A Celebration of Young Poets

South – Fall 2006

Creative Communication, Inc.

A Celebration of Young Poets
South – Fall 2006

An anthology compiled by Creative Communication, Inc.

Published by:

CREATIVE COMMUNICATION, INC.
1488 NORTH 200 WEST
LOGAN, UT 84341

ISBN: 978-1-60050-077-0

Foreword

Poetry is alive and well! Each year we receive thousands of entries in our contests. The daunting task of reading each poem and judging it is one that our judges truly enjoy. I am continually told that the job of being a judge is both entertaining and educational. As most of the poems we received were not invited to be included in this anthology, we are pleased to present you with a book of the best poems from the contest.

Reading these poems can help you escape to a place where time is taken to watch the leaves on an autumn day or snow fall quietly outside; a place where friendships are easily made and tragically broken. Through the safety of words, these poets share the poetic images of the world around them.

We are proud to provide an outlet to these young poets. We receive hundreds of letters each year that tell us how our contest is a catalyst in changing a life or motivating a poet to do better in school. The letters also tell the story behind the poems. Many poems are written after an event in the poet's life. These young poets write on many of the same topics that poets have throughout history. They write on love, nature, tragedy and triumph. They write from the heart. As you read these poems, we thank you for joining in this "Celebration of Young Poets."

Thank you,

Gaylen Worthen, President
Creative Communication

WRITING CONTESTS!

Enter our next POETRY contest!

Enter our next ESSAY contest!

Why should I enter?

Win prizes and get published! Each year thousands of dollars in prizes are awarded in each region and tens of thousands of dollars in prizes are awarded throughout North America. The top writers in each division receive a monetary award and a free book that includes their published poem or essay. Entries of merit are also selected to be published in our anthology.

Who may enter?

There are five divisions in the poetry contest. The poetry divisions are grades K-3, 4-6, 7-9, 10-12, and adult. There are three divisions in the essay contest. The essay division are grades 4-6, 7-9, and 10-12.

What is needed to enter the contest?

To enter the poetry contest send in one original poem, 21 lines or less. To enter the essay contest send in one original essay, 250 words or less, on any topic. Each entry must include the writer's name, address, city, state and zip code. Student entries need to include the student's grade, school name and school address. Students who include their teacher's name may help the teacher qualify for a free copy of the anthology.

How do I enter?

Enter a poem online at:
www.poeticpower.com
or
Mail your poem to:
Poetry Contest
1488 North 200 West
Logan, UT 84341

Enter an essay online at:
www.studentessaycontest.com
or
Mail your essay to:
Essay Contest
1488 North 200 West
Logan, UT 84341

If you are mailing your poetry entry, please write "Student Contest" at the top of your poem if you are in grades K-12. Please write "Adult Contest" at the top of your poem if you are entering the adult division.

When is the deadline?

Poetry contest deadlines are August 15th, December 5th, and April 4th. Essay contest deadlines are July 18th, October 17th, and February 14th. You can enter each contest, however, send only one poem or essay for each contest deadline.

Are there benefits for my school?

Yes. We award $15,000 each year in grants to help with Language Arts programs. Schools qualify to apply for a grant by having a large number of entries of which over fifty percent are accepted for publication. This typically tends to be about 15 accepted entries.

Are there benefits for my teacher?

Yes. Teachers with five or more students accepted to be published receive a free anthology that includes their students' writing.

For more information please go to our website at **www.poeticpower.com**, email us at editor@poeticpower.com or call 435-713-4411.

Table of Contents

States included in this edition:

Alabama
Arkansas
Georgia
Kentucky
Louisiana
Mississippi
Missouri
North Carolina
Oklahoma
South Carolina
Tennessee
West Virginia

Fall 2006 Poetic Achievement Honor Schools

* Teachers who had fifteen or more poets accepted to be published

The following schools are recognized as receiving a "Poetic Achievement Award." This award is given to schools who have a large number of entries of which over fifty percent are accepted for publication. With hundreds of schools entering our contest, only a small percent of these schools are honored with this award. The purpose of this award is to recognize schools with excellent Language Arts programs. This award qualifies these schools to receive a complimentary copy of this anthology. In addition, these schools are eligible to apply for a Creative Communication Language Arts Grant. Grants of two hundred and fifty dollars each are awarded to further develop writing in our schools.

All Saints' Episcopal School
Morristown, TN
> Betty Golden*
> Angie Smith

Alpena Elementary School
Alpena, AR
> Sherry Choate
> Holly Kelley
> Dawn Keys
> Stella Maberry
> Wanda Massengale
> Ms. Star

Alvaton Elementary School
Alvaton, KY
> Debbie Deaton
> Cheryl Hughes*
> Jane Kirby*
> Mary-Anne Powers
> Cindy Rider*
> Paula Strain*

American Heritage Academy
Canton, GA
> Sue Buffam
> Sandy Dranzek
> Mrs. Griffin

Armorel Elementary School
Armorel, AR
> Cynthia Sullivan*

Arnaudville Elementary School
Arnaudville, LA
> Debbie Cormier
> T. Duvall
> H. Hollier
> Tonia Meche*
> Patrice Montgomery

Atkinson Elementary School
Hendersonville, NC
> Diane Smith*

Baylor School
Chattanooga, TN
> Fontaine Alison*
> Amy Cohen
> Sally Naylor*
> Roger Vredaveld

Beck Academy
Greenville, SC
> Debbie Sanders*

Bellwood Discovery School
Murfreesboro, TN
Cindy Jones
Kristy Mall*
Suzie Trussell

Benton County School of the Arts
Rogers, AR
LaVona Cerna*

Bonaire Elementary School
Bonaire, GA
Connie Long*

Briarwood Christian Elementary School
Birmingham, AL
Martha Bickford
Jenny Burdick*
Mrs. Cuneo*
Mrs. Griffin*
Mrs. Hutchinson*
Susan Johnson
Miss Jones
Mrs. Pardue
Joanne Peterson
Mrs. Petty*
Mrs. C. Smith
Mrs. Starr*
Miss Wagner
Amanda Westbrook*

Brilliant Elementary School
Brilliant, AL
Dana Bryant
Betty Mitchell

Broadway Elementary School
Broadway, NC
Susan Brown*

Brogden Middle School
Durham, NC
Jennifer Haycraft*
Elizabeth Hunter
Samantha Magee

Calloway Smith Middle School
Mobile, AL
Amer Rhodes
Della White

Cathedral School
Raleigh, NC
Diane Lee*

Central Arkansas Christian School
Sherwood, AR
Mrs. Chapin*

Charleston County School of the Arts
North Charleston, SC
Ms. Drennan
Mary Ann Henry*
Rene Bufo Miles*

Cherokee Elementary School
Hardy, AR
Kim Circle*
Deloris Ray*
Kim Thomas*

Christ Episcopal School - Middle School
Covington, LA
Peggy Aultman
Maurine Magne

Clarksburg School
Clarksburg, TN
Jeannine Stokes*

Cleveland Elementary School
Oklahoma City, OK
Richard Kleffman
Alice Pettit

College View Middle School
Owensboro, KY
Sandra Roberts*

Community Christian School
Wilson, NC
Julie Provo*

Contentnea Elementary School
Kinston, NC
Birta Battle*

Cool Spring Elementary School
Cleveland, NC
Aimee Adkins*
Tonya Cassidy
Stephanie Flammang
Carmen Graham*
Mandy Harrington
Kenneth Lindstrom
Monica Williams

Cottonwood Public School
Coalgate, OK
Mrs. Barrett
Tammy Daniel*

Crestwood Elementary School
Crestwood, KY
Holly Fink*

Debusk Elementary School
Greeneville, TN
Tamara Wykle*

Desoto Central School
Southaven, MS
Rachel Harris*

Drayton Hall Elementary School
Charleston, SC
Mrs. McGrath*

Dyer Elementary & Jr High School
Dyer, TN
Lee Hudson*

East Jones Elementary School
Laurel, MS
Shirley Sellers*
Nancy Walters*

East Marion Elementary School
Columbia, MS
Libby Aaron*

Edmonton Elementary School
Edmonton, KY
Rachel Dial
Peggy Redmon*

Eminence Middle School
Eminence, KY
Jennifer Montgomery
Terry Walther*

Etowah Elementary School
Etowah, NC
Mrs. Furris
Elaine Kirkpatrick*
Shirley Robinson*
Diane Smith
Mrs. Wells

Evangelical Christian School
Germantown, TN
Shireen Brandt
Becky Jernigan
Lindy Murley
Tammy Umlauf
Annette Wright
Barbara Yelverton

Geggie Elementary School
Eureka, MO
Marlene Bequette*
Mrs. Krey

Goshen Elementary School at Hillcrest
Prospect, KY
Barbara Link
Kristy Mattingly
Mrs. Miller-Bennett

Graham Elementary School
Talladega, AL
Donna Edmiston*
Susie Pressley

Guntown Middle School
Guntown, MS
Manya Chappell*
Laci McClung*

Harrisburg Middle School
Harrisburg, AR
B. Davis*

Hayes Elementary School
Enid, OK
Susan Brinley
Suzanne Johnson*

Haynes Academy for Advanced Studies
Metairie, LA
Janet C. Gubler*
Juliet Hohan*
Princess LaCroix
Peggy LeBlanc*

Heartland High School and Academy
Belton, MO
Doreen Gibson
Julie Paul
Cindy Scott

Holy Rosary Academy
New Orleans, LA
Rae Ann DiMaggio
Judith Malouse

Islands Elementary School
Savannah, GA
Kevin Bowden
Lisa Long

J E Holmes Middle School
Eden, NC
Virginia Hall
Mrs. Lawson
Linda Reynolds*

Joann Walters Elementary School
Dierks, AR
Patricia Bissell*

Lake Castle Private School
Slidell, LA
Christine Monnin*
Stephanie Songy

Landmark Christian School
Fairburn, GA
Mrs. Bulger
Patty Burdette
Mrs. Cusumano
Gail Emanuel
Nancy Gunter
Becky Joiner
Mrs. McAllister

Lee A Tolbert Community Academy
Kansas City, MO
Trasi Ashley
Angela Boley
Piper Crawford
Candace Ford
Tori Hirner
Natasha Moorer
Amber Parks
Crystal Piper
Erica Templeton
Dana Tiller
Janice Yocum*

Leland Middle School
Leland, NC
Christie Tisinger*

Leonville Elementary School
Leonville, LA
Barbara Jesclard*

Lewis Vincent Elementary School
Denham Springs, LA
Chantel Taylor*

Livingston Middle School
Livingston, TN
Mrs. Dillon
Mr. McCormick
C. O'Brien
Debie Taylor*

Lost River Elementary School
Bowling Green, KY
Nancy Stevenson*

Magnolia Springs Baptist Academy
Theodore, AL
Ms. Brown
Mr. Lawson
Mrs. Mack
Sandra Moody
Mrs. Nichols
Ginger Pierce
Mrs. Richardson
Mrs. Williams*

Martin Elementary School
Parkersburg, WV
Mrs. Forshey
Mrs. Halbert

Midway Covenant Christian School
Powder Springs, GA
Mrs. Terrell*

Montessori Community School
Durham, NC
Michelle Irinyi
Peter Piche
Karen Richardson

Mount Zion Christian School
Greenville, SC
Laura Phillips*

North Iredell Middle School
Olin, NC
Sandra Ellis*

Orange Grove Elementary School
Gulfport, MS
Stephanie Schepens*

Our Lady of Fatima School
Biloxi, MS
Marcia Todd
Mrs. Torricelli

Paint Lick Elementary School
Paint Lick, KY
Pam Canter*

Palmetto Christian Academy
Mt Pleasant, SC
Dianne Williams*

Pembroke Elementary School
Pembroke, NC
Gelena H. Chavis*
Ivene Jones Hunt*

Pine Tree Hill Elementary School
Camden, SC
Cheryl Watson*

Pleasants County Middle School
Belmont, WV
Carol Hysell*

Providence Academy
Johnson City, TN
Lynne Little*

Queen of Angels Catholic School
Roswell, GA
Christine Bordnick*

River Trail Middle School
Duluth, GA
Christina Kim
Jacqueline Lavi*
Paula Warnicke*

Rock Mills Jr High School
Rock Mills, AL
Jeffery Thompson*

Russell Babb Elementary School
Harrah, OK
Connie Jewell*

Salem Elementary School
Bryant, AR
Beth Oppenhuizen*

Scotts Creek Elementary School
Sylva, NC
Laura H. Wallace*

Shirley Elementary School
Shirley, AR
Mrs. Clark
Lynda Tharp*

South Nodaway Elementary School
Guilford, MO
Nicole Carter*

South Topsail Elementary School
Hampstead, NC
Wendy Strickland*

St Cecilia School
Broussard, LA
Jean Cantrell*

St Elizabeth Ann Seton Catholic School
Edmond, OK
Mrs. Hammons
Sara Harjo*

St Mark Elementary School
Kingstree, SC
Ms. Kent*

St Mary Cathedral Elementary School
Cape Girardeau, MO
Monica Macke*

St Teresa's School
Albany, GA
Judy Jaros Johnson*

St Thomas More School
Chapel Hill, NC
Mrs. Beachler
Hilda Bukowski
Pat Killian
Jennifer Sullivan*

St Vincent Elementary School
Perryville, MO
Bonnie Guyot*
Ronda Rowland*

Statesville Middle School
Statesville, NC
Brenda Bradshaw*
Geoff Crosson
Carole Pickett

Stephens Elementary School
Alexander City, AL
Andrea Patten*

Stokesdale Elementary School
Stokesdale, NC
LaWonne McCoy*
Ms. Moses

Sullivan Elementary School
Kingsport, TN
Susan Cassidy*

Sycamore Elementary School
Sugar Hill, GA
Ruth Beichner*
Patty Kambiss
Cindy Taylor

Tamassee-Salem Elementary School
Tamassee, SC
Susan B. Smith*

Tates Creek Elementary School
Lexington, KY
Brenda Jackson*

Temple Hill Elementary School
Glasgow, KY
Cynthia Wilson*

The Mountain Community School
Hendersonville, NC
Laurie Roberts*

Tomlinson Jr High School
Lawton, OK
Mary Hanson*
Pam Rodriguez

Trenton Middle School
    Trenton, MO
        Pamela Johnston*

Walker Intermediate School
    Fort Knox, KY
        Vicki Pitcher*

Walton Verona Elementary School
    Verona, KY
        Deborah C. McNeil*

Western Hills Elementary School
    Little Rock, AR
        Swayzine Horton*
        Ms. Warren

Wohlwend Elementary School
    St Louis, MO
        Wendy Soell*

Woodland Presbyterian School
    Memphis, TN
        Carol Percival*

Language Arts Grant Recipients 2006-2007

After receiving a "Poetic Achievement Award" schools are encouraged to apply for a Creative Communication Language Arts Grant. The following is a list of schools who received a two hundred and fifty dollar grant for the 2006-2007 school year.

Aaron Parker Elementary School, Powderly, TX
All City Elementary at Jane Addams, Sioux Falls, SD
Barstow Intermediate School, Barstow, CA
Benton Central Jr/Sr High School, Oxford, IN
Broome High School, Spartanburg, SC
Carver Jr High School, Spartanburg, SC
Clarksville Elementary School, Clarksville, VA
Dunlap Middle School, Dunlap, IL
Edward Bleeker Jr High School, Flushing, NY
Emmanuel-St Michael Lutheran School, Fort Wayne, IN
Florida Youth Challenge Academy, Starke, FL
Fort Towson Jr/Sr High School, Fort Towson, OK
Fox Creek Jr High School, Bullhead City, AZ
Galena Primary School, Galena, IL
Hancock County Middle/High School, Sneedville, TN
Harrison County High School, Cynthiana, KY
Lehi High School, Lehi, UT
Lester B Pearson Catholic High School, Gloucester, ON
Lincoln Jr/Sr High School, Alma Center, WI
Little Flower Day Care Center & Prep School, Brooklyn, NY
Madison Park Technical Vocational High School, Boston, MA
Marsh Grammar School, Methuen, MA
Miller City-New Cleveland School, Miller City, OH
Northeast Baptist School, West Monroe, LA
Onsted High School, Onsted, MI
Roselle Park Middle School, Roselle Park, NJ
South Nodaway Elementary/High School, Barnard, MO
Spring Creek Elementary School, Laramie, WY
Springfield Local High School, New Middletown, OH
St James Catholic School, Abbotsford, BC
St John the Baptist School, Silver Spring, MD

Language Arts Grant Winners cont.

St Thomas More Academy, Burton, MI
Tahoka Middle School, Tahoka, TX
Thomas Lake Elementary School, Eagan, MN
Turner Middle School, Kansas City, KS
Virginia A Boone Highland Oaks Elementary School, North Miami Beach, FL
Washington School, Greenville, MS
Willamette Christian School, Eugene, OR
Woodcliff Middle School, Woodcliff Lake, NJ
Woodcrest School, Tarzana, CA

Young Poets
Grades 4-5-6

Note: The Top Ten poems were finalized through an online voting system. Creative Communication's judges first picked out the top poems. These poems were then posted online. The final step involved thousands of students and teachers who registered as online judges and voted for the Top Ten poems. We hope you enjoy these selections.

Top Poem Grades 4-5-6

Seasons

Seasons come and seasons go.
The wind lies quiet, then it blows.
Summer is here, now comes the fun,
Swimming and boating and days full of fun.

Now here comes fall rolling in,
Cool crisp days start to begin.
Down come the leaves one by one,
Now summer days are finally done.

Here comes winter, it gets quite chilly.
I wear my pink sweater that's soft and frilly.
Soon the ground is covered with white,
Fire logs are burning on these long cold nights.

Showers are coming and flowers begin to bloom,
No more days filled with gloom.
Birds are singing and wedding bells ring,
Thank goodness it's spring.

Sydney Bailey, Grade 4
Stephens Elementary School, AL

Top Poem Grades 4-5-6

Moonlit Storm

Silvery sheets
Cascade in gray tendrils,
Everything shimmers
In the lily-white moonlight.
God's hammering thunder
Sends shivers through the forest,
The sky alights
As bolts crash the clouds.
An old battered rosebush
Thwacks wet, dappled glass;
The ever-graceful cat
Purrs in mingled moonlight.
A tired girl
Does not stir.
Bittersweet wind thrashes
The glittering woods one last time,
Finally, all is silent.
A velvety cloud brushes by,
Revealing the lunar sun
Hanging in the sky
As an ominous sign to all.

Rachel Fairchild, Grade 6
Appalachian Christian School, KY

Top Poem Grades 4-5-6

The Three Letters for Love

A beautiful woman with an inspiring charm,
A tender heart with loving arms.
A knowledgeable star with a caring soul,
A grown lady with an important role.

I can confide in her when things go wrong,
She compares my life to part of a song.
She wipes my tears before they fall,
Oh, how can a person know it all?

She stands by my side in every way,
Her duties do not stop night or day.
She has done so many wonderful deeds,
Her intelligence spreads like the wind blowing seeds.

This woman is amazing just like a dove,
I address her with the three letters for love.
These are some reasons that I am proud to call her my M-O-M.

Jessica Horne, Grade 6
Statesville Middle School, NC

Top Poem Grades 4-5-6

God's Return

The grass will move aside to let Him pass.
The wind will proclaim His presence.
The lightning will light His path.
The leaves will dance and swirl with grace and beauty.

Flowers will spring up wherever He steps.
The water sings His praises.
Its splish and splash sounds like music.
So beautiful, rhythmic, and peaceful.

The sun and moon will shine and glow.
The rainbow will be His crown.
The rain will stop to watch Him.
The clouds will part to see His glory.

The fish will walk to lay eyes upon Him.
The beasts will halt at His hand.
The birds will fly like the wind.
Thus is God's return.

Abigail Johnson, Grade 5
Providence Academy, TN

Top Poem Grades 4-5-6

Look What God Made

Look what God made.
He made you and me.
He made the animals and plants.
He also made the sea.

He made the ground and trees,
And the grass that grows.
He made the little birds that fly
And the wind that blows.

And when I look around
I'm glad that I can see
That God's love is everywhere.
And He loves you and me!

Bryan Landreth, Grade 5
Quail Run Elementary School, GA

Top Poem Grades 4-5-6

Respect Our Flag

Doth she not maketh thy first flag to show thee liberty?
Then why doth thy treateth it like it doesn't show thee importance?
Thy forefathers hath given thee a liberty and justice
    That ye cannot taketh away.
Only thy Father Whom dwells in high places can taketh this away.
But I, being shown under God, humbly ask that ye respect thy flag.
For our country, for ye forefathers.
For the Lord God Almighty Who giveth thee food and clothing in times of need,
And for liberty and justice that He hath given us.
    Respect our flag,
      O nation of people that live free to this day.
    Respect our flag.

Kaitlin Odneal, Grade 5
Heartland High School and Academy, MO

Top Poem Grades 4-5-6

Fall

How do you know when it's fall?
The lark and sparrow seem to call.
The field turns yellow and leaves are red.
It's been dark for awhile when you go to bed.
There's a chill in the air and warm things to wear.
That's how you know when fall is there.

Madison Pittman, Grade 4
Bethlehem Christian Academy, GA

Top Poem Grades 4-5-6

Memories

I drove past that old trailer
I saw her standing there on the porch
Then all of a sudden the memories came running through
Memories of the nicest woman I ever knew
Memories of me hugging her and telling her I love her
Then as the memories started hitting me harder tears started to fill my eyes
That was when my nanny passed away.

Katrina Reynolds, Grade 4
Cave City Elementary School, AR

Top Poem Grades 4-5-6

The Remembered

Blazing hearts
Went down together
One would take the loss for the other
243 lost their lives
And so many more than that
Five years of hurt pass you by in an instant
Hearts pound with love and some tremble with fear
Their eyes swell with tears as they remember the pain
All the innocent people who lost their lives
Just for the sake of national hatred
Where do you stand in this hurtful battle that we face?
On our side, the side of freedom,
Or theirs the side of dictatorships and supreme rulers
What do you see when you look at our graceful but wounded nation?
You should see the hope that we have for what is to come of tomorrow
The compassion we show toward our neighbors who have been cut deeply
Those who are still hurting but yet no one bothers to look their way
Those who sit next to you but you just "don't see"
The ones you really don't care to look at
That is what our nation was built upon
That is what you should see.

Alexandria Sheffield, Grade 6
Woodland Presbyterian School, TN

Top Poem Grades 4-5-6

Still My Best Friend

Make new friends but keep the old one is silver the other gold
those words ring in my head as the warm tears make their way down my cheeks

I am alone I do not talk or smile
my best friend is gone I wanted her all to my own, but she didn't

I was safe and she was wild I was lucky she even liked me
we were close without her I was nobody I had nobody

She changed my life I hope I changed hers and just as quick as we were friends
our friendship ended a new girl came in

I didn't give her a chance I left and made new friends
in a way we still understand each other
even though we are not with each other

We still hold each other's secrets whenever we are together
we are best friends like we used to be she and her new friend are still friends

But I have accepted it I should treasure a friend
and I didn't make new friends but kept the old one
one is silver and she was gold

Abigail Simpson, Grade 6
The Mountain Community School, NC

Drought

A bad drought
The hard ground cracks.
You are wishing for rain.
The dying plants,
The dying crops,
I am wishing for rain.

Sam Clifton, Grade 5
St Vincent Elementary School, MO

Fishing

Fishing is the very best.
We sometimes have a fishing fest.
My lures sometimes get stuck in moss.
I also fish at Lake Foss.

Landon Brown, Grade 4
Horace Mann Elementary School, OK

Basketball Practice

I walk towards the
girls' room to change
when I get there I change
into a blue and white jersey
and blue shorts
I run to the gym and stretch
then we do a drill
after we're done the coach says
wait, let's run
when we finally get done,
I go home tired and
rest

Kara Gilmore, Grade 6
Dyer Elementary & Jr High School, TN

Halloween

Chilly skies, falling leaves,
Children believe in pumpkins,
Goblins, toilet paper trees.
They open up the door
And say BOO!
We love candy, how about you?

Ian Sattely, Grade 5
Prince of Peace Catholic School, SC

Love

Love is as deep as the ocean.
It's as wide as the sea.
Love is as bright as the sun,
It's always between you and me.
Love is as beautiful as the
horizon setting across the lake,
And it's there every time I wake.
Love is like a burning fire.
Love is special.
Love is kind.

Ashlea Brazil, Grade 5
Salem Elementary School, AR

I Am Pretty and Funny

I am pretty and funny.
I wonder about the future.
I hear sounds.
I see my friends and family.
I want a cell phone.
I am pretty and funny.
I pretend that I can do anything.
I feel like someone is watching me.
I touch the sky.
I worry about war.
I cry when I am sad.
I am pretty and funny.
I understand we all have to grow up.
I say God is real.
I dream I can be famous.
I try not to be shy.
I hope my knee gets better.
I am pretty and funny.

Katie Bushman, Grade 6
Hayes Elementary School, OK

Moms, Moms, Moms

Tall moms
Short moms
Happy, sad, mad moms
Those are just a few!

Pretty moms
Ugly moms
Grand, kind, clever moms
Hilarious, loving, marvelous moms
Great moms too!

Excellent moms
Pleasant moms
And don't forget cheery moms!

Last of all
Best of all
I like friendly moms!

Ben Wood, Grade 5
Salem Elementary School, AR

Rain

The raindrop runs and
slips off the thundercloud and
then it begins to freeze.

Matt Julian, Grade 5
St Vincent Elementary School, MO

Pollen

Pollen all around…
It's in the trees and the breeze…
Pollen makes me sneeze!

Elizabeth Milano, Grade 6
Queen of Angels Catholic School, GA

Multiple Colors

Yellow is the color of the sun,
Red is fire that makes you run.
Blue is a flower that you smell,
Orange is a carrot that tastes very well.

Rylie Eller, Grade 4
Horace Mann Elementary School, OK

My #1 Maw, Maw

She is sweet like honey.
She makes me feel better when I'm hurt.
She takes me everywhere.
She is a helper.
She loves everything I do.
She makes me feel better when I'm blue.
I love her and she loves me too.
She is my friend.
She is pretty.
She is smart.
She is a great dancer.
She is good to me.
She never does anything wrong.
My #1 Maw, Maw
I love her.

Kristina Gomez, Grade 4
Lewis Vincent Elementary School, LA

Animals

They are big.
Some are small.
Some are just tall.
They climb and crawl.
They cherish and love.
They have stripes and dots.
Some even have spots.
They have elephant ears and pig's tails.
They help, heal, and guide.
Animals are not just creatures.
They are people too.

Alona Wachlin, Grade 6
Our Lady of Fatima School, MS

Your Soul

Your soul has a second life.
When you die…
Your soul lives on.

Blake Blankenship, Grade 4
Vanoss Elementary School, OK

Loves

L ovely, kind, and ever true
O dd and knows very few
V ery smart and loves her shoes
E ver kind and ever true.
S pecially for a kind person like you.

Jaycie Freeman, Grade 6
Midland Elementary School, AR

Oceans

It is all deep blue.
The waves are like a city.
It is glorious.

Libby Hennington, Grade 4
Briarwood Christian Elementary School, AL

The Fall Leaves

The fall leaves are bright and orange.
They fall from great big trees.
They fall from tall, tall trees.
They fall from small, small trees.
Little kids love to play in fall leaves.
They pile them up and JUMP!
If they start playing in them they never stop.
Fall leaves can come in many colors and sizes.
They also come in many shapes and varieties.
They look so beautiful and gorgeous.
They are orange, yellow, brown, and red.
If I like fall I know you will too.

Amanda Swearingen, Grade 5
Stokesdale Elementary School, NC

Gone

How I wished I could go back
To the wonderful world of glee
My parents, best friends, and family
Gone.
How I wish I could go back
And watch movies and DVDs all day
Like I had all the time in the world
Gone.
How I wish I could go back
To school even, learning math and science
Laughing at lunch, running around in gym
Gone.
As I think of the happy memories that have happened
And the memories now
I cry with regret as anger fills my heart
And all those happy memories, the laughing moments
Are now Gone.

Alina Clay, Grade 6
Woodland Presbyterian School, TN

Pumpkins

Orange and joyous
They are awfully spacious
have scary faces.

Katy Broughton, Grade 4
Briarwood Christian Elementary School, AL

The Killer Whale

The killer whale jumped
out of the water, made a
splash and got us soaked

Matthew Lovell, Grade 4
Briarwood Christian Elementary School, AL

Autumn Leaves

An autumn leaf is like the sea,
swaying back and forth,
slowing down as the wind catches it again,
flying, soaring gracefully,
landing on the ground,
waiting for another.

Mikayla Absher, Grade 4
First Wesleyan Christian School, NC

Snow

Snow looks like a baby hare just born.
Snow looks like soft sheep's wool just cut.
Snow is like pureness or holiness.
But snow is a beautiful creation from Jesus Christ our Lord.

The problem with snow is it's very cold, burrr!
Snow is very beautiful and very tasty.
Snow reminds me of the gift of the Lord Jesus Christ.

It is soothing just like Jesus Christ our Lord.

Victoria Tanner, Grade 5
Magnolia Springs Baptist Academy, AL

The Black Cat

There once was a black cat whose name was Jerry.
Jerry met a cat whose name was Carry.
Jerry thought she was very pretty.
Jerry asked Carry to marry him.
She told him "yes" they were talking about having a family.

Courtney Jackson, Grade 6
Livingston Middle School, TN

School

Feels like a headache after a test
Looks like old books first being opened at the first of the year
Smells like new pencils first being written on a blank paper
Sounds like key chains hitting and dangling off of book bags
Tastes like a bitter Monday after every weekend

John Wise, Grade 5
Briarwood Christian Elementary School, AL

Fall

Fall is a nice season.
The trees are all different.
There are some different colors,
red,
yellow,
and brown.
Some have no leaves.
Fall is also different in weather,
cold,
hot,
in between.
Fall is a nice season.

Haylee Elizabeth Nadicksbernd, Grade 5
Walton Verona Elementary School, KY

little kitties

little kitties in the sun
little kitties having fun
little kitties it's time to eat
now they run out of the street
little kitties "munch munch munch"
and eating up all their lunch
little kitties lap lap lap
now it's time to take a nap
they've eaten now they can't go out
so little kitties just go pout
when they wake up to say good morning
little kitties see rain pouring

Brittany Farrell, Grade 6
Graham Elementary School, AL

Days of Winter

Winter brings snow fights
by the fire we warm ourselves
and we make hot s'mores

Trey Davis, Grade 6
Tomlinson Jr High School, OK

Angel and Devil

Angel
Generous, precious
Loving, giving, sharing
Halo, wings, horns, pitchfork
Frowning, sassing, arguing
Bossy, cross
Devil.

Molli Schmitt, Grade 4
Harahan Elementary School, LA

Purple

Purple is beautiful,
a violet just waiting to be picked.

Purple is a rose,
trying to pierce through the Earth.

Purple is amethyst,
a gem on thy royal head.

Purple is a tiny butterfly,
hiding in my heart.

Purple is a seashell,
lying on the beach.

Purple is my best friend,
always by my side.

Purple is the sunset,
kissing the world good night.

Kelsey Howard, Grade 6
College View Middle School, KY

Best Friends

B is for always being there for each other.
E is for everything we do together.
S is for sticking together through times.
T is for taking the blame for one another.

F is for friendliness we will share throughout our lives.
R is for remembering why we are best friends.
I is for ignoring any obstacles that might try to break our friendship.
E is for everything we will go through with each other.
N is for never forgetting each other when someone else is around.
D is for doing something special for each other.
S is for saying something that will bring happiness and joy to your best friend.

Kayla LaGrange, Grade 6
Arnaudville Elementary School, LA

I Am From

I am from where the bluegrass grows,
Where the skies are almost always sapphire blue,
And a place where thoroughbred horses run in the grassy plains.
I am from where the angels fly in my God's Heaven…including my grandma.
She is an angel, too, who flies high.
I am from the Lord, the maker of Heaven and Earth.
I was born in God's hands.
Jesus is waiting for me in Heaven.
We are all from where His tears fall.
I am from my whole family of five: Dad, Mom, Blake (aka Bubby), Justin, and me.
I am from times of frustration and temptation…
From Blake slamming his doors, blaring his music and video games, and more!
Sometimes I respond by stomping my feet.
This temporarily makes me feel complete.
I am also from cheerful times…
Raising and riding horses on my granny's farm,
Watching movies with the whole family,
Playing my two brothers' video games,
AND
My cousins coming over to visit me at my house.
These are all of the people, places, and things that I'm from.

Nikki Lay, Grade 5
Burgin Independent School, KY

Golden Leaves in the Swaying Breeze

The shimmering sun glistens upon the blacktop
As you look across the street you see the bare beautiful trees
As you listen you hear the swaying flag as a symbol of our freedom.

Leaves are lying peacefully along the ground
As you see them you feel the mid-November breeze
If you listen closely you can hear the chirping birds
You can see the leaves swirling to the ground.

Engines are roaring
Petals are falling from the red bush
As I sit across from my 6th grade teacher I think…
Isn't this neat.

Kelsey Nicole Bray, Grade 6
Temple Hill Elementary School, KY

What's in the Sky?

When I look at the sky I see things that others don't see.
They are pictures that God gave only to me.
I look so far in the sky my thoughts start to fly,
Like the birds soaring high,
My eyes tend to wander,
While they fly past the pillows in the sky.
The pillows are perfect in their own way,
Just like a sunny day.
The pillows move at a steady pace,
Each one in the race,
Flowing through the air,
I can't help but stare.
They have feelings like we do.
They get pearly white when they are glad,
And turn dark gray and cry when they are sad.
I am filled with peace and love all around,
Tears of joy running down.
What I see through my eyes is
These beautiful clouds in the sky.

Kayla Margin, Grade 6
Mount Zion Christian School, SC

True Work of Art

What wonders await in a blank piece of paper?
A sonnet, a ballad, a masterpiece?
What thoughts awaken in a ball-point pen?
A story, a poem, a drawing?
Can you measure the worth of a pencil?
In a sketch, a picture, a cartoon?
Can you imagine the importance of the eraser?
In words, in art, in song?
Could you make a work of art with a pencil and paper?
Could you shade it with a fine ink pen?
Could you erase inadequate lines with the eraser?
And how many times could you do it over again?
So draw me a masterpiece; write me a song.
Write me a beautiful poem.
The beauty of the arts is here.
The beauty of all hearts is near.
Release the artist inside.
The poet inside.
The musician inside.
Create a masterpiece with your own hands and heart,
And you will be the true work of art.

Katie Murphy, Grade 6
Queen of Angels Catholic School, GA

Sharks

S is for the slithery giants of Earth
H is for the hungry hunters they are
A is for the attitude they can possess
R is for the rangers of the water
K is for kindless hearts
S is for swimming the seven seas of the world

Michael Steven Edgar Brown, Grade 6
Scotts Creek Elementary School, NC

Magic White Cotton

Big, puffy cotton balls floating gently in the sky,
Capable of making rain, sleet, or snow,
Hail or tornadoes,
Huge, white globs of whipped cream
Can cause much trouble
Yet whip up some beautiful things!
Like rainbows, when blinding sun shines through
And rain.
This magic white cotton is made from the waters of
Rivers…ponds…lakes…oceans
When filled up by undersized dust crystals,
God will turn the knob
And the heavy rain will flow from the huge white faucet
The winds will pick up,
The trees will dance
And God's bowling ball will strike the pins,
Making heavy sparks.
So wicked strong that it might snap a tree in one blow.
Then, it all stops,
And the heavy ring of fire rises to brighten the day
Putting on a show…so magical!

Ryan Pollak, Grade 4
Big Creek Elementary School, GA

Oceans

Oceans are such fun
There are treasures in the sea
Each a mystery

Allison Pugh, Grade 4
Briarwood Christian Elementary School, AL

I Am

I am a blossom.
I wonder if anything in the world shall turn against me.
I hear the wind that is always calling my name.
I see paint blotches from painting the world.
I want to be successful.
I am a blossom.

I pretend I am friends with the constellations above me.
I feel I am strong.
I touch angels' hands.
I cry if I hear harsh words about me.
I am a blossom.

I can be as wonderful as you want to be.
I always struggle.
I never want to fail on important things.
I understand if you don't respect me.
I say to do your best.
I dream of magical worlds.
I try hard to achieve my goals.
I hope to change the community.
I am a blossom.

Katie Hyatt, Grade 4
Walnut Grove Elementary School, AL

Nightmare!

Dark and spooky, as the color black
The mysterious trees go clickity, clack.

The street lights flicker on and off
Laying on my pillow that feels so soft.

Gasping at my creepy feelings
In my bed staring at the ceiling.

Shadows, noises, all those things
Just to creep me out, it seems.

Figments of my imagination
Trapped inside with no escaping.

Fantasies, weird stuff is what I mean
I wake up and realize it's just a dream.

Justin Gaddy, Grade 6
Brogden Middle School, NC

All About Me

D aring at football
A real friend
R eally great at basketball
I ndividual personality
U nderstanding
S uper at science

Darius Smiley, Grade 6
Brogden Middle School, NC

The Unknown Death

I was never even close
To become one to boast.
Never to my eyes, even than before
Every moment of my life
Very quickly flashes a light.
Even if God gave me back
Reckon I would meet the Devil.

Because I have been ordered
I have pledged
To kill those who are different
As some allege
They are in war, like us
Not so different, they can be.
Just different beliefs, you see.

For I am a soldier
Never thought to be a killer
Will he come for me?
Will he forgive me?
I shall not know as nobody does
Less trust in country
More faith in God.

Sierra Hensley, Grade 5
Etowah Elementary School, NC

The Dream of Earth

I once have dreamt
I was the Earth
The mother of all
In which, the birth

Of living things
And non as well
Live and grow
Sleep, dream and dwell

And Mother Earth
Prays to her child
To keep the peace,
Yet keep the wild

Where the fiery wind
And tumbling sea
Have made a dream
For you and me

Molly Mulroy, Grade 6
Campus Elementary School, TN

Christmas

C heer is spread
H olly is hung
R ed is the color
I nside and out
S ongs are sung
T insel is hung.
M any people
A re celebrating this
S acred season.

Abigail Riley, Grade 6
Eminence Middle School, KY

An Ode to Snow

Oh, snow is falling,
What a pretty sight.

Snow is falling,
It plays with the light.

Snow is falling,
It plays a game.

Oh snow is falling,
It makes everything that is different,
Look the same.

Snow is falling,
It blinds all who see.

Snow is falling,
It hides from you and me.

Cardayshia Jackson, Grade 4
Pines Elementary School, NC

Saints

S aints are awesome
A thletic team
I n the Dome
N o losing
T alented team
S aints rule

Alex Stephens, Grade 6
St Cecilia School, LA

War

War
Dark, cloudy
Running, fighting, flying
Scary to be in
Death

Logan Smith, Grade 5
Bonaire Elementary School, GA

Lakes

Lakes
Lakes are cool
Lakes are fun
Lakes seem to carry joy
Lakes, lakes, lakes
Lakes are awesome
Lakes are really neat
Lakes

Matt Glendening, Grade 5
Faith Christian School, SC

If You Were Here

If you were here right now,
I'd leap in your arms.
I'd feel safe and secure
For you'd keep me from harm.

If you were here right now,
All my troubles would disappear.
I wouldn't worry one bit
For you'd erase all my fears.

If you were here right now,
How happy I'd be!
Feeling safe and secure,
In your arms you would hold me.

Alexis Penaloza, Grade 6
Fayetteville Christian School, NC

Snow

Snow
Fun, cold
Playing, falling, slipping
Today at school it snowed
White

Briana Byars, Grade 5
Bayyari Elementary School, AR

Christmas Morning

Looks like Mom and Dad are ready with the camera.
Smells like cinnamon in the air.
Feels like the warmth of the fire.
Tastes like gingerbread cookies.
Sounds like laughing and playing with all the new toys.

Tyler Shulman, Grade 5
Briarwood Christian Elementary School, AL

Veteran

V ery happy of you!
E veryone is very afraid that you are gone!
T ogether we trust in you!
E ach of us is nervous about you!
R ights is what we need!
A merica is free!
N ow it is safe for us!

Katlyn Elliott, Grade 4
Cherokee Elementary School, AR

God

Very powerful
so he can defeat evil
and protect us

Wesley Hardin, Grade 4
Briarwood Christian Elementary School, AL

Blue

Blue looks like a big blue sky when I'm on the ground.
Blue feels like a cold winter day in the snow.
Blue smells like my mother's blueberry pie.
Blue sounds like the ocean waves clapping together.
Blue tastes like a glass of refreshing ice cold water.
Blue is what you see in me when I'm happy.

Ashley Schwinn, Grade 5
Geggie Elementary School, MO

Bullies

Thy has a problem with bullies you say?
Beating thou up and taking your stuff.
Telling thou to give his pay.
Thinks he's cool, but really he's tough.

Thou is scared for his life every single day.
Don't want to go through with it, so school we miss.
Getting blamed all the way.
Since all of this is happening, we are sent to the office.

But thou's friends are there to help.
To help thou through those hard times.
So thou no longer has to yelp.
And thou won't have to lose any dimes.

So make sure thou has a friend,
Because friends are there 'till the end.

Krishna Mehta and Andrea Williams, Grade 6
Radloff Middle School, GA

His Game

When I pray, I call it rappin' with the "Big J."
Jesus is His name. My life is his game.

When I'm feeling down, I've got someone around.
Jesus is His name. My life is His game.

When I am happy too, he's there for me and you.
Jesus is His name. My life is His game.

When I have a test, the "Big J" thinks I'm the best.
Jesus is His name. My life is His game.

If you've lost touch my friend, it's time to call on Him.
Jesus is His name. Your life is His game.

The "Big J" loves us all, no matter how big or small.
Jesus is His name. Our life is His game.

Joshua Hebert, Grade 4
Holy Rosary Academy, LA

Stars

The stars twinkle all at night
They always light up my sight
They can help me where ever I am
They are so amazing.
They always make me happy when I'm sad
They light up my heart always,
When I look up in the sky and
see how beautiful they are in my eyes.

Katie Owens, Grade 5
Shannon Forest Christian School, SC

Hope Is Growing

Hope is a rainbow — filling our life with color.
Green is the strength with which we carry our faith.

Red is our heart…shining like a jewel.
Yellow is education. We learn in school.
Purple is the color of peace…
    For all the world.

Pink is the garden growing flowers of happiness.
Blue is the ship of hope sailing across the ocean.
White is the cure for disease.

I wonder…will hope remain?
Will this rainbow carry us through?

Brittany Teasley, Grade 5
Breitling Elementary School, AL

Creepy Spider

The spider is neat
The web has a great design
It is very cool

Mary Emma Campbell, Grade 4
Briarwood Christian Elementary School, AL

My Small Wobbling Fire

Finally! A fire
After all this work
I finally lit a fire of my own

It hobbles and wobbles
And finally stays
It starts to grow small,
So for wood I go search

For what seems an hour,
My small fire blazes
Between the cold snow
That surrounds these places

I go get some water
And come to find out
My small fire has vanished
For the warmth it once brought
Is no longer alive.

Maria Ferreira, Grade 6
Richards Middle School, GA

Egypt

Dam on the Nile
Holding back water

Crocodile on the riverside
Waiting for prey

People talking in the market
Waiting for gold

People in the temple
Praying to the gods
Matthew Fishback, Grade 4
Easley Elementary School, NC

Best Friends

Best friends are there,
When you are in need.
Best friends are there,
To do a good deed.
Best friends are there,
To have a good time.
You got to have a blast,
Even with the best friend of mine.
As I said, best friends are there,
When you are in need.
Even you have to be,
A best friend you see.
When you see your best friends,
They jump to galore
Because that is what,
Best friends are for!
Taylor Fain, Grade 5
Paint Lick Elementary School, KY

When I See Thanksgiving

Turkey, gravy, mashed potatoes, dressing
That's what most people think when they see the word Thanksgiving
But what I see isn't food galore
What I see is much much more
What I see is my cousins, my brothers,
My father, my mother
What I see is my family whom I love so
And without them I'd have nowhere to go
And to me that is better then turkey and dressing
I wish everyone would see that when they see the word Thanksgiving

Krystal Cook, Grade 6
Guntown Middle School, MS

Red

Red looks like a juicy apple sitting on my teacher's desk.
Red feels like a silk petal on a rose in a garden.
Red tastes like a plump cherry popping in my mouth.
Red smells like a fresh fall day on a cool morning.
Red sounds like the Cardinals hitting a homerun to win the World Series.
Red is the fire that burns in my heart when I play soccer.

Kyle Gardner, Grade 5
Geggie Elementary School, MO

Graceful, Beautiful, Cats

Oh, the fascinating creature the cat,
How swiftly, silently, and gracefully the cat will catch a rat.
If you admire them just right,
They will be more beautiful than sprite
To me they do not appear as a stale rye,
But as a beautiful butterfly.
But there are two cats at my aunt's house that get a lot of devotion,
When there is too much commotion.

Ian Taylor, Grade 4
South Topsail Elementary School, NC

Brown

Brown looks like a big rocky mountain in the distance.
Brown feels like my soft guinea pigs when they snuggle up to you.
Brown tastes like a big chocolate brownie just out of the oven.
Brown smells like a big fat cinnamon stick.
Brown sounds like a big brown bear roaring in the distance.
Brown is the color that begins my life.

Allie Webb, Grade 5
Geggie Elementary School, MO

If Voice Were a Color...

If voice were a color, it would be very bright,
It'd make you keep reading all through day and all through night.

If voice were a color, it would be like red,
It'd make you pick up your book and hop right into bed.

If voice were a color, it would shine like gold,
It'd make you feel happy, adventurous, and bold.

Ryan Carroll, Grade 4
Big Creek Elementary School, GA

Snow Day!

Snow flurries blow so cold,
As they whoosh and whish through the air,
Back and forth.

Karly Hodgson, Grade 5
American Heritage Academy, GA

Pickle

In the big glass jar
lies the delicious pickle
of truth, and triumph.

Peyton Dabbs, Grade 4
Briarwood Christian Elementary School, AL

The Boy Who Lived

Lord Voldemort drove Harry Potter crazy,
While killing his parents when he was only a baby;
He tried to kill Harry but didn't get far;
Through all his efforts, he left only a scar;
When he was twelve, Hagrid knocked on his door
To say he would live with his mean aunt and uncle no more;
Hagrid said, "You're a wizard, Harry;
I know this is scary;"
When he went to Hogwarts, he wasn't alone;
With Ron and Hermione he found the Sorcerer stone.

Ashleigh Sokie, Grade 6
St Anne Catholic School, SC

Iron Bowl

Football football everywhere
The smell of hot-dogs in the air
Watch Bama fall on the ground
While Auburn gets a touchdown
When the Tigers make a good play
All the crowd screams YEAH
When the game is over Mike jumps around
He nearly falls on the ground.

Peyton Phillips, Grade 6
Graham Elementary School, AL

An Unused Toy

What happens to an unused toy?
Does it blow away
like a soft breeze?
Or pack up its things and leave
like a college student?
Does it haunt your mind
like a ghost within the shadows?
Or linger near your heels
like a puppy counting your steps?

Maybe it pouts
like an angry child

Or does it just wait?

Shelby Studebaker, Grade 6
Charleston County School of the Arts, SC

Mommy

Sitting drawing pictures
creating things just for you
or sitting sticking photos with albums, paper, and glue.
Sitting with the radio on old memories in records, quite a few
or sitting, simply sitting you're in everything I do.

Brooke Pinkard, Grade 4
Brilliant Elementary School, AL

Black Cat, Black Cat

Black Cat, Black Cat comes only at night.
She walks in the shadows, staying out of sight.
Black Cat, Black Cat always silent and alone
Roaming and wandering without any home.
Black Cat, Black Cat very hungry and weary.
How can we help you, so you won't feel leary?
Black Cat, Black Cat can we give you a home
Name you and feed you and make you our own?
Black Cat, Black Cat here once more
Waiting and watching outside of our door.
Black Cat, Black Cat needs a new name.
We'll call her Raven, and we'll give her safe haven.
Black Cat, Black Cat lying on my bed
All warm and cozy after just being fed.
Black Cat, Black Cat has found a good home,
And knows she will never more roam.

Ian Fraski, Grade 6
Crocker RII School, MO

The Holocaust

People everywhere scared and misled,
Little do they know they're going to be dead.
The worry, the fright in people's faces,
Why would you kill these poor human races?

The panic, the innocence in people's eyes,
Some of them even had to get in disguise,
If you lived in those times you had to be brave,
You might even have to go live in a cave.

The Nazis were evil, mean people to hate,
You had no choice but to cooperate,
Tragedy and ignorance lingered in the air,
People were suffering everywhere.

Madison Immesote, Grade 5
Heber Springs Elementary School, AR

I Am A...

I am a clock on the wall at school,
Always the same, always in the same place.
But always moving,
My three hands always changing.
Tick, tock, tick, tock,
I show when it's time for the bell,
And when the day ends.

Clint Prevallet, Grade 6
St Vincent Elementary School, MO

The Moon and the Sun
The sun gathers the moon in its arms,
And takes away night.
And kills the little flickering lights.
As friends they work,
The sun and the moon,
Together.

Amanda Breig, Grade 5
St Vincent Elementary School, MO

Spring Days
Spending days outside
Watching butterflies flutter
And flowers in bloom.

Veronica Muniz, Grade 6
Tomlinson Jr High School, OK

A Day in Heaven
Heaven is pink.
It sounds like church bells.
It tastes like chocolate.
It smells like flowers.
It looks like amber fields of gold.
It makes you feel like singing.

Aubree Allen, Grade 5
Salem Elementary School, AR

July Fourth
J ust sit and watch the fireworks
U se the colorful fireworks
L ights and sparks light the dark
Y oung kids like the fireworks

F our different colors of showers
O ur whole family is here
U nited States always celebrates today
R ed explosions everywhere
T he lighters need to be full
H ave you had a good time?

Dustin Roan, Grade 5
Frankford Elementary School, MO

Soccer
I love soccer
I'm a blocker
  I even kick my locker.

I love soccer
I'm a kicker
  I'm even a defender.

I love soccer
I make a goal
  I kicked an ant hole
I love soccer.

Logan Frederick, Grade 5
Arnaudville Elementary School, LA

My Heart
The smile was brief,
My heart was light,
I could actually sleep at night,
But now it's all different,
It's all wrong,
You broke my heart,
Our love is gone.

"Sorry" can't heal my pain,
I won't show my secret sham,
You said you'd help,
You were wrong
You broke my heart,
Our love is gone.

I cried when you left me once,
I cried when you left me twice,
I couldn't cry a third time,
You ended my emotional life.

Jordan Munn, Grade 6
Kitty Stone Elementary School, AL

I Can't Write a Poem*
It's hard
It's not fun
I'm allergic to poems
I have ape hands
I think I'm dying
My pencils keep breaking
I think it's Saturday
Aliens have taken me
Time's up? Uh oh!
All I have is this dumb
list of excuses. You like it?
Really? No kidding. Thanks a lot.
Would you like to see another one?

Alex Brooks, Grade 6
Armorel Elementary School, AR
*Patterned after "I Can't Write a
Poem" by Bruce Lansky

Ice
Freezing slick cover
Clear crystals hanging from eaves
Slipping sliding down

Tyler Dyson, Grade 4
Broadway Elementary School, NC

Football
Football
I have the ball
Touchdown
Touchdown
I made a Touchdown!

Brandt Mathews, Grade 4
Cave City Elementary School, AR

Fourth Grade
F un
O pen and different
U nique
R un to learn
T here are lots of friends
H ere there is a wonderful teacher

G ood
R un in P.E.
A wesome
D aring
E xciting

Mackenzie Harris, Grade 4
Landmark Christian School, GA

Lawmaker
  L aborist
  A chieve
  W ell-bred
  M ankind
  A ccomplish
  K indhearted
agre **E** ment
wo **R** k

Lexi Pitts, Grade 4
East Jones Elementary School, MS

Best Friends
I've never come across anyone
As great as them
Ones who stuck by me whenever
I needed them
We might not be the most perfect
Set of friends
Yet we think that the love we
Have for each other couldn't be better

Yeah we fuss and we fight
But we'll always be tight
We know that we can call
On each other whenever we're alone
We are best friends; Yasmine,
Calia, and me, Allyson Jones

Allyson Jones, Grade 6
Brogden Middle School, NC

Veteran
V ictory in America
E verlasting love
T rust and truth
E mbrace truth and justice
R espect in America
A wesome America
N ature in justice

Autumn E. Boggs, Grade 4
Cherokee Elementary School, AR

Brown

Brown looks like hot chocolate on a cold winter day.
Brown feels like brown leaves breaking in my hand.
Brown tastes like chocolate from a candy store.
Brown smells like BBQ wings on a plate.
Brown sounds like wood getting sawed.
Brown is one of my favorite colors.

Alex McCracken, Grade 5
Geggie Elementary School, MO

Spring

Smells like the new bloomed flowers
Feels like lying down in the sunny grass
Tastes like fresh ice tea
Looks like no time but to relax
Sounds like all the baby birds are chirping

Caroline Fields, Grade 5
Briarwood Christian Elementary School, AL

Seconds

Turkey, potatoes, macaroni and cheese
What I wanna know, can I get some more please?
Food, food, food galore
The question is, can I get some more?
In a bowl, on a plate, or even a stick
I need some food now and I need it quick
Your food is so good, moist, and creamy
If I were the food, I wouldn't want to see me
I would eat the food in the quickest hurry
No chance for the food to try to scurry
The end for the food, the beginning for me
This is the end of my food rhymery

Micah Proctor, Grade 6
Brogden Middle School, NC

Our Soldiers Overseas

The risk their lives,
and make the ultimate sacrifice.
They all do it willingly,
never thinking twice.

Our men and women are out there,
on the frontline.
They get in small skirmishes,
time after time.

They volunteer to go out there,
all have the nerve.
They are always in some danger,
but they're still willing to serve.

Our American soldiers are out there,
fighting to keep us free.
Because the land we are today,
is the land we were meant to be.

Hunter Pabst, Grade 6
Haynes Academy for Advanced Studies, LA

Pet Love!!

How good is pet love you ask?
Pet love is great the whole world should know.
Gray, white, brown, black, or yellow any color,
It doesn't matter as long as you love it, and it loves you.
Love is what the world goes around.
Love is in the air.
It's all around us.
If you don't know about pet love you haven't seen nothing yet.

Danielle Miller, Grade 5
Debusk Elementary School, TN

Our Flag

This is our flag,
Let us not mistreat it.
Nobody else can defeat it.
This flag stands for love and freedom.

Every stripes means our thirteen colonies,
And every star stands for our fifty states
And how our country has grown.

Our flag is inseparable.
So let us stand up for our flag and our country.

We fought and we won.
And that meant that we were done.

We are under authority of God.
Our flag means we have freedom and that we have rights.

So let us win our fights.

Sarah Johnson, Grade 6
Heartland High School and Academy, MO

Kindergarten

My first day of kindergarten
Little kids that I have never met before
Meeting the teacher
Parents leaving
Making new friends
Lunch
Walking to the cafeteria
Standing in line took forever
Finding a seat took forever also
I meet this nice girl named Taylor
Taylor wasn't in my class though
The end of school
When they would call the buses
Standing in a big line going back to the cafeteria
Finding my bus table
Seeing my friend that lives in my neighborhood
Meeting my bus driver
Having a great day of…
School

Dee Dee Russell, Grade 6
Beck Academy, SC

The Feather

Smooth and rough feather
laying on the brown dirt ground,
black and white feather
Matthew Ayala, Grade 6
St Joseph Institute for the Deaf, MO

Veteran

V olunteering to fight for us.
E very day of their lives.
T rying their best,
E ven if it's hard.
R eady to get up and go.
A nd fight for their lives.
N ative America is ready to fight.
Samantha Stovall, Grade 4
Cherokee Elementary School, AR

What Is Blue?

Blue is the lake.
The color of the sky.
Blue is the color of
My favorite book.
Also the color of the blue jay.
Blue is the color you don't want to be!
Monica Weaver, Grade 5
Trenton Middle School, MO

My Puppies

They play.
They run.
They tug at each other.
They bite at each other.
They pull at Robinhood's ears.
They walk.
They sleep.
They chew on their bones.
They love you and love you for years.
They like to sit in your lap.
They love to lick on your face.
They are cute and adorable.
And they can't be replaced.
Rachel Kathleen Stiles, Grade 6
Scotts Creek Elementary School, NC

Black and White

Some people are angry and lie
and their forked tongues pierce
Some people make you tremble and cry
and they are cold and fierce

Some people love and are helpful
and their intents are pure
Some people always tell the truth
it's them God will hear
Tanner Smith, Grade 6
Central Arkansas Christian School, AR

A Whispering Sound

The wind whispers in my ear saying a silent sound,
and when the wind blows hard it grows and goes round and round,
It sinks up in the deep blue sky saying a whispering sound,
and he said, "Why is a whisper a whisper, and why is the sky so blue,
no one knows because a whisper is a whisper and it whispers only to you."
Kiana Roshel Rambo, Grade 5
Franklin Elementary School, OK

Cheer!

Go! Shoot! Run!
When you are at a game here is how to make it extra fun!
CHEER! Basketball, soccer, baseball, or football
Start a cheer by making a call
Cheer on the court, field, or dugout
If you don't know any cheers just shout!
Cheers can be fun and silly
Even if it's just plainly Go Billy!
Anything that will encourage your teammates is great
If he/she swings or hits too late
Don't go and cry or get mad
No matter how bad
While sitting on the bench with nothing to do
Make up a cheer, soon, very soon
Cheer with your family and friends
And when the game is nearing the end
Do not be afraid to shout till you go hoarse
Just make sure the cheers don't turn to sayings mean and coarse
When the buzzer beeps and the clock stops
Stand up and cheer with all you've got!

Madeline Baker, Grade 6
Queen of Angels Catholic School, GA

Go Find Each Other

A girl by a waterfall,
A boy sitting in a tree,
"Go find him," a voice called,
"He's somewhere in a tree."
Altogether lost in hope,
She ran faithfully,
Wondering if she'll go back,
Or if she'll find that tree.
There he was, watching her from the tree,
Wishing to break free and flee,
For he was trapped by vines divine,
Hoping that she could call him, "mine."
For only true love could break those vines,
Those vines so divine,
So he called to her, "you're mine."
And she answered, "forever and ever, you're mine."
The vines let loose and set him free,
And so he leapt from the tree,
And ran to her,
As she ran to him.
"Forever and ever, we'll be in those vines so divine together," she said.
Olivia Sartain, Grade 6
Bellwood Discovery School, TN

Brothers

B is for brother's who get under your skin.
R is for rough and dirty shins.
O is for oblivious and clueless thoughts.
T is for terrible and terrifying things.
H is for helpful, which they're not to me.
E is for extinct, which I wish they could be.
R is for ridiculous in every sort of way.
S is for scallywag, which my brothers appear to be.

Chrissy Bolesky, Grade 4
St Thomas More School, NC

Mammoth Cave

A smiling face beamed as I opened my eyes
Outside bodies are gearing up for a long chilling ride
Chills cover my body as we make our entrance
Stinging rises to nip at my nose
Warmness hugs me as we make our exit
Stinging feet make me almost fall
Flames warm me as I rest
Tired I walk toward the jumpy goats
Nipping at my hands I feel their hunger
I rise into the air as my dad's clutch tightens
Leaving I look back at the wonderful place I love
I wake up, we are already home

Morgan Huninghake, Grade 5
Cline Elementary School, KY

Christmas

C hristmas is the time for joy, spirit, and presents
H aving a good time ripping presents open
R ed, blue, and green wrappings
I have a blast having snowball fights
S anta Claus comes and delivers presents
T he most wonderful day
M y stocking is filled with candy
A spectacular time it is that day.
S omething makes it a special holiday.

Austin Jones, Grade 5
Sullivan Elementary School, TN

Boys Are Yuck and Birds Have Not So Much Luck!!

I am the reader of my class.
But what I hate the most is some
Boys tend to pass gas.
They say, "Oh, my bad."
I am so not glad.

I am in a class with geeks and nerds.
When one day there was a bird.
I said, well hello there cheerful thang.
But then there was a bang.
Down fluttered the little feathers.
But just to think I have to go back to school.
Where it is so not cool.

Whitney Williams, Grade 5
Cottonwood Public School, OK

If I Had

If I had a wishing star,
That I could make a wish upon,
I would wish for a better world,
That I could live on.
There are so many things that I would
Like to change down here,
Like drugs and hate that may cause fear,
These are just a few but a good place to start.
I would place love where hatred had been in the
HEART!

David Sparks, Grade 5
Paint Lick Elementary School, KY

Snow Is Everywhere

Snow is everywhere,
I jumped for joy,
Snowy day are fun,
For girls and boys.

You put on your winter clothes,
And then go on out,
You can roll and throw the snow,
That is what snow is about.

Christmas is coming,
I hope it comes soon,
All of the leaves and trees will be covered,
From morning 'til noon.

Snow is everywhere,
I will have so much fun,
I hope it will snow forever,
Just to leave out the sun.

I love snow days,
How about you?
Go and get some hot cocoa,
And think it through.

Kelly Dorsey, Grade 6
William J Fisher Elementary School, LA

Rain Forest

Smells like unique flowers, moss and bark
Looks like birds in the air, trees everywhere
Feels like trees giving shade, dirt and leaves
Tastes like exotic fruit and newly fallen rain
Sounds like rushing water and animal life all around

Taylor Bass, Grade 5
Briarwood Christian Elementary School, AL

The Raindrops

Raindrops are falling
Everywhere seeds are sprouting
The spring is coming!

Isabella Powell, Grade 4
Briarwood Christian Elementary School, AL

Stars

S oaring
T winkling
A ir born
R adiant
S hining

Kelly Wilson, Grade 4
Moyock Elementary School, NC

What Is Wisdom if Not a Tree?

What is wisdom if not a tree?
Thoughts waiting to be picked
Subject branching new ideas
Aging, sprouting tree rings

Thoughts waiting to be picked
Knowledge budding leaves
Aging, sprouting three rings
Watching years go by

Knowledge budding leaves
Death, chainsaw hacking into life
Watching years go by
The bigger it is the older it can get

Death, chainsaw hacking into life
Subject branching into new ideas
The bigger it is the older it can get
What is wisdom if not a tree?

Stephanie Soendker, Grade 6
Pioneer Ridge Sixth Grade Center, MO

My Love

My love
Could be
Should be
Or
It is to be
Nobody knows
Because love is a mystery
Love is a secret
It is a story
Love is not to be hurt
It is not to be killed
Love is life
Love is,
The world.

Madelaine Beitzel, Grade 4
Clonlara School, NC

My Jesus

Jesus is the Savior
He saves us all…
When God comes down to Earth
The devil shall fall.

Corbin Kellum, Grade 4
Southside Elementary School, AR

Witch's Stew

Deadman's toes,
And one frog's nose,
Eye of a lizard,
Snow from a blizzard,
Hair from a wizard,
Bark of a dog,
Smell of a log,
Taste of a chicken,
And some nose pickin'.

Samantha Rader, Grade 6
St Vincent Elementary School, MO

Sports

Sports are fun
But they're not silly games
Sports are hard work
You can win
You can lose
You get booed
You're a star
You go far

Dylan Spinelli, Grade 5
Drayton Hall Elementary School, SC

The Four-Wheeler

Fast as the wind
Swift as an arrow
Down the road
Into the woods
The four-wheeler goes
Passing the trees
Passing the bushes
Going faster and faster
Like a red flash
The four-wheeler goes
Down the hill
Through the creek
Splashing in the water
Sliding in the mud
Up the other side
The four-wheeler goes
Over the bank
Across the fields
Into the sun
Into the wind
The four-wheeler goes

Kenny Renegar, Grade 4
Cool Spring Elementary School, NC

Autumn Leaves

Watching autumn leaves
is like watching water
trickling over the rocks in a waterfall
until they land soothingly.

Harrison Brooks, Grade 4
First Wesleyan Christian School, NC

Creative Art

Your pencil runs,
Your colors flow.
You think great things,
So all your ideas go.
Your mind wanders about,
Just drawing whatever comes,
And in the end, it is Creative Art.

Jessica Wilder, Grade 6
St Peter School, MO

Deer Hunt

I shot a deer with my new gun
That son of a gun was on the run
I walked and ran
I was out of breath
Then I saw him at his death
I showed my wife
She started to cry
Then I told her it was time for him to die

Dillan Alvin Vandeven, Grade 5
Zalma Elementary School, MO

My Baby Brother

My baby brother is about four,
And all he says is he wants more.
My baby brother is so cute,
He gets a lot of attention,
So I wish I could put him on mute.
And when he eats,
In his diaper come treats.

Wesley Bodin, Grade 6
St Cecilia School, LA

Veteran

V icious battles are everywhere
E nduring soldiers are fighting
T orture is here
E ager to get through the battles
R ampaging fighters are retreating
A rmed forces are helping
N ot all will see home

Austin Himschoot, Grade 4
Cherokee Elementary School, AR

Fluffy

Fluffy my dog is so funny!
She is like a scientist
Always exploring new things.
She is very curious, sweet
And rambunctious!
I love to watch her protect her house
Like a mom protects her child.
Fluffy talks to me every night
And lulls me to sleep.

Jessica Austel, Grade 5
Bonaire Elementary School, GA

N.C. State Red

N.C. State Red sounds like the football team
hitting pads on a cold fall night.

N.C. State Red tastes like a sweet apple
going in my mouth.

N.C. State Red feels like a wolfs fur
while it's running in the breeze.

N.C. State Red smells like a wolfs breath
after it just ate.

N.C. State Red looks like the fans
going nuts at the game after they just made
a touchdown playing against Carolina.

Ross Robinson, Grade 5
Cool Spring Elementary School, NC

My Father

My father is nice.
You will love to be around him.
Five of my friends wish he was their dad.
All of the time he buys me things.
The same day he gets paid he gives me 20 dollars.
He is the best father I've ever met.
Every day we watch TV together.
Really I love him so much.

Sabria Williams, Grade 4
Stephens Elementary School, AL

Thank You God

The friends I've got,
Touch my heart just like
My Mom and Dad.
Things they say to me,
I'll always keep within.
My Mom's look shines down on me,
My Dad's music so very sweet,
So sweet I could almost hear it now.
The soft breeze,
On my face feels so very good.
The most important thing in my life,
Is God Almighty.
He fills the empty hole in my heart,
And that's where
I want Him to stay,
Right there with me.

Renata Roussell, Grade 6
Haynes Academy for Advanced Studies, LA

On the Web

A little spider.
It spins its web big and neat.
And catches its food.

Ryan Murphy, Grade 4
Briarwood Christian Elementary School, AL

Rainy Moments

Rain, dripping onto houses and into rain gutters
Pounding on my bedroom window
In a matter of minutes all I hear is rain on my window
It silenced my music for my attention
Feeding Mother Nature and her children
Through day and night it pours
As dawn nears, sunrise moves gracefully, as does the sun,
up into the sky, as it evaporates the water into thin air
All of my rainy moments; disappear leaving me with nothing
but my memories, rainy memories

Hannah Quire, Grade 4
Big Creek Elementary School, GA

Colors

Colors for you and colors for me
Blue for the sky and blue for the sea
Green for the grass and green for a pea
Yellow for the sun and a bumblebee
Mother Nature has so many colors
That's why it would be too long to name the others

Marissa Doucet, Grade 5
Arnaudville Elementary School, LA

The Ocean

Feeling the warm sun on my back.
Tasting the cool drink in my mouth.
Hearing the people splashing in the water.
Seeing the seagulls flying overhead.
Smelling the salty air.

Madison Thames, Grade 5
Briarwood Christian Elementary School, AL

My Red-Hooded Sweatshirt

You, my red-hooded sweatshirt,
were the shiniest one in the world.
You were extra-large and the kids at school
thought you were too big.
But as I got older, you became a perfect fit.
Then my house caught fire and you burned to ashes.
I saw another red-hooded sweatshirt at the mall.
I tried it on, but it wasn't a perfect fit.
It was like my life ended when yours did.

Levi Gotto, Grade 5
St Vincent Elementary School, MO

Pranks

A whoopie cushion on a chair,
put an insect in her hair.
Sneak a banana peel on the floor,
tear the picture off the door.
Do something that will make her weep,
even do it when she's asleep.
Stick wood in her shoes and she'll get a blister.
The pranks I pull on my older sister.

Linnea J. Galletta, Grade 5
Shannon Forest Christian School, SC

Playing Pool

Oh, how I like to play pool,
people who challenge me must be a fool,
I don't usually win,
but at the end there's a grin.

Oh, how I love to play pool,
when I knock the ball in,
I feel cool,
then again I grin.

Oh how I love pool,
so wonderful, so sweet,
they say I rule
to play pool, it's a treat.

Eric Gauldin, Grade 5
Stokesdale Elementary School, NC

Roses

On a summer day
I like to watch roses grow
Until the fall comes

Jennifer Snyder, Grade 5
Etowah Elementary School, NC

Christmas

C hrist died for us.
H e loves us.
R esurrected for us.
I will always love him.
S peaks to us.
T ells us what to do.
M ighty king.
A wesome God.
S aves us.

Evan Rainey, Grade 6
Desoto Central School, MS

Leaves

Falling down,
Racing each other,
Down to the ground.
Tagging each other.
Like children playing.
Like falling stars
Twirling down
In the air
Flying,
Diving,
Down,
Down,
Down,
Gliding on air,
Wishing they
could float forever.

Katie Grubb, Grade 4
Crestwood Elementary School, KY

What's in My Journal

The black and white horse galloping across the field,
Mane flowing with every stride.
The intensity in the air,
Sweat dripping off the faces of the young athletes,
The ball is hit with everyone staring, waiting for their turn,
Yelling, screaming, BUMP, SET, SPIKE!
Quiet, not a sound is heard except the jingle of the bridle,
The thunder of the hoof beats against the hard ground.
Snow falling on my face, I am looking down this massive monster,
I am falling, but meaning to,
We are in tandem, my family and I,
Skiing in 'S' patterns down the giant mountain.
Verdant walls, brass bed, the colorful, fragile quilt my grandmother made me,
Checked comforter, long pillows stretched out like tired dogs.
Looking out the window into the bright black sky lit up by shining stars.
Stepping into the front row, rusted from years of use.
I grip the handle bar so tightly it makes calluses on my freezing hands.
We come to our first drop, going deeper in the darkness,
So fast I feel as if I cannot breathe.
As fast as it started, the ride is over.

Rachel Travis, Grade 6
Baylor School, TN

My Favorite Wood

I used to sing sweet songs,
I used to feel so good,
but that was before they cut down my favorite wood.

I used to hear the song of nature,
I used to touch silky flower petals,
but that was before they turned the land into harsh, cold metals.

I used to see beautiful nature,
I used to smell sticky sap,
but that was before they turned my favorite wood, into a big, 'ol, gap.

Hope Pungello, Grade 5
Montessori Community School, NC

God

There is a Heaven above,
And also a white little dove,
Who stops by my house every day
And moves in its own special way,
And soon I learned it was an angel,
And blessed it with my own soul,
When it told me that God was a special Person,
And soon when I go to church I'll be glad I worshipped Him,
I went and praised His name,
When I saw everyone doing the same,
I felt wonderful because I noticed I wasn't the only one
who was tapped by the dove,
And now since I was at church all God did was told me to give love,
I didn't understand at first but now I do,
All that time God was trying to tell me to love myself and to love Him too.

Zakiya Smith, Grade 6
Brogden Middle School, NC

Love

It is such a strong word to say,
Moreover, you wonder if he does day by day.
You kiss and hug,
Talk and play,
You wonder every single day.
Indescribable and heartbreaking
As people say —
Love hurts.
Parents say, "You're too young,"
We say, "But we're still in love."
Plan your wedding and your life
Elders tell you it is all a lie.
They say you should wait
'Til the time comes
He might not be the special one.
He hurts you; you hurt him.
Then you go away thinking
What you can do to keep it working
In addition, it still does not follow
Then you think…
Whether it's really *LOVE*.

Ty'Shian Innocent, Grade 6
Newbern Middle School, GA

The Red Tree

A wonderful sight
The leaves turn red in the fall
Fall makes things different!

Katie Sanders, Grade 4
Briarwood Christian Elementary School, AL

People

Some people are nice
Some people are mean
And some are so angry you think they'll turn green.

Some are crazy some are smart
Some are so good they can do art.
Some can even keep a today chart.

Some people like to cook
Some make a cook book
Some just like to read a book.

Some like to play
Some people work and bosses pay
Some just like to have their way.

Some are happy
Some are sad
Some are mad
But that's okay because
People will be people
And I am glad.

Emily Holiday, Grade 5
Macedonia Elementary School, SC

Puppies

puppies don't weigh much
you could pick some up with a touch
they don't play
they're to young they sleep most of the day
snuggling together
in any weather
when they are young they get sick
in a lick

Louisa Fine, Grade 4,
NC

The Blue Sea

The ocean waves crash
The color is aqua blue
It is beautiful

Mary Catherine Touliatos, Grade 4
Briarwood Christian Elementary School, AL

Face Your Fears

I drop my head into the water
Because the sin inside me is to be slaughtered

I feel refreshed I feel so good
Like taking drugs out of a bad neighborhood

I'm being pulled up without hesitation
To open my eyes to a crowd clapping

What has happened? What have I done?
Oh yeah I was baptized in front of everyone!

Jack Dolan, Grade 6
The Mountain Community School, NC

Rose/Tree

Rose
beautiful, sweet
blooming, smelling, dying
garden, bush, forest, leaves
rooting, absorbing, growing
tall, leafy
Tree

Miles Bragdon-Hall, Grade 5
Briarwood Christian Elementary School, AL

All Around

Red leaf
Yellow leaf
All leaves around,
Kids raking,
Kids running
And playing all around.

Leaves are on roads, yards and much much more,
Leaves are all around just as before.

Faith Mercer, Grade 5
Debusk Elementary School, TN

A Tree

Once a tree loved me
every time it saw me
it danced and sang out
I ran to it and it hugged
me and cradled me like a baby
I loved it and it loved me
until it moved on never to
see me again but I'll never
forget the tree who loved me

Kaitlyn Carter, Grade 6
Armorel Elementary School, AR

A Windy Day

On a windy day
I like to play in the snow
And sled all day long.

Lori Pace, Grade 5
Etowah Elementary School, NC

Jamie

Jamie is gone.
He is now in the air.
He is flying high.
Up, up, up.

So long to Jamie.
I'll miss him so.
We had many good times,
But he had to go.

Bye, bye, bye.
He's up in the sky.
On a journey so long.
It breaks my heart to think he's gone.

It doesn't feel right
Without him beside me.
It doesn't feel right
Without him to guide me.

Now I'm here all alone.
I'm waiting for Jamie.
I feel so bad, I'm going insane.
It's hard to see him fly off in the plane.

Raegan Andrews, Grade 6
Beck Academy, SC

The Promise

It is beautiful
It is red, blue, green
And purple and pink, yellow
Is supposed to have gold at the end
It's God's promise
It's a rainbow.

Bryant Lee Bailey, Grade 4
Crossville Christian School, TN

Sun

The sun rising
Large, magnificent
Rising, shining, gleaming
Slowly rising over my head.
Setting, creeping, fading,
Beautiful, colorful
The sun setting

Sydney Carr, Grade 6
Pulaski County Middle School, GA

Snow, Snow, Snow

Snow, snow, snow!
It's always cold out in the snow.
Snow, snow, snow!
You get to miss school when it snows,
Out in the cold.
You can make the best snowman ever,
Out in the snow.
Snow, snow, snow!

Stephanie Stephens, Grade 4
Hayes Elementary School, OK

Wild Horses

Wild horses running free,
So beautiful and elegant,
Out on their own,
On this beautiful land.
I wish I could be,
A wild horse running free.

Mercedes Nute, Grade 5
North Shelby Elementary School, MO

Hunting

Hunting is fun!
So hurry up and
Get-R-Done!
Up early —
Hunting all day;
Stop and take
a little break
We're all REDNECKS;
That is true!
Come and join us?
How about you?
hang in the trees:
hide in the bush!
Stop!
Be quiet!
shush!
    shush!
        shush!
listen for the sound
of a bear or dear or a long-eared hare!
come home late, eat a bite, go to sleep!

Hunter W. Gass, Grade 6
Scotts Creek Elementary School, NC

Flying

I was flying in the sky,
I flew way too high,
I reached the sun,
I knew my life was done,
I fell down dead
until you said,
"I think, I think,
I think you're dead."

McKinley Martin, Grade 4
Landmark Christian School, GA

Day and Night

Day
light, warm
warming, enlightening, awakening
brightness, sun, darkness, moon
cooling, darkening, brooding
dark, cool
Night

Victoria Zimmerman, Grade 5
Prince of Peace Catholic School, SC

Autumn Days

A pples on the ground
U sing a knife to cut the pumpkin pie
T idying up the house
U nselfish people
M ountains covered in leaves
N aughty and nice

D rugs stores closing
A corn whistles
Y oYo's going wild
S un setting in the sky

That is what I call "Autumn Days."

Matthew Mulvaney, Grade 5
Palmetto Christian Academy, SC

God

Your words can crumble any mountain.
Your breath can freeze any fountain.

God helped Moses part the Red Sea.
He sent Jesus to save you and me.

He helped Noah survive the flood.
All of this is good.

The deaf will hear. The blind will see.
He does all this for you and me.

God is glorious man.
He has a glorious plan.

Frank Guida, Grade 6
Mount Zion Christian School, SC

Nature

Nature is one of my favorite things
I stay there until the church bell rings
I stroll through the meadows
While the grass tickles my toes
I go there to calm down
For it isn't as loud as town
I sit down on the grass
Just to relax
For when I go home I have
A fine feeling in my heart
For nature is my favorite part
Of earth's heart

Olivia Mann, Grade 5
St Thomas More School, NC

By the Brooks

By the brooks crickets
Are chirping a noise of peace
A beautiful green

Caroline Kerr, Grade 4
Briarwood Christian Elementary School, AL

Animals

In the air soaring
fish swimming in the ocean
and on the land wild and free

Jake Harrell, Grade 4
Briarwood Christian Elementary School, AL

Giant

An undersized little oak tree, barely any leaves or branches,
Just a minor stick. Rising into the full-size blue sky,
Branches stretching farther. As it drops a puny acorn,
Falling into the green grass.

Green ovals hanging there, on the dark even branches.
Trunk as thick as an elephant's foot. Giant reaches higher.

Growing thicker, wider, crooked, too. Watching the birds land,
On the branches full of leaves. Listening to the wind whistle.
As the seed grows into a tiny sprout.

With ragged brown leaves, giant gets older.
Starting to rot. Clasping with a loud…THUMP!!!
All that's left in the dark soil is the little tree,
That grew into a GIANT!

Caroline Sadlo, Grade 4
Goshen Elementary School at Hillcrest, KY

A Leprechaun Named Reid

There once was a leprechaun named Reid,
He loved to plant one lucky little seed
But when Rover came over,
He ate Reid's four leaf clover

Reid Parker, Grade 4
South Topsail Elementary School, NC

Sullivan's Island Hill

Sullivan's Island Hill
overlooks Charleston.
From the top of the mound,
I see the Ravenel Bridge
that looks like two sailboats
drifting on the Cooper River.
Whether I climb to the top,
or drive the rocky path up,
it still makes me feel
like a bird soaring through the sky.
Pieces of cardboard
litter the hill,
and I use them to slide down
the bumpy worn grass
that covers the knoll.
I feel like a penguin gliding
through the snow
with a smile on my face.

Ashley Beth Prentice, Grade 6
Charleston County School of the Arts, SC

My Chopper

When the rain is coming down and all is wet
I can't ride my chopper or play around
But when the sun comes out and all is clear
I can ride my chopper all about
So I like the sun better cause there's more to do
When it is raining I get all wet
When I ride my chopper down the road
I feel free and happy and full of life

Jessica Worrell, Grade 6
Dyer Elementary & Jr High School, TN

I Am a Military Child

I am a military child, born in Fort Hood Texas.
I wonder what is going on when tanks are firing.
I hear the loud explosions from tanks firing.
I see my friends moving from their houses.
I want my father to be around when I need him.
I am a military child.

I pretend that I'm with my father shooting tanks.
I feel happy every time my dad comes home.
I hug my father to show my love.
I worry about my brother while playing football.
I cry when my parents do not understand me.
I am a military child.

I do not understand that my father can leave at any time.
I say to my mom why dad has to leave.
I dream that one day I can fight for freedom.
I try to grab the flags in flag football.
I hope one day I can protect my country from evil.
I am a military child.

Benjamin Waga, Grade 4
Walker Intermediate School, KY

Wednesday

Today I ate my cat,
Tomorrow I'll eat my hat,
Friday I'll eat my bat,
Boy oh boy am I going to get fat!
Julia Ross, Grade 6
St Cecilia School, LA

The Super Sonic Beast

I am veracious like an earthquake
I have a vortex of doom
I am a beast you never want to meet
I will kill you like lightning
I will spin you into a shark's mouth
I am petrifying like a Hurricane Katrina
I am loud like a twister
I will run over you like a powerful train
I am your worst nightmare
I would watch out
I will give you no warning
I will get you because you can't hide
I will find you wherever you go
I am a tornado
Jade Hunt, Grade 5
Pembroke Elementary School, NC

My Mittens

I have some purple mittens,
They're always nice and fitted,
They kept me warm,
Since I was born,
That's why I love my mittens!
Sarah Arceneaux, Grade 6
St Cecilia School, LA

Life

There is a game called life
But life is not a game
Life is what you make it
So don't make it a shame

There is a cereal called life
But life is not a food
So always use good manners
And don't be rude

Life has some good times
And some bad one's too
But if you stay positive
You'll make it through

So don't complain about life
Just try to smile and laugh
And be very very thankful
For the life that you have
JhaBrelle Hall, Grade 6
Brogden Middle School, NC

Who Am I?

Hey you, can you guess who I am?
Nature created me, I am tougher than a ram!
I come down from sky.
Lots of people seem to wonder why.
I am black and gray in color and am made of dirt and wind.
I can take down gigantic trees and all of a sudden make them bend.
My body twirls around and around.
Especially when I touch the ground.
Now have you guessed who I am?
I am a deadly tornado. I will take you out with a bam.
Kelsey Mariah Locklear, Grade 5
Pembroke Elementary School, NC

Dark Angel

The black wings of my angel, my darkest sin…
The scars of my tormented soul…

They cannot see me, they cannot see my wings…
They cannot see my luster of ecstasy

I have taken the kiss of hatred…I feel the bliss of allegiance
I taste the pleasure of sorrow…

They cannot see…I can see
I can see their malice as they laugh their twisted laughs…

These wings are my reminder my reminder that I don't belong…
The curse of my darkness…

My broken dreams…My faded hopes…My forgotten paradise
I of the black wing, walk in the shadows

Wade in the black lake of tears forever I drift my angel and I,
Deeper into the darkness the only place my wings are accepted
Kali Kokolis, Grade 6
Chapin Middle School, SC

America, a Wonderful Place for Me!

I am proud to be an American,
a wonderful place for me.
When the sun rises, I see God's face telling me you're okay.
Tears of family members
are running down their faces.
I always think of you in the war and
I'm hoping that you are okay.
I pray to God
that the angels are watching over you.
We dream of everyone
being okay in the war.
As night comes, I look into the stars
and make a special wish for all the soldiers in the war.
Always remember that
all the angels are watching over you and they are protecting you,
Thanks for making our lives safe!
Dorie Darbonne, Grade 6
Leonville Elementary School, LA

Glistening Raindrops

If I were rain
I would drip out of clouds
And explode once I hit the ground
Like a cannonball in a battlefield

If I were rain
I would make ripples glide through glassy water
And tap on tin roofs
Drowning out all other sounds

If I were rain
I would glisten and sparkle
as I splash on the smooth black pavement

If I were rain

Darby Brown, Grade 6
South Oldham Middle School, KY

The Monkey

The curious monkey gazes about,
as the sun rises through the trees.
There is much to do, he has no doubt,
as he scurries through the tempestuous breeze.

The funny monkey hops around,
searching for his daily meal.
He wiggles his tail up and down,
spotting an insect that is teal.

The playful monkey chases his friend,
running and jumping limb by limb.
They chase each other to the river bend.
The sun goes down as the light dims.

The sleepy monkey climbs into bed.
He stretches, he yawns,
he falls and bumps his head.
He closes his eyes, as he waits for the next dawn.

Erica Murret, Grade 6
Haynes Academy for Advanced Studies, LA

The Beautiful Flowers

Little pink roses
Did not get enough water
So they will not grow

Aleah Hutchinson, Grade 4
Briarwood Christian Elementary School, AL

What's That Coming Up the Stairs?

Shhhh! Do you hear the creeeeeak of the stairs?
I can hear tiny whispers at the end of the hall.
Tap, tap, tapping of wandering feet.
(Gasp) Something's knocking on my door!…Ahhhhh!
Ohhhh…it's my mom.

Morgan Beam, Grade 5
Ascension Elementary School, KY

If I Were in Charge of the World

If I were in charge of the World
There would be upstairs in every house,
     So I can look over rooftops
Then I can take a ladder and get on my house.
     If I were in charge of the world
There would be a better cure for cancer,
     And give them a life they've never had
Like going to Kentucky Kingdom for a ride.
     If I were in charge of the world
There would be no more poor people
     They would have big and clean houses.
And that's if I was in charge of the World

Cory Sheffield, Grade 6
Eminence Middle School, KY

Together

T ightest Thanksgiving hugs come from Momma,
O ldest daughter, Aunt Gloria,
G ives the most kisses. Around the table we
E njoy
T elling
H umorous jokes. The Williams Family
E nveloped in
R espect, harmony, and love.

The youngest granddaughter,
Sostine Williams

Sostine Williams, Grade 6
Nathaniel Hawthorne Elementary School, MO

All About Thanksgiving

T urkey baking in the oven
H appy people talking
A ll of us bow our heads in prayer
N ow we all eat
K iller turkey
S melling fall in the air
G iving people respect
I miss people over in Iraq,
V eterans sacrificing for us
I n God we trust
N ow we always will remember these days when we
G row up.

Brandon Harris, Grade 5
Sullivan Elementary School, TN

The Seasons

Winter
cold, damp
snowing, raining, learning
bonfires, snowflakes, flowers, vacation
playing, running, skipping
hot, joyful
Summer

Alex Gantt, Grade 5
Briarwood Christian Elementary School, AL

Ode to Dad

When I was 7
my dad got sick.
People told me but I
thought it was a trick.
Now I'm 11 and he is in Heaven.
I wish I could go back to being 7.

Jacob Keyes, Grade 6
Our Lady of Fatima School, MS

The Best Summer

Playing with my friends
going to the beach to swim
summer is the best

Ashley Tullos, Grade 6
Tomlinson Jr High School, OK

Praise

P ray
R espect God
A lways read the Bible
I dolize Him
S urrender to Him
E nter into the Heavens

Konosha Chew, Grade 6
Desoto Central School, MS

Winter

I feel the cold breeze.
It makes me weak to my knees.
I can hear the wind blow,
When I play in the snow.

Grayson Venters, Grade 4
South Topsail Elementary School, NC

Ode to Drugs

Students and staff
Are clean and drug-free
The school is kept clean
By ev'rybody.

This poem's made up
For me and for you
And everyone who
Stops to look at this, too.

The students keep learning
The teachers keep teaching
At really high levels
that drugs still aren't reaching

Red Ribbon Week's past
And gone in a wink
But let's still remember
That drugs really STINK!

Andrew Preisack, Grade 5
Bayless Intermediate School, MO

Thanksgiving

T urkey we share,
H eavenly care,
A ngels in the sky,
N ighttime's good-bye,
K ids running around,
S ome laugh real loud,
G ift of good,
I s it good?
V ery good friends,
I s there an end?
N obody's mad, just
G lad, glad, glad!

Dylan Richardet, Grade 6
St Vincent Elementary School, MO

Stay in School

School is fun not dumb
We have spelling, math, and English too
So if you want to be cool
Stay in school

Granston Locklear, Grade 5
Pembroke Elementary School, NC

Cats

Cats are little tigers.
That have very pointy ears.
They are very nice.
Cats are nice little critters.
That's why I think cats are nice.

Jacob Severns, Grade 5
Shirley Elementary School, AR

Performance Day

I walked on stage,
And started to play,
I felt so excited,
In a beautiful way.

I am happy,
Do you know why?
Because I conquered the habit,
Of being shy.

I woke up this morning,
Not knowing the day,
I thought I'd be shy,
I'm glad it ended this way.

Tiana Ferguson, Grade 5
Sycamore Elementary School, GA

Fall

leaves fall, sun, birds play
sunflowers, trees, rotten, cat
songbird, rake, walking

Shalea Jones, Grade 4
East Jones Elementary School, MS

Obey

Obey your mom,
Obey your dad.
Obey your sister,
Obey your brother.
Obey your elders,
And don't forget —
Obey Jesus!

Chelsi Harper, Grade 4
Ava Victory Academy, MO

Dogs!

Dogs,
Dogs,
Dogs,
Black dogs,
Gray dogs,
Big playful dogs,
Small happy spotted dogs,
These are just a few.
Dumb dogs,
Smart dogs,
Funny strange stray dogs,
Good bad sad dogs,
Nutty dogs too.
Silly dogs,
Sticky dogs,
Don't forget crazy dogs.
Last of all, best of all,
I like white dogs.

Christopher Eugene Whittlesey, Grade 6
Lost River Elementary School, KY

Spinach

Do you know the green stuff
on your plate?
You might think it is lettuce.
Well your wrong, it's that nasty stuff
don't even say it…
S-P-I-N-A-C-H
Don't even describe what it
looks like either
It looks like
"Oh boy here we go again."
My mom had just put
some more on my plate.

Mackenzie Taylor, Grade 4
Cool Spring Elementary School, NC

Brianna

Brianna
Smart, sweet, funny
Smiling, sharing, hugging
Loves to play and have fun
Bre

Brianna Goins, Grade 6
Leland Middle School, NC

Leaves and Pumpkins

Leaves are very fun.
Autumn weather, cooler days,
Gigantic pumpkins.

Andrew Akins, Grade 4
Briarwood Christian Elementary School, AL

Chase

Chase is fast
Chase is cool
Chase knows when to be good
Chase is my best friend forever for life
Chase is there for me when times get really tough
I never had a friend like him
He's never late
He's never slow
He always comes to my call
He's my dog forever and for life
He never fails at his task
He's in my prayers every night
It was best friends at the very first site
He's my one and only very close friend
My best friend forever and eternity.

Amanda Kerby, Grade 5
Paint Lick Elementary School, KY

Too Many Struggles

There's too many struggles in the world today
People trying to make money the wrong kind of way
Too many people on the streets
Some are even getting beat
"Too many struggles"

Who chose the president?
Cause there are too many people without a residence
Unable to pay their bills,
So they have to sit at home with the chills
"Too many struggles"

The price of gas is way too high
Some can't even afford to fly
They can't buy their medication
Or pay for their education
"Too many struggles"

Kayla Kinard, Grade 6
Brogden Middle School, NC

Veteran

V ivacious and violent
E quipped to fight our foes
T hey keep our country safe
E ager to get on the battle field
R ifles are loaded and set to fight
A merica, Sweet Home America,
N ever give up on us Sweet Home America.

Hayley Foust, Grade 4
Cherokee Elementary School, AR

Friends Forever

From kindergarten to 4th grade, friends forever
From 5th grade to 8th grade, friends forever
From ninth grade all the way through college, friends forever
Through tears, drama, and happy times, friends forever
In times through gain and loss, friends forever
Popularity and prettiness don't matter, all that matters
Is that we are friends forever
When we have grandchildren, friends forever
When we are laid down under ground, friends forever
No matter what happens, friends forever

Paige Sanders, Grade 6
Harrisburg Middle School, AR

Friendship

Some are friends forever
Some maybe never
Some may make you laugh
Some may make you cry
Some will always be there to wipe the tears from your eye
I hope that you can always see
That you can always count on me
A true friend I will always be.

Leighann Elliott, Grade 6
Queen of Angels Catholic School, GA

Myrtle Beach

Painful waves splashing forcefully
Scorching sand sleeping on the beach
Boasting seagulls squawking thunderously
Enormous laughter spreading resoundingly like a train
Flapping stingrays are kings hurrying loyally
Agitated horseshoe crabs crawling as slow as a baby
Vaporizing saltwater racing in the ocean
disintegrating driftwood like dead fish rotting slowly
Rich pancakes cooking perfectly
Crunchy bacon sizzling freely
I feel joyful and grateful.

Dalton Tant, Grade 5
Bailey Elementary School, NC

After the Rain Comes a Rainbow

It's musty, cold, and gray.
The children can't laugh or play.
Cats are meowing, dogs are barking, and the birds are silent.
Because in the sky is a miracle of colors…a rainbow.

Margo Morton, Grade 4
Wilder Elementary School, KY

Ice

Cold, wet
Outside on ground
Makes me want to skate dance
Creating eights with my new blades
Sparkling

Brooke Godfrey, Grade 5
Broadway Elementary School, NC

So Many Friends

Friends, friends, friends
I have many friends
so many friends
how will I ever pick
my best friend of all
do you have any suggestions
you should pick the ones
you can rely on
and trust
I guess that narrowed it down
that was a great suggestion
thanks that really helped.

Cierra Wilson, Grade 6
Dyer Elementary & Jr High School, TN

When Puppies Attack

When puppies attack
They jump in the air.
When they eat your food
It doesn't seem fair.
During the night
They give you a fright.
When puppies attack
You better beware.

Eliza Demos, Grade 5
Prince of Peace Catholic School, SC

I Don't Understand

I don't understand
Why the sky is blue.
Why the wind blows.
Why clouds make shapes.

But most of all
Why homework takes forever.
Why pencils break every 5 seconds.
Why folders are heavy.

I understand most
Why people like Clemson.
Why Carolina stinks.
Why football is the most watched sport.

Chase Thompson, Grade 4
Pine Tree Hill Elementary School, SC

Shoes

So many shoes
But only two feet
I wish I could buy
Every pair that I meet
You say heels
They just kill
I say heels
Are best on huge hills

Alyson Henry, Grade 6
Harrisburg Middle School, AR

Lone Memories

Loner walks to a grassy mound
With glittering eyes he looks around
Then raises his head and begins to sing
His voice is as clear as a bell ring
He sings of mist, clouds, and rain
And of his heart's terrible pain
For his pack is gone, they never were there
He fixes everything with a stony glare
This lone wolf has no home
He has always been alone
An orphan, an outcast, an unwanted pup
All he ever wanted was a little love
Instead he was faced with turned backs
Because his coat was reddish and theirs were black
Kicked out of the pack, left by himself
Feeling as tiny as the smallest elf
How he survived he doesn't know
But he still doesn't have a place to call his own
He lowers his head and the song ends
But still seems to continue beyond the river bends
Many hear it and look for its source, but he has vanished, without a trace.

Ashley Huemmer, Grade 6
Martin Middle School, NC

Yellow

Yellow looks like beautiful stars at night.
Yellow feels like a soft daisy flower.
Yellow tastes like an excellent smiley face cookie.
Yellow smells like a tasteful cool cup of lemonade at a lemonade stand.
Yellow sounds like a charming bee flying by.
Yellow is a lovely bright color.

Ashley Stevens, Grade 5
Geggie Elementary School, MO

He Plays His Flute

In the 1600s many years ago, a young man
sat in a beautifully designed chair playing a flute.
In the realist painting, the boy is in the foreground.
In the background hangs a wooden crafted violin.
Next to the violin on the wall was a small, smooth record.
As his eyes gaze upon the bright light shining in his face
the boy runs his fingers across the dark flute
creating a wonderful melody.
His face has pale tints of white.
The boy's white silky collar compliments his dark woolen suit
and his crimson red velvet hat.
This child must come from a wealthy family.
In the oil painting, the child has slight movement.
The boy sits in positive space. The air is the negative space.
The child is the focal point.
The young man's hand in front of the flute has a light tint of white to it.
His other hand has shades of darkness.
This young man is serious about his music.
Maybe even till this day, he plays his flute.

Leah Mager, Grade 5
Saffell Street Elementary School, KY

Winter

Winter is when the leaves fall off,
Winter is when our hands get cold,
Winter is when we all love snow,
Winter is when we throw snow balls,
Winter is when some stay inside,
Winter ends with us all cold and wet from all of the snow.

Derek Merritt, Grade 5
Paint Lick Elementary School, KY

Horses

I feed my horses every day, I feed them corn,
I feed them hay.

I feed them all. I sometimes stay with them until dark,
Alone with my favorite Uncle Mark.

On their back is where I ride,
With my legs down by their side.

There are two horses I love the most,
One is Max one is Ghost.

Max is covered with spots,
I like to ride him as he trots.

Ghost is very fast,
he'll never come in last.

Everyone should have a horse can't you see,
I love my horses and they love me!

Paige Cummings, Grade 5
Pembroke Elementary School, NC

The Race

Cars are slick, cars are fast
Cars to me are a blast
Some have windows like the night sky
Sometimes they sound their battle cry
Some have doors that open like drawbridges
Some have hydraulics that shoot to the moon
Oh boy, I'll be there soon

Ben Blowers, Grade 4
Robert E Lee Elementary School, TN

Time to Go

I look at the time, in tears I cry
I cry until I cannot cry anymore
My eyes are dry, but I'm still sad
As my loving dog is gone forever.
I guess it was really time for her to go.
Her puppies wait for their dear mother,
But they can't see her until it's their time to shine
I hope the saying is correct that all dogs go to heaven
Trisha was one really special dog; and loving too.

Shaana Vigé, Grade 6
Arnaudville Elementary School, LA

Jesus Christ

Jesus Christ came down from above;
Even to the sinners, he showed love.
His mission was to love and forgive
In order for us to eternally live!
Hung on the cross as the crowd yelled "crucify!"
Rose in three days, and that's no lie!
Went up to heaven though still loves us all;
Nothing comes between us,
Not even a wall.
Now in my heart, and he's my best friend;
I know he'll stay with me until the end!

Lindsay Corbin, Grade 6
Scotts Creek Elementary School, NC

Texas

I want to go to Texas
Maybe even get a Lexus
I want to live in Austin
No! No! Not in Boston
I want to play softball
Or maybe even basketball
And no matter what anyone says
My heart will still be in University of Texas

Casey Nicole Fitts, Grade 6
Maplewood Middle School, LA

Piano Paradise

Each time you play me,
I sing and dance a song of glee.
Every note is a little word,
To tell you I can chirp like a bird.
When a melody is done,
I plead that you play another one.
So when you tickle me again,
I enjoy the time together we spend.
But when a sad song comes along,
I try to use soothing words to calm your mourning heart.
I am your other world,
Your ebony and ivory piano.

Kendra Little, Grade 6
River Trail Middle School, GA

Our Christmas Tradition

Christmas traditions are different for every one,
Every year new ones begin.

Stockings, pajamas, and presents just to name a few,
Traditions carried from the old to the new.

Together we share in family games and fun,
There's always something for everyone.

Christmas traditions from the old to the new are
Always special for me and hopefully you too.

Alexis DeBord, Grade 5
Paint Lick Elementary School, KY

Thank You for Thanks
Thank you for the sun,
The bun on my plate.
Thank you for my dog,
The turkey that he ate.

Thank you for the cat,
And the fish that he can take.
Thank you for my room,
And that big chocolate cake.
Peyton Jones, Grade 4
St Bernard Academy, TN

The Pirates Search for Treasure
The blasting of the cannon,
The clanging of the sword's blade,
After all the fighting,
They needed the first aid.

It was a clear day today.
That is when they found land.
Then they found the treasure
There buried in the sand.

On the ship someone was being bad,
So he had to walk the plank.
The treasure was too heavy
So the pirate ship sank.
Stephen Calcote, Grade 4
Evangelical Christian School, TN

I Wonder
I wonder, yes, I wonder.

I wonder why the grass is green.
I wonder why the sky is blue.
I wonder why the sun is yellow.
I wonder why I think these things.

I wonder, yes, I wonder.
Could you fly without a plane?
Could you drink without a glass?
Could you write without a pen?

I wonder, yes, I wonder.
I wonder why sheep feel so soft.
I wonder why there's no air in space.
I wonder why we go to the moon.

I wonder, yes, I wonder.
Could you think without a brain?
Could you sing without a voice?
Could you see without an eye?

I wonder, yes, I wonder.
Brian Hasl, Grade 6
North Oldham Middle School, KY

Spinach
The first time I tried spinach,
My taste buds went to heaven.
It tasted so good,
I thought I was eleven.

Spinach is my favorite food,
So creamy and green.
One thing that people think is,
SPINACH IS MEAN!!!!!!

I love spinach so much,
Because it makes you strong.
I could live off of spinach.
It makes me live so long.
Nicole Clarke, Grade 5
American Heritage Academy, GA

Stranger
Hello stranger it's me again
remember I'm your best friend.

You lay in the heat, out in the street
and that is something I cannot beat.

Your eyes are blue who could have
knew that I would want to be friends
with you.

I lay in bed at night with lots and
lots of fright just because I'm thinking
of you. Remember this stranger
you are brand new! Please
represent yourself as you
Savannah Thompson, Grade 6
St Mark Elementary School, SC

Messy
Some people are very messy
They're just born that way
Sometimes it's a good thing
Sometimes they have to pay

I am one of those people
And I can't really complain
Except when I look and look
And can't find anything!
Evan Tillman, Grade 6
Benton County School of the Arts, AR

Dog
A dog has a paw,
That it uses to crawl,
It has a nose,
That it uses to sniff out clothes.
Joseph Sylvia, Grade 4
South Topsail Elementary School, NC

The Cat
She waits by the door,
listening to the sounds.
She squats on the floor,
while no one is around.

She plays alone,
and with her other too.
She hides in the traffic cone
while her owner has the flu.

She is a speedy demon,
and bites her owner's wife.
Always near her owner, beaming;
this is how she spends her life.
Aidaana Amanbekova, Grade 6
J D Meisler Middle School, LA

Presents
Presents
Presents
Presents
Surprising presents
Big presents
Fat, humongous, nice presents
Cool, sweet, awesome presents
Fat presents
Smelly presents
Nasty, disgusting, large presents
Red, white, blue presents
Danielle Olson, Grade 5
Tates Creek Elementary School, KY

Favorite Saint
I have a favorite Saint
If you think he's dead, he ain't
On his shirt is number 25
He helped his team stay alive.

But now he's my favorite man
Because he helped when others ran
Now I watch him run and run
Watching the Saints is really fun!
Dalton Flauss, Grade 5
Holy Rosary Academy, LA

I Sing
I sing the mighty power of God
That made the mountains rise
And spread the flowering seas abroad
And built the lofty skies
I sing the wisdom that
Ordained the sun to rule the day.
The moon shines full at his command,
And all the stars obey.
Katie Andrew, Grade 6
Pleasants County Middle School, WV

Thankful

I'm thankful for my family and my friends.
I'm thankful for the things I got.
I'm thankful for things I do.
I'm thankful for all the things I have.
And I'm thankful to be sitting here
Talking to you about what I'm thankful for.

Kody Edwards, Grade 5
East Marion Elementary School, MS

Waves

Waves are bluish
Waves are strong very strong
Waves are greenish

Carson Cupo, Grade 4
Briarwood Christian Elementary School, AL

Giving Thanks to Veterans

T hank you for everything you've done
H ow happy we were when you came home
A rmistice Day, now Veteran's Day
N obody stood in your way
K ids were happy to see you!

Y ou are very special
O n your way home!
U ndertaking the difficult tasks!

Thanks For Everything!

Megan Dykes, Grade 5
Sullivan Elementary School, TN

Cheetah

With their spots,
Oh, they have lots.
They blend in,
And sit down very Zen.
Waiting for their prey,
They won't sit there all day.
Then the cheetah runs at the speed of light,
To be attacked by it would be a fright.
Soon, they catch their meal.
Man, what a deal!

Anna Kean, Grade 6
Queen of Angels Catholic School, GA

Windy Day

The wind is blowing,
The leaves are flowing.
It is a very windy day,
But many people are having fun at the bay.
It is a lovely day,
And I would like to play.
But, I can't play because I'm sick,
I can't even go to the picnic.

Hope Gutierrez, Grade 4
Cleveland Elementary School, OK

Hummingbird Eggs

Little young inside
Tiny as a small walnut
Someday a small bird

Abbie Gauldin, Grade 4
Briarwood Christian Elementary School, AL

The Flag

The flag is true.
With its red, white, and blue.
Its beautiful stars and stripes.
Blow gracefully through the wind.
It flies high.
In the pure blue sky.
I live in a free country.
As long as the flag may blow.
We celebrate our flag on the 4th of July.
Sometimes the fireworks are so pretty I cry.
But even in the midst of the fire.
Our flag will fly higher.

Amie Gatewood, Grade 6
Heartland High School and Academy, MO

My Little Poodle

His big, glimmering eyes
Look at me in delight
his tail waves happily
when I come into sight.
He can't even contain himself.
He's so happy and filled with glee,
his favorite thing in the world
is just being with me.
Yet the saddest pup you'll ever see
only appears once I leave.
When I come back his fluffy face lights up,
I bet he knows he's a real lucky pup.
He always gives me unconditional love,
and I love him more than the stars above.

Ashlyn Williams, Grade 6
College View Middle School, KY

The Mid South Fair

It's finally here, it's just over there
The Mid South Fair is in the air!
Chaotic rides and many surprises
Coasters, flume rides, drops and rises
It's never too late to go to the fair!
Cotton candy, candy apples, and Pronto Pups
But you really shouldn't eat before you ride the downs and ups.
If you haven't ridden the flume ride yet
You should, so prepare to get wet!
At the fair, it could get hot in the sun
But it's worth it, so come have some fun!
The Mid South Fair, the Mid South Fair
It's finally here, it's just over there!

Justin Jabbour, Grade 6
Woodland Presbyterian School, TN

The Old Yellow Leaves

The emerald green.
Is gone from the old yellow leaves.
The trees will grow.
But it shall not snow.

It is fall.
With few people out at all.
The dogs will play.
The day away.

Temple Hill School.
Is a place that's cool.
There are students there.
And you see them everywhere.

Winter is forthcoming.
Summer is through.
The emerald green.
Is gone from the old yellow leaves.

Wesley Clay Buckley, Grade 6
Temple Hill Elementary School, KY

I Always Like Axis and Allies Best

I always like Axis and Allies best
For the strategy
Moving troops, buying tanks
Planning and adjusting

I always like Axis and Allies
For the mind-bending decisions
Deciding where to attack and defend
Getting one step ahead of my dad

I always like Axis and Allies best
For the challenge
Each turn meticulously planned
My dad trying just as hard

I always like Axis and Allies best
For the time with my dad
I try to out think him
As I learn new strategies

I always like Axis and Allies best
For the relationship it strengthens
My dad and I
Getting closer together

Nathanial Long, Grade 6
South Oldham Middle School, KY

The Wolf

The separated
Wolf tries to find his wolf pack
The pack is now back

Dalton Bender, Grade 5
Sycamore Elementary School, GA

Your Life

Your life, the pages in a book,
when you read all the pages your life ends.
Then your life is being read by someone else,
and they find deep secrets hidden on the pages.
So now you know that your life is just one big, old book.
Inside on the first page, you find moments when you were happy and sad;
good and naughty, and all the mistakes in between, but you
think if you had made a mistake in your life you wish
you had taken the other choice that you had.

Shady Mrier, Grade 4
Nesbit Elementary School, GA

A Little Brother

I have a little brother and when he was only one,
He stomped on all my legos and only just for fun.

I have a little brother and when he had turned two,
He gobbled up my play dough and began to chew.

I have a little brother the day he turned three,
He learned to ride his dirt bike and ran over me!

When my little brother turned the age of four,
He pushed me out the house and laughed when he locked the door.

I can't remember if it was five or maybe it was six,
He pulled my shorts down in a crowd and all just for kicks.

Now my brother's seven and I just cannot wait
To see what torment he'll put me through the day he turns eight!

Brennen Reed, Grade 4
Lewis Vincent Elementary School, LA

I Am

I am a pretty girl with a great family.
I wonder what year I will graduate college.
I hear cars rushing through the wind.
I see myself as a cheerleader at UNC Wilmington.
I want an iPod nano.
I am a pretty girl with a great family.

I pretend to be a business woman.
I feel shimmering water rushing against my feet.
I touch a great white shark bigger than the world.
I worry about what will happen to me in the future.
I cry when someone in my family dies.
I am a pretty girl with a great family.

I understand that anybody can be different.
I say everybody is a hero.
I dream about going to Florida watching my brother play baseball.
I try to make different friends.
I hope to cultivate different rocks.
I am a pretty girl with a great family.

Grayson Griggs, Grade 4
Easley Elementary School, NC

For the Doubtful

Don't leave yourself behind from your own life
Because life isn't life, unless your life filled with strife
Don't put yourself behind because of your size or height
Doubtfulness will just start a mental fight.
Don't think being imperfect puts your under not right
Because your self goes behind human sight
Don't put being on popular your most deadly fright
Because that barely compares to not being bright
So if you need advice this was made to inform you
If life gives you lemons you know what to do
And when life passes you by you must catch
But you must be patient don't snatch
Because you might think I'm just on a roll
But this is just soul poetry for the doubtful soul

Malachi Smith, Grade 6
Brogden Middle School, NC

Racing

Racing is so fun.
Racing is the most fun under the sun.

I wish I could race every day.
But no is what my parents say.

When the green flag drops
I never want to stop.

The laps count down
as we roll around.

I see the checkered flag wave.
Shucks I didn't win…it was Dave.

Next week I will try again.
Maybe then it will be my turn to win.

So here I sit wishing for the race day to arrive.
The next week passes by slowly, but I will survive.

Finally race day is here again.
Yay it was my day to win!

Michael Garmon, Grade 6
Edmonton Elementary School, KY

America

America, America, home of the brave.
We fought for our country through,
The blood and the pain.

We fought and fought 'til the night was done.
For the next day was realized we had won.

America, America, where the flag still waves for the red, white,
and blue 'til this very day.

Baylee Kitchens, Grade 5
Joann Walters Elementary School, AR

Homework Is Dumb

H omework. Homework is so boring.
O h, why do we have to have homework?
M ean teachers only give us homework.
" **E** asy," said the teacher, but it is not.
W ork, work, work is all I ever do.
O h no! I forgot to do my homework!
R un away so I don't get a detention.
K ry, cry, cry. It's okay.

I will never go to school ever again.
S upervisor kicked me out of school.

D ad is angry at me.
U h, oh!
M om doesn't care about anything.
B oring homework. I told you so.

Kayla Conradi, Grade 6
St Joseph Institute for the Deaf, MO

Bright Star

Bright star
shining so bright
do not whine or lament
in the summer night you are rich
oh, star

Christian Candler, Grade 5
Briarwood Christian Elementary School, AL

My Dad*

My dad is a great dad helping me build a deer stand.
He is like a monkey in a tree.
He is a great dad because he is helping me.
He makes me laugh.
We all think he's crazy but he's still a good dad.
He is good to all of us as he works for us.

He is the best dad you will ever find, at least that's what I think.
He helps me with a lot of things like fixing my four-wheeler.
Dad lets me help him a lot
I really like him.
We make fun of him, he makes a joke out of it and we all laugh.
He is the greatest dad in the world anyone would like him.
He is the Best Dad!

Luke Goodman, Grade 4
Alvaton Elementary School, KY
*Inspired by my dad

Bonfire

Bonfires are places to gather and chat,
To roast marshmallows and do this and that,
But be careful and don't get too close,
It can burn your body and singe your clothes,
Bonfires are very fun and cool,
And if you're careful you won't be their fuel.

Elliott Brewer, Grade 6
Queen of Angels Catholic School, GA

The Silver Phantoms

The first time I was ever
in a soccer tournament
the Silver Phantoms, fifteen people
playing an orange team
for first place
I was in goal
for the third quarter
hurt face
kicked with the ball
tried to block, crying
ball went flying
into the goal
sidelines, with no action
five minutes gone
back in the game
fifteen minutes passed
no scores, whistle blew
like a steam engine
final score 2 to 1
more crying
second place.

Emily Gregoire, Grade 6
Beck Academy, SC

Autumn in Charleston

Autumn is here
Christmas is near
Trees are losing their leaves
Say good-bye to short sleeves
Thanksgiving food,
I'm in the mood!
Family is comin'
We're gonna be hummin'

Mac and Cheese is scrumptious
Yams and Turkey are luscious
The leaves are losing their green
Sadly we see them leave
Autumn in Charleston…
It's comin'

Sydney Copleston, Grade 5
Palmetto Christian Academy, SC

Sports

Soccer is my favorite sport,
I also like the tennis court.
Basketball is lots of fun,
Lacrosse is my second favorite one.
Hitting, throwing, catching balls,
Softball umpires make the calls.
I like volleyball in the sand,
And football half-times with the band.
Swimming and diving in the pool,
All these sports are really cool.

Taylor Jones, Grade 5
Prince of Peace Catholic School, SC

The Troops

You're always on my mind
You mean a lot to me
Thanks for being so kind
You keep our freedom free

I know that I'm just a kid
And my voice not very loud
But the job that all of you did
Makes even us kids feel proud

It must be very bad
Always being gone
Please do not feel sad
God is with you, so you're never alone

I pray for your safe return
One day you'll be home to stay
The title of hero you've earned
GOD BLESS THE USA!

Makayla Pierce, Grade 5
Quail Run Elementary School, GA

Springtime Is Here

When butterflies fly
that is when springtime is here
flowers and fresh air.

Carol Perez, Grade 6
Tomlinson Jr High School, OK

Christmastime

Beautiful, beautiful, beautiful lights
Santa Claus creeps all through the night
Don't wake up if you dare
Santa will give you a little scare

It is time for holiday cheer
Don't mess up by drinking beer
Presents, presents, lots and lots
I wonder what my parents brought

It is time to open the big toy
Let's cheer with a little more joy
I want a PS3
I'm going to get it from under the tree

La Toya Jones, Grade 6
St Mark Elementary School, SC

Thanksgiving

Thanksgiving means thanks to me.
It means prayers that people pray.
The love they pass around.
The forgiveness they forgive.
The smell of lemon pie and turkey.
Thanksgiving.

Kiefer Sutherland, Grade 6
Guntown Middle School, MS

Hunter

The greatest hunter
He is swift, clean, and quiet
Brave still full of speed.

Wyatt Carroll, Grade 4
Cleveland Elementary School, OK

Love

Love is great;
Love is kind;
It does not lie.

Love is good;
Love is sweet;
It does not hurt.

Love is happy;
Love is wise;
It does not hate.

Love is love.

Crystal Frederick, Grade 4
Vanoss Elementary School, OK

The Mad Man

There once was a black bus,
who made a big man fuss.
The bus did not stop,
so he jumped on top,
and waved good-bye to us.

Arizona Stipes, Grade 4
Judsonia Elementary School, AR

Birds

Birds can come in many colors,
red, blue green and yellow.
Some have a ring,
most like to sing "Ding ding."
Birds hit the windmill,
no they do not kill.
It is said they have small heads.
But are very smart. Hay!!!
You can survey them on a chart.
Birds birds everywhere.
Red and yellow, blue and green.
God created them fair and square.
They eat pears.
Some people say who cares.
I say how dare you say that I care.
Birds can fly here and there
they can fly everywhere.
They can fly to the sky.
I love birds.
Do you ever wonder if a bird is a dove?
I do.

Emily Treece, Grade 5
Shirley Elementary School, AR

Blue

Blue is the color of the sky up above
Blue is the color of my mitten and glove
Blue is the color of the sea at the shore
Blue is the color of the house next door
Blue is the color of the candy bar in my hand
Blue is the color of the grand marching band
Blue is the color in New York
Blue is the color of moldy pork
Blue is the color of the flower outside
Blue is the color of the swirly ride
Blue is the color of rock n' roll
Blue is the color in my soul

Lane Poag, Grade 5
St Thomas More School, NC

Thanksgiving

Feels like the cool, fall air
Sounds like leaves crunching under my feet
Looks like red and yellow everywhere
Smells like pumpkin pie in the oven
Tastes like turkey, dark and light

Philip Johnston, Grade 5
Briarwood Christian Elementary School, AL

Hope Is Growing

When a wife loses her husband
    she knows that the hope is within her soul.

When a young girl realizes that all she has lost,
    she knows that the hope has always been inside her.

When a grandmother dreams of "days gone by,"
    she knows that hope will bring us through.

When an uncle is ashamed of himself,
    He remembers that hope is a friend who he can turn to…

When life comes,
    we all know that hope has always been inside of us…

Abbi Stringfellow, Grade 5
Breitling Elementary School, AL

Tree

You are no ordinary tree
You are special.

Just the right one for me.
With your spread out green leaves

And a good small size
Just like me.

You are perfect
And always will be.

Kendall Kramer, Grade 5
Christ Episcopal School - Middle School, LA

Things I Like to Do and Say

I am beautiful inside and so are you.
I love to play outside and swing on swings
And go to the park too,
But the most things to do is to eat things up yah!
But I am still beautiful inside,
Those are the things I do and say!

Latosha Walker, Grade 5
Romine Inter District Elementary School, AR

The Haunted

In the past I was haunted by,
The weird clowns that were at the circus,
The boogeyman who once lived in my closet,
The horror movies that my uncle watched,
That's what I was scared of in the past.

In the present I am haunted by,
Poisonous spiders that can take lives,
Poisonous snakes that will leave you to suffer,
Crocodiles that will eat you whole,
That's what I am haunted by in the present.

In the future I will be haunted by,
A car crash that will end my life,
World chaos that will destroy citizenship and friendship,
Bazookas that will damage cities,
That's what will haunt me in the future.

Jonathan W. Sutton, Grade 5
Eminence Middle School, KY

Two Siamese Himalayans

Black, gray, and brown
Two twins meowing to get petted,
Running, chasing, and hissing at each other,
Running into doors
Crazy as a dog chasing its tail.
"One nice, one mean,
Both cats."

Almost the softest thing I've felt.
At night they sleep at the bottom of my bed,
Purring quietly.

Never stopping the noise
Giving me a bad headache.
Walking around my legs,
All they're wanting to do
Almost like they're saying
"Feed me, pet me,
Give me more."

Chasing after them,
Grabbing them in my arms
Carrying them around everywhere.

Hannah Causey, Grade 4
Goshen Elementary School at Hillcrest, KY

College of William and Mary

C hildren in colonies received different amounts of education.
O lder boys studied to be priests.
L essons were hard for the boys.
L arge towns like Williamsburg had rules that only boys could go to college.
E ducation for both boys and girls included strict lessons in manners.
G eorge Washington, Thomas Jefferson, James Monroe, and John Tyler all attended the College of William and Mary.
E very year, in the 1700s about 100 boys attended.

Mitch Corder, Grade 5
Alvaton Elementary School, KY

The Wind

I sat there, in the light of sunrise, the wind howling at my face. Cool air gently touching my lips.
I watched as the silent wind swayed the tall blades of grass.
I saw the wind rustling the tree leaves. The clattering of the leaves making me overcome with joy.
I saw the wind making the white, glazed, picket fence clang against its lock.
I saw the wind making the autumn leaves fly off its tree making a pile into our yard.
The colors of the leaves were extraordinarily beautiful, containing the colors red, orange, yellow, and a handsome brick red.
I heard the wind gushing throughout the sky with a faint smell. The wind making the sky dark and gray.
I knew then a storm was coming. A storm with gusty winds and hideous cold rain.
A storm that happened because of the wind.

Rachel Leachman, Grade 6
Freedom Intermediate School, TN

I Am Haunted!

I was haunted by something under my big wooden bed that lived in the cracks in the floor
that might jump out and eat my hand or foot off.

I am haunted by old haunted homes that make squeaky shattered noises when you
walk up the old wooden stairs, and things that go bump and, boom in the night.

I will be haunted by walking through a gory graveyard and looking at one of the headstones
and the body will jump out and get ya!

Audreanna McClain, Grade 5
Eminence Middle School, KY

Thanksgiving Forest

As I walk among the trees, I smell my mom's turkey and hear her call my name. I know I should go back, but I don't. I hear her shut the door. My cheeks are cold as ice. I hear the cheerful music, I see my parents dance, everything is so cheerful, but my feet won't move. They're anchored to the ground. I hear the leaves rustle, and I feel a chilly breeze. My cheeks are probably red by now, in this place among the trees. I walk a little farther, it's silent as the grave. My mom calls me again, and says the family's here. My feet come unbolted, and I rejoin the cheer.

Emily Wheeler, Grade 6
Guntown Middle School, MS

What Is Childhood?

Childhood is cooking with my mom.
Childhood is going to the skating rink because you love to skate and listen to music.
Childhood is being scared of the dark because you had bad nightmares.
Childhood is sleeping and playing with a fuzzy blue bear.
Childhood is wanting to be a cosmetologist.
Childhood is traveling to Smokey Mountains, and wanting to go to Florida someday.
Childhood is falling when skating.
Childhood is going to the dentist.
Childhood is wanted to grow up and be just like my mom, and wanting to be the best at whatever I do.

Crystal Miller, Grade 6
Lost River Elementary School, KY

Dogs

Dogs, dogs, dogs,
A great joy of life!
In fact I have two,
And when you're blue,
You should think they love you!

Dogs, dogs, dogs,
So many to choose from,
And you know they are known to be,
A man's best friend!
So you know they will guide you till the last day,
Because they love you!
Bark! Bark!

Megan Rasp, Grade 4
Hayes Elementary School, OK

Brittany

Brittany
Artistic, loving, energetic
Daughter of Toni
Who loves swimming, outside, and math
Who feels lovingly about her family
Who needs education, home, and a family
Who gives friendship, toys, and clothes
Who fears spiders, bugs, and bad dreams
Who'd like to see her uncle James
Who dreams of being a teacher
A student of Ms. Swain
Britt-Britt

Brittany Ledford, Grade 5
Windsor Elementary School, NC

Movie Theater

Smells like buttery popping popcorn
Tastes like lots of delicious colorful candy
Looks like an 8 foot plasma TV
Feels like red velvet chairs rubbing against my back
Sounds like loud surround sound speakers

Sellers Mulvaney, Grade 5
Briarwood Christian Elementary School, AL

Oak Tree

Oh I'd like to have a coke
underneath an old oak.
I'd be with someone to poke and joke with
and just maybe tell them a myth.
And so I did
without blowing my lid.
I chose my brother
although I had another.
The birds are chirping
because it's such a pretty day today.
And a bee is under this old oak tree.

Preston Byrd, Grade 5
Stokesdale Elementary School, NC

Black Stallion

The massive stallion,
It's sometimes very wild.
It rides very fast.
They are beautiful.

Marly King, Grade 4
Briarwood Christian Elementary School, AL

Summertime

Grass is blowing on the hot dry field,
Hearing the sound of the old vacant windmill,
Flowers are blooming red, blue, and yellow,
Country frogs are sleeping in the meadows,
Children are playing, babies are crying,
I can hear the sounds of the blue jay flying,
Temperature is high. The weatherman don't lie,
Smelling the smell of a hot baked apple pie,
Boy! I love the season of summer,
Sometimes I say, "Can it be a little longer?"

Alfonsa Kyles III, Grade 6
Calloway Smith Middle School, AL

School Is Out

Yes, today is the day
No more social studies or geography.
No more math or science tests.
Today is the day I get to play my video game.
No more teachers or any rules.
No more reading or writing.
Today is the day I watch TV all day.
No more CCC or spelling.
No more music or media lab.
Today is the day I say HOORAY!

Taylor Airington, Grade 5
Cottonwood Public School, OK

Dreaming

I had a dream that you were gone.
You died of cancer so very young
As we put a flower upon your grave
We say we wish you could have been saved.
We cried and cried the minute you died
Now, half of your life has been left behind
Now, we surely will miss you a lot
Because it wasn't just a dream.

Bethany Colvin, Grade 6
Pleasants County Middle School, WV

What Would I Do?

What would I do
If I didn't have you
Would I pray for you
Or would I turn black and blue
Oh what would I do
I would look for eternity searching for you.

Eric Boggs, Grade 5
Beaver Elementary School, WV

Forever Gone

One time I met you
So nice you were to me that day
Even though I only saw you once
It does not take away the pain
Because now you are gone
And will never return
Although I am a little relieved
Because you were in so much pain
Just a stranger you were to me
Then why am I so sad today
One day you're there and then
You're gone

Kyle Hall, Grade 6
The Mountain Community School, NC

Spinning Spider

The door closed behind us
and I told my mom,
"This is going to be fun!"

The spider started and then it stopped
so others could climb on.
When it was full
we started moving slowly at first.

Faster, and faster, and faster
we turned 'round and 'round.
All of us screamed, "Ahhh…!"

When the spider finally stopped
I felt dizzy but I was ok.
"I'm not getting on another ride."
But of course I did!

Diana Rodriguez, Grade 5
Etowah Elementary School, NC

A Day in Kentucky

In Kentucky it's always cold,
but the leaves are so bold!
The colors are red and yellow;
it makes me a jolly fellow.

Football games are held in the day,
Kentucky and Louisville play.
Baseball season is over
and the field is covered in clover.

Thanksgiving is here,
it brings cheer.
Pumpkin pie is great
but it makes me stay up late!

I love fall —
it's a ball!
Richard Fowler, Grade 5
Palmetto Christian Academy, SC

A Guy

There once was a guy
That wished he could fly
He fell in a lake
Got bit by a snake
And now he wants to cry
Nick Betit, Grade 5
Bonaire Elementary School, GA

Christmas

C aring
H appy
R udolph
I ce
S anta
T iming
M ake cookies
A ll of my family
S nowing
Shaylisa Crawford, Grade 4
Wohlwend Elementary School, MO

The White

Stitch by stitch snow falls
sewing a quilt white as paper
attracting energetic joy to the world.
William Bukowski, Grade 4
St Thomas More School, NC

Bubble Gum

I love bubble gum
I can't wait till I get you
But I hate it
When you stick to my shoe
Sometimes you are sour
Sometimes you are sweet
Getting to chew you
Is such a treat
Alone or with friends
No matter what
The fun never ends.

Kayla Pate, Grade 5
Macedonia Elementary School, SC

Summer

Hot, sweaty, lazy,
Birds, pretty, sunny, flowers,
Trees, butterflies, bees
Houston Hutto, Grade 4
East Jones Elementary School, MS

Birds

I like my new bird
I like that wonderful bird
I love that new bird
Jalene Brown, Grade 5
Coldwater Elementary School, AL

Snowman

I am a snowman
I wonder if I will melt someday
I hear kids playing
I see them all playing
I want to meet new people
I am a snowman

I pretend I am not alive
I feel lonely
I touch the ground
I worry I will have no friends
I cry because I will melt someday
I am a snowman

I understand the animals
I say I am cold
I dream of kids playing in the snow
I hope it stays cold
I try to talk
I am a snowman
Alyssa Sciaroni, Grade 4
Wohlwend Elementary School, MO

The City

There are tall buildings
There are people who are nice
"Ring" "Ring" there's a bike
Michael Ashby, Grade 6
Martin Elementary School, WV

Clickity Click

Clickity click, clickity click!
Where is that clickity click?
I hear over there, there and there.
I think it's everywhere.
I look here. I look there.
Where is that clickity click?
Silly me.
It's just Grandpa's feet!
Tommy Rudy, Grade 4
West Elementary School, MO

Hunting

I saw a bird
in a tree,
That's when I heard him sing,
I said to myself
that's the best song you've ever sang
Quietly I took my aim
and held my breath.
Pow!! I pulled the trigger
and smoke filled the sky.
I looked for the bird everywhere,
but heard him as he sang good-bye.
Tanner Collins, Grade 5
Pembroke Elementary School, NC

The Bad Things About Hiking

When you go hiking it is quite fun
but when you are done it can be very icky
you found out you got itchy
and then you get squiggly and twitchy
after that you count out 53 dots
oh no, you have itchy spots!

Kallen Schmidt, Grade 5
Walton Verona Elementary School, KY

Thank You, Nouns!

Nouns can be a person, place or thing;
nouns are also ideas, thoughts or feelings.
They may be singular or plural,
possessive or not, concrete or abstract,
common or proper.
No matter what, nouns surround you.

Nouns are you, nouns are me;
they are animals and plants.
Nouns can be nice or mean,
attractive or gross.
Nouns are everywhere.

Nouns can be tall or short,
whatever form they take.
Nouns help us in many ways.
Without them we could not,
communicate, write, or read.
Thank you, nouns!

Jacob Brumley, Grade 5
Saffell Street Elementary School, KY

Explosion

"Boom, Bang, Bam!"
These are the sounds of explosions.
Just look at those flames and smoke!
That fire looks so beautiful I could faint!
I go near the source of the flames
And it's hot breath is blown down my back.
"Stay away!" it says.
"My flames will burn you!"
BOOM!
The fuel ignites
And there is one last
EXPLOSION!

Cole Stover, Grade 5
Bonaire Elementary School, GA

A Blessing for Piano Players

May your keys work when you play a song.
May your song be played beautifully.
May your notes be played correctly.
May your practicing get the song perfect.
May you have confidence in playing a song.

Maggie Hillhouse, Grade 6
St Francis Xavier School, AL

Life

Life
Life is like a chain
A chain strung through
The minds of young and old
From young to old
Life
Happy
Sad
Memories
Life

Heidi Merk, Grade 6
International Community Charter School, GA

The Piano

The piano, the piano
Putting notes together, creating a piece as light as a feather
Add more, add more, the conscience seems to implore
The piano, the piano.

The piano, the piano
Pressing the pedal below, the music begins to flow
Pumping each part, playing like a beating heart
The piano, the piano.

The piano, the piano
Oh what a wonder, hear the melody yonder
Across the rooms, each stanza looms
The piano, the piano.

The piano, the piano
Such beautiful sounds, as the fingers fly down
Each keystroke ripples and pours, as the soul soars
The piano, the piano.

John Robertson, Grade 5
Providence Academy, TN

The Flag

I love my flag because
    it is a sign of freedom.
My flag is a sign of peace
    in times of darkness and conflict.
I believe that the flag is its own reward,
That all who stand with it should treat it
    with respect and dignity,
That we have a freedom of religion,
    of speech, and
    a freedom of the press, and
That it is a great honor to have a free republic.

Our flag is our country's symbol.
Our flag should always fly tall.
It should be flown outside every American home,
    and all should love it.

Nathan Martinez, Grade 6
Heartland High School and Academy, MO

Sunset

Sunset
Orange, pretty
Glowing, gleaming, brightening
Fun to watch
Daylight

Ally Spees, Grade 5
Bonaire Elementary School, GA

Sea Shells' Paradise

The bright sea shells' color
Belongs to the sand and waves
Where they live always.

Ryann Roberts, Grade 4
The Reading Center/Schola Maxi, AL

Friends to the End

As we were growing up,
in a very small town.
Everywhere my brother went,
I was around.
We had fun in the summer,
as we grew up.
My big brother Jeremy,
taught me a lot of good stuff.
Now that I'm grown,
I look back to then.
I know now what it means,
to be friends to the end.

Taylor Cowan, Grade 6
Brogden Middle School, NC

Christmas

Christmas is a very happy day
A time to give gifts and celebrate
Jesus' birthday that's what makes
Christmas fun the joyful holiday
deserves a special thanks to Santa
Claus and Jesus' day we
celebrate with foods, lights,
trees and nice clothes when
the time comes we will
watch Rudolph. I'm glad
Christmas is a holiday we
celebrate with nice things
Christmas day.

Kayla Dickerson, Grade 6
St Mark Elementary School, SC

Ponies

Ponies
Playful, cute
Galloping, jumping, plodding
They are very charming
Horses

Saralynn Willhite, Grade 4
Russell Babb Elementary School, OK

Music

There are different kinds of music,
some people like Pop some people like Rock.
My parents tell me to make good grades,
but I make them anyway.
Music helps me concentrate and gets me to sleep,
then I feel like I'm in deep.
Like Gretchen Wilson and Tim McGraw,
when some people hear their name they either say naw or yehow!
People are always talking about Nick Lachey,
but when I come around they say "Your cra-zay."
Whatever music you like don't worry,
everything will be all right.

Bailey Sartin, Grade 5
Graham Elementary School, AL

A Knight

A knight is brave, strong and true.
In gleaming armor guarding the king in all his glory.

A knight will walk on the wall and defend it to the end of time.
Lords and ladies admire him, so young lads pretend to be him.

A knight is a defender of the people; He is like the soldiers today.
When the knight rides his steed down the road as all the peasants cheer hooray.

Conner Rorrer, Grade 5
Paint Lick Elementary School, KY

Blue

Blue looks like a dolphin jumping out of the sea.
Blue sounds like the water splashing in the ocean.
Blue smells like the people walking by eating ice-cream.
Blue tastes like the salty ocean water.
Blue feels like the water rushing up on the sand touching your feet.
Blue is the beautiful cloudless sky.
Blue is the water splashing as it goes down the fountain
Blue is the blueberries we smell on a bush.
Blue is the cotton candy we eat at the fair.
Blue is the sweetness you get when you relax on a swing.

Taylor Souther, Grade 5
Cool Spring Elementary School, NC

Wild Horses

Wild horses —
    they run so fast through the night
            and in the sun.
Never stop —
    they go on!
Of beautiful horses —
    I am so fond!

My horse and me —
        forever friends!
And I know that will never end!

Beautiful eyes and pretty manes;
Easy to ride, but hard to tame.

LeeAnne N. Cook, Grade 6
Scotts Creek Elementary School, NC

Riding a Horse

Galloping by the seashore the horizon falling on you
The sun is setting
You're in heaven
It's just you and the horse
Communicating in silence
The loud thudding of the horse's hooves pack into the sand
But you can't hear it
You are trapped in your own mind
Your own world
Wishing that you can stay in this wonderful place forever

Corey Coleman, Grade 6
Montessori Community School, NC

A Second Home

There's a quiet little place where I like to go when I'm alone,
It's like a second home.

But it's not just a little house with garden gnomes.
It's a place that I can call my own.

Sometimes I just crawl into my room,
And stand like a broom.

But, then I feel better when I go
To the place I call a second home.

Rachel Weaver, Grade 5
Mountain Road Elementary School, GA

School

School I hate it makes me mad
but to some people without it makes them sad
I hate the work it could make me hurl
I would rather kiss a girl
I do like the teachers and what they teach
but still I'd want to be at the beach
If it could disappear
I wouldn't be sitting here

Duncan Davis, Grade 4
St Thomas More School, NC

Bronco

Bronco is my dog
He is very fluffy
Bronco is four
His nickname is Broncie
Bronco is small
He is a little mutt
Bronco is a Norfolk Terrier-Shitzu mix
His fur is a rusty brown color
Bronco's bottom row of teeth sticks out
He is very, very protective
Bronco is the cutest dog in the world
I love Bronco

Caroline Grace McHam, Grade 5
Midway Covenant Christian School, GA

Ode to a Pillow

Oh pillow you're so fluffy,
You're big and round and very puffy.
Pillow, pillow you're bendy in every way.
Pillow, pillow this is what I have to say…

"Dear pillow you help me sleep
All through the night I don't make a peep.
I will be grumpy if I didn't have you.
What I'm trying to say is that I love you!"

Leslie Cooper, Grade 5
Walton Verona Elementary School, KY

Baseball

You pitch the ball,
it goes real fast.
When the player hits it,
it rolls in the grass.
You dive for the ball,
but miss it.
When you reach it and throw it,
the ball goes "swish."
When the catcher caught the ball,
it was a real close call!
Baseball is fun for all!

Hayden Chighizola, Grade 6
Haynes Academy for Advanced Studies, LA

Red

Red sounds like a fire engine racing across town.
Red looks like a fire blazing through the wind.
Red tastes like a cherry lollipop.
Red smells like ketchup.
Red feels like a hermit crab's shell.

Caleb Langdale, Grade 5
West Bertie Elementary School, NC

The Terrible Darkness of War

The terrible darkness of war
What a terrible, terrible thing
I scream at the sound of a missile around
The terrible darkness of war

The soldiers are fighting all through the night
to set our country free
the buildings are burning
The people are learning
Of the terrible darkness of war.

The twelfth day of war
The twelfth day of fighting
The twelfth day of people screaming and hiding

A white flag appears on the horizon
which signals the end of the war.

Elizabeth Barbour, Grade 4
Elon Elementary School, NC

The Clock

A clock it ticks,
And when morning comes,
It rings in my ear.
It wakes me up
for the day to begin.
It ticks when it's homework time,
It rings when it's
time for me to play.
I even hear it at the end
of every day.

Justice Bradburn, Grade 4
Cool Spring Elementary School, NC

Books

Books,
Books,
Books,
Funny books,
Skinny books,
Thick books,
Colorful books,
Those are just a few
Guide books,
Chapter books,
Picture books too,
Game books,
Test books,
Don't forget text books,
Last of all, best of all,
I like comic books.

Benjamin Page, Grade 6
Hayes Elementary School, OK

I Can't Write a Poem*

I ripped my paper
My pencil lead broke
I'm sick!!!
Can I go to the nurse
I'm feeling a bit wheezy
I broke my writing hand
My hand is stiff.
Can I lay my head down it hurts.
I have make up work
I'm leaving around writing time
She is stabbing me with a pen
I have to go to see the principal
I have to take down the flag
Time's up? Uh oh!
All I have is a dumb list of excuses.
You like it, Really? No!
Kidding! Thanks a lot. Would
you like to see another one?

Tyler Wagganer, Grade 6
Armorel Elementary School, AR
*Patterned after "I Can't Write a
Poem" by Bruce Lansky

The Sea

The sea
The sea is beautiful
The sea is filled with mean animals
The sea is quiet
The sea is scary to some
The sea has a lot of things in it
Fish, rocks, boats, people, trash, water
And those are the things in the sea.

Stephan Tacker, Grade 5
Arnaudville Elementary School, LA

A Tickle Feels Like

A tickle feels like happiness
Spreading through your body
Making a giggle
Become a bowl of laughter

A tickle feels like family
Warmth and kindness
That spreads through your heart

A tickle can make
A frown turn around
Just from the touch
Of someone's fingertips

A tickle replaces
The sadness that lurks
Within everyone's body
Now the sadness
Is nowhere to be found

A tickle feels like everything
Between happiness and warmth
Even on sad, sad days

Caitlyn Brown, Grade 6
South Oldham Middle School, KY

Christmas Season

Snow falls on the roses
Brightens up our noses
Snow fights we are having
Now we are sitting up and laughing
People want to know
Why we sit and play in the snow
We tell them, "It's the Christmas season
And that's our only reason!"

Viershanie Latham, Grade 6
Mildred Jackson Elementary School, AR

Dirtbike

Dirt, bike, clutch, brake, motor,
Honda, kick start, oil, gas, race, paddle
helmet, goggles, boots, gloves, red

Nathan Walley, Grade 4
East Jones Elementary School, MS

Thanksgiving

Turkey, turkey,
All kinds of turkey!
Big ones, little ones
It doesn't matter,
Because we're all going to have a feast
and that will be delicious!

Justin Stewart, Grade 4
East Jones Elementary School, MS

Grades

Grades, grades
If I make an A
I get to play charades!
If I make a B
I will go to plan C
I might as well go to plan B
For me I can't make a D
'Cause then it will be over for me!

Tyler Gunter, Grade 5
Graham Elementary School, AL

The Animal in Me

There is a kitty in me
With skin like a frog
And acts like a monkey
It purrs like a goat
It walks like a skeleton
It lives in my brain
And makes me feel weird
I wish it weren't in me

Andrea Henggeler, Grade 5
South Nodaway Elementary School, MO

Grandma

To someone special we all know
Whose heart and love warms our soul
Who has a bright, gleaming glow
That's my grandma we all know

Emily Giles, Grade 6
Inola Middle School, OK

Baseball Fun

You need a baseball mitt
And maybe a base hit
If you do all these
You can surely play with ease

Travis Howell, Grade 4
Horace Mann Elementary School, OK

Bed Time

It is time to go to sleep.
I can hear a noise go beep.
I darted to Grandpa Dock
and realized it was only the clock.

Alexis Fluharty, Grade 6
Martin Elementary School, WV

For a Little While

I think it would be fun to be an actor,
instead of always being myself.

I would like to know what it feels like to be someone else,
even for a little while.

I would like to be a character who lives far away from here,
and does new and exciting things.

I would like to be the girl who has lots of friends,
the girl who gets the guy, and lives happily ever after.

I think it would be fun to be an actor,
even for a little while.

Emily Harris, Grade 6
Holy Rosary Academy, LA

I Am Thankful

I am thankful for my family.
They love me and I love them.
My mom takes care of me.
She gives me food, a home, and a life.
When I hear my heart having fun
She is playing with me.

I love my dad
He gives me things to play with.

Sometimes in my sleep I see a unicorn and horses.
They make a happy sound, I am thankful for my dreams.

I love my grandmother.
She takes me to the Center at the Landing to play.
I go to church with her.

Most of all I love my dog, her name is Princess.
She is always coming to my room.
She will not forget me,
We are best friends forever.

My sister and me like to play together.
She sings, plays and dances with me.
We make jokes, and bake heart cookies together.

Jeeneva Brown, Grade 4
Lee A Tolbert Community Academy, MO

The Trampoline

The wind feels me as it goes up, down, and around
Exploding as my weight hits the springs
My body flies as I reflect off the platform
Bouncing higher and higher at every touch
Bodies collide as we spring backwards and forwards
Hair screams at every sudden movement
Freezing forms end our meandering

Andrew Szovati, Grade 5
Cline Elementary School, KY

If I Were in Charge of the World

If I were in charge of the world
There would be no rules or laws,
No one would be sick,
People would never have to get shots,
Kids could play outside whenever they wanted,
And there would be no killing.

If I were in charge of the world
There would be no school,
There would be no rules,
We would have no homework,
We could pick our own lunch,
And we could eat candy.

If I were in charge of the world
People would not be punished at home,
Kids could drive their parents cars,
Have all the TV channels I want,
And we could paint our walls any color.

Josh Witt, Grade 6
Eminence Middle School, KY

Avalanches

Weather's no big deal, but when there's an avalanche
RUN!!!!!!!!!!!!!!!!!!!!!!!!
It looks like lots and lots of marshmallows rolling down a hill
Flippin n' Floppin
Gaining speed
With a blink of an eye
Its right on me
Running inside with everyone else
Seeing who will reach a house first
After running and running
I've reached my prize
My soft downy house
Safe and sound
Thumping and teeth chattering
Freezing hands and feet
Looking out a window to see the rocks
Once the coast is clear, I go outside to see the snow
It's over my house
My o' My I can't play now
It gives me a scare
But when it's over "Wahoo!"

Cameron Bennett, Grade 4
Big Creek Elementary School, GA

Wind

The wind blows up, down,
And all around like two people
Chasing each other in a circle and
When they catch each other they
Settle until the next battle.

Adison Nikolai, Grade 5
American Heritage Academy, GA

Sleep

Life is but a great sleep.
I have good and bad dreams.
What about me when I die.
I awake and see.
That Jesus died for me.
Now I'm in heaven.
Yes, you see.

Ryan Dowell, Grade 6
Cathedral School, NC

Child Abuse

Another child hurt
Another one dead.
Think about it; use
Your head. Don't
Sit around Stand up
Today because a
Child needs your help
In each and every
Way.

Addison Sprinkle, Grade 6
Statesville Middle School, NC

Berries

there are some red berries
they are on a big green bush
they smell really really good

Sarah Fish, Grade 6
Livingston Middle School, TN

I Can't Write a Poem*

My brain hurts!
It's not fun!
I love my mom!
My stomach hurts!
It smells very bad!
My heart is stopping!
I can't see!
My dog died!
The person next to me won't be quiet!
I have x-ray vision!
My leg is gone!
It's dark in here!
I left the stove on!
People keep staring at me!
I'm wanted!
There's eight planets in our solar system!
There is a good looking girl next to me!
Time's up? Uh oh.
All I have is this dumb list of excuses.
You like it? Really?
No kidding? Thanks a lot!

Blake Davidge, Grade 6
Armorel Elementary School, AR
*Patterned after "I Can't Write a
Poem" by Bruce Lansky

Red

Red looks like a big shiny cherry
Red feels like a soft velvet curtain
Red tastes like a hot squishy cherry pie
Red smells like a fragrant apple candle burning
Red sounds like a strawberry falling on the floor from a long fall
Red is the best

Rodney White, Grade 5
Geggie Elementary School, MO

Seeing Her the First Time

I open my eyes and I see your face,
A face of joy, of peace,
And tears running down your soft white face —
The eyes, the eyes, the lips, the lips, as smooth a skin as mine, as mine.

Her name I did not need to know, to me she was an angel.
But woe to me, I did not see,
Behold she was my mother —
The eyes, the lips, as smooth a skin as mine.

She held me like I was a fragile soul,
And thus she knew I was.
A man came in laughing with joy to see me, a little baby —
The eyes, the lips, as smooth a skin as mine.

I close my eyes and never do I wake,
But wake I in heavenly bliss,
To see Him looking at me —
The eyes, the lips, smoother skin than mine.

Averie Blackmore, Grade 5
Providence Academy, TN

My Granddaddy

My granddaddy is resourceful,
He made wooden bows and arrows as a child and hardly ever missed
My granddaddy was a student,
He never missed a day in kindergarten through high school.
My granddaddy is responsible,
He always took care of his younger siblings.
My granddaddy was a chemist,
He worked for Ralph Lauren for about ten years.
My granddaddy is a listener,
He will listen to any question or story I tell him.
My granddaddy worked in the Korean War,
He built bridges and retired a Lieutenant Colonel.
My granddaddy is special,
He likes to tell stories of the old days when he was a boy.
My granddaddy is loving,
He loves when I come and sit in his arm chair with him.
My granddaddy is smart,
He has always answered any question I ask him.
My granddaddy is strong,
He's had eight bypasses, two open heart surgeries, and a stroke.
My granddaddy is a survivor.

Taylor Cates, Grade 6
Tyro Middle School, NC

I Am Haunted

I am haunted in the past by the damp, dreary, dark
The spooky, scary movies made me terrified
The dark hallways would whistle my name.

I am haunted in the present because my mom might die
I might be scared and left alone, and brokenhearted
I might be poor if she dies.

I am haunted in the future because I might be in a car wreck
If I die in a car wreck I would leave my family
My family might be scared that I won't come back.

Jackson McGuire, Grade 5
Eminence Middle School, KY

Land/Ocean

Land
dry, hard
moving, quaking, shaking
animals, humans, fish, reefs
flowing, living, freezing
wet, salty
ocean

Evan Russell, Grade 5
Briarwood Christian Elementary School, AL

Feast

Thanksgiving is great at least for someone,
If possible you can have a lot of fun,
So grab you a turkey and have a great feast.
It may be good to get a pound of yeast.
Maybe you will get some cranberry jam.
One good thing is to get some ham.
Invite some people to debone the turkey,
Sometimes it feels like a clump of beef jerky.
Have a great and fabulous feast.

Austin LaBrune, Grade 6
Guntown Middle School, MS

Pearl Harbor

Pearl Harbor and its dangerous threats,
The day Americans will never forget.
Japan invaded America by air,
They brought bombs, guns, weapons that we cannot bear.
Many people died on that day,
Japan also demolished that beautiful bay.
Some just wanted the killing to end,
But others wanted sweet, sweet, revenge.
"A day that will live in infamy" is the quote,
Because they devoured the U.S. by air and also by boat.
Everybody will remember the ones that rest in peace.
The brave soldiers that were once beat.
The attacking of Pearl Harbor is a day we will all remember,
The beautiful place that went down in embers.

Kevin Lee, Grade 6
River Trail Middle School, GA

Rain

Swish swish swish
The rain never stops
Coming down in very big drops
One night it's here the next it's there
Falling down through the silent air

Swish swish swish
It is here again
Wetting all the good men
It comes down hard in an angry way
Oh I wish it would go away

It keeps falling through the night air
Pounding all people without a care
It knocks down trees with a mighty wind
Hitting all people even the hens
Tearing through houses without a doubt
Knocking down people who scream and shout

The rain stops falling
It finally clears
Uproars rise with people's cheers
It covers the land like a great lion's mane
The rain the rain it's finally tame

Michael Simmons, Grade 6
Pulaski County Middle School, GA

The Hockey Hero

There once was a hockey player named Marian,
his shot was harder than a charging ram,
his check is hard,
his face mask is bizarre,
but his stick is big and makes a bam.

Nick Ludwik-Alfi, Grade 5
American Heritage Academy, GA

Thank God for Our Soldiers

I am proud to be an American
where stars are twinkling
in the night time sky
while we sleep in our cozy beds.
Soldiers are fighting for us
in the night.
You can hear the rain drops
on the window sill.
When you see the cemetery
you think of all the tears that flowed.
A diamond ring can't buy happiness,
that your family member
or friend went to war.
The dogs are barking loudly.
People are rejoicing and praying
in their bibles; the war is over!
Thank God that the soldiers are safe and help keep us free!

Megan Lanclos, Grade 6
Leonville Elementary School, LA

Knights

Battle on horseback
Wear sixty pounds of armor
Lancers they fought with
Noah Bacon, Grade 4
Easley Elementary School, NC

Adieu

Adieu to thee, goodbye to thee.
I'm going away now
To Heaven where I am going to live.
Forever.

When this I go up to thy Lord,
I leave my head here.
My soul goes up to thy Lord in Heaven.
Forever.

Will thou go up with thee?
Or will thou go down
And suffer for all eternity?
Forever.

Adieu thy is going up now like a bird.
I pray thy will see thee in Heaven
To abide with our Lord.
Forever.
Abby Smith, Grade 5
Providence Academy, TN

Winter

Winter is frost,
Winter is snow.
Winter is ice,
And a great icicle show.

Winter is apples,
And oranges too.
Winter is coal,
So be good all of you.

Winter is Christmas,
Winter is fun.
Winter is candy and presents,
And getting in the snow to run.

Winter is evergreens,
Covered with decorations.
Winter is toys and gifts,
And Christmas Day celebrations.

Winter is New Years,
And champagne and a baby.
Winter is a count down,
And a lot of people going crazy.
Justin Baker, Grade 6
Brogden Middle School, NC

See Through

Can't you see that I'm here
Now?
I've traveled such a long way just to see
If you remembered me.
But I came and left
And there were still no loving words.
Can you see right through me?
Do I blend with the colors on the wall?
I long to know you better,
But I'm not sure
That you feel the same way.
I wish that you would count the days
Until I'd see you again.
But instead,
You dread them.
So tell me,
Do you love me?
Will you show it?
Or am I just
See through?
Olivia Daniels, Grade 6
Myrtle Beach Middle School, SC

Mom and Dad

Mom
Sweet, funny
Caring, loving, driving
Friend, female, male, buddy
Hugging, working, cooking
Tall, nice
Dad
Miranda Hancock-DeLima, Grade 5
Sycamore Elementary School, GA

Moms

Moms, Moms, Moms!
Some can be a pain.
But I know they contain,
A secret part of love.

Moms, Moms, Moms!
Telling you what to do.
Maybe yelling at you.
But deep down inside,
I know that they hide,
A secret part of love.

Moms, Moms, Moms!
Never telling a lie.
Never ever shy,
So when I grow,
I really really know,
That I'll have
A secret part of love.
Maggie Ruding, Grade 4
Hayes Elementary School, OK

Red Kangaroo

Red kangaroos are
the giant plant eaters of
their hot Outback home
Nefeli Jay, Grade 5
Orchard Elementary School, AL

The Pig Who Hated Pink

There once was a pig who hated pink
she sat all day without a blink
so she painted herself blue
and changed her name to Sue
then everyone gave her a wink!
Elizabeth Thornburg, Grade 6
Martin Elementary School, WV

woods

all the woods out there
have a bunch of animals
like deers, birds, and coons
Holden Lacy, Grade 6
Livingston Middle School, TN

Ashley Had a Pony

Once upon a time
Ashley had a pony
His name was Sunny
They would ride through the meadow
So happy as could be
And Ashley would pick him an apple
From an apple tree
Ashley Boyd, Grade 5
East Marion Elementary School, MS

Pie

I like pie and pie likes me
especially with a big glass of tea.
It is good, it is sweet
it is my favorite afternoon treat.

Apple, cherry, lemon or lime
I want it to be all mine.
Slice or half or the whole pie
it's the apple of my eye!
Austin Shiflett, Grade 5
Graham Elementary School, AL

Fall

Fall is cool
but you can't swim in a pool
rain is coming
leaves are falling
soon it might be snowing
Halloween is there
go trick or treating if you dare!
Katherine Matthews, Grade 5
Midway Covenant Christian School, GA

My Dream

I sat impatiently waiting,
wondering when my laptop computer would come.
I had been watching out the window for hours.
Waiting for that brown UPS truck.
I imagined the man stepping out, with a big package.

I continued to stare out the window, angrily waiting.
I imagined me snatching the package from the man,
opening it and pulling out a new laptop
while screaming with joy.

Suddenly I heard a noise.
It sounded like a truck.
I ran to the window and peeked out.
My dream had arrived.
My laptop was finally here.

I screamed loudly with joy,
hopped up and down with excitement!
Quickly I peeled off the tape
and opened it up and pulled out a beautiful laptop.

It was shiny silver with black keys.
It was my dream come true!

Carissa Whitaker, Grade 5
Etowah Elementary School, NC

Basketball

When you go to the gym
you need to get a ball
and shoot a basket!

William Laatsch, Grade 4
Briarwood Christian Elementary School, AL

The Four Seasons

Summer is the season I love the most
    it makes me laugh and play.
When spring is at its nearest
    I always say "Hooray."
When fall comes I get out the rake
    and sometimes get paid.
When winter comes I get out the coats
    and practice constructing the snow.
Seasons, seasons, seasons, so many things to do.
Seasons, seasons, seasons, you better get ready too!

Koby Morton, Grade 5
Parker Road Elementary School, MO

Math

Math
Hard, tough, boring,
Too many numbers giving me a headache
Blah, blah, blah…we need a break!
Is anything worse than math?

Parker Millican, Grade 5
Landmark Christian School, GA

My Mommy and Daddy

My Mommy and Daddy are always there
My Mommy and Daddy are the ones who care
My Mommy and Daddy are lots of fun
My Mommy and Daddy love me a ton
My Mommy and Daddy are really cool
My Mommy and Daddy never let me miss school
I love My Mommy
I love My Daddy
And that's how it always will be

Shilo Canady, Grade 6
Pershing Middle School, MO

The Fall

In the fall
Great teams play football.
We always run around the house
And sometimes play quiet mouse.
Every morning we go to play
Always expecting an exciting new day.
After school,
We act like fools.
When all our homework's done
We're always ready for more fun.
That's what Fall is all about;
Being able to run, jump, play, and shout.

William Trout, Grade 4
Stephens Elementary School, AL

A Saturday Nap

I look at the ticking clock.
8:30 A.M.
Then I sigh.
Saturday morning I have to get up and work.
I don't want to get up.
Drag myself out of bed,
put on my clothes with my eyes drooping down,
and crawl
to the steps.

Gotta go to work.

Time inched by working at the airport:
helping people board,
scheduling flights.
Could this day go any slower?

Finally 2:30 P.M.
I can't wait to get home.

I run to my room,
dash to my bed,
jump in and pull the covers over my head.
At last, a Saturday afternoon nap.

Storm Edwards, Grade 5
Etowah Elementary School, NC

What Is It?
It drops,
    it falls,
    it splatters,
what could it be?

It falls in sheets,
    mists,
    showers,
    and sometimes
    even storms.

It's cold,
    clear,
    slippery,
    dirty,
    and soft.

It's also piercing,
    cool,
    light,
    and it's definitely
    wet.

It's a raindrop!!!

Brian Franklin, Grade 5
Saffell Street Elementary School, KY

October
October is fun
October is sweet
Fall comes, the leaves fall, this is so neat.
It's cool and rainy, the great fall
I love it all.

Sadie Powers, Grade 4
Western Hills Elementary School, AR

Birthdays
Birthdays are pink and blue.
It sounds like a lot of laughter.
It tastes like yummy candy.
It smells like awesome cake.
It looks like a lot of fun.
It makes you feel ecstatic.

Ashley Callier, Grade 6
St Vincent Elementary School, MO

Veteran
V ery brave
E mbracing
T errific
E mpowering
R ecieve love from us
A wesome as can be
N ice to us!

Brooke Cole, Grade 4
Cherokee Elementary School, AR

My Tadpoles
My tadpoles are tiny and they're speedy, too.
They zip through the water like a speedboat and they're super cute.
I love my tadpoles and my sister does, too!

Rodney Scott, Grade 5
Woodlawn Christian School, NC

The Football Team
This football team, with four crystal footballs,
Plays the game of football, with many rules and laws.
This team's power comes like booming storms,
Their name? The Longhorns.

The Longhorns' offensive line is an iron bar,
Their backfield is a sight,
It's always ready for a fight,
Their backs are quick and always ready for a pick.

The Griffin twins, who love to win,
Are very good and try not to lack,
They can hit the other team with a whack!
The Griffin twins are very good.

The Longhorns are an unstoppable force of serious unstoppableness,
They are quite unstoppable!
I just love to cheer,
For this bunch of steer.

Sterling Fooshee, Grade 5
Providence Academy, TN

Devil's Hand
Rain pouring down from the heavens,
    Hail thudding on the rooftop,
A lonely dog howls, longing to come inside,
    As the wind beats against the window,

Horror thrives through the house,
Devil's hand reaches down toward the land below,
    Fear wrenches my chest,
Lights flicker on and off as if a ghost is in our presence,

All is black as the power leaves the lights,
    Families retreat to their basements,
    Hand reaches down miles away,
    Preparing to destroy everything,

His hand ripping God's creation from the Earth,
    Killing, hurting, destroying,
    Suddenly he stops, feeling tired,
Collapsing into his flaming den, where he is waiting to arise once again,

All is calm,
The dark clouds roll away in the night sky,
    All is black,
    As God tucks us in.

Cole Morgan, Grade 4
Goshen Elementary School at Hillcrest, KY

Thanksgiving Dinner

Every year I go to eat Thanksgiving dinner with my family…

But this year is different, I sat down beside my sister. Then we passed around the food after giving thanks.
And my sister dropped gravy in my lap. O boy did that make me mad. (And this is why you never ever sit
by sisters at dinner.) So I dropped some dressing in her lap. And what do you know she threw turkey at me
and we got in lots of trouble. So that's why you never sit by sisters at Thanksgiving dinners.

Danielle McArthur, Grade 6
Guntown Middle School, MS

Waiting

Waiting waiting for the first snowflake to fall.
When summer's fading and that's not all.
When the bluebirds stop singing and the robins go home, autumn is almost gone.
With lawns full of leaves that are turning brown it is getting colder in everybody's town.
It was gloomy and gray when the first snowflake fell.
We are no longer waiting for the first snow to fall.

Madeline Small, Grade 6
Richardson Elementary School, MO

Christmas

The night before I put up stockings and set out some cookies and milk for Santa Claus,
I may even sneak a bite or two.
I go to sleep early so Santa can come and leave me lots of presents,
I will wake up first in my home and yell out with glee.
I'll wake up my family and maybe my neighborhood, too.
I'll need to look in my stocking, and what do I find?
A candy cane, a book, and a hairpin, too.
Oh, such treasures! I'll keep them forever!
I wait on my brothers and sister, Mom and Dad too.
I go running to the Christmas tree.
I will find lots of presents for me and everyone else in my household.
I run to the kitchen, and what do I find?
A crumb of cookie and drop of milk on the plate where Santa Claus ate!

Logan Ellis, Grade 5
Paint Lick Elementary School, KY

The American Flag

Not long after the Declaration of Independence was signed, the American Flag was carefully designed.
The colors chosen were red, white, and blue. It was to symbolize freedom for more than a few.

One day Betsy Ross sat sewing. Her needle bobbed and weaved.
In the past, the citizens had grieved. But now the flag is flowing.

The flag means a lot to you and me, what a glorious sight it is to see,
On the battlefield the enemy will flee, when it waves everyone jumps up with glee.

Our country fights for freedom, we honor leadership and bravery.
From many countries they come; our country believes in victory.

Please acknowledge the American flag. Don't use it as clothing or as a hand bag.
Remember to take care of it, or our flag will tear bit by bit.

We honor our country and its liberty. When we win a war, we are filled with glee.
We are comforted because you see, in the United States, we are all free.

Thomas Kyzer, Colin Shearer, and Tristan Creasey, Grade 5
Heber Springs Elementary School, AR

Open Road
a road trip with bikes
see birds and have lots of food
music on the way
Michael Pradier, Grade 6
Tomlinson Jr High School, OK

Thankfulness
I'm thankful for God.
I'm thankful for me.
I'm thankful for life that I live with glee.
I'm thankful for friends, family too.
But most of all I'm thankful for you.
John D. Coffman, Grade 6
All Saints' Episcopal School, TN

The Letter S
Slithering
Snakes
Silently
Stalk
Slippery,
Slimy Salamanders
So
Softly
Sings
Slowly
So
Solemnly   Sounds
Soundless Sound
Stephanie Floyd, Grade 6
Pulaski County Middle School, GA

Christmas
C aring
H appiness
R estless
I mmovable
S haring
T hankfulness
M agical
A micable
S leepless
RaKeem Williams, Grade 6
St Mark Elementary School, SC

War
War is red and orange
It sounds like screaming
It smells like sadness
It looks like tears
It makes me feel like
I just want to go up
To both armies and say "Stop!"
Jacob Wallace, Grade 4
Cleveland Elementary School, OK

One Friend
I have one friend,
Her name is Kristen.
She is shy and kind and always cares.
She loves not hates.
She gives gifts, not mad faces.

I have one friend,
Her name is Kristen.
When I come over, she plays with me,
Not throwing paint at me.

I have one friend,
Her name is Kristen.
She always has a joy-filled heart.
Willow Griffith, Grade 4
Hayes Elementary School, OK

Best Friends
You are my best friend
to the end
You are nice, smart
and funny
You brighten my day
when I'm lonely
You will never lie
to me
You are the best

You are the friend
a Best Friend
can have
Jamillah Carter, Grade 6
Brogden Middle School, NC

Verbs
Read, sing, dance, and play
Jump, drink, laugh, and say
Swim, push, drive, and write
Chew, eat, kick, and bite

Pull, take, and swing side to side
Bring, prance, carry, and hide
Move, run, stomp, and blink
Get, wait, sit, and clink

Hike, paint, put, and snap
Scratch, found, blow, and nap
Talk, roll, roar, and dress
Brush, spin, splash, and rest

Ring, type, publish, and go
Clap, believe, giggle, and show
Stand, wiggle, drop, and draw
Cut, limp, imagine, and crawl
Chelsea Patma, Grade 4
Nesbit Elementary School, GA

The Girl Who Loved Jelly
There once was a girl named Kelly
She loved to eat jars of jelly
She brought some to lunch
Then she gave it a munch
And now big is her belly!
Hannah Starnes, Grade 6
Carmel Elementary School, GA

My Grandma's House
My grandma's house is full of love.
It's there I feel joy and happiness.
She plays a game of Go Fish.
That brings a smile to me.

My grandma's house is full of love.
We watch her favorite show.
And she tells me stories of old.
That brings a smile to me.

My grandma's house is full of love.
After school, she's there waiting,
To share another time of treasure.
That brings a smile to me.
Lexus Hulet, Grade 4
Hayes Elementary School, OK

Christmas
A blanket of snow comes every year,
As a simple sign that Christmas is here.
No school, no work, no more Math,
Just plain fun and a game of Smath.

See the Christmas lights on doors,
And also, on the wooden floors.
There's not any Grinch in sight,
Have a happy Christmas night.
Varun Ramachandran, Grade 4
Nesbit Elementary School, GA

Titanic
My daddy took me 'board this ship,
During our yearly summer trip.
We gazed up at the Titanic so grand,
So excited about this trip we'd planned.
No one predicted the iceberg we'd hit,
The one that made this huge ship split.
Cold water starts to pour inside,
Off the balcony I quickly slide.
Plunged in the water freezing cold,
This never ending nightmare unfolds.
The rescue boat comes to my aid,
I climb in, terrified, afraid.
We sit, watch in terror, panic,
Sinking remains, 'o the great Titanic.
Alisha Goel, Grade 6
River Trail Middle School, GA

I Dream

I dream of a gorgeous garden
I can just picture it in my head,
I can see flowers of all pretty colors and trees of green.
I can also see a path made up of smooth stones for a nice,
Quiet morning walk.
I can hear in my head birds singing a calming song,
A fish leaping out of the pond.
I see a fountain pouring out dreams.
Every time I get this image in my head,
I think to myself, this garden is beautiful,
Like Me!!!

Courtney Privette, Grade 6
Brogden Middle School, NC

Owls

Owls fly through the night,
So silently you can't hear their flight.

They hunt for food like voles and mice,
They sleep during the day and soar at night.

Some owls are huge, some are small,
They have beautiful feathers all.

Living in trees high above the ground,
Many are endangered, never to be found.

From Elf to Great Horned and all in between,
They are all amazing and always will be.

Joe Piscitelli, Grade 5
Cameron Park Elementary School, NC

White

White is the last name of Snow and many more,
White is the color of my front door.
White is the elephant that makes everyone look,
White is the color of the cover of my book.
White is the color of my grandfather's hair,
White is the fur of a polar bear.
White is the color of a little harmless lie,
White is the color of a cloud in the sky.
White is the color of the President's House,
White is the color of a little blind mouse.
White is in the name of a Great White Shark,
White is the color that chases the dark.
White is the milk in the carton in your hand,
White is the color of the beaches' sand.
White is the color of stripes in our flag,
White is the sugar in a ten-pound bag.
White is the color of a softball you can throw,
White is the color of no more sorrow.
White is this paper before I had begun,
White is the presence of all colors that run.

Regina Andreoni, Grade 5
St Thomas More School, NC

Scary Is a Fright

We looked out to the night sky.
We saw the moon hidden in a tree.
We heard owls coo, coyotes howl.
We wandered on hearing the night sounds.
We saw skeletons, monsters, mummies, and goblins.
And all of a sudden boo! Ahh!
Oh! It's just Halloween night, Trick-or-Treat.

Alexis Brooks, Grade 5
Etowah Elementary School, NC

Veteran

V ictorious troops fighting for America.
E ager to get out of the war
T ake down the enemy with an iron fist
E very day waiting for our loved ones to come home
R ifles firing off every moment
A merica is our home
N ever will we give up

Noah McComas, Grade 4
Cherokee Elementary School, AR

Halloween Mayhem

Ghost and goblins oh my
Witches and wizards boo!
Warlocks and mummies of all sorts
Evil and good
Scary and spooky
Nice and mean
Evil and spooky
All trick or treating on the night of Halloween
Awaiting it on All Hallows Eve
To go out and trick or treat on Halloween night
What a fright

Kate Moffitt, Grade 5
Walton Verona Elementary School, KY

Middle School

First day of middle school, oh, what a fright
I stayed up the whole entire night

Sights and smells of a new school
I think this place is so cool

Visions of getting to class on time
Ran through my head like a Boeing 49

Instead of putting my feelings on a shelf
I've gained confidence and belief in myself

Touching the lock for the first time
Sends chills up and down my spine

Sounds of bells rrrrrrringing in my ear
The first day of middle school is finally here

Tori Peavy, Grade 6
Pulaski County Middle School, GA

Some People

Some people smile and pick flowers
and other people like to frown
Some people get to sleep
and others act like clowns

Some people hate the clock
others love the pool
Some girls hate dogs
now others have to go to school

Mason Smith, Grade 6
Central Arkansas Christian School, AR

Halloween

Halloween is very fun
even though it's not in the sun
I like to get lots of candy
it makes me feel very dandy.
Halloween comes once a year,
it's hard to decide what to wear.
At Halloween there's so much to do
I'd really like to go haunting with you!

Samantha Cowan, Grade 4
Frederick Elementary School, OK

An Ode to Sophie

Oh Sophie, you are really a cute kitty.
Oh Sophie, you really are bad.
When you run away it makes me sad.
Oh Sophie you are really nice.
I understand you like to catch mice.
Just be yourself and have fun.
I also know you like to run!

Justine McNair, Grade 4
Pines Elementary School, NC

Mr. Ol' Sycamore Tree

Mr. Ol' Sycamore tree
You are the perfect one for me.
You are as sturdy as can be
Mr. Ol' Sycamore tree.

There is a place on you that's flat
So I can sit back and rest my back.

Mr. Ol' Sycamore tree
You are the perfect one for me.

Emily Davis, Grade 5
Zalma Elementary School, MO

Bells

Bells on the trees, bells on bees
Bells in the tress, bells on knees
Bells in the sky, birds fly by
Bells, bells, everywhere there is bells.

Erica Brown, Grade 5
Hatfield Elementary School, AR

The Beautiful Flower Garden

My family is a random assortment of flowers, watered by the rain.
Never growing far apart, but sometimes falling apart.

My grandmother is the solar energy, for my aunt.
High in the sky.
Smiling for all the world to see.
Giving off energy for her to live.
Kissing and blessing her with sunshine.

My aunt is a red rose.
Filling everyone with splendor.
With her red rosy color, she brings everyone to her.
Sparkling with delight, as the sun goes down.
Still sparkling, she awaits for its return.

Now in the end, they are still friends.
But they come with their own packaged,
Heart with love and consequences.

Allison Judd, Grade 6
Bowling Green Jr High School, KY

Chips

Chips with dip
sometimes make you flip
and break your hip.

The chip sounds crunchy
when you put it in your mouth; it sounds munchy.

They smell of the chips go according to what kind of chips you get,
but the kind I would get is Ritz.

Quentin Mabry, Grade 6
St Mark Elementary School, SC

Leeks

Once a day and twice a week, I go to the store to buy a leek.
Leeks have leaves like trees.
But sway sweetly in the breeze.
How sweet the taste of a leek.

Apples are red, oranges are orange.
But a leek is green and shines with a rosy sheen.
I tell you my friend there is nothing more sweet than a leek.
How sweet the taste of a leek.

Leeks are candy to me.
They help me move my weak knee.
They walk upon the earth, only to be buried in the throat of a gray old goat.
How sweet the taste of a leek.

I could die for the taste of a leek.
If you ask me to give up a leek, I will tell you to come back next week.
A leek for you a leek for me.
How sweet the taste of a leek.

Noah C. Huskey, Grade 5
Providence Academy, TN

Cassadie's Bio
Cassadie
Funny, caring, cheerful, curious
Sister of Nate, Gabe, Mason, Grace
Lover of animals, talking, candy
Who feels happy when playing with guinea pigs
Who gives friendship, money, help
Who needs animals, laughter, candy
Who fears dying
Who would like to see a candy factory in my house
Oklahoma City
Oglesby
Cassadie Oglesby, Grade 4
Cleveland Elementary School, OK

The Indian Ocean Tsunami: The Doom's Day
When the waves came groaning,
The people started soaring and drowning.
As the big and heavy wave hit the land,
It went way past the sand.
Everyone ran out of sight,
And safe from this awful fight.
Each person that lived in a village on the shore,
Lost someone that they used to adore.
Everyone cried in sorrow,
They hoped that it wouldn't happen tomorrow.
People worked day and night,
To reconstruct the horrible sight.
Many volunteers helped the poor,
With words to treat their mental sore.
Doctors and nurses cure patients,
With much patience.
Organizations were willing to share,
They gave so much care.
People were so hurt because of this cause,
And so we will never forget this dreadful pause.
This tsunami was the worst,
And so this tsunami should be cursed.
Divya Sukumar, Grade 6
River Trail Middle School, GA

Frogs
Frogs are all sizes.
They are different colors.
Frogs can jump sky high!
Kaitlyn Hennesy, Grade 4
Briarwood Christian Elementary School, AL

The Thrills of Autumn
As I sit on the porch reflecting the day
I see the leaves one by one as they blow away.
The pumpkins in the neighbor's yard
are big and round but rather large.
The thrill of autumn is just months away
it's a perfect end to a perfect day.
Austin Holbrooks, Grade 4
Tamassee-Salem Elementary School, SC

The Ocean
Looks like dolphins jumping
Sounds like waves crashing
Smells like stinky fish
Feels like the salty cold water
Tastes like salt.
Anna Forester, Grade 5
Briarwood Christian Elementary School, AL

A Friend Is
A friend is a kind person.
A friend is a good citizen.
A friend is a kind speaker.
A friend is a buddy, pal, and bff.
A friend is a person to look up to.
A friend is a person to ask a question to.
A friend is a person that can help you do anything.
A friend is a person that won't curse.
A friend is a person that won't be in a fuss.
A friend is a person who will smile.
A friend is a person to smile for while.
A friend is like my friend Ashton.
A friend is like my friend Elizabeth.
Rickkia Manuel, Grade 5
Franklin Elementary School, OK

Silly Words
Abracadabra, hocus pocus
these are words that need focus

Holy moly, and thing-a-ma-jigger
means something is much bigger

Shake that thing and raise the roof
are groovin' down phrases like high-wire goofs

"Goober" is one "what-cha-ma-call-its" another
these are words I learned from my mother
Drew Burns, Grade 5
Walton Verona Elementary School, KY

Bugs
If I were a bug
And I'm glad I'm not,
I'd never roam the street
I'd do my best
To stay away
From peoples giant feet

If I were a bug
I would run from cars
And I'd fly high
To the sky
So that my butt and face stay very far apart.
Alex McLeod, Grade 6
Benton County School of the Arts, AR

The Terrible Tornado

I am vicious as a beast
I am faster than the Tasmanian devil.
I am your family's worst nightmare.
I will give you no warning.
I will start by spinning in a deadly way.
You will be very furious,
When I come your way.
I come when you're asleep.
I come when you're awake.
I am determined to destroy,
what gets in my way.
That's why I'm called a tornado

Tisha L. Locklear, Grade 5
Pembroke Elementary School, NC

Prayer of a Fish

In the big wide ocean
with swordfish trying to be free
I must hide for protection
from hungry fish and big mouth teeth!

Derrick Moore, Grade 5
Mark Twain Elementary School, MO

Tyler Fay

I saw Tyler Fay
Digging in some hay
I thought he was raking
He thought I was faking
I think he just wants his way

Tyler Fay, Grade 5
Sycamore Elementary School, GA

Autumn Fox

Autumn fox
Brown leaf fur
Autumn fox
You are so pure
Autumn fox
You should know
In the forest
Where to go
Autumn fox
Run and play
Blue sky green grass
A beautiful day!

Grace Brintnall, Grade 5
Etowah Elementary School, NC

Hare

Hare
hopping and playing
running fast
like the wind blowing
If only I could have two.

Caleb Waugh, Grade 4
Riverside East Elementary School, AR

Veteran

V ery violent
E veryone looked sad
T ogether everyone fights in tanks
E ach enemy's eyes were in pain
R ights, we have rights
A ttack the mean people
N ot all people will live.

Dakota Cheyenne Ringstaff, Grade 4
Cherokee Elementary School, AR

The Gun

Finally I have a real gun.
It's so beautiful and shiny.
It's everything I imagined,
Brown, black, silver, long, skinny.
It's like a dream come true.
I can be just like my dad and uncle.
I can go hunting with friends and family
And spend quality time.
That, you can't buy in stores.

Trey Gibson, Grade 6
North Iredell Middle School, NC

Numbers

Counting numbers, always with glee,
they go over, infinity.
Two plus two,
always equals four.
Adding is fun,
but there is much more!
Six minus five,
has got to equal one.
Adding, subtracting,
oh, isn't this fun!
Seven times six
equals forty-two.
That's one more,
but there's still another to do.
Turn around multiplying,
and you can divide.
Write that answer down,
Full of pride.
Numbers are really fun,
but now I tell you
this poem is done.

Ellie Harrison, Grade 5
Meramec Elementary School, MO

Snow

Snow
Soft, white
Playing, eating, flaking
Everything is a piece of heaven and joy
Snow

Eric Bahena, Grade 5
Bayyari Elementary School, AR

I Am Haunted

I am haunted by war
I am afraid those terrible terrorists
Would come into town.

I am haunted by Waverly Hills
The big black ghost
That haunted the window
Whenever I go up the hill
I shiver and my knees quiver.

I am haunted by scary spiders
I am afraid they will bite me
And poison me with the venom.

Sean Hoagland, Grade 5
Eminence Middle School, KY

Las Vegas

My trip to Las Vegas
Fun and exciting
Lots to see and lots to do
Never thought it would take so long
Could not wait to get there!
Flying high above the sky
Like a bird with flapping wings
Saw many lights flickering
Like candles on a birthday cake
Could gamble in casinos
Pretty women dressed in costumes
Money jingling like bells chiming
People screaming "jackpot!"
Slow moving gondolas passing by
As I devour strawberry gelato
Mimes moving in different directions
Trying to follow me around
But I escape to my room
Where a white, puffy cloud awaits me
I lay down on my bed, soft as snow
And gently drift to sleep.

Taylor Bour, Grade 6
Beck Academy, SC

At the Shore

Ten wide whales all in a row
Nine swift sharks way down below
Eight diving ducks up in the sky
Seven big boats with sails so high
Six soft seals lying in the sun
Five playful porpoises having some fun
Four gray gulls standing in the sun
Three strong swimmers heading for land
Two cheery children playing with a ball
One crawling crab climbing a wall
Everyone goes to the shore you'll agree
To look at the things that live by the sea

Joseph Jackson, Grade 6
Mildred Jackson Elementary School, AR

I Am From

I am from Deanie and Stephen
From friends and family
From action packed movies like *Lord of the Rings*
From *Fable* the video game
From *Harry Potter* too
From fishing for crappie to fishing for bass
From basketball too

Cody Compton, Grade 5
Tates Creek Elementary School, KY

Pumpkins

Round, decorative
God's beautiful creations
Big and skinny shapes.

Emmie Leath, Grade 4
Briarwood Christian Elementary School, AL

Going Through the Woods

When I ride my four-wheeler,
I see trees, deer, spiders, turkeys, and fallen leaves
I step off, and pace toward the river.
The river is cold as winter.

I hike up the hill,
and discover little caves. I gaze
down in them and hear water waves.
I touch the rocks,
They feel smooth as socks.

I go back home
and think if I should go back
with my brother to the cold
river.

The End
Katie Beth Douglas, Grade 4
Alvaton Elementary School, KY

What Am I?

I am gigantic and unstoppable.

If you are in my vortex I will pick you up and throw
You anywhere even in the Pacific Ocean.
I am a deadly beast.
I am taller than a skyscraper
I smell like a dumpster
I will destroy anything in my path.
I'm determined to destroy everything.

So don't stand in my way or I will be furious and vicious
I go at super sonic speed.

I am a Tornado!
Porshia Steen, Grade 5
Pembroke Elementary School, NC

I Love Fall!!

Fall is here,
Ball seasons here,
Animals getting ready to hibernate,
All rabbits, bears, and deer.

Leaves fall on the ground,
I love their crunchy sound
we'll rake them in a pile,
we'll jump, it'll be worthwhile.

Thanksgiving's almost come,
Mashed potatoes, Yum!
Mom's busy in the kitchen,
Hurry; lets cook that chicken!

Fall has come and gone,
but soon it won't be long,
'till Fall is here again,
I LOVE FALL!!!

Brooke Bottone, Grade 5
Palmetto Christian Academy, SC

Veteran

V eterans fighting for victory
E nduring terrifying moments
T errorism is all around us
E xtreme sadness and sorrow
R ed, blood-stained battle fields
A lthough not all will ever see home again
N ever will our Nation give up

Kevin French, Grade 4
Cherokee Elementary School, AR

A Blessing for a Dancer

May your shoes stay tied and taps stay on
May your turns be sharp and leaps be high
May your dance stay on beat and you remember your dance
May you dance with excitement
And may you dance with a smile on your face

Abby Fields, Grade 6
St Francis Xavier School, AL

Our Fight

You said some things that weren't very nice
But that didn't give us a reason to fight
I yelled and screamed
You hit me and other things
I was sad
And you felt bad
I refused to speak
But you tried for weeks
You apologized again and again
So I thought to begin
I would say sorry and be your friend

Mary Carol Butterfield, Grade 5
Prince of Peace Catholic School, SC

A Story About God

One morning God woke up,
Said good morning to everyone
But no one was in sight
It was all dark
So God said let there be light
There was
So God said let there be animals, trees,
Plants, stars, and there was a lot more
And it was
Then he made Adam and Eve
To take care of all the stuff
He had created by hand
And God saw it was good

Danielle Rickman, Grade 6
Dyer Elementary & Jr High School, TN

Horses

Running, thundering
With spirit in their hearts
And as free as the wind

Darrian Short, Grade 5
Bonaire Elementary School, GA

Thank You for Fighting for Me!

I am proud to be an American
in the great outdoors.
the clouds are moving far
in the deep black sky.
the grass is green and cold.
My dog is chasing every car!
My neighbors are outside cooking.
I know my aunt is watching me
from above.
The fragrant smell
from my mom's cooking
smells good!
I'm thinking about the soldiers
in Iraq fighting for me.
Thank you for fighting for me!

Brennan Lafleur, Grade 6
Leonville Elementary School, LA

Thanksgiving

T hanking
H im for his
A wesome
N ame for the
K indness He has
S hown
G iving in a
V ery
I ncredible way, He is a
N ever failing
G od

Kim Kham, Grade 6
Victory Christian School, OK

How Words Make You Feel!

Words you use them every day.
You use them from morning until night.
Words can make you feel happy, sad, or sometimes mad.
You must choose your words carefully.
According to how you use your words
you can make someone happy with just a few nice words.
You can make someone sad if you choose to use words that can hurt.
When someone is feeling down you can bring them up
and they will treasure your friendship forever.
Words can make new friends and keep your old friends.
Words can make a difference in this world.
So use your words carefully
and the world will be a better place to be.

Alex Darden, Grade 4
Lewis Vincent Elementary School, LA

Words and Images Everlasting

The dictionary, the old memory box.
The knowledge and information, from present and past.
Some say data is infinite, and some say their past has or hasn't lasted enough.
The dictionary, the big book of words, with its passionate use of language.
The old memory box of ancient, valuable accommodations.
They remind us of back then, usually good times.
The old memory box, the dictionary containing unlimited intelligence.
Telling descriptive passages that go on and on.
The dictionary, the memory box.

Selaem Hadera, Grade 5
Nesbit Elementary School, GA

Where I Am From

I am from watching movies, camping, reading books, vacationing, inventing, cooking
Defending friends in need, dancing and singing everywhere I go, playing the flute,
Learning in school, and performing in plays.

I am from cheerleading, basketball, baseball,
Kickball, mat ball, catch, football, gymnastics, and *swimming*.

I'm from jewelry, arts and crafts, music
Cats and dogs
And riding bikes.

I'm from public swimming pools, parks in other towns, church, and the world!

I am from friends, like Savannah and Lauren.
We share toys and secrets.
Sometimes...
I have to watch my little brother, Michael, and my little sister, Alyceson, at home, too.

I am also from God and the world, like everyone else.
Nobody is perfect. Treat people the way you want to be treated,
And take this lifelong advice.
Worship God. He is our Lord and Creator.

This is where I am from.

Jessica Angeloff, Grade 5
Burgin Independent School, KY

What Is Green

Green is the plant we all grow,
Green is the crayon all dull and old,
Green is the color of apples in the trees,
Green is the grass below you and me,
Green is the color of the murky sea,
Green is the envy we all hate to see.

Green is the grape vine hanging down,
Green is the lily pad floating around,
Green is the top of the carrot that is never clean,
Green is the alligator that is so mean,
Green is the olive on a sandwich.
Green is the color of a salad with spinach.

Itchy poison ivy is also green,
Makes me itch until I want to scream.
Green is the color of elves in the North Pole,
Green is the leprechaun protecting their gold,
Green is the color of water and leaves,
Green is the color of faded trees.

Bradley Thomison, Grade 6
Lost River Elementary School, KY

The Thief Lords

One night in the cold streets of Paris, there were two thieves.
They enter houses at night just like cats.
Their names are Sheila and Sly.
They can always come up with a really great lie.

They use different disguises to sneak by guards.
The people they have to fight are at large.
With the help of their friends Bentley and Murray.
When they sneak in a house they don't have to hurry.

When the cops are on their tails.
They can escape by sliding on some rails.
Carmelita can never catch the two crooks.
But Sly and Sheila always give her challenging looks.

The brother and sister pair can always win.
Sometimes they can steal things that are golden.
Some days they just sit down and rest.
With their two friends they think are the best.

Kiana Whyte, Grade 6
Orange Grove Elementary School, MS

Cow Burger

Cow
Slow, fat
Grazing, digesting, cowtipping
Lazy, dirty, yummy, juicy
Spilling, frying, melting in my tummy
Spicy, fat
Hardee's Jalapeño Burger

Christian Rodgers-Smith, Grade 5
Nathaniel Hawthorne Elementary School, MO

Clouds

They can be white, they can be gray
There can be none at all.
If they're there they sit beside a glowing yellow ball.

They are nestled in a sky of blue not purple, brown or gray.
Then at night when the sky turns black they seem to run away.

In winter they bring snow, in summer they bring storm,
In spring they bring us tornadoes, causing us to mourn.
If you know what this is, you surely should be proud,
You just figured out I'm defining a *cloud*.

Lilly Echols, Grade 5
Lula Elementary School, GA

Beautiful, Wild World

The birds fly by,
The clouds drift in the sky.
A deer grazes in the plain,
The wild horse shakes its mane.
A lone wolf cries out its lovely song,
For a pack it will long.
The tree limbs twist as a breeze comes through,
It ripples the lake that is so blue.
This beautiful, wild world is so heavenly it may seem,
This beautiful, wild world can disappear like a dream.

Sami Baudry, Grade 6
Queen of Angels Catholic School, GA

Our Flag

Our flag is a symbol of freedom.
Our flag is a symbol of states.
So always love it with no hate.

God watches over the U.S.A. every day.
He cares, loves, and wants us to obey.

When the flag flies high in the big blue sky.
We can remember the soldiers who fight every day.
And always remember to love the U.S.A.

Kaylinn Baker, Grade 4
Heartland High School and Academy, MO

My Stuffed Rabbit Hippy

Hippy is my rabbit.
He is pink, yellow, orange, purple, green, and blue.
I have had Hippy
Since I was two
Hippy is really special to me
Because I sleep with him
Every night.
Having him with me
Makes me happy
When I sleep

Hannah Kenyon Ashby, Grade 5
American Heritage Academy, GA

Ode to My Football Helmet

Ode to my football helmet
because without you I
would have a bad headache

Keith Spillman, Grade 5
Walton Verona Elementary School, KY

Thoughts of a Struggling Poet

This is quite a difficult task,
Yet oddly enough I get it.
As soon as I write something good,
I will receive the credit.
Let me try the English style.
Young Lochinvar is too old.
How about a nursery rhyme?
Too childish to be told.
Maybe I will write a narrative
About a child named Billy.
To me it seems,
A poem like that
Would just be far too silly.
Perhaps I'll write a free verse.
It won't have to be so terse.
I'll have to be persistent though
Through times when I'm perverse
I can't believe what I'm seeing
This all seems so queer.
I thought about writing the perfect poem,
And look what I found here!

Justin Bryant, Grade 6
River Trail Middle School, GA

Moon

I look out my window,
In the foggy night sky,
I see the moon lighting my way.
I keep on looking at it all night.
Then the moon just fades,
like a rainbow in the sunlight.
It looks like
it's sliding away, and then it vanishes
just like life.

Rebecca Crain, Grade 4
Crestwood Elementary School, KY

Christmas

C hrist was born
H appiness was found
R emember Lord Jesus
I love Him
S ay your prayers
T alking to Him
M ake Him happy
A ngels will appear
S ing "Silent Night"

Kelsey Ward, Grade 5
Trenton Middle School, MO

Winter Wonderland

Winter brings cozy fires
around Christmas
with presents and wrapped gifts.

Alec Wright, Grade 6
Tomlinson Jr High School, OK

Lace Monitor

Like a dragon a Lace Monitor looks.
Hunts animals of every kind.
You can't even pull it in a wagon.
Could it be color blind?

Oscar Newton, Grade 4
John Will Elementary School, AL

Christmas

C ookies and milk
H oliday spirit
R ough bark on the Christmas tree
I love Christmas
S anta Claus
T oys
M any Christmas presents
A very Merry Christmas
S now

Danny Ambriz, Grade 6
Brogden Middle School, NC

Amputa

Amputa
sand-colored fur
burrows for food
disguised to the eyes of predators
Mammal

Sam Nichols, Grade 5
Indian Springs Elementary School, AL

When the Waves Hit

As the rising waves hit
the sandy ground,
it completed my soul.

Walking to the campsite
near the beach,
I still could hear the waves crashing.

Pushing to the shore,
pushing to the shore,
then back to the sea.

It's time to go,
and the waves do not hit.
Nothing completes me now.
Next summer,
the waves complete my soul again.

Juan Pablo Retamal, Grade 5
Etowah Elementary School, NC

My Family Lives in a Closet

My family lives in a closet
Emily is a prom dress,
Beautiful, but isn't with us much

Katie is a T-shirt
Plain white,
doesn't like fancy things,
and is the middle,
the hardest place to be

Dad is the jackets,
that keep us warm and close.

Mom is a jewelry box
full of sparkling jewels

Felix is the buttons,
cute and likes to cling

I am the hangers,
that give my family support.

Sarah Ulber, Grade 6
College View Middle School, KY

Poems

P ersonable
O riginal
E xciting
M agnificent
S atisfying

Simone Cowan, Grade 4
Landmark Christian School, GA

I'll Fly Away

One of these days, I'll fly away.
I will go up the only way.
The Lord knows I want to fly,
So one day I'll have to say good bye.
I flap my wings and take to the sky,
as long as I keep flying up, I'll never die.
It is time for me to land,
this place where I am is name brand.
As I walk to the huge gate,
I'm hoping I'm not too late.
Oh great! I'm on time,
but I have to go to the end of the line.
I heard a voice but didn't see anything,
I knew that could only mean one thing.
The Lord Almighty, who I wanted to see,
I'm here now and I can be.
At last I came to the gate,
for I didn't have to wait.
Like I said, I'll fly away,
I'll go up the only way.

LaNiyah Hicks, Grade 4
Stephens Elementary School, AL

Soccer

Soccer is fun, soccer is great
To score a goal you must concentrate
To get in shape you must exercise a bunch
If you crash into someone it makes a loud crunch
A couple of moves are the cutback and header
When you practice these you get better
To be a good team you must cooperate
And to be a good player you must participate

Hannah Street, Grade 5
Graham Elementary School, AL

The Perfect Gift

Dad, I could not afford flowers this year
Or a fancy trip for two;
I couldn't even find chocolates
With your favorite goo.

So, Dad, my gift to you this year
Is a gift so fine and dear,

It may not be much,
But it is a gift with your daughter's touch.

So, Dad, my gift to you this year
Is a heart full of love
From me to you.

Kelsey Kimble, Grade 5
Evangelical Christian School, TN

I Am Haunted

I AM HAUNTED in the past by scary snakes
They might come and bite me
They might be poisonous

I am haunted in the present by haunted hospitals
They might give me a shot
They might have nasty food

I am haunted in the future by my mom and dad dying
I'm afraid they might have creepy cancer

LaTisha Singer, Grade 5
Eminence Middle School, KY

It Is Rain!

It can sprinkle, drop or fall.
It can also splash, pound, or smack a wall.
Sometimes it pours, drips or even hails.
It can come down fast, slowly, lightly, and softly
It can land on the ground or in a pail.
It can be warm, cold, clear, dirty or even slick.
Sometimes it may feel like a needle or a sharp stick.
It can be ice, dew, mist or come down in sheets.
Sometimes it is liquid on our little feet.

Garrett Pritchert, Grade 5
Saffell Street Elementary School, KY

Thanksgiving

Thanksgiving is a time to share
a time to give
and a time to help people
during their time of need.
Thanksgiving is a great time of year
especially if you like turkey and stuffing.
So this Thanksgiving spread a little cheer.

Katelyn Grandin, Grade 6
Guntown Middle School, MS

Summer/Winter

summer
hot, sunny
swimming, running, laughing
grass, ocean, snow, ice
skiing, freezing, skating
cold, bare
winter

Ryan Lavoie, Grade 5
Briarwood Christian Elementary School, AL

My Backyard

My backyard is the place I love to be.
I go swimming.
I go skate boarding.
I even play football.
My backyard is my dream house,
and I even have a tree house.
It has a rope tied to it and to a tree.
My backyard is awesome.
I never want anything to happen to my backyard.

Matt Erwin, Grade 4
Lewis Vincent Elementary School, LA

Birthdays

Birthdays: like roses in spring
    smelling like sweet warm pie in a window sill
    with a strong gentle breeze blowing by
Birthdays: tons of magic to look for
    when you blow out your candles
    no matter how many there are
Birthdays: another year older than the last
Birthdays: something to look forward to year after year.

Josie Harms, Grade 6
Lutheran School Association, MO

Drawing

I like drawing.
It makes me happy.
I do it when there's nothing else to do.
It helps me express my feelings.
I don't like to be interrupted
because it blows my focus.
Drawing is one of my favorite things to do.

Alex Bain, Grade 5
Shannon Forest Christian School, SC

Music

There's AFI, Green Day,
Talking Back Sunday,
Flyleaf, Blink 182,
Evenesense, U2,
The Rolling Stones, The Killers,
Nirvana, and The Gorrillz,
Some overplayed, some never heard,
There's always time to rock out,
WORD!

Jessica Henry, Grade 6
Brogden Middle School, NC

The Little Boy

In the early morning in the fall
a little boy plays with a ball.
It was time to eat lunch
his family was in a bunch
he put down the ball and ran inside
only to find they all lied.
A birthday cake was on the table.
I could eat it all if I was able.
I was happy cause they loved me so
I never wanted to let them go!
Selena Fowler, Grade 6
Graham Elementary School, AL

Dream Writer

If I had the time to write
And just dream away all day and night,

Then I'd be as free as could be.

If I had the time to think
About the things I would repeat

Then I'd be as free as could be.

If I had time to play
Then I would do that all day

Then I'd be as free as could be.

If I would have the perfect life
Then I could do all of that…

And my hope is that
I will.
Lydia Stellwag, Grade 6
Greenville Montessori School, NC

Baseball

Bat, pitcher, dugout
Baseball, left fielder, catcher
Base, coach, home plate
Braxton Taylor, Grade 4
East Jones Elementary School, MS

My Favorite Place

Swoosh, swoosh. I look out my window and see the ocean
    Glistening in the moonlight.

Swoosh, swoosh. I hear the waves crash on the rocky shore.
    Shells are diamonds on the sand.

Looking out, seeing the never ending waters. With the sands
    As fluffy as cushions.

Wading into the water, feels like walking through a soft bed of flowers.
    When I dive into it, I feel the waves take me away.

All of the fish make the ocean look like a colorful painting.
    The summer breeze makes the water ripple.

Swoosh, swoosh. The smell of salt water fills the air.

Swoosh, swoosh. The ocean rocks me to sleep.

Martin Donzella, Grade 6
Beck Academy, SC

My Brother's Sleepover

Crazy, jittery filled atmosphere lined with superior smells
My body bursts with energetic laughter and sings of joy
All were hysterically horsing around
Rainbows of bright and neon sparks filled the air
I delightfully sketched over his head
Neon streaks were sparky and striking
Bright shining bulbs were warm and inviting
Sparks darted then pounded together like a horse's hooves meeting the ground
Then sadness crept into the room as I had to depart
Ally Garcia, Grade 5
Cline Elementary School, KY

Festival

Getting ready to leave my house,
Hoping that the lines will be short.
Walking to the school seeing all the cars in the parking lot.
People rushing inside from the pouring down rain.

Going inside to see inflatables as tall as trees,
Hurling the ball at the dunk tank.
SPLASH!!!
Seeing the person fall in the cold water,
Smelling the scent of hot dogs cooking like I'm at a baseball game,
Feeling cheerful and excited as I see the person fall in the cold water,
Wondering why people cry when they miss,
Dashing to get to the mechanical bull.
Hoping that I will win the prize.

Leaving to go home to get in my warm bed.
The sky getting darker as I leave,
More and more people leaving as I go inside.
Feeling as happy as can be.

Jake Howe, Grade 4
Goshen Elementary School at Hillcrest, KY

A Football Game

Sounds like cheering fans
Smells like sweat and grass
Tastes like water and mouthpieces
Looks like crowds and athletes
Feels like pride

Philip Benson Botes, Grade 5
Briarwood Christian Elementary School, AL

Smells

The wonderful smells in the air!
Turkey, dressing and biscuits on the table!
Let your emotions run free.

Jacob Henson, Grade 6
Guntown Middle School, MS

All About Me

Hello!
My name is Taylor!
If I were a color
I'd be pink
Like a big heart on Valentine's day
If I were an animal
I'd be an animal that swims peacefully!
Like a dolphin!
My favorite place is Disney World
When their having a parade
And when we go shopping!
My favorite snack is vanilla ice cream and strawberries
The strawberries are so yummy and the ice cream is cold!
From the western sizzlin in Lugoff.
I really get upset
When I have to clean my dog's room
And I have to do it all by myself!
I love listening to the printer
When it makes that noise when
Someone makes a bad grade!

Taylor Woodrow, Grade 4
Pine Tree Hill Elementary School, SC

Christmastime

Christmastime is almost here,
Time for those whom you hold dear.
Putting up the tree and holly,
Everyone should be jolly.

My Christmas list is almost done,
A top, a whistle, and a toy gun.
If you listen closely you might hear,
Santa Claus, and his reindeer.

Christmas day has arrived,
and I hope I will be surprised,
With my presents.
Time to eat Christmas crescents!

Cassie Fulton, Grade 4
St Elizabeth Ann Seton Catholic School, OK

I Am Haunted

I am haunted in the past by *clowns*
because I saw a movie that was scary and
I went to bed and I saw a clown
it had creepy long nails that would grab me.

I am haunted in the present by *gross guys*
because they will grab little girls and
they will not see their mom or their dad no more.

I am haunted in the future *by being fat*
and I will be called names like Fatso and
Fatty and other mean names.

Emily Dixie, Grade 5
Eminence Middle School, KY

December

In December the weather
is cold it may even snow
and the wind might just blow.
But most of all I love it when the stars glow.

Katelyn Rochelle Woods, Grade 5
Briarwood Christian Elementary School, AL

Garden Fragrances Smell Terrific

Looks and smells so sweet
yummy treat for butterflies
makes you act surprised

Madilyn Algren, Grade 4
Briarwood Christian Elementary School, AL

December

December is a time when the angels from heaven celebrate
by showering us with white confetti.

When you look out your window on Christmas day,
you see a vast, white blanket of fluffy pleasure.

It fills your heart with comfort and joy, freeing your mind of
all distractions, and filling it with happiness.

December is a time of Jesus's birth,
when we celebrate his coming to earth.

Zach Soberano, Grade 5
St Thomas More School, NC

Veteran

V iolent and vicious
E veryone scared
T orches, tanks, and torpedoes
E liminate everyone
R ifles and guns
A mbush and attack
N eed nurses and doctors, but it is too late.

Chase Pinkonsly, Grade 4
Cherokee Elementary School, AR

Smell

Smell the clean, fresh air
Big green leaves smell like bath soap
Honey-scented oaks
Masha White, Grade 6
St Joseph Institute for the Deaf, MO

I Wonder Why

I wonder why
People do drugs
Do they try
To be thugs
I wonder why
I wonder why
They don't go to school
Do they not try
Or do they think it's cool
I wonder why
Nicholas Hammonds, Grade 5
Graham Elementary School, AL

My Mother

Mother
Nice, cuddly
Loving, caring, sharing
Love to hold close
Ebony Tone
Shyla Hutchins, Grade 4
Stephens Elementary School, AL

Haley

Haley Hill
nice, smart
swim, play, dance
I like to help others.
Haley Hill
Haley Hill, Grade 4
East Jones Elementary School, MS

Puppies

P uppies are so cute
U sually everybody likes them
P uppies are so awesome.
P uppies are so cool.
I love puppies.
E mma and
S ami just got two new baby puppies.
Emma Williams, Grade 6
Martin Elementary School, WV

Missing Home

No more waterfall rhythms
No more lions roaring,
We moved to another city,
I wish I were back in Arizona.
Chloe Wofford, Grade 4
Western Hills Elementary School, AR

Chocolate

Chocolate,
Chocolate,
Chocolate,
Good chocolate,
Bad chocolate,
Sweet, yummy, gooey chocolate,
Big, little, thick chocolate,
Those are just a few.
White chocolate,
Dark chocolate,
Excellent, melty, messy chocolate,
Hershey's chocolate, too.
Reese's chocolate,
Chunky chocolate,
Don't forget milk chocolate.
Last of all, best of all,
I like delicious chocolate!
Colton Jackson, Grade 6
Hayes Elementary School, OK

Christmas

C arol
H appily
R iding
I s nice
S howing love
T hings
M orning
A nnual
S urprise
Savannah Sparrow, Grade 4
Wohlwend Elementary School, MO

I Like to Fight with All My Might

I like to walk, I like to talk,
I like to fight with all my might.
If I may with all delay.
I like to fight with all my might.
Baylee Roper, Grade 4
Lula Elementary School, GA

I See You

In the dark sky
I see you I see you
In the dark sky
I can feel you're coming
But when.

Are you big
Are you small
Can you tell me before
I fall off this big dark cliff

PLEASE JUST TELL ME!
Desiree Ehler, Grade 6
Curtis Inge Middle School, OK

Take Me to Love

Show me the way, take me to love.
Wounded birds fly high.
Roses bloom, never die.
Show me the way, take me to love.
Is this place even real?
Is it real to the touch?
'Cause that's not what I feel.
Take my hand and guide me.
Show me all the sights there is to see.
Show me the way, take me to love.
Elizabeth Alimi, Grade 5
Stokesdale Elementary School, NC

My Terrible Puppy

My terrible puppy
Reese eats so much.
He looks like he's
going to blow to pieces.
He growls and barks
'til it gets too dark.
All day long he scratches
and bites,
but he sleeps all night.
Shaina Beals, Grade 5
Canute Elementary School, OK

Thanksgiving

Good food,
Day pilgrims came to us,
Beautiful leaves.
Red, brown,
Yellow, and even orange colors.
Being with
Your friends and family.
Having fun.
Nikki Robinson, Grade 6
Guntown Middle School, MS

Come to the Baseball Park

See the children playing ball
Hear the shouting of the fans
Touch the cool wet grass
Smell the wonderful burgers
Taste the juicy sizzling hot dogs
Cole Hinson, Grade 5
Bonaire Elementary School, GA

So Very Happy

Happiness is violet red.
It sounds like tap dancing.
It tastes like cookies.
It smells like daisies.
It looks like a deer.
It makes you feel like playing.
Alyssa Humphrey, Grade 5
Salem Elementary School, AR

If I Was in Charge of the World

If I Were In Charge Of The World.
I'd be the boss of my house.
I'd make my family healthy.
I'd be the richest person on the earth.
I'd make my mom and dad speak English.
I'd spend more time with my dog Short.

If I Were In Charge Of The World.
I'd be the principals of all school.
I'd fire all the teacher, but Mr. Douglas
I'd change the school hours to 3 hours of free time
1 hour of lunch 4 hours of gym.
I'd have no bullies.

If I Were In Charge Of The World.
I stop all wars.
I stop global warming.
I'd stop winters.
I'd let all Mexicans come to the United States.
I'd make white people work for Mexicans.

Jesus Ramos, Grade 6
Eminence Middle School, KY

The Night Sky

The night sky is like the earth
It lasts forever for everyone to see
It stays still till the break of day
It contains plenty of mysteries.

The night sky shines brightly
Filled with stars and planets
Even the moon shines
Along with space rocks.

As comets dance in space
As galaxies flicker in the distance
As long as matter continues to exist
People will always wonder about the universe.

Nijel Gajuan Johnson, Grade 5
Macedonia Elementary School, SC

Sore Throat

I went to school, thought I was fine.
But I didn't know about this throat of mine.
I walked into class kinda slow.
But I still didn't know.
Social studies class came around.
I was the sickest guy in town.
I told my teacher, "I am sick!"
My head hurt and my tongue was thick.
My tonsils were swollen,
Gosh they were sore.
I didn't want to feel that way anymore.

Brandon Stiles, Grade 5
Paint Lick Elementary School, KY

When I Think of You

I do hurt when I think of you,
but I just think of how Jesus loves you.
I turn my head, I see your face,
but I know you are in a better place.
All this I know was for a reason,
but in my mind just not in the right season.
I wish I could be with you,
anything just to see you.

Julia Willcoxon, Grade 6
Desoto Central School, MS

Legos

I like Lego blocks;
I snap them together until each one locks;
Their colors are so brilliant;
I can show my talent;
Building cars, trucks, planes and more;
I built a house with windows and a door;
I put them together and tear them apart;
It's always fun to start and restart.

Zachary Shrift, Grade 5
St Anne Catholic School, SC

Homework

White lined paper
Sharp pointed pencil
Boring words on paper
Hard, annoying,
"Here's your homework, boys and girls…"
Is anything worse than homework?

Hayley Bylsma, Grade 5
Landmark Christian School, GA

Waiting in the Darkness

Waiting patiently in the darkness of the night
really gives me a fright.
Waiting, Waiting all alone,
my heart plays a gothly tone.
Darkness, darkness

No one to hug you or say goodnight.
As I wait in the darkness of the night.
As I lay against the dark wall,
I feel lonely.
There is no one with me at all.

Carmen Stowe, Grade 4
Stephens Elementary School, AL

If I Could Fly

If I could fly, I would soar high in the sky.
If I could fly, I would fly away.
If I could fly, I would fly to the roof of my house.
If I could fly, I would go places.
If I could fly, I would fly with the eagles.

Kelcey Gathright, Grade 5
Oark Elementary School, AR

Baseball Is Fun

Baseball
My favorite sport
The lights glisten like the sun
Cheers wash over the
Players as they step up.
A swing and a hit!
It goes to the outfield
The coach signals to take
Second
Going…going…safe!
Baseball is fun!

Patrick Koch, Grade 5
St Teresa's School, GA

Popcorn

Popcorn, popcorn everywhere
Popping high in the air
Smelling butter in the room
Oops, I just heard it boom!

Careful opening
It is hot
But I don't care
I eat it a lot!

Popcorn, popcorn everywhere
It's so good
Why don't you try it
I think you should!

Popcorn, popcorn
It's so neat
Even though it has hot heat
Can you tell it's my favorite treat?

POP!!

Shea Troutman, Grade 4
Sequoyah Elementary School, TN

Fall

Fall is here —
There's a fire in the forest,
Lightning bugs fly over water —
Men go fishing at the lake,
There is the smell of Thanksgiving.
Smoke comes out of chimneys,
Turkey is cooking in the oven.

Cheerful boys play football —
Women are making jam,
Men are cutting wood.
Leaves are changing color
The pumpkin patch is open —
What a wonderful season!

Andrew Mulvaney, Grade 5
Palmetto Christian Academy, SC

I Am a Military Child

I am helpful and funny for my mommy when she needs a hand when daddy is gone.
I wonder what my daddy does while he is in Kuwait, Iraq.
I hear Army soldiers marching in the early morning.
I see my best friend getting ready to leave for Australia.
I want my daddy to stay home forever.
I am helpful and funny for my mommy when she needs a hand when daddy is gone.

I pretend to be a soldier in my daddy's old uniforms.
I am happy when I hug my daddy's neck.
I touch my heart and say the Pledge of Allegiance every day.
I worry my daddy will get hurt.
I cry when I see my daddy leave.
I am helpful and funny for my mommy when she needs a hand when daddy is gone.

I understand my daddy has to help our country.
I say the military tries to help others.
I dream that daddy will come home safely.
I try to spend time with my mommy when I feel sad.
I hope daddy will be home for my tenth birthday to go with me to get my ID card.
I am helpful and funny for my mommy when she needs a hand when daddy is gone.

Cierra Scarpill, Grade 4
Walker Intermediate School, KY

Fall Leaves

When fall comes the leaves will turn red, orange, and yellow.
They will then fall to the ground.
The dads will rake them up into piles so the children can jump into them.
The wind will blow the leaves into the air so the dads must rake them up again.

Josh Gibson, Grade 5
Palmetto Christian Academy, SC

Thanksgiving Time

Thanksgiving is a time for family, neighbors, and friends,
wonderful food that your mawmaw cooked
"mmm I can smell it now warm turkey with dressing mmm,"
to spend time with your family, for you to laugh and just enjoy yourself.

Brooke Lindsey, Grade 6
Guntown Middle School, MS

A Seed's Growth

As the glistening seed waits,
the majestic wind picks it up and takes it somewhere.
When it falls,
it drops to the grassland's ground.
Soon it will sink into the soft and fertile soil,
awaiting for the drizzling rain to come,
along with the sun's rays of light.
The pouring rain rushes to the waiting seed,
the bright sun will give light to the seed,
and the see will germinate into a seedling.
This takes several weeks for the seed to grow into a young plant,
weeks have passed, and the see is in a young plant form,
but suddenly in a day's worth of time it grew into adulthood,
and now can send out new sees that will carry on this amazing process.

Kevin Lam, Grade 6
Haynes Academy for Advanced Studies, LA

Dream

If you have a dream follow it.
When you dream you are happy and delighted.
But if someone comes in the way of your dream,
Then tell them to move out of the way!
Don't let anyone stop you or your dream from coming true!
It is very good to dream good things!
Always dream — never stop!
If you stop then your dream will fail!

Christian Dunn, Grade 5
Parker Road Elementary School, MO

Citadel Football Games

Oh how I love the Citadel football games.
The food, the fun and the games.
Montrell Lee, Gary Domanski, James Wilson and Chris Murray.
oh how I love the Citadel football games.
The adrenaline waiting to go on the field.
Oh how I love the Citadel football games.

Bobby Ruff, Grade 5
Drayton Hall Elementary School, SC

New Orleans

New Orleans was a city full of music and fun.
New Orleans was home to many people.
Millions of people loved New Orleans.
It was one of the greatest cities in the world.
It was.
It was until…KATRINA.
On August 29, 2005 the worst natural disaster hit NOLA.
It wiped out 377 square miles of people,
Of homes,
Of lives.
Katrina devastated one of the greatest cities in the world.
It hit us.
It hit…New Orleans.
It hit a fun musical town.
Many thought we would not recover,
But we will prove them wrong.
We will rebuild and we will come home.
We will be the great city we once were.
We were, and still are
NEW ORLEANS.
Welcome home.

Heather Held, Grade 6
Haynes Academy for Advanced Studies, LA

A Winter Day

S now is falling down
N one of the trees have leaves
O ne by one the snowflakes fall,
W onderful things happen!
M y house is covered in snow
A nice winter day,
N o one works because it is cold!

Cierra Bodrick, Grade 4
Elizabeth Traditional Elementary School, NC

Colonial Dancing

When dancing mind you, don't curtsy too deep,
For your corset will put you to sleep.

Be nice to the gentleman that calls you his pretty,
For he is a rich man that lives in the city.

Don't stay too late, nor leave too early,
So people don't think that you're rude, or unruly.

The dancing we do is really quite hard,
The Virginia Reel and Minuet all filling my dancing card.

Maddie Powers, Grade 5
Alvaton Elementary School, KY

My Dog Ate My Homework!

Oh I'll admit it
My dog ate my homework.

How you say?
I was taking a walk in the park
I sat my frog on a log
piece of paper
homework down.

My dog thought it was a real frog on a log
and jumped
and crunch
there went my homework.

Oh you say
I don't have a dog

Um, Um,
Well, this is what really happened, well…

Elizabeth Bright, Grade 4
Alpena Elementary School, AR

Leaves on the Trees

They are colorful.
They store water in their leaves.
Red, brown, yellow, green.

Lacy McClung, Grade 4
Briarwood Christian Elementary School, AL

November

N ative Americans came before American people did.
O ther people around the world do not celebrate.
V isitors go to holiday parties.
E ven homeless celebrate holidays.
M any people have birthdays on holidays.
B abies when they have teeth they eat holiday food.
E very year in a month a holiday comes
R elatives come on holidays.

Charynez Dukes, Grade 6
Western Hills Elementary School, AR

Thanksgiving

T hanksgiving
H olidays
A blaze
N ovember
K ind
S pecial
G iving
I mpossible
V ery
I nteresting
N oble
G ood

Anna Boykin, Grade 4
East Jones Elementary School, MS

Stars

Stars are twinkling in the sky
Stars are gleaming in a baby's eye
Stars are as beautiful as apple pie
And soon the stars will be back tonight
Madalyn VanWinkle, Grade 4
Cave City Elementary School, AR

Freedom

America is free
America is brave,
Because of many soldiers,
That fought for many days.

Many lives have been lost,
So our freedom could remain.
Families have been torn apart.
They will never be the same.

I will always hold my head up high,
Because I know I'm free.
Old Glory will always wave proudly,
From sea to shining sea.
Andrew Sirmon, Grade 5
Joann Walters Elementary School, AR

Toads

Bumpy, lumpy
Really jumpy
Toads;
Green, not mean
Fly-eating machine
Toads;
They're cool
They don't drool
They aren't a fool
Toads;
Toads are really great;
And easy to appreciate.
Gabrielle Hurley, Grade 4
Blessed Teresa of Calcutta School, MO

My Little One

Sing with me dance with me
My little one,
Go with me play with me
My little one,
Talk with me walk with me
My little one
And you will make the birds sing.
Morgan Brower, Grade 4
Tri-County Christian School, MO

Orange, Green, Blue

Orange, green, blue
I think I've got the flu,
My face is red,
I feel plain dead,
How about you?
Brianna Coffee, Grade 6
Cottonwood Public School, OK

Living Our Lives

Life isn't that long you have to live it,
You don't breathe forever,
You have to feel it,
Put aside complaining until tomorrow,
Fill today with love and compassion.

Do good not bad,
Be happy not sad,
Feel your life with strength!

Be with those you love,
Don't make enemies but friends,
Have laughter no weeping,
Have neverending joy,
Act like there is no tomorrow,
And be forever you!
Elizabeth Meynardie, Grade 6
Martin Middle School, NC

Christmas

I love when Christmas comes to town,
With all the pretty trees,
Everyone says, "Wow."
I think Christmas is really cool,
Because none of it is a drool.
I hate when Christmas has to go,
Because some people did not find out
About the true meaning of Christmas,
And some will never know.
But soon it will be back again
And we'll be able to tell about,
The true meaning of Christmas
How Jesus grew up and died,
For our sins.
Katelyn Dewrell, Grade 4
First Assembly Christian School, AL

Rainbows

After rainy day
Spectrums of hues form arches
In waiting clear sky
Michaela Patterson, Grade 4
Broadway Elementary School, NC

An Ode to Christmas

Christmas, Oh Christmas,
So much joy.

So many new things,
Like a cool toy!

Everyone needs to remember,
Why we celebrate the season.

We celebrate this holiday,
Because Jesus is the reason!

We sing old Christmas carols,
From door to door.

This helps us enjoy an ode to Christmas,
More and more!
Tatyana Claude, Grade 4
Pines Elementary School, NC

Buddy

There is a "meow,"
and a scratch at the door.
He comes parading in
with his tail up
high…Purring
Because he knows the attention
he's going to get.
He's there when I'm sad,
there when I'm scared.
I love him because…
he's my cat!
Kira Wilson, Grade 6
Scotts Creek Elementary School, NC

My Brother

My brother often loves me,
As long as I love him.
He asked me to climb trees,
And then we often grin.

If you want to keep him,
That's fine with me too.
Just don't come back again,
I'll say this once more
Don't come back again
And may luck be with you.
Haleigh Parson, Grade 4
Lula Elementary School, GA

Gracie

When we met you were small and cuddly.
Then you grew as fast as the honeysuckle.
You are as sweet as one too.

You look like a Polar Bear.
You think you're a bunny.
You are as soft as one too.

When I get home you greet me with a funny, smiling face.
You try to hug me like the rest of my family.
You are as loving as them too.

You love the snow as much as I do.
You pull me in the snow like Santa's reindeer.
You are as strong as them too.

You are sweet, soft, loving, and strong.
Most of all I love you!

Cayle Reese, Grade 5
Paint Lick Elementary School, KY

Thank You for All You Do

I am proud to be an American
standing free with the cold blue icicles hanging from houses.
Soldiers fighting while it's cold
And we are warm in our houses.
Doves cuddled up shivering,
water in the pond is frozen.
Walking along the red dirt road,
Finding a diamond and bringing it home to my mother.
Running with the beautiful sunset
with God watching me and shivering.
Thank you for all that you do.

T.J. Maddie, Grade 6
Leonville Elementary School, LA

Freedom

Freedom
Flags flying
Freedom
Stars and stripes waving
Freedom
Soldiers fighting and dying
Freedom
Families crying
Freedom
Doing what we want
Freedom
Saying what we want
Freedom
Going where we want
Freedom
Proud, safe, home sweet home.

Rebecca Helms and Jamie Henderson, Grade 4
West Elementary School, MO

Stephano

S wimming is his sport
T akes things seriously
E ats a lot
P lays a lot of games
H as a good personality
A lways can help
N ever hurts anyone
O n the ball!

Stephano Derrell Arnez Johnson, Grade 5
Calhoun Academy, SC

Penguins

P enguins live in icy areas
E very penguin eats fish
N ight is bad for them because of their enemy, seals. They
G et the poor little penguins from
U nder the breakable
I ce so they can eat them.
N ow, penguins are endangered animals.

Abby Bishop, Grade 5
Sullivan Elementary School, TN

Friends

Friends can come and go all of the time.
Friends can turn their backs on you for somebody else.
Friends cannot always be so true to you.
Friends can start talking about you to other people.
Friends, friends, I have no true friends,
not now, ever —
but it always depends.

Alexis Traylor, Grade 5
Parker Road Elementary School, MO

If I Were a Book…

If I were a book,
I wonder who would write me.

What would they say?

Would they write fondly of me?
And remember me?

Or would I be placed upon a dusty shelf,
Unfinished and Forgotten.

When I grow old, worn, and tattered,
Will children still see the soul that
Beats like a heart inside of me?

As you read along,
Will you trust in my characters?
And will they stay their course, and fight to the very end.

And will I be what the author wanted me to be?

Howard K. Menser III, Grade 6
South Oldham Middle School, KY

Fall Changes

During the Fall many things happen.
Leaves change colors and fall.
Pumpkins grow, pumpkin patches open; that's what happens.

During the Fall the weather changes.
It may snow, it gets colder, it might rain, fire places are on, it's warmer inside; that's what happens.

Lots of changes on the calendar.
Thanksgiving is coming, Santa is packing his sleigh, crops die, farmers are sad, Christmas is coming; that's what happens.
Isn't Fall FUN!

Carson Keeter, Grade 5
Palmetto Christian Academy, SC

What Does Thanksgiving Mean to You

Thanksgiving means to me going over to my grandmother's house and eating food celebrating Thanksgiving. And then we will go back to her house for supper. And we will spend the night at her house. And when Sunday comes we will go to church and at night go back to church and have a meal at church. So it means to me going to my Grandmother's house.

Dominic Neisler, Grade 6
Guntown Middle School, MS

Light Blue

Light Blue looks like the Florida waves hitting the rocks and leaving a shower of tiny droplets of water.
Light Blue sounds like kids screaming and trying to dodge the ocean waves.
Light Blue smells like the salty fish, mixed water.
Light Blue tastes like the disgusting salt filled water leaving a bitter taste in my mouth.
Light Blue feels like the pointy rocks jabbing at my feet as I walk through the shallow water.
Light Blue is the ocean waves rolling back and forth.
Light Blue is the kids swimming and playing in the ocean
Light Blue is the salty sand in the ocean.
Light Blue is the chips I eat for a snack while running on the sand.
Light Blue is the scratches on my hand from collecting sea shells all day.

Miranda Parks, Grade 5
Cool Spring Elementary School, NC

Gazing Out the Window

The boy, playing his flute, sees all the shadows of the instruments hanging on the light green tinted wall.
The young musician listens to the soothing music he is playing.
His clothes, oh, so rich from head to toe;
His clothes look like they're from centuries ago.
On his head there sits a hat of rose color.
His jacket is a deep brown and tinted silky collar.
The young magician looks so real.
This is an oil panting.
He looks so engaged, but his fingers are moving.
The young musician looks, oh, so calm.
As he runs his fingers up and down his flute making wonderful melody,
he is focused on his music.
The boy and his silky flute are in the foreground.
The young musician's hand-carved violin and recorder sits in the background.
While he is playing his flute, his right hand slightly shaded, the left hand is tinted.
As the hand-carved violin hangs vertically on the tinted wall,
the young musician in his ornate chair diagonally sits from the wall.
His flute sits horizontally while he is playing it,
as he sits gazing out the window.

Lindsey Bowman, Grade 5
Saffell Street Elementary School, KY

Freedom

Freedom does not come free.
You have to earn it. It costs the lives of many men
and women of the armed forces who fought our wars
for us throughout our history.
To earn freedom you have to have discipline and work hard.
It takes us all to earn freedom. Everyone is responsible
for making freedom last.
Freedom does not come free.

Hunter Morphis, Grade 5
Cool Spring Elementary School, NC

Spring

Spring is a special time of year
Nature makes it all clear
The birds hatch out of their eggs
The little ones for food beg
When the early dew falls on the leaves and grass
The warm sun casts sun rays and rainbows do pass
Some might think that spring is queer
I think it's the best time of the year.

Laarni Lapat, Grade 5
Windsor Elementary School, NC

Razorbacks

I love to watch the Razorbacks,
And Mitch Mustain, our quarterback.
Darren MacFadden was named All-American First team,
I bet when he was a boy that was his dream.
You better watch out for big ole Sammy O,
He'll rock your world like you don't know.
K-jack is having a very good year,
Since he made that interception,
Quarterbacks look at him in fear
Marcus Monk has made some pretty awesome plays,
Lance Alworth was like him back in the old days.
D-Mac is awesome, but Felix is too,
He'll probably be just as good when D-Mac is through.
Gus and Houston make a real nice pair,
But I don't think we'd make it without Reggie there.
The defense is good, but the offense is great,
To see them play this Saturday I can't wait.
Mike's done well, but we sure miss Paul.
I bet up in heaven he's leading the hog call.
Imagine in Atlanta he'd say with pride,
MacFadden the 10, 5…Touchdown Arkansas…Oh my!

Mikayla Feemster, Grade 5
Joann Walters Elementary School, AR

Fall

Rainbow of colors fall to the ground
Can't wait till Fall comes around
Running and jumping in crunchy old leaves
Hearing all the wonderful sounds
I can't wait till Fall comes around

Hannah Richie, Grade 6
Bellwood Discovery School, TN

VeggieTales

They are with each other
when they are on tape gladly
singing and dancing

Anna Hommerson, Grade 4
Briarwood Christian Elementary School, AL

Black and White

The hot summer sun burns above
while the ocean foam lies on the shore.
A time of darkness is at hand.

A black ship appears on the horizon.
A woman in a long, gloomy dress
weeps on the beach.

She stands, not on sand, but on black ashes.
Her tears fall and white steam rises.
In her trembling hands
she holds a colorless bottle.
Murky, black oil falls to the ground
and the black ashes explode into flame.

Her ghostly skin is blackened
and her black dress slips into the white heat.
The white sand is scorched,
the white sun is swallowed by the black ocean.
The tranquil night chases away the last light
as the world forgets this black day.

Eric Davidson, Grade 6
Charleston County School of the Arts, SC

The Dream

One dreary day I was watching the rain.
My mother told me not to complain.
I was feeling really bored and blue,
But now I know just what to do.

All of a sudden something magical happened.
I closed my eyes to rest.
When I opened them it was the best.

I had a skit playing in front of me.
It showed a forest, ocean, desert,
And the most glorious tree.
I couldn't believe what I had to see.

So many things to explore.
I want to see more.

But then I awoke and noticed
It was only a dream.
I couldn't believe it.
It was too extreme!

Rachel Mayo, Grade 5
Pine Ridge Elementary School, GA

Raindrop

a raindrop is like a
sprinkle from God's sprinkler.

a raindrop is like a
sprinkle from a very big waterfall.

a raindrop is like a
tear from my eyes.

Jadan McGill, Grade 5
Cool Spring Elementary School, NC

Time to Forgive

Thanksgiving is a time
to thank family, friends,
and loved ones
who are no longer with you,
to be forgiven
for things you
never meant to do
then you think
that thanksgiving
is not only
for the food or turkey.
It's about the love
and friendship
to others.

Marinda Newcomb, Grade 6
Guntown Middle School, MS

Beauty

It runs in some families
But not in others
Super models have a cat walk to walk

We all have beauty
But it is always not discovered
Until we are old
Beauty is what is on the inside

Linzy Jameison, Grade 5
Walton Verona Elementary School, KY

Winter

Winter, winter,
Got a cold,
Winter, winter,
I drink cocoa as I'm told,
Winter, winter,
I'm froze,
Winter, winter,
So are my toes,
Winter, winter,
My blankets are cozy,
Winter, winter,
I'm kind of dozy.

Lane Clay, Grade 4
Cave City Elementary School, AR

What Is Halloween?

Halloween is a day that people celebrate
witches, ghost, and goblins.
Trick or treating is done.
Scary things are in the air.
That's Halloween.

Kyle Crutcher, Grade 4
Western Hills Elementary School, AR

Soccer

kick, run, score, soccer,
goalie, starter, fun, play, win,
team, ball, team colors

Sara Wilkinson, Grade 4
East Jones Elementary School, MS

The Beach's Wonder

The way the sun
Breaks down on my back
The waves washing away
Shells with beauty that do not lack

I lay here thinking
About the wondrous sights
The blue of the ocean
And the sun that is providing lights

The sand in my small toes
As it starts to wash away
And the wind flying in my face
All the children are starting to play

Sailboats in different sizes
Beach balls and colored umbrellas
All of the things that you need to know
About the water and the sandy rolls

Hayden Carlos, Grade 6
Alexandria Middle Magnet School, LA

My Dog, a Boston Terrier

P lenty of fun.
U ncommon breed in this area.
G ood to everybody.
S ometimes scared of cats.
L oves to greet me when I come home.
Y ou'd love to have a dog like him.

Shaun Whitson, Grade 5
Sullivan Elementary School, TN

Jesus

Jesus
Good, responsible, nice
Saving, loving, caring
The Lord sacrificed
Leader

Shayla Ortega, Grade 5
Shirley Elementary School, AR

The Big Frog

Big frog with red stripes
Jumping on a lily pad
With his mom and dad

Patsy Conley, Grade 4
Hillcrest Elementary School, TN

Test

The night before a test,
makes everything a mess.

I can't play or watch TV,
until my parents are at ease.

They want me to make an "A,"
but a "C" is fine with me.

So I must study through the night,
until the signs of first daylight.

Hopefully things will go just great,
I'll get an "A" that would be neat.

Studying, studying is such a bore,
I think I'll turn over now and snore.

Matthew Pearson, Grade 6
Community Christian School, NC

Mountains

Mountains are snowy
Some mountains are really big
Some aren't big at all

Zack Barr, Grade 6
Martin Elementary School, WV

About My Cat

I like pickles.
My mom does, too.
Why Sox my cat doesn't
I haven't got a clue.

My dad likes chicken,
Pork steak, and roast beef.
Why Sox eats with Dad
Is just beyond belief.

Jacob Lisotta, Grade 4
Northeast Baptist School, LA

Horseback Day

Yeah, yeah, it's horseback day!
Time to ride and feed them hay.
Brush them down and tack them up.
Then take them out and giddy-up.
Gallop, canter, jump, and run.
Oh, horseback day is so much fun!

Elizabeth Dias, Grade 5
Prince of Peace Catholic School, SC

Prayer

Bow my precious head
Pour out my heart to the Lord
He always listens.

Abigail Shirey, Grade 4
Briarwood Christian Elementary School, AL

Freedom of America

In the land of the free.
Where the eagle flies so carelessly.
We fought for freedom in the night.
It was such a horrible sight.

Where the soldiers are free.
Who fight for you and me.
In the home of the red, white, and blue.
The people are free who love me and you.

Eron Harner, Grade 5
Joann Walters Elementary School, AR

Children

Children are like flowers, they grow with love and care.
They are sweet like candy.
They are nice like friends.
Most of all children are like children.

Katharine Michie, Grade 6
Our Lady of Fatima School, MS

Horrible Storm

I am deadly like a Cotton Mouth
If you get in my way I will hurt you like a Lion

I can suck your home up like a hawk picks up a rat
I am mean like a Rattle Snake

I cannot be stopped like a T-Rex going for some sinew
I am furious like a Tiger

I am horrible like a Grizzly Bear attacking you

I am powerful like a Gorilla
I am fast like a Cheetah
I am loud like a freight train
I am a Tornado

John Bullard, Grade 5
Pembroke Elementary School, NC

Summer…

Summer…
    Looks like pools getting filled up
    Sounds like family BBQ's
    Feels like wonderful times with family
    Tastes like delicious homemade foods
    Smells like fall coming!

Tenasha Bonnett, Grade 5
Trenton Middle School, MO

The First Day of School

The first day of school
All ready to go.
I've got paper and pencils,
All straight in a row.
Go out the door,
Raring to go.
I see Darin and Caren.
On the go.
I'm running to school!
I open the gate…
OH MY GOSH
I THINK I'M LATE!!!!!

Claudia J. Hoffmeister, Grade 4
St Mary Cathedral Elementary School, MO

Autumn

Crunching, falling, sliding leaves,
Yellow, orange, red, purple, and even brown leaves,
Piling them up to the stars,
Jumping in them over and over again,
Rainy, windy weather blowing them away,
Aaaaaahhhhh!!!!!
Getting so mad because I have to do all my hard work again,
Crows as black as coal and loud as a whistle,
Getting all the coats out,
Wishing it was winter already,
Fall

Amber Michelle Dethridge, Grade 6
Alvaton Elementary School, KY

St. Jude's

S t. Jude's is a loving and caring place
T he doctors and nurses are really friendly

J oyful and hopeful sounds coming from every room
U nafraid children having chemo treatments
D octors helping parents and patients
E very little child getting hugs from family
S omeone there for you every minute.
    Thank you for taking care of my brother!

Julia Light, Grade 5
Sullivan Elementary School, TN

Skateboarding

Jump, skid, laugh and play
I could do this every day
Run, skip, laugh, and fall
I wish I could skateboard in the mall
Skateboard, oh skateboard
Too bad I can't bring you today to go play
But since I broke you yesterday
We can't run, skip, fall, or play
Since yesterday was the last day
we could go and say, "yeah!"

Jonathan Yarnall, Grade 5
Walton Verona Elementary School, KY

God Makes the Wind Blow

God makes the wind blow
from my head to my toe.
God makes the wind blow
as easy as the wind blows.
God makes the wind blow
as you and I can tie a bow.
God makes the wind blow
to give us a breeze you know!

McKayla Harrington, Grade 4
Brilliant Elementary School, AL

My Dancing Day

Dusk till dawn my dancing day.
Between these hours there is no play.
Jazz, pointe, ballet and tap.
To the music along we snap.
Competitions at our door.
Wanting us to dance some more.
When we're back with trophy in hand.
We'll know we're the best of the land.
We flash our smiles in all directions.
Showing them our dancing connection.
We'll dance until the day is done.
Just to show you we're #1.

Jill Foster, Grade 6
Southeast Middle School, NC

Lawmaker

L abor
A lert
W arden
M ighty
A mazing
K ind
E ducated
R everent

Akeelah Jones, Grade 4
East Jones Elementary School, MS

King Parrot

King Parrot's flying
On a scorching summer day
Gliding over heads

Sherman Winchester, Grade 4
Indian Springs Elementary School, AL

Madison

M addog is my nickname
A dorable and all together
D elightful and distinguished
I ntelligent and important
S mart and sweet
O rganized and original
N ice and neat

Madison Buhler, Grade 5
Qulin Middle School, MO

Baseball

A baseball player is what I want to be.
I love the game baseball; a baseball player is what I want to be.
I like to hear the smack when the ball hits the bat.
I like to run to each base a home run is where it's at!
I love to hear the fans on the bleachers as they cheer.
The fans give me confidence I can hear them with my ears.
Baseball is my game I think about it all the time;
I go to bed with baseball on my mind.
A baseball player is what I want to be.
I love the game baseball so much I think I'll play in the major league.

Trenton Curtis, Grade 6
Calloway Smith Middle School, AL

I'm a Tar 'Buckeye' Heel

Before I knew it, my dad had me in scarlet and gray;
I was wearing Buckeye colors on my very first day.

For the longest time, it made no sense to me;
What is a Buckeye? Is it a nut or a tree?

As I grew older, I understood my dad's love for the OSU team;
Because when they won a big game, you would hear a loud scream.

But I live in the South, my home — Chapel Hill;
Watching the Tar Heels gives me a thrill.

So what would it take to test the team I like best?
A battle of Buckeyes and Heels would be the test.

They finally would play in the Dome named for Dean;
Roy Williams' Tar Heels, and Thad Matta's Buckeye Machine.

When tip-off was here, my dad wondered aloud;
Was I a Tar Heel, or am I Buckeye proud?

What team do I pull for, Oh, Me, Oh, My, Oh?
You guessed, I did it — it was O-H-and-I-0!

Benjamin Linke, Grade 4
St Thomas More School, NC

My Country

You grand old flag,
You wave so high for everyone to see.
Even in bad times you still wave so high.
You wave when there are floods, tornadoes, and earthquakes.
You make me think what this country stands for,
And how your forefathers fought for our freedoms.
You make me feel the freedom and glory that our country has.
Like letting us pray and read the Bible,
And believe what we want to believe.
You also make me think what the red, white, and blue means.
Red and white stripes stand for the first thirteen colonies,
And blue and white are for the many states we have in our country,
And what we stand for.

Stephan Munsell, Grade 5
Heartland High School and Academy, MO

Olie

Running around barking,
Snorting like a pig.
Strolling around the neighborhood,
Coming home tired and hungry.
Scratching on the window wanting to come in.
Why does Olie scratch on the window?

Coming in all wet and dirty,
Hearing him bark as we put him in the bath,
Making bubbles as they pile on each other,
Trying to get out when we are holding him in,
Looking like a wet rat with shampoo on him.
Why does Olie hate the bath?

Watching TV on the couch together,
As he starts sleeping on the sofa,
As he is curled up in a ball.
He looks like a bunny rabbit with short ears.
Then we start to fall asleep.
Why does Olie fall asleep?

Bradley Dean, Grade 4
Goshen Elementary School at Hillcrest, KY

Rain

Rain trickles down on my
window as I watch it fall.
Rain
Fall, fall fall, down to the ground.
It falls fast and sometimes
it falls slow, but it always goes down.
Down, down to the ground deep in the rocks and soil.
Rain

Madison McElheney, Grade 5
Drayton Hall Elementary School, SC

Sunset at the Beach

Shining oceans waters play,
As the fading sunbeams of an exhausting day,
Dance upon the horizon.

The swells beat gently against the shore
In a steady rhythm.

The world in color —
One final flash —
Then — it's over
'Til dawn.

Sarah Milowic, Grade 6
Cathedral School, NC

Faith

Faith is religious
Faith can be shown anyway
Faith is meaningful

Elizabeth Shepherd, Grade 4
Briarwood Christian Elementary School, AL

The Beast Tornado

I am a terrible tough frightening storm
I smell like garbage
If you get in my way I will destroy you
I tear up cities and towns
I'm ugly, angry, and look like King Kong
I even look like an ugly beast
My winds are strong and tough
I will destroy you so bad you will wish
you weren't on Earth
I look like the devil trying to destroy you
So if you see me you better run you can't hide
Because I'm a tornado

Victoria L. Lowery, Grade 5
Pembroke Elementary School, NC

Yellow

Yellow looks like a daisy blowing in the wind.
Yellow sounds like the yellow leaves crunching on a fall day.
Yellow smells like a fresh fall day in November
Yellow tastes like the fresh cheddar cheese from the oven.
Yellow feels like a cheerful day for all of us.
Yellow is the color of a daisy's petal.
Yellow is the sound of crunching leaves in the wind.
Yellow is the sweet aroma in the fall.
Yellow is the sweet taste of pumpkin pie.
Yellow is the touch of the sun on my skin.
Yellow is a good color

Montana Barnette, Grade 5
Cool Spring Elementary School, NC

Halloween

Halloween is coming it's so much fun
Happiness and laughter we even get to run
Candy and food it's so yummy
Just sitting there in my tummy

When we put on our costumes it's time to go trick-or-treat
To go get all that candy that you just love to eat
I'm sorry that I must go
But this will be the end of the show

Alexis Guidry, Grade 6
St Cecilia School, LA

Green

Green is limes hanging from fruit trees
It is overgrown bushes and sycamore trees
Dark green is a watermelon rind containing juicy fruit
Wondrous caterpillars inching to a feast of fresh leaves
Green dye drip dropping into clay
Broccoli, cabbage and spinach no use in eating them
Weeds so desperately needing to be pulled
Green is grass growing tall and long
The fresh smell of newly cut grass

Stephen Isaac Breeding, Grade 6
Alvaton Elementary School, KY

Lawmaker

L abor
A cknowledgement
W riter
M oney
A ccomplishment
K eeper
E lect
R anger

Shaquetta Parker, Grade 4
East Jones Elementary School, MS

Smartie Pants

S mart
M ath
A rithmetic
R eading
T utoring
I ntelligent
E ncouraging
S tudents

Megan Jarrett, Grade 6
Clarksburg School, TN

Pumpkins, Pumpkins, Pumpkins

Big pumpkins
Small pumpkins
Rotten, ugly, pretty pumpkins
Weird, cool, smelly pumpkins
Those are just a few!

Skinny pumpkins
Fat pumpkins
Slimy, rough, smooth pumpkins
Awesome, common, unique pumpkins
Scary pumpkins too!

Sad pumpkins
Happy pumpkins
And don't forget nasty pumpkins!

Last of all
Best of all
I like unusual pumpkins!

Kaci Mann, Grade 5
Salem Elementary School, AR

Summer/Winter

Summer
Hot, refreshing
Swimming, playing, running
Gorgeous, sunny, beautiful, white
Freezing, snowing, shivering
Cold, snowy
Winter

Beisia Quintana, Grade 5
Sycamore Elementary School, GA

An Ode to a Football

Oh football!
You are so big and round!

When I have you in my hands,
I get tackled to the ground!

Sometimes they don't catch me,
And I run like I am free…

Francisco Alonzo, Grade 4
Pines Elementary School, NC

Rain

Pitter
patter
everywhere
now there's some
time to spare
no playing outside
or
walking our pets
pitter
patter
everywhere

Micki Biehl, Grade 5
Walton Verona Elementary School, KY

Squeakers

My little hamster,
Will play,
All night and day.
He gets on my mom's nerves at night,
however he doesn't have a fright.
He runs in his wheel
no matter what time,
my mom thinks that's a crime!

I love my furry friend,
I would go to the end,
just for him.

His wheel is annoying
and sometimes he smells
however, I love him the same,
but if he doesn't squeak
I may change his name.

Katelyn Kirtley, Grade 6
College View Middle School, KY

The Mat

There once was a cat,
that slept on a mat.
It was not comfy,
it was quite lumpy.
The cat's name was Pat.

Ina Toddy, Grade 4
Judsonia Elementary School, AR

Veteran

V ictory to our soldiers.
E verybody is hoping and crying.
T roops fighting against enemies.
E veryday wanting to go home to stay.
R ifles are going off every moment.
A merica is my home to stay.
N ever failing for our freedom.

Shelby Lambert, Grade 4
Cherokee Elementary School, AR

My Dog Ate My Homework

My dog ate my homework,
He promised to do it for me,
but he got so hungry,
he threw it down his throat.
The bad thing is
I can't turn in my homework,
It's been slobbered all over.
I walk in my class with no
homework for my teacher,
She explains, *Go back home*
and go to bed!
Oh, well, I was tired anyway.
I guess my dog didn't do so bad.

Leah Campbell, Grade 4
Cool Spring Elementary School, NC

Leaves

Leaves are falling in colors of rainbows.
Leaves are saying "so long"
To their trees.
Dancing and swaying leaves
Say good bye to me.
They say good bye because
They will get crunched
And spring will come again.

Hannah Marr, Grade 4
Atkinson Elementary School, NC

Buddy

This is my dog,
His name is Buddy.
I like my dog,
He is such a honey.

This is my dog
He is the best.
My dog is very happy,
My dog can rest.

This is my dog.
My dog likes to jump and play,
Leaving his footprints,
On the kitchen floor they lay.

Zachary Hudson, Grade 5
Heber Springs Elementary School, AR

Waiting for the Dove

There is a man
who has black, Spanish eyes.
He wears a starched white shirt
and a deep, dark tan.

A snowy dove perches on his arm
about to be sent off into the black wedding night.
The bride stands in white next to her new husband.
She waits for that one, timeless moment.
His black tuxedo contrasts her silken, white gown
that wraps around her slender waist.

She breathes hard with anticipation
as she leans into his ink colored warmth.
The keeper of the dove flashes her a dazzling smile.
With a toss of his long onyx hair,
he thrusts the ivory dove into the air.
They watch it soar into the night's abyss
as the bride tosses her bouquet of lilies.

Emily Thomas, Grade 6
Charleston County School of the Arts, SC

So Many

So many brothers
So many sisters
So many acres
So many rooms
So many fish in the pond
So many clouds in the sky
So many places to go
So many places to see
So many things to do
So many stairs for me to climb
I have seen so many things around me,
and still I see so many stars in the midnight sky

Amanda Kriska, Grade 5
Stokesdale Elementary School, NC

The Water Park

I like the water park
going to the water park.
Getting in the nice
cold
water
like an ice cube
running d your skin
o
w
n
Feeling like laying in it all day long.
Water dripping
dripping
dripping down your flesh.

Blake Dethridge, Grade 4
Alvaton Elementary School, KY

Mad Mathematics

There once was a girl name Cierra Flax.
She loved math.
Every morning she would count her cereal pieces,
1, 2, 3, 4, 5, 6, 7, 8, 9, 10…
Then she would eat them.
She took the school bus to school each morning,
    counting the cars that went by.
When Cierra got to school, she would turn in her homework,
    then go straight to work.
Of course she was working on math.
In P.E. she would count, then multiply
    all the students by random numbers.
Next came Spanish and music.
She would count as high as she could in Spanish,
    which usually took the whole time.
In music she would do the same, but in English.
Then it came time for math.
Cierra Flax loved math!
Every time here teacher, Mrs. Bestion, asked a question,
    Her hand shot up with the right answer in her mind.
Cierra Flax loves math!

Maggie Katzman, Grade 5
Meramec Elementary School, MO

Christmas

C andy canes we love to eat,
H aving and giving on this day,
R ound the tree with all different decorations,
I t's a great way to celebrate this special day,
S aving or giving money to the poor,
T o a day of planning or having fun,
M any people don't have that chance,
A different way to celebrate it every year,
S omething on this day always brings happiness.

Tabitha Crawford, Grade 5
Sullivan Elementary School, TN

The Animals

The animals are in winter hibernating.
Every day I can hear them snoring,
With every sunset.
I can listen to them rolling over.
The bugs are listening so hard they vanish.
It's getting warmer outside.
The animals are waking up,
The bugs come back.
Winter is heading north.

Megan Onnen, Grade 6
Armorel Elementary School, AR

Sunrise

In the morning sky
orange, red, purple, and blue
different colors.

Hannah Hall, Grade 4
Briarwood Christian Elementary School, AL

Stars

There are stars in the sky,
Fraught too much for the human eye,
We gaze upon them,
With endless awe,
Then we think back on what we just saw.

The stars serve as light,
On a dark, moonless night,
And the stars in the sky,
Are so numerous to count,
They pile up as high as the tallest mount,
The stars are endless

William Miller, Grade 6
Jackson Christian School, TN

Thanks to Soldiers

America is the place for me;
could not live anywhere else.
But there are things I never did,
I want to do these things.
Have never gone to the moon,
touched a blue whale,
seen a polar bear,
ice skated,
went to the equator,
swam in the Atlantic Ocean,
never even played in the snow.
Thanks to soldiers,
I can dream of these things.

Seth Mistrot, Grade 6
Leonville Elementary School, LA

Music

Music is like water,
Flowing like a river.
Music is feeling,
Feelings with love and thought.

Music is an art,
Like a painting that warms my soul.
Music is eternal,
Like the light of a synagogue.

Music is the source of life.
Music is the essence of the world.
Music is the god of love and peace.
Music is my soul.

Stephen Langellotti, Grade 6
Riverwood Middle School, NC

The Ocean

Blue ocean waters
Shining just like sapphire
Cool watery mists

Joseph Schumann, Grade 4
Wohlwend Elementary School, MO

The Big Buck

In the woods I must hide, behind a tree or in a hunting blind.
I hear the leaves rustling, could it be the big buck?
There he stands 8 points in all; all I can say is "yee-haw."
My hands start to shake as the shot I must make, my heart starts to pound,
then boom, and he hits the ground.
I'm heading home in my hunting truck; with my trophy I'll call the Big Buck.

Aaron M. Kimmel, Grade 6
Scotts Creek Elementary School, NC

A Blank Look

Oh, dear student I hope you see,
that you have not written a thing on me.
I am not but a worthless sheet
until your pencil and I meet.

You are only to define five words which are easy as can be.
And, yet, you sit and stare at an old dead flea.
If you turn me in blank, your grade will go down.
Then your parents will make a nasty frown.

In three minutes, you have to finish and go to bed.
But you doodle on the side and make funny noises instead.
I really don't see why you won't write
the one definition of the word "light."

It is now time for you to go to sleep.
Hopefully, you will do your homework instead of counting sheep!

Natalie Owens, Grade 6
Kitty Stone Elementary School, AL

Raindrops

I awake in the morning to the sound of small drums beating on the roof and windows.
The pitter-patter of the rain, its drone…
Splashing into puddles, and splattering on umbrellas,
Viciously attacking the road,
Infiltrating the nooks and crannies of my jacket,
Slowly easing off…slowly…slowly…

Erik Stammers, Grade 6
Cathedral School, NC

Christmas

Today is the day to say Merry Christmas Day.
On Christmas Day we celebrate the day that Jesus Christ was born.
On that day we care to say thank you, Jesus, for that wonderful day.
So on that day remember to say thank you, Jesus, for this day.

Julia White, Grade 6
St Mark Elementary School, SC

Santa's Yearly Ride

Toys, toys, toys, for little girls and boys,
Santa stops by and then goes to the sky for his yearly Christmas ride.
The children wake up and know to go to the tree with glee;
Where Santa left wonderful toys for the good girls and boys.
All of this occurring on his yearly Christmas ride.

Mason Strong, Grade 5
Debusk Elementary School, TN

Girls

Hannah
prissy, pretty
cheerleader, smart
funny, fast, laughter
volleyball player, talented
musician, strong, dancer
talker, loving, kind
Caleb

Hannah Wambsganss, Grade 5
Briarwood Christian Elementary School, AL

The Wind

The wind is strong and can break windows.
It has many enemies and foes.
The wind also rattles leaves,
Which is one of my pet peeves.
The wind is weird and strict.
It's causing lots of conflict.
But still it tickles my nose
When I take a doze.

Sam Rider, Grade 4
Cleveland Elementary School, OK

Rain

There is nothing to explain about rain,
Except it comes on silent cat feet,
Then it breaks into pieces...
It leaves behind a loud noise like thunder,
Boom!
Then a streak of light,
Nothing is there.

Savannah Bryan, Grade 5
Etowah Elementary School, NC

Christmas

C elebrating, young and old.
H aving a family to love.
R eaching out and shaking gifts.
I magining what the next Christmas will bring.
S miling with joy as you reveal your gifts.
T hanking your aunt for the socks she got you.
M emorizing every verse of "Deck the Halls."
A lways being with family.
S haring precious moments.

C-H-R-I-S-T-M-A-S
A time to love and be loved

Cheyenne McDougal, Grade 6
Alvaton Elementary School, KY

Fall Leaves

beautiful leaves are
everywhere lots of crunchy
colorful fall leaves

Gabby Bell, Grade 4
Briarwood Christian Elementary School, AL

My Favorite Place

Warm and squishy sandy too crabs
In the water kids screaming
when...
The wave gets them
the waters go up and down
Left   and   right
Sea shells all around the warm sandy beach
the Fish in the sea
sharks and turtles all around
Swimming and surfing on the waves

Monica Benavides, Grade 5
Stokesdale Elementary School, NC

The Beach

Looks like a water wonderland
Sounds like children playing in sand
Tastes like Mom's sandwiches from the cooler
Smells like salty mist on the breezes
Feels like warm sun on my face.

Sarah Cressman, Grade 5
Briarwood Christian Elementary School, AL

The Pier

Clouds above me
Ocean below
Birds flying past
Fishing the undertow
Waves splash underneath
Making silent dome
A seagull calls out
Crying "Where's home?"
Light slices the water
Waves crowd the pier
Getting higher each time
Getting closer
Coming near.
Passing the railing
The light leads me home
Lost and alone
Doomed forever to roam.

Darbi Mulkey, Grade 6
Christ Episcopal School - Middle School, LA

Life

Life is like a rolling sand hill
It goes up and it goes down
And it can sometimes stink like a paper mill
But then it can be as happy as a rainbow
Or a winter with snow
But then life can be in-between at times
It can stink or be as black as ink
Then one point in your day you say
"I will never give up I should be proud in every way!"

Shelby Bailey, Grade 4
St Thomas More School, NC

Falling

I'm falling
Down there someone's calling
I keep falling
While I'm falling
I'm hoping soon I'll land,
In soft fluffy sand.

Jeremy Snyder, Grade 4
Cave City Elementary School, AR

Me, Myself, and I

Me, myself, and I,
I wish I could fly.
Soar over clouds
And never come down.
No one is with me
Even if the sky is empty.
Me, myself, and I,
I wish I could fly.

Jakayla Jackson, Grade 4
Stephens Elementary School, AL

When You Look Outside

When you look outside
Full of pride
You see something white and cold.
So you take a scarf, mittens,
And a nice warm coat.
You go outside
Full of pride.
All of a sudden the sun starts to shine.
You go inside full of pride.
You sit there and say goodbye
To all that snow.

Amanda Minch, Grade 6
Mount Zion Christian School, SC

Snow

Snow, snow on the ground
Falling, falling all around
Icicles glistening in the night
Dripping, dripping out of sight.

The snow is leaving 'til next year
Then the flowers will appear
Through the grass and through the trees
Comes the gentle summer breeze.

Colton Nutt, Grade 6
Pleasants County Middle School, WV

The Crying Fly

There was a fly who had to cry
When we told him he had to die
We built him a tomb
And we called it a tomb of doom

Zach Scott, Grade 5
Trenton Middle School, MO

Christmas Means…

C heerful places
H appy faces
R omantic maybes
I nnocent babies
S mall dolls
T ennis balls
M any different games
A unts and uncles with different names
S ometimes it's hard to remember
    I guess I'll wait 'till next Dec.

Antonio West, Grade 5
Graham Elementary School, AL

Veteran

V eteran's
E xperience
T elephones are busy
E veryone in pain
R eloading rifles
A ware of attacks
N urse saving lives

Becca Sinclair, Grade 4
Cherokee Elementary School, AR

Video Games

They are fun
They are cool
Everyone loves them
I do too.
Most are fun
some are boring
But I'm the best
at all of them.

Tanner Ellis, Grade 6
Armorel Elementary School, AR

Christmas

I love to get presents
I don't want a peasant
I put up the Christmas tree
My mother screams about a bee
My grandma and I play a game
My cousin says I'm lame
We all eat deviled eggs
My cousin acts like she has no legs

Aaron Lindsay, Grade 4
Wohlwend Elementary School, MO

Snow

Snow
White, soft
Melting, falling, covering
As light as feathers
Ice

Kimberly Gutierrez, Grade 5
Bayyari Elementary School, AR

Shevva

This is my dog
She is so big and strong,
With very quick speed,
She's always barking a song.

This is my dog,
She sleeps in my bed.
Her belly is holding puppies,
So she looks well fed.

This is my dog,
She is like a turtle dove.
I will say this more than once,
My dog, I will always love.

Michael Marble, Grade 5
Heber Springs Elementary School, AR

Little Angel

An innocent soul in the wrong place
Hides every scar-every mark on her face
Beaten and bruised by a man not brave
Now she lies in her own grave
The life she hated is gone and done
She can now be a child
She can now have fun
Now, the sweet girl
With the teary-eyed face
Now is the girl in a wonderful place.

Kyli Boley, Grade 6
Pleasants County Middle School, WV

My Fishing Day

One day I went fishing,
just me and my mom,
the fish weren't biting
but we really did have fun.

First, we had a picnic
and then played catch,
next we climbed trees,
but we were afraid we
would break our necks!

The sun started to set
our day was coming to an end,
we'll come back to catch the "big one,"
one day real soon, my friend!

Ky Foley, Grade 5
Canute Elementary School, OK

My Parents

Mom is good, Daddy is mean
Mom gives me anything.
My daddy just leaves.

Shalea Jones, Grade 4
East Jones Elementary School, MS

I Am a Military Brat

I am a Military Brat.
I wonder when my dad will retire.
I hear helicopters soaring over head.
I see planes taking my dad away.
I want my dad to stay home.
I am a Military Brat.

I pretend I am in a tank.
I feel happy to see my dad back.
I touch my skateboard to remember my dad.
I worry that something might happen to him.
I cry when my dad leaves.
I am a Military Brat.

I understand he'll be gone a lot.
I say my dad is a great hero.
I dream he'll come back safe.
I try to represent my dad.
I hope everything will be peaceful.
I am a Military Brat.

Joseph Tafoya, Grade 6
Walker Intermediate School, KY

Sadness

Looks like: a cloudy sky
Sounds like: a baby crying
Tastes like: sour juice
Smells like: old food
Feels like: the wind taking your breath away

Magie Steinhoff, Grade 5
Trenton Middle School, MO

Victoria's Bio

Victoria
Honest, nice, pretty, bookworm
Sister of Gabe
Lover of books, puppies, and soda
Who feels joy when reading
Who needs books, food, and friends
Who gives hugs, drawings and encouragement
Who fears bees and spiders
Who would like to see kids never get sick
Oklahoma City
Flowers

Victoria Flowers, Grade 4
Cleveland Elementary School, OK

Green

Green looks like grass after it has been mowed.
Green feels like leaves after it rains.
Green tastes like a crisp green apple picked from a tree.
Green smells like a kiwi that has been cut open.
Green sounds like a grasshopper singing on a summer night.

Marina Keller, Grade 5
Geggie Elementary School, MO

Snowman

I am a snowman
I wonder if the kids are going to throw me
I hear the kids
I want to live forever
I am a snowman
I pretend that I'm not alive
I feel really cold
I touch the scarf it is melting me
I worry that I will melt
I cry when I am
I am a snowman
I understand why I melt
I say I don't
I dream there is an ice age
I hope there is
I am a snowman

Samuel Dominguez, Grade 4
Wohlwend Elementary School, MO

Victory

I love football, don't you?
Even if I hurt a finger or two.
Let me tell you about the game
About the game that gave me fame.

It was fourth down, no completion
The other team were not even Christian
The coach put me in, I was in the game
This is the game that brought me fame.

Me, in the game. I almost died
I was as nervous as a duck going to get fried.
All the sudden the ball came whizzing at me.
Could I catch it? I did! I was happy as can be.

I ran like I never thought I could
I scored a touchdown, didn't think I would.
After the game the other team got saved
God's victory was better than the fame I craved.

Andee Atkins, Grade 5
Providence Academy, TN

Sticky Icky Snowmen

when snowmen are hot they melt
like a boiling pot
when snowmen get cold
they sometimes fold.
So sticky so bright
they make my heart go right.
They are so white especially at night
where they fight
snowmen hate the light 'cause it's so bright
it's a fright to their sight.
This is the protector from the sun 'cause it's no fun.

Shawn Stankavage, Grade 5
St Thomas More School, NC

Little Frog

Little creepy frog
In delicate resting pond
Playing with great friends
Arianna Garner, Grade 4
Hillcrest Elementary School, TN

Ode to Earth

You are my mother Earth,
you give me air to breathe.
You give me water to drink
and food to eat.

You give me a place to live
and a place to sleep.
You give me a place to play
and a place to sit.

You give me a place to talk
and a place to cry.
You give me a place to live
and a place to die.
Sachin Joshi, Grade 6
River Trail Middle School, GA

Christmas

Children making their lists
Hoping for all the gifts.
Elves make every new toy
With hopes to bring children joy

Santa Claus is on the roof.
Children not hearing a single hoof.
Parents clean many dishes.
Hoping for all their wishes

Children are hanging lights
With the lights shining very bright.
Now everyone goes to rest
To hope for the very best.

We think Christmas is about gifts
Or making a list.
Christmas is about Jesus Christ
Who treated everyone nice.
Lorie Dukes, Grade 6
St Mark Elementary School, SC

November

Growing darker every night
Birds commence migration flight
Majestic oaks nearly bare
Fields of grass will fade and tear
Wind rushes through the trees
Children chase cascading leaves
Emily DeMoss, Grade 6
Whitefield Academy, GA

People of the World

We are different and yet the same.
We are different colors, but so are all the things we make.
We have and will always be different.
It doesn't matter that we are different.
We can be red, black, white, or tan and it won't make a difference.
We are all God's creation,
We stand hand in hand.
Haley Williams, Grade 5
Orange Grove Elementary School, MS

I Am a Military Child

I'm Davion Brown and I'm a military child.
When I hear the tanks shooting, I wonder if he is going to come home.
I see air planes fly over my head.
I want the war in Iraq to end.
I'm a military child.

I pretend that he is here at home hugging me.
I feel that he is not going to Iraq.
I touch my heart then I realize he is still here with me.
I worry if my dad passes away and my heart will be broken.
I cry when my dad tells me he is going to be all right and I hug him tightly.
I'm a military child.

I understand that he has to go to support our country.
I dream that he made it and so did the other soldiers.
I try to keep my grades up so I can be a football player.
I hope that the military will be safe.
I'm a military child.
Davion Brown, Grade 6
Walker Intermediate School, KY

I Remember Savannah

I remember Savannah…
Hearing the slow waves, feeling the hot sand, tasting the good food

I remember Savannah…
Relaxing in the Jacuzzi, swimming in the cool pool, drinking sweet tea

I remember Savannah…
Sleeping in a warm bed, eating at a clean table

I remember Savannah
Azaria Irvin, Grade 5
Sycamore Elementary School, GA

Isn't It Sad

Isn't it sad how people are dying left and right.
Isn't it sad how people aren't even trying to make it right.
Isn't it sad how we end up in war to restore lost peace.
Isn't it sad how the Towers fell to the ground.
Just think of all the sadness in that town.
Isn't that sad how we have drug dealers who call themselves healers.
Isn't that sad?
Desireé Yvette Dominguez, Grade 5
Parker Road Elementary School, MO

Me?

for what i see could this be me
could it be me
who questioned and pondered at every sight of danger
me when only a few years back
i was free
to roam as i pleased
for what i see this isn't me
who cherished thee
to be who thee wants
to be
to feel free once more
this is not me
i say to thee as i look in a mirror
this is truly not me

Gisell Cisneros, Grade 6
Henderson Middle School, GA

Finding My Way

I am walking through the darkness,
Trying to find my way
With only a candle to guide me,
I am trying to find my way
Walking down a dark dark hall, wandering, searching,
Trying to find my way
With the thunder booming, my heart pounding,
Trying to find my way
I see a light, I run, I run as fast as I can,
I run 'till I'm able to run no more,
Trying to find my way
I am lost, I am lost, I am lost in the darkness,
Trying to find my way.

Saxon McDonald, Grade 5
Nature's Way Montessori School, TN

Abraham Lincoln

Abe Lincoln was a famous man,
Who came up with a master plan.
Elected President of the USA,
He was quite important in a major way.
Lincoln was a help to our land,
Because he took such an important stand.
The North and South became at odds,
And Abe had support from his wife Mary Todd.
The Battle of Gettysburg was a bloody one,
And Abe knew many had lost a son.
Abe shouted, "Let's end slavery, once and for all,"
And across the land he made this call.
The South surrendered and Abe was glad,
But the many lives that were lost, made him sad.

To Ford's Theater he went to see a play,
Never knowing it would be his last day.
John Wilkes Booth, didn't like Abe's plan,
And shot him dead, which shocked every man.

David Scaff, Grade 6
River Trail Middle School, GA

Thanksgiving Time

Thanksgiving is great, I will not lie.
The wonderful smell of sweet potato pie.
Happiness while the turkey is cooking,
I stare at the turkey. I can't stop looking!
How happy I'll be when it is done.
I stare out at the November sun.
It's Thanksgiving time that's what it is now.
Oh, how can it be so wonderful? I wonder how.
No other time of the year can beat it.
Now here comes the food and I must eat it.

Ben Warnick, Grade 6
Guntown Middle School, MS

Thanks

I am thankful for my mom
I love it when we go to church
And I like the smell of new shoes.

I have a dog and
I like it when
She licks my hand.
I feel cold and tickly.

Sometimes me and my Grandma
Are in the kitchen
And she cooks.

I like the times when
Me and my sister laugh together
We all watch movies and eat popcorn.

Rissiah Sanders, Grade 4
Lee A Tolbert Community Academy, MO

Painted Fall

See the colors sweet
Red, golden, brown colored trees
It is painted fall

Maggie McDavid, Grade 4
Briarwood Christian Elementary School, AL

My Gym

Looks like a bunch of crazy people,
Smells like people's sweat,
Sounds like Coach John yelling,
Tastes like popcorn during the break,
Feels like flipping through the air.

Maggie Benner, Grade 5
Briarwood Christian Elementary School, AL

The Ocean

Pretty, blue ocean
water hits against the rocks
the water splashes.

Laiken Pearson, Grade 4
Briarwood Christian Elementary School, AL

Go

To go is to travel,
Going is fun.
Going is challenging,
I like to go.
How about you?
Wesley Wright, Grade 6
Desoto Central School, MS

The Great Depression

It all began on Black Tuesday
Stock markets began to crash.
Many citizens were unemployed
People's lives had turned to ash.

Not many people had food to eat
Nor did they have much money.
Their lives were dark and gloomy,
No longer bright and sunny.

People got in very long lines
Just to get a bite to eat.
They got bread and soup for meals,
And considered this a treat.

They lived in shacks called Hoovervilles
The government helped people succeed.
This event was very tragic and sad
A depressing time indeed.
Jacqueline Frederic, Grade 6
J D Meisler Middle School, LA

Respect Your Mummies

M ummies are not really dummies
U sed as fuel for engines
M any sold as medicine
M agicians used them to get rich
Y ou should really know more before
you call a mummy a dummy.
Domonique Davis, Grade 6
Clarksburg School, TN

The Stars

The stars in the
Night sky so bright
Each one like a small
Ball of light
Shining in the sky
Giving the whole world
Light during the night
The stars
Dancing next to
The moon letting
The whole world shine
At night.
Jasmine Hunter, Grade 6
Cathedral School, NC

Read Wherever

People read.
Read the Constitution
If you're in the White House.
Read a map if you're at sea.
Read a book if you're at school.
Read a sign if you're on the road.
But wherever you are,
Read anything, anywhere
Just read!
Shanna Nichols, Grade 5
Pleasant View R-VI School, MO

Autumn Leaves

Jumping in the brown leaves
zooming to the bottom of the pile
hearing the crunchy sound
all the leaves flying up
drifting down
scraping them up again.
jumping in
That's the fun of Fall.
Cassidy Meador, Grade 4
Alvaton Elementary School, KY

The Sun

The fiery ball
that sits in our sky
known as our sun,
shines brilliant light
on our wonderfully
shaped world.
Houston Cunningham, Grade 6
Dyer Elementary & Jr High School, TN

Soccer

Soccer is the greatest sport
At least it is to me
I love to run, and jump, and kick
Like a fox going after a snorting pig.

Isn't the game 90 minutes long
And is it 90 minutes of great fun
The goal is 24 feet wide
And all the players look sublime.

If I steal the ball it's pretty much mine
It's really fun to score a ton
The opponent is my enemy
But my team is the only friend of me.

I kick the ball through 12 pairs of feet
Once they get to me they are dead meat
We usually play under the sun
After the game it is all pure fun.
Daniel Dube, Grade 5
Providence Academy, TN

Halloween

Halloween
Ghost and witches
Smelling fear
Owls and werewolves howling
Smoky taste of burning candles
The foggy air rubbing on your body
Halloween
Tanner Roach, Grade 4
Tamassee-Salem Elementary School, SC

A Mysterious House

I walk on cobblestones
Just when I come to see
Some bright blue house
Sitting by the sea
I hear some strange sound
So I listen to it close
I cannot hear at all
Because the wind blows
When I walk into the house
I hear another sound
Some kind of music
I hear it all around
It sounds like classical
It's my favorite kind
It transports me away
Because it's music of the mind
Nolan Gosnell, Grade 6
Alexandria Middle Magnet School, LA

Halloween

H owling ghosts
I ll-tempered vampires
J ack-o'-lanterns with creepy smiles
K eep away from the werewolves
They're coming to get me!
Megan Sole, Grade 5
Trenton Middle School, MO

Signs

Signs, signs all around.
Some make me smile,
some make me frown.
Some say stop.
Some say go.
Some say even slow.
Signs, signs all around.
Payten Townsend, Grade 4
Brilliant Elementary School, AL

Chocolate

Roses are red,
Violets are blue,
Chocolate is not as sweet as you!
Preston Poole, Grade 5
Midway Covenant Christian School, GA

A Match and a Fire

On a dry windy day, a careless match hits the dry grass.
Then the roaring sound of a train is heard for miles.
Not a real train, but a fire.
The red, orange, and yellow flames scorch sides of the trees.
Smoke settles into the valleys as it goes out.
New grass and trees will be seen again in the spring.

Tracy Bodenhamer, Grade 5
Etowah Elementary School, NC

Ocean and Desert

Ocean
refreshing, salty
swimming, playing, building
waves, surfing, cactus, rocks
threatening, hunting, burning
hot, dry
Desert

Lily Leath, Grade 5
Briarwood Christian Elementary School, AL

Seasons

Leaves are falling everywhere.
There are different colors in the air.
I hear lots and lots of sounds;
birds, squirrels, dogs, and hounds.
Fall goes by so fast,
winter is here at last.
We will play in the snow, "Ho, ho, ho."
We will freeze and shiver.
I hope grandma does not cook liver.
Yeah, here comes spring.
It's time to sing.
Flowers start to fill the air.
They are good for gifts and good to share.
God gave us everything with care.
Now is summer, hot and mild.
The kids are really, really wild.
Outside fun and swimming pools.
We were definitely not cool.
All the seasons were really grand,
but now I'm back where I began.

Jennifer Knox, Grade 4
Stephens Elementary School, AL

An Ode to a Chocolate Chip Cookie

Oh Chocolate Chip Cookie,
Your chocolate melts in my mouth.

When I eat you I think of dancing mice,
Just one bite, I go crazy.

After I eat you I make a "MMMMM!" sound,
And then my eyes go hazy!

Davion Davenport, Grade 4
Pines Elementary School, NC

Wind

Wind blows through my hair
in the autumn it feels cool
every day it's cool

Natalie Kidd, Grade 5
Briarwood Christian Elementary School, AL

It Ain't My Thang

Rappin is not my thing, but I will spit a few verses,
Sorry for the inconvenience, no time for rehearsin,

I was born with many talents, but this ain't one,
Close your ears tight because this is a dry run.

To some of you guys this may be boring,
But for me I am just exploring.

I dibble and I dabble a little here and there,
A bunch of cluttered words but I am almost there.

So listen my friends to what I have said,
Because my mother is telling me it is now time for bed.

KaDarrius Rattler, Grade 6
Calloway Smith Middle School, AL

Atlantic Beach

The enormous ocean crashing thunderously
Small sailboats like ballerinas flowing peacefully
Vast waves breaking nosily
Quick serious seagulls squawking ineffectively
Gritty sand is play dough squishing strangely
Protective suntan lotion rubbed carefully
Salt water smelling fishy
Exotic fish like divers swimming so slowly
Genuine alligator fried tastily
Coarse sand blowing like a blizzard
I feel relaxed and at ease.

Makenzie Wood, Grade 4
Bailey Elementary School, NC

The Great Outdoors

I like the great outdoors it's really really fun,
But sometimes I have trouble from being hot in the sun.
I like the great outdoors and to play by the creek,
But sometimes I feel like a geek.

I like the great outdoors it's really really fun,
But sometimes I have trouble from being hot in the sun.
I like the great outdoors and to play hide and seek,
And sometimes my cousins find me down by the creek.

I like the great outdoors it's really really fun,
But sometimes I have trouble from being hot in the sun.
I like the great outdoors it's really really fun,
So sometimes you should come too, and have lots of fun.

Jessica Lynn Rouse, Grade 4
Tazewell/New Tazewell Elementary School, TN

Leprechauns

A leprechaun running free,
Turned around and looked at me,
He urged me toward his pot of gold,
But then I saw it was all mold.

Landis Alexander Brannan, Grade 4
South Topsail Elementary School, NC

What My Name Really Means!

S aturday is my favorite day of the week.
E njoys playing basketball.
R espectful to others.
A mazing in schoolwork.

Sera Berisa, Grade 6
Lost River Elementary School, KY

The Land I Dream Of

Far, far away
Over the rainbow
Behind the clouds
Above the sky
There is an area I love,
The place I dream of.
Such a colorful spot,
It makes me smile and smile a lot.
I love to go there.
It's like a retreat.
The land I dream of
Has tables and chairs.
Such a shady, relaxing space.
I will never forget this place.
Never…Never…

Callie Monk, Grade 4
Ode Maddox Elementary School, AR

Airplanes

Zap, zoom
This way and that
Airplanes are so fast
There's B-2's and
Tomcats,
Blackbirds and Hornets,
Zap, zoom,
I want a ride,
Take me up high,
As high as you can,
Down, down, down,
I see the runway
What a smooth landing,
Can I go again
Up, up
Will you take the day off,
For me, please?
Take me up and down
All day long, please, please, please???

Emilie Warman, Grade 5
Walton Verona Elementary School, KY

TarHeel Blue

TarHeel blue looks like the jersey that is on the team
TarHeel blue sounds like the crowd cheering when the team scores a goal.
TarHeel blue smells like the sweet flying of the players.
TarHeel blue tastes like ice cold Kool-Aid I'm drinking in the crowd.
TarHeel blue feels like the happiness of the crowd cheering when the team wins.
TarHeel blue is the color of my shorts I wear to the game.
TarHeel blue is the sounds of the crowd cheering with astonishment.
TarHeel blue is the sweat smell of the ice people are sipping on in the crowd.
TarHeel blue is the taste of the slushy I'm eating in the crowd.
TarHeel blue is the color of my hoodie I wear to the game.

Nathan Elmore, Grade 5
Cool Spring Elementary School, NC

Red

Red looks like a fresh boiling cherry pie.
Red feels like the hot fire sun.
Red tastes like blasting strawberries.
Red smells like sweet awesome cherry blossoms.
Red sounds like the Cardinals screaming when they won the World Series.
Red is a blasting, boiling wonderful color.

Brittany Margherita, Grade 5
Geggie Elementary School, MO

Egypt: A Historian and a Boy

Egypt is   Egypt is
amazing
                                          a bore!
I am   I am
a historian.
                              a five year-old boy. With all of its
pyramids
                                   and millions of kings,
Egypt is   Egypt is
fantastic
                                          confusing
magnificent
                                          a bore!
Egypt is fantastic and amazing. They believed
in many gods and goddesses and they   (plugs ears)
believed their pharaoh was a god on Earth. They were very religious
and they willingly served him. They even built the Great Pyramid for
a pharaoh called King Khufu. So, you see, Egypt is amazing and important.
                                                    Not!
    (glare)
                                                    Sorry!

Emily Hudson, Grade 6
Beck Academy, SC

Thanksgiving

Thanksgiving is a time when we take time to thank people for what they do for us.
Thanksgiving is when we take time to think about what people do for us every day.
Thanksgiving is when we fellowship with our families and friends.
Thanksgiving is when we take time to communicate with others.
That's what Thanksgiving's all about.

William Crump, Grade 6
Guntown Middle School, MS

Color

Red is the color of a beautiful rose
Green is the color of a leprechaun's nose
Yellow is the sun shining so bright
Black is the color when you turn out your light
Orange is a pumpkin sitting in your yard
Blue is the color of a cheerful card
What do you see in these colors?

Michael Ritter, Grade 5
Ascension Elementary School, KY

Squirrel Hunter

Everybody likes football, but hunting is my game.
I spot a squirrel in the woods and I aim.
Bang! I miss.
But I won't accept the blame.
Must be the gun.
Run run squirrel run!

Collin Gilbert, Grade 4
Brilliant Elementary School, AL

Love and Hate

Love and hate
Paced alongside each other
Love is for the kind people
But hatred rings above my head
Taking place of love and all that is good
Hatred comes by convincingly
But love stands lonely
Who am I to say hatred is better
Love is harder to accept harder than a letter
Which is why love has conquered all
Hatred stays behind but love is on the ball.

Gabriela Rodriguez, Grade 6
Riverwood Middle School, NC

Fire Burning

Someone screams then yikes!
A fire burning in the night,
people run away.

Allyson Payne, Grade 4
Briarwood Christian Elementary School, AL

The Pirate

One day there was a pirate so bright,
He said instead of a boat I will take a flight.
No! Never could he take a flight,
For a pirate this is not right,
He found himself in the deep blue sea.
As always his boat was right by me,
He stood in his boat with his 24 men,
And shot balls out of the cannon like ink in a pen.
The island they went to was covered with ice.
Returning home was so nice,
They were served hot beans and rice.

Shirla Wyles, Grade 4
Western Hills Elementary School, AR

What Ifs of the Bible

What if Adam had not sinned?
What if Abel had lived and his blood had not cried out of him?
What if the ark had sprung a leak?
What if at Babel someone would speak?

What if Jacob had fought back?
What if God believed that speech Moses lacked?
What if Joshua did it his own way?
What if Israel would obey

What if Ruth had gone away?
What if David had been afraid?
What if Solomon had stayed with God?
What if Joel had died like a dog?

What if Jesus had not died?
What if Saul had not been blind?
What if Paul had not written to the Church?
These are what ifs of the Word.

Austin Wright, Grade 5
Providence Academy, TN

Santa Claus

Santa, do you get tired of delivering presents every year?
Do you get tired of dealing with your reindeer?
Do you get bored of riding your sleigh through the mist?
Do you feel bad placing naughty kids on your list?

Tyler Stowe, Grade 5
Heber Springs Elementary School, AR

Rainbows

I have seen a rainbow
Have you?

I've seen the pretty
Colors of it too.

As the wind goes
Through my hair.

As I can smell
The beautiful air.

I have not kept
A gold coin from a rainbow.

But, if I do
I will give it to you.

I have no place to go.

But the end
Of a rainbow.

Elizabeth Kight, Grade 4
St Mary Cathedral Elementary School, MO

Monkeys

Monkeys are pretty
They are very full of play
Monkeys are my friends
Molly Gore, Grade 6
Livingston Middle School, TN

Football

In the fall
We have a game called football.
Some people get to carry the ball
The referee gets to make the call
The quarterback calls the play
The receiver makes the day
As he scores
You can hear the crowd's roars
Heard throughout the town
Can't wait for another down
To get a touchdown
Devin Savoie, Grade 6
Arnaudville Elementary School, LA

Without Math

Without math we wouldn't know
How many fingers or toes we have.

Without math we would starve
For we couldn't cook.

Without math we wouldn't know
What time it is.

Without math sports would be
No fun because you couldn't keep score.

Without math we would all be
Naked for we couldn't sew!

If you were injured
You couldn't have surgery.

Without math life would be
Bad and dangerous.
Liam Dougan, Grade 5
Meramec Elementary School, MO

Food Colors

Red is the color of Apples.
Yellow is the color of Lemons.
Green is the color of Cucumbers.
Blue is the color of Blueberries.
Purple is the color of Plums.
Red is the color of Strawberries.
Green is the color of Watermelons.
Pink is the color of Grapefruit.
Miranda Simon, Grade 6
Hayes Elementary School, OK

Tractors

Tractors,
Tractors,
Tractors,
Green tractors,
Yellow tractors,
Big loud red tractors,
Colorful huge popping tractors,
These are just a few.
Rusty tractors,
Shiny tractors,
Smokey screeching thumping tractors,
Humming hissing noisy tractors,
Thundering tractors, too.
Strong tractors,
Dirty tractors,
Don't forget clean tractors.
Last of all, best of all,
I like working tractors.
Chase Harnage, Grade 6
Lost River Elementary School, KY

Veteran

V ery nice and ready to come home
E ngaged in fighting
T ough and hardworking
E veryone's heroes
R ising to the call
A wesome at work
N ice to us
Dakota Williams, Grade 4
Cherokee Elementary School, AR

Santa Claus

S aint Nick
A ll knowing
N aughty or nice
T oys for kids
A lways jolly

C andy in stockings
L oving
A lways nice
U p above naughtiness
S leigh rider
Terry Baker, Grade 5
Tates Creek Elementary School, KY

Christmastime

Christmas is green.
It sounds like jingling bells.
It tastes like warm apple pie.
It smells like fresh gingerbread cookies.
It looks like glistening white snow.
It makes you feel joyful.
Vanessa Petzoldt, Grade 6
St Vincent Elementary School, MO

Snow

Snow
cold, white
Melting, falling, playing
Snow is cool, cold, and fun
Winter
Vianca Valdovinos, Grade 5
Bayyari Elementary School, AR

The Owl

His eyes are golden amber,
Shining like the sun.
Seeing all, watching all,
But always noticed by none.

His beak is sharp as steel,
The color of dull gold.
They release an echoing "who"
Or so I'm told.

His wings are slightly ruffled,
Designed for silent flight.
To swoop down on prey unnoticed
In the dark of night.
Irene Lin, Grade 6
River Trail Middle School, GA

Cats

Cats have really sleek fur.
Cats always like to purr.
I really enjoy my cat.
I sometimes wear him as a hat,
But I don't think he likes that.
I'll see you when the scratches heal.
Until then, I'll pretend they're not real.
Katie Leenders, Grade 4
Cleveland Elementary School, OK

At the Beach

There is fun
at the beach
Waves you can hear from a distance
at the beach
Watching my brothers build a sand castle
at the beach
I see a surfer
at the beach
There are airplanes in the sky
at the beach
In the water there are
fish, crabs, shells, sharks, dolphins
at the beach
There is happiness in the air
for everyone to share
at the beach
Katie Allison, Grade 4
Alvaton Elementary School, KY

Wild Ponies

They grazed,
They ate grass
And they gazed at me.

They were black,
White, brown,
And gray too.

I named them
Smoke, Star,
Woody, and Smog.

I fed one,
It was a hog.
That one was Smog.
He was a hog.

Katie Emmendorfer, Grade 4
St Mary Cathedral Elementary School, MO

October

October is my favorite month of the year
In your garden, a pumpkin may appear.

In October, there are many fairs
And you can feel a chill in the air.

In October, the leaves fall off the trees
And what beautiful colors you will see.

In October, the World Series you can watch.
The players will step it up a notch.

In October, football and soccer are played
With lots of great plays being made.

I love October!

Jacob Andrew Baird, Grade 4
Contentnea Elementary School, NC

My Family

My family is very kind and loving.
If I did not have them,
I would be nothing.

I thank God
For my loving family.
They feed me,
Support me,
And give me shelter.

I could not live without them.
I know I love them,
And they love me too.

Adam Pope, Grade 4
St Mary Cathedral Elementary School, MO

Kittens

Kittens, kittens so so cute feel his rough tongue,
and his soft furry back I love it when he looks at
me with his BIG, ROUND EYES because it
makes me feel all good inside.

Jessica Thornton, Grade 4
Moyock Elementary School, NC

9/11

Remember all those planes,
Now scraped up by cranes?

Remember all those people running around,
When those Towers hit the ground?

WHAT A SOUND!

Remember all those people who died,
And all their families that cried?

Remember all the Firemen just doing what they do,
Remember Flight 93 and don't forget it, too?

Remember the many prayers prayed that sad, sad day,
From New York City all the way to L.A.?

Do you remember all those kids who questioned why?
But no one can explain no matter how hard they try!

REMEMBER 9/11!!

Drew Kitchens, Grade 5
Holsenbeck Elementary School, GA

Poems

Poems are neat,
Poems are fun,
Poems can be done by anyone.

Poems are great,
Poems are cool,
Poems do not have a single rule.

Sometimes they may be challenging,
Sometimes they may be tough,
But if you think and think,
Ideas you'll get enough.

From yummy ice cream to cows going "moo,"
You can write about anything,
Any idea will do.

Poems can be quick,
You have a good time,
All you have to do
Is to write words that rhyme!

Derek Chan, Grade 5
St Ann Elementary School, NC

Pumpkins

Pumpkins,
Pumpkins,
Pumpkins,
Scary pumpkins,
Nice pumpkins,
Fat, tall, frightening pumpkins,
Rotten, stinky mean pumpkins,
Those are just a few.
Short pumpkins,
Skinny pumpkins,
Orange, juicy, slimy pumpkins,
Hairy, cute, square pumpkins,
Round pumpkins, too.
Squishy pumpkins,
Flat pumpkins,
Don't forget bright pumpkins.
Last of all, best of all,
I like big pumpkins.

LeAnn Walker, Grade 5
South Nodaway Elementary School, MO

Someone to Hold

You need someone to hold,
Hold when you're alone.
You need someone to guide you,
Guide you through the dark.

You need someone to protect you,
Protect you from a broken heart.
You need someone to carry you,
Carry you home.

You need someone to love you,
Love you until you're apart.
Life isn't pleasant without,
Without someone to hold.

Zachary Redden, Grade 5
Etowah Elementary School, NC

Veteran

V eterans can make a difference
E veryone knows it
T ogether if they work together
E veryone will be saved
R ights will be saved
A nd no more wars
N ow it's time to go my friends

Emma Johnson, Grade 4
Cherokee Elementary School, AR

Bees

Buzz Buzz goes the bees
Don't get too close they might sting
Ouch that bee stung me.

Morgan Trippett, Grade 6
Martin Elementary School, WV

He Is in Heaven

Heaven, what a wonderful place to be.
He is there in Heaven walking with Jesus on the streets of gold.
He is singing and dancing and nothing is wrong.
His heart is better and his bumps and bruises have disappeared.

The life He lived on Earth was troubled and hard,
in heaven everything about it is perfect.
He has no more struggles, no more hardships, and no more deaths.
His life here is over but his life there has just begun.

Every night when I'm lying bed,
I wonder what it will be like in heaven
I think about my Grandaniel and I
Know I felt happy every time I saw him
I know he fits in perfect in heaven.
That's where he belongs.

Every time I think of my Grandaniel
I know, He's in Heaven.

Kristin Rockhold, Grade 6
Magnolia Springs Baptist Academy, AL

Colors

All colors depend on my day
All colors are in my own way
Blue is when I'm feeling down.
Red is when I'm steaming like a hot chili pepper.
Green is when I'm feeling sick.
Pink is when I'm perky.
Yellow and orange and purple is when I'm feeling normal or fine.
That's when I love poetry
Because I can express my emotions.

Mariah Domings, Grade 5
Drayton Hall Elementary School, SC

The Hunt

The day had turned to dusk
Dad and I had just discussed
Which one would take the first buck
The decision was made as we left the truck
I climbed the tree stand all alone
I could only reach dad by cell phone
My thoughts wandered as I watched the field
It got darker by the minute as my watch would soon reveal
Suddenly there was movement 50 yards away
Could it then finally be my day
I shot and down went the deer
Not a sound was heard by the human ear
It was strangely quite except for the sound of my own heart beating
With this big deer down I knew what we would be eating
Dad joined me by my tree stand
He calmed me down and shook my hand
I will never forget the hunt that day
The time I had with my dad what can I say!

Chase Gibson, Grade 6
Our Lady of Fatima School, MS

Faith

Faith is the thing that holds us together,
and gets us through all the bad weather.

Sometimes you need faith to fulfill your dreams,
and it can help you through all extremes.

Faith isn't just a little story,
it's a part of history.

The biggest thing you should have faith in is God,
because he gets the most applaud.

He's the best thing in my life,
better than my bowie knife.

James King, Grade 5
Quail Run Elementary School, GA

The Ocean

The ocean is blue
The ocean is pretty too
The ocean is fun.

Breeanna Dillard, Grade 4
Briarwood Christian Elementary School, AL

Swans

Swans…
Gliding gently across the water…
Tiny ripples spread slowly across the surface…
Like a stone thrown into water.

Swans…
Feathers as white as snow…
Their presence is unknown…
Their serenity as they glide by
Is like a dejavu of the past…

Swans.

Matthew Johnson, Grade 5
Evangelical Christian School, TN

The Beach

Tastes like crab claws and lobsters
Looks like shells and Palm trees
Smells like fish and salt water
Feels like sand and water.
Sounds like seagulls calling and wave crashing.

Chanah Fallin, Grade 5
Briarwood Christian Elementary School, AL

True Friends

Friends are who you trust to tell your secrets to.
Friends will help you make a breakthrough!
Good or bad, thick or thin,
True friends will have your back to the end!

Essence Weary, Grade 5
East Marion Elementary School, MS

Where Is She?

Where has she gone? Where did she go?
Do any of these people really know?
Has she gone through the clouds up above us?
Is she dead in the ground?
If she's near us, is she making a sound?
Can you hear her heart pounding?
Why did she leave us?
Will we see her again?
Will she send us a message to let us know she's still here?
If she's still with us, I want to see her again.
But, if not, I already miss my kin.
Will she be here tomorrow?
Will she be here today?
Will she ever say?
If she is in pain, is she still fighting?
I don't know, it's too confusing.
Is she doing better?
Is she doing her best?
Is my great-grandma finally at rest?

Sierra Burris, Grade 6
Hot Springs Middle School, AR

Rose

There once was a girl named Rose
Who liked to blow her nose.
She blew so much she started to quiver
But she was cured when she jumped into the river.

Morgan Kane, Grade 4
Robert E Lee Elementary School, TN

Playing Football

Whenever you make a touchdown
Everyone screams very loud.
People play football to have fun
Or to be a famous player.
You could see millions of people
Routing your name out.
It's not all about winning,
But it is about to have fun.
If you play football, don't be afraid
You will be the best one they've ever seen.
If you want to play football
Play and you might be the best one they ever had.

Dylan Periou, Grade 5
Arnaudville Elementary School, LA

Pig Pig

My binder said
I'm full of papers!

Please, stop it, right now, I don't think I can take it anymore.
See, just look at me I'm thick and heavy. I can barely shut.
I'm so fat I look like a pig. See just look at yourself.

Jessica Rice, Grade 5
Walton Verona Elementary School, KY

Mittens

A mitten
Should not be bitten,
For when it is worn
It would look torn.
Conor McVeigh, Grade 4
St Thomas More School, NC

My Best Friend

My best friend is from California,
she has short blonde hair,
there is nothing she would not dare!
Her smile is like the shining sun,
together we have lots of fun.
Whenever we are playing together
or eating apple pies,
I see friendship in her big green eyes.
Cristy Cabrera, Grade 5
St Teresa's School, GA

Did You Catch That?

All the boys said I was
fly, but I don't have
wings. Is it hot in here,
or is it just me? I took
a trip in my dance class.
Did your computer catch
that mouse fast? They
call him a pig, but he
doesn't live in a sty. Can
boys really catch your eye?
Whitney Law, Grade 6
Armorel Elementary School, AR

The Animal in Me

There is a tiger in me
With teeth like a chain saw
And eyes like a flashlight
It roars like a mountain lion
It claws like a wolverine
It lives in my heart
And it makes me dangerous
I wish it would give me superpowers
Collin Salsbury, Grade 6
South Nodaway Elementary School, MO

Summer Days

Summer days are very long,
Each summer day is a brand new song.
Summer days, we spend at the sea,
Summer days, it's just you and me.
Summer days, I enjoy the most,
To summer days, I give a toast.
Now the summer days are done,
A new school year has now begun.
Elizabeth Whiteside, Grade 5
Shannon Forest Christian School, SC

October

O ver the
C ool fall leaves
T ons
O f children play
B ecause of the fun
E ntertainment of
R umbling on the ground
Clayton Cottrille, Grade 6
Martin Elementary School, WV

Sisters

Sisters are nice.
Sisters are fun.
Sisters are great friends.
Sisters play together.
Sisters laugh together.
Sisters love each other.
Sisters are there for each other.
My sister is my best friend!
Kayla Sexton, Grade 6
Friendship Christian Academy, MS

Valentines

chocolate, candy
love, Valentine's cards,
pizza, friends, party
Mikala Baughman, Grade 4
East Jones Elementary School, MS

Roses Are Red

Roses are red,
Violets are blue.
If I had the Omnitrix,
Here's what I'd do.

First, I'd go Four-Arms
Then I'd go Upgrade
I'd fix electronics,
But just to get paid.

Ben 10's so lucky,
Well, not any more.
Since I made a bored character,
He was never again bored!

This poem's getting annoying,
And I'm glad its about done.
I really can't stand it,
'Cause, this poem's no fun!!

I want it to be over,
Wait! It nearly is!
Just two more sentences,
And this poem will fizz.
Lorenzo Christina, Grade 4
Nesbit Elementary School, GA

All About Me

Hello!
My name is Sabrina Steen.
If I were a color
I'd be mix
like people.
If I were an animal
I'd be nice with a tail
like a dog.
My favorite place is home
When babies are over
and you can play with them.
My favorite snack is ice cream
The movie store has.
I really get upset
when my sister April cries.
and I have to deal with it.
I love listening to music
when I get mad or sad.
Sabrina Steen, Grade 4
Pine Tree Hill Elementary School, SC

My Dog Does Tricks

My dog does tricks at home every day
he begs and sits up for my candy
there's one problem with Sandy
he gets too excited when I give him
a bit and he slobbers all over me.
Brandon Pinkard, Grade 4
Brilliant Elementary School, AL

The Night

One night I went over to
My friend Katie's house
We played tag
We played hide and seek
Finally dinner came
We ate chicken with rolls

We fled outside
We climbed on the trampoline
We both started jumping
Five o'clock came
It's pitch dark
We heard sounds
We took turns screaming
We peered under the trampoline
Her cat Charcoal purred at us.
Danielle Prosser, Grade 4
Alvaton Elementary School, KY

Ants

They live in dirt holes
They like to eat picnic food
The ants have six legs.
Billy Gibson, Grade 4
Russell Babb Elementary School, OK

Christmas

Christmas is a time when you have joy
but some people think Christmas is all about a toy.
Some people think Christmas is all about snow
but it is other things that they don't know

Christmas is full of a lot of things
Even angels and their cute little wings
Christmas is a day that Christ was birthed
Just make sure that Christ comes first

Even though we're out of school
the kids think it is cool
I ask myself all about Christmas
I wonder if I could make a few wishes

Alexis Wilson, Grade 6
St Mark Elementary School, SC

Halloween

Ghosts and goblins everywhere,
Are coming out to give a scare!
Witches, mummies, pumpkins galore,
And so much more!

All around the town tonight,
Come and say hello, all right!
All around the neighborhood,
That's why Halloween's so good!

Trick or treat,
Give me sweets!
Make it fun to walk the streets!
To find some yummy things to eat!

From street to street and all around,
Kids are dressed up like witches and clowns!
Some look scary, and some look sweet,
But they are all after one thing; a sugary treat!

Taylor Terracina, Grade 6
St Cecilia School, LA

War and Peace

War or peace, such a hard choice
If we are poor with a punchbuggy
Or rich with a Rolls Royce
War is like the Grim Reaper
It makes the death toll much deeper
War is the vile yin and Peace is precious yang
Peace is a provider of life
But War is the Devil's fang
War waits for a victim like a snare
Peace rids us of our pain and despair
We fight for Peace and cause War
If this keeps up, humanity shall be no more

Ilyes Benslimane, Grade 6
Haynes Academy for Advanced Studies, LA

The Deep Blue Ocean

The large blue ocean
Very deep and colorful
You'll love it, it's great

Summer Waterman, Grade 4
Briarwood Christian Elementary School, AL

The Motorcycle

There is a motorcycle riding down my street
So fast, so loud, so exciting
At night I sit in my bed
Quietly, still
Then out of nowhere the loud machine comes roaring
Down the street like a lion protecting its cubs.

As I jump out of my bed and peek out of the window,
All I see are the marks from the tires.
Then I think where does he go.
Then as the sound fades out I think
Maybe one day I can ride with that big blue
Motorcycle.

Dominick Vellucci, Grade 6
Cathedral School, NC

Baby Jesus

While the birds are singing and the trees are sighing,
Baby Jesus is crying.
As the Owls are hooting and the shepherds are coming,
Baby Jesus is in the manger.
Mary and Joseph are pleased for this child.
As the wind is calm and the stars are bright,
The farm animals lie in the night.
Oh Hallelujah! The Savior has been born!

Natalie Jacobs, Grade 4
Briggs Elementary School, SC

Fall

Fall is here,
Everyone give a cheer!
Even though Major League Baseball's done,
You can still have fun.
I still wish we had the sun,
But the cool breeze is still fun.

In the oven, turkey is baking,
Leaves fall down for raking,
Playing outside is a blast,
Even though you can't run very fast,
When the cool breeze gives a big blast!

Now, we're at the table to eat some food,
We are smiling and having a happy mood,
So let's have some turkey and stuffing,
And potatoes like fluffing,
Because it's Thanksgiving!

Zachary Douglas, Grade 5
Palmetto Christian Academy, SC

I Have a Monster

I have a monster
made out of clay.
I have a monster
that likes to play.
He likes tea and pizza too.
But I haven't seen him.
Oh no he's gone.
Where can he be?
He's not in the closet.
He's not in the tree.
Oh no where can he be?
Look he's over there.
Oh no what happened?
He's skinny.
Did he go on a diet?
No that's not him.
My monster's been hiding.
But where?
In my room of course!

Christine Williams, Grade 4
Islands Elementary School, GA

Fall

Fall, fall come and play!
Blow all the leaves away, way, way, way!
Summer is hot. Winter is cold.
Can't you see the melody?
I like fall the best.
The leaves are pretty.
The weather is cool.

The trees are changing
Red to yellow, to green, to orange
Not blue, or pink, or black.
Just bright and pretty.
Not dark like bark.

In winter, it's cold.
There is now as white as cotton.
I like it. But there is no color.
For spring has flowers,
But I love fall the best!!!

Marlynda Steiner, Grade 5
Etowah Elementary School, NC

Be Thankful

Whatever you're feeling
should be kindness or joy
to give thanks for life,
to give to others,
to share the love from your heart,
to live your life in security,
to live among people who care for you,
be thankful for what you have always.

Marley Donegan, Grade 6
Guntown Middle School, MS

Rough Pups

My dogs waiting patiently at the door, to be let out.
Barking in a high pitch, and they're off.

Speeding down the white deck, chasing the other dogs.
Heading towards the swing set, running like a herd of cheetahs.

On the other side of the fence, there're other dogs.
Growling and yelping loudly, trying to communicate their excitement.

Once at the door again panting. Waiting to be let in.
Seeing their glaring eyes, begging for water.

Now they're in. Trotting to the water,
Hearing the click clack of their paws, sucking down a big gulp.

Now they're hydrated. Heading to the couch,
Snuggling up. Tired from the chase.

Madison Callery, Grade 4
Goshen Elementary School at Hillcrest, KY

Grandfather

Even though it feels as if the time we had was not enough,
I'll never forget all the great memories we had together.
I remember the time we went shopping
Because I was jealous of all the discounts you got.
I'll never forget your afternoon arguments with grandma,
And how you always liked it when I made you tea.
Or the time you said I could have candy if I washed your car,
And instead of candy, you gave me a Slimfast bar.
I remember how you asked for your cricket scores every day,
Even when none of the teams had a game to play.
Or how every morning you had to shave for at least an hour,
Or until grandma yelled at you to get into the shower.
But the thing I remember the most about my short time with you,
Was how you said "The end" and a new page was turned.
As this chapter ends, a new page turns.

Shivam Patel, Grade 6
Desoto Central School, MS

My Dream

I dreamed I danced with fairies, with magical wands and wings,
I dreamed I walked over glassy water, lit up by the glittering moon.

I dreamed I climbed a rainbow, the magnificent colors and all,
I dreamed I flew with eagles, soaring through the puffy white clouds.

I dreamed I swam with dolphins, leaping and diving through,
I dreamed I explored an ancient land, with fossils and dusty stones.

I dreamed I ran like a unicorn, ripping my legs through the air,
I dreamed I was a prosperous queen, with the throne of a gorgeous land.

I dreamed I was a rich captain, sailing through the deep sea,
I dreamed all these miraculous things actually happened to me.

Brooke E. Hasl, Grade 5
Goshen Elementary School at Hillcrest, KY

Life

Life is a plane trip, with many decisions, it's all up to you, you control when to end it.
It's you who controls it, it's your own business, whatever you do, and whatever you witness.
You call all the shots, because it's your life just be careful what you do because you live it once not twice.
Follow your heart and believe in yourself, because you can make it from poor to the wealth.
Life might hurt but you can take it, just believe in yourself and you will make it.
Life is too short, for you to just waste it, make something of yourself and get an education.
You might have some problems, but you can fix them.
It's a well-known fact that you live when you live, and you get what you get because of the decisions that you have made.

Maurice Walker, Grade 6
Orange Grove Elementary School, MS

I Am a Military Child

I am a true Southern Belle who was born at Shaw AFB, South Carolina.
I wonder if I will ever join the military and be like my dad.
I hear the guns go off near my house on post, and I imagine it being my dad shooting them.
I see the United Trucks pulling up near my house.
I want my dad to stay home and never leave again.
I am a true Southern Belle who was born at Shaw AFB, South Carolina.

I pretend that Dad puts me in his parachute before he jumps so I can go too.
I feel the excitement when we know my dad is coming home.
I touch my mom's hand when the National Anthem is played and think about my freedom.
I worry not knowing about when we will move or when my dad will leave for Iraq.
I cry when I think about losing my friends each time we move or when my dad isn't home at night.
I am a true Southern Belle who was born at Shaw AFB, South Carolina.

I understand that my dad works long hours and can't be with us.
I say a prayer each night before I go to sleep to thank God for my freedom and my dad's bravery.
I dream that everyone will come home safe from Iraq and Afghanistan and everyone will be happy.
I try to understand the job my dad does and respect the country which we live in.
I hope that the war ends in peace and that each and every country can work together.
I am a true Southern Belle who was born at Shaw AFB, South Carolina.

Sierra Coker, Grade 5
Walker Intermediate School, KY

Colors

Brown, Green, Red, Blue and other colors do not like each other.
"I'm special, you're not." the colors say to one another.
But one color, a loving nice color, said one day,
"Stop, you must learn to work together."
"What?" they all questioned looking at one another,
"If you work together, you all will be important."
Then they all worked together and thanked the loving, nice color who showed them the way.

Lori-Ann Kesten, Grade 4
Moyock Elementary School, NC

On the Mountain

As I sit under the mountain I thought I felt rain drops
but it was my mother's tears as she sits above me on the mountain
thinking of the mother she once had and all of the good times they had once shared
she was here one day then in a blink of an eye she was gone
even now I have never seen her but I feel like I've known her my entire life from the stories I've heard
as I sit and think of her rain drops have started showering down now
when I die I hope I get to be with my grandma and get to know her a little bit better.

Jessee Guthrie, Grade 6
Edmonton Elementary School, KY

Penguins

Penguins are awesome.
Penguins are very cuddly.
I really like them.
Brandon Franks, Grade 5
Shirley Elementary School, AR

My Garden

Blooming dusty roses,
Sprouting fresh and new,
Sweet aroma of vivid flowers,
Filling my nose with such delight,
Lovely colors clashing and blending,
Spring is time for fresh new starts,
Summer is time for growing,
Fall is time for harvesting many crops,
Winter is time for sad good-byes,
My garden of many colors.
Preston Thomas Parrish, Grade 6
Alvaton Elementary School, KY

Watches

Watches make a tick, tick, tick.
This lets me know when time goes by.
But…
If the battery is dead, dead, dead
Then we'll be late and not know why.
Nicholas Freeland, Grade 4
Claiborne Christian School, LA

I Am A…

I am a rifle.
My owner holds me firm.
He pulls the trigger,
and I am fired.
The bullet flies through the air,
and hits a deer.
My owner climbs down the deer stand
and tries to find the deer.
We find the deer.
It is a ten point buck.
He is happy that he got a big buck.
I am put away and will be
used again when the time comes.
Derek Unterreiner, Grade 6
St Vincent Elementary School, MO

Day/Night

Day
warm, shining
playing, running, scattering
sun, light, moon, stars
sleeping, meowing, snoring
cold, dark
Night
Samantha Lindsay, Grade 4
Cleveland Elementary School, OK

I'm a Monster

I am a Beast
I am strong
I am a gigantic monster
I am a horrible nightmare
I am your largest fright
I am a mean machine
I am a big monster
I am a disaster
I am determined
I am a Gigantic Horrible Monster
I am a big mean fighting machine
I will destroy you
I am unstoppable
I am a skyscraper
YOU MIGHT NOT KNOW BUT
I'M HERE
I am a tornado
Jessica Franklin, Grade 5
Pembroke Elementary School, NC

War

W ater torpedoes
A tom bombs
R ockets
Colton Moore, Grade 6
Clarksburg School, TN

A Hawaiian Luau

I'm ten now! Watching
The hula dancers, a flower in
My hair. The sunset is
Perfect. I'm having so much fun!

Eating food from all over
The world is so cool! Dessert,
The best part. The words
"Happy Birthday" are
Written in chocolate on my plate.

I even have something to
Remember it by. I have a
Great picture with my family
In front of the Maui sunset.
Caila Yates, Grade 6
Beck Academy, SC

Veteran

V icious soldiers who are
E quipped
T o fight
E very day of their lives
R unning to
A ttack other enemies
N ever going to stop for our country
Sierra Henry, Grade 4
Cherokee Elementary School, AR

Softball

S oftball is fun
O uts we make
F ielding the ball
T he friends you make
B ase hits
A ll about team work
L earning new things
L ove this sport!
Kelsi Stanford, Grade 4
Brilliant Elementary School, AL

Halloween Night

One Halloween night
The ghost and goblins
Came out for a fright!

The underground drool
Came to fool.

I found a goblin
And his name was Evan.

When the sun comes up
The ghost, goblins, and drools
Go in until next Halloween night.
Marcus Barnett, Grade 5
Etowah Elementary School, NC

Dirtbike

Racing, trailbike, big
Motor, shocks, gas, clutch, pads, black
Brakes, kick start, oil, wheels
Devin Goble, Grade 4
East Jones Elementary School, MS

Sleep Over

Go to friend's house
spend the night
have lots of fun
Have pillow fights
put makeup on
play dress up
stay up all night
Most times spend
too much time together and
get into big fights
Sometimes don't
This was one of those sometimes
We had a great time
hours went by
had to say good bye
mom said maybe next weekend
At least I got to go home to a loving,
peaceful family.
Lauren Cati Pence, Grade 4
Alvaton Elementary School, KY

The Team
A flaming martial artist wrist burning bright
seeking foes to fight
he is fared by friend and foe alike
great in the arena and contest to a fighting and fire type
and is very kind to his trainer and him race across the land
together they make the team of Tom and blazeken
Daughtry Wright, Grade 6
Brogden Middle School, NC

My Favorite Place
The place I go to ease my soul
The place I go to plan my goals
The place to filter all my thoughts
The place to keep all I was taught
When I need to visit my magical place
I close my eyes and let my mind race
For my place isn't somewhere you can physically go
It is somewhere special that everyone knows
Somewhere I go anytime of day
Somewhere where my thoughts are mine to put away
My place lets all my feelings take part
For my favorite place is my heart
Megan Wemyss, Grade 6
River Trail Middle School, GA

Autumn Leaves
Autumn leaves are like snowflakes falling down,
like a ball falling down,
like raindrops watering the plants.
They fall from the tree
landing safely.
Akshay Desai, Grade 4
First Wesleyan Christian School, NC

Reflections on Black and White Things
jet,
a silhouette, at night
ebony
the blind one's sight

pearl,
the snow, a blinding blur
ivory
coats of mink fur

crow,
a Bengal tiger's stripes
a horse's mane
the black of night

dove,
a snowy owl's plumes
white butterflies
the sand on dunes
Jessie Drannon, Grade 6
Charleston County School of the Arts, SC

Can You Guess Where I'm From?
I am from the Bluegrass state…
Where thoroughbreds roam across the pasture,
Where the never-ending cornfields s-p-r-e-a-d
To be BIGGER and BIGGER.

I am from the place where every year in May
The special derby is held in Louisville on a Saturday,
Where the prettiest countrysides are located,
Where the greenest of muddy swamps are,
And where the homes of coal miners rest in the mountains.

Yes, Kentucky is where I'm from.
Harley Poynter, Grade 5
Burgin Independent School, KY

The Place I Belong
The golden waxed floor
And the rather high hoop
The clock ticking just waiting to buzz
Pumped up players ready to run
And the glistening sweat of the hardworking point guard

Popcorn and cokes in the mouths of the viewers
Cool blue Gatorade filling my taste buds
Children playing, playing tag, popcorn in hand
Screaming, kicking, yelling, and crying fills this open gym

I feel like I belong here yet I don't know why
This court is like a kiss it just feels right and nice
The way I feel makes me wander
Why I go to any other place
Madison Preece, Grade 6
College View Middle School, KY

Green
Green looks like the greenest grass nature has made.
Green feels like a caterpillar crawling on my hand.
Green tastes like a fresh picked apple.
Green smells like a sassafras tree.
Green sounds like tree leaves rustling on a breezy day.
Green is the color of all the wonderful seasons.
Kimberley Beeson, Grade 5
Geggie Elementary School, MO

Farm Life
Life on the farm is never boring
Work constantly needing to be done
Up early in the morning, bed late at night
Milk the cow, feed the pigs, fix the fence
Plow the field, swath the hay, work, work, work
If your day was easy just wait till tomorrow
Something will happen to ruin your routine
Farm life is an adventure only few can handle.
Amber Kupka, Grade 5
Canute Elementary School, OK

Winter's Joy

Winter's spreading cheer
steaming cocoa everywhere
presents here and there

Marisa Campos, Grade 6
Tomlinson Jr High School, OK

Tollbooth

I see the tollbooth
The tollbooth sees me
The tollbooth wants my money
No siree
One dollar every day
I don't see why to pay
So just skip the toll road
And go on with your day
First it was a quarter
Then it came to fifty cents
Then it rose to seventy-five
Now it's at its peak
One dollar every day
Oh dear, I can't go on this way
So here's some good advice
Keep that dollar in your pocket
Oh, that feels so nice.

Margaret Louise Taylor, Grade 5
Shannon Forest Christian School, SC

Boo!

Boo!
the wind rustles,
the trees blow.
The spells churn,
The clock turns.
It strikes midnight.
I scream with a fright.
Bones rattle, werewolves howl,
Witches laugh over the cauldron.
Zombies grow, bats fly.
Can you hear the children cry?
I've never seen such a sight,
Until this very Halloween night.

Kelly Welker, Grade 6
St Vincent Elementary School, MO

Bunnies Make Me Laugh

I love bunnies,
Yes I do!
I love bunnies,
How 'bout you?
When they hop around,
I fall on the ground!
It is me that they tickle,
And then I giggle!
Bunnies make me laugh!

Mary Cazalot, Grade 6
St Cecilia School, LA

Thank You for Helping Our Country

I love being in America.
Black birds are flying
around the big oak tree.
It is very windy and sometimes cold.
The orange, yellow and red leaves are falling out of the pretty trees.
Beautiful dogs are playing in the yard.
My brother is playing basketball
in the backyard.
In church I am reading
a holy book and
learning about God.
At night the stars whine very bright.
Butterflies are flying
around in the yard.
Thank you for helping our country.

Malcolm Jones, Grade 6
Leonville Elementary School, LA

I Am From

I am from going to Herrington Lake on weekends
For swimming and tubing.

I am from playing with and training my dog, Angel,
Being entertained by my cats: Stormy, Cupcake, and Red:
And finger-training my parakeet, Katara, with Mom's help.

I am from typing stories on cold, rainy days
To drawing pictures for them.

I am from playing basketball with Dad in our driveway
And going to Burgin Elementary School.

I am from talking to friends (like Cheyanna, Callie, Alyssa, Jake, and Savannah)
And making new friends on vacations (like Courtni and Sarah from Tennessee).

I am from playing computer games,
Fighting with my brother, Chris,
And baking cookies and cakes with Mom.

That is where I am from.

Lauren Ferguson, Grade 5
Burgin Independent School, KY

Carolina Blue

Carolina Blue looks like the uniform as they swish around the court.
Carolina Blue sounds like fans cheering and jumping up and down on the benches.
Carolina Blue smells like the breeze off the players as they go by the crowds.
Carolina Blue tastes like the raspberry slushy at the concession stand.
Carolina Blue feels like the warm blanket as I sit it on my lap.
Carolina Blue is the color of the light blue sky.
Carolina Blue is the sound of people munching on the food from the concession stand.
Carolina Blue is the smell of sweat rolling down the face of the players.
Carolina Blue is the taste of the ice cold drink at the game.
Carolina Blue is the feel of sadness of the crowd after we lost the game.

Brandi Campbell, Grade 5
Cool Spring Elementary School, NC

The Ocean Blue

Crashing waves making
Mist, rocky shores, transparent
Water deep and blue

Mary Davis Barber, Grade 4
Briarwood Christian Elementary School, AL

My Grandpa

My grandpa died oh, yes, he did.
I guess you can't really have people for as long as you wish.
I'm really sad, you want to know why?
It's because I never really got to see him.
Now and then I see him, but only in my dreams.
I was only in my mom's stomach when my grandpa died.
He died two weeks before I was born.
I guess it's really hard to let go of your loved ones.
My sister always says that I'm bad luck.
My grandpa died because of a heart attack.

Luisa Muñoz, Grade 4
Lula Elementary School, GA

Me

Justin
Child of Jimmy and Kathey Duncan
Sibling of no one
Love pool
Love to skate
Love fishing
Who is loved by aunts, uncles, mom, dad
Who wished to be the best pool player
Who dreams of being the best skater
Who wants to catch the biggest striper in the world
Who wonders when I die
Who fears nothing
Who needs a pool table
Who likes snakes
Who believes I'm a pool shark
Who loves God
Who plans on going to heaven
Who would like to see God
Whose destination is heaven
Duncan

Justin Duncan, Grade 4
Tamassee-Salem Elementary School, SC

Christmas

It's Christmas! It's Christmas! I look at the tree,
But all that I see just surprises me.
500,000 presents galore,
I wonder if there are any more.
I seek, I search, I look high and low,
I even look under the big old bow.
But for when I open one out shoots a stream,
I then wake up and it's only a dream!

Dominic Indelicato, Grade 4
Wohlwend Elementary School, MO

Blue

Blue looks like a flowing stream of water
Blue feels like a blanket of dark blue sky
Blue tastes like a fresh blueberry in a nice cold smoothie
Blue smells like a flower under a light blue sky
Blue sounds like a bundle of bluebirds singing a peaceful song
Blue is the color that begins my world

Lauren Stacks, Grade 5
Geggie Elementary School, MO

The Author and Best Friend

The pen sat on the desk
Waiting to be used
And a paper
Not yet written on
It will just set there
'Til dawn
He came home
He had a story waiting to be told
The pen on the table ready for him to hold
He wrote a story about a man so brave and bold
Then it was night and getting cold
He leaves, it sets there 'til morn.
The next day a brand new book was born.
He became famous and lived happy all his life.
And so did his lovely wife
Until she fell; it caused her death
Just the thought made him feel ill
At the funeral he just stood still
He finally learned to love again
And now he's my father and my best friend.

Gabrielle Flanagan, Grade 6
Pleasants County Middle School, WV

Christian

Laughing, playing, having fun
Those are the things you do with your son!
Baseball, soccer, sports in all
Just watching your son grow so tall.
There he is that baby boy.
God made him and he brought you so much joy!
You vow to always love him so.
Placed in the cradle out the door you tiptoe.
Days passed to months first birthday on the way
Then one morning the excitement fades away.
The beat of that heart you greatly loved to hear.
Now it was gone and it brought a tear.
At the grave you pray down low.
You know Heaven is the place he'll go.
You remember that sad day,
He unexpectedly passed away.
Then in four years there came a smile,
God blessed you with a lovely child.
Throughout the sorrow and all the pain
He was the loss but she was the gain.

Brenna Coyle, Grade 4
Sequoyah Elementary School, TN

Wind

Listen
All hear the wind
Colored leaves falling down
Floating and heading toward wet ground
Blowing

Autumn Melby, Grade 5
Broadway Elementary School, NC

The Ball

I bought a ball.
When it became fall,
I decided to throw the ball
with my brother.
The ball hit me in the head,
and I didn't wake up
'til the summer.

Derek Spicer, Grade 5
Midway Covenant Christian School, GA

Veteran

V ery grateful to those people
E ntertaining to hear stories of them
T aking care and protecting us you do
E xciting to see you
R eturn safe protectors
A ll together you are strong
N ow we love you warriors

Dasha Artsykhovska, Grade 4
Cherokee Elementary School, AR

Drop Zone

My heart is pounding.
I was feeling faint,
as I stood in line for the Drop Zone.

Finally our turn came.
Taking off my shoes,
I scurried over and buckled up.
Soon we started climbing
the 160 ft tower.

Up and up I went.

Finally we were at the top.
Sitting there waiting, then suddenly we
DROPPED!
It felt like I was riding a tornado
going 100 miles an hour.

It slowed down.
Relieved.
My heart was in my throat.
My legs were like jelly as I got off.
I am never riding the Drop Zone again.

Cassidy Dale, Grade 5
Etowah Elementary School, NC

Not Gone

I am not gone
Though it seems that I am.
I have moved on
Nothing will end.

I am not gone.
I am in your heart,
Your mind, your soul.
I am not gone.

I will never leave you alone.
I will never leave you depressed.
I cannot leave.
I hope you believe that I am not gone.

And someday you'll come
And join me above,
So we will be together
Forever and ever
For now, I am not gone.

Alexandra Brown, Grade 5
Lead Mine Elementary School, NC

Holidays

Thanksgiving
Colorful, chilly
Greeting, cooking, eating
Feast, holiday, birthday, celebration
Snuggling, caroling, wrapping
Snowy, jolly
Christmas

Melanie Hayduk, Grade 5
Sycamore Elementary School, GA

My Loving Dog

My dog is so fury.
But when he goes outdoors,
He gets cold!
He shakes and shivers.
We put his sweater on.
Then he is warm and cozy.
This is my loving dog in the winter.

Logan Hall, Grade 5
Paint Lick Elementary School, KY

My Dog

We have a new dog
His name is Zoot
You would like him
He's fuzzy and cute
His tail is like a ball,
His hair is like a noodle.
Yep, you guessed it,
Zoot is a poodle.

Courtney Reed, Grade 5
Graham Elementary School, AL

I Am Santa

I am Santa
I wonder who is good or bad
I hear sleigh bells
I see kids making me lists
I want to make kids happy
I am Santa

I pretend I am an elf sometimes
I feel joyful
I touch my sleigh
I worry kids don't believe in me
I cry when my sleigh breaks
I am Santa

I understand what kids want
I say "Ho Ho Ho"
I dream kids always believe in me
I hope I will be ready to get in my suit
I try not to eat too many cookies
I am Santa

Roger Hall Thomas, Grade 4
Wohlwend Elementary School, MO

Here Comes Autumn

I like autumn for several reasons,
It's very cold in autumn and it's
beautiful too.
I like it because my sister and I
always rake up the leaves and then
jump in them.
The leaves look like colorful
frosted flakes.
I always have liked how the trees
get bare.
I also like the way the leaves spin
down from the trees.
It looks like a ballerina falling
from a high tree.
The best thing about autumn is the
cool colorful leaves.
I like them because, they're not just
plain old green.

Justina Roberts, Grade 4
Washington Lands School, WV

Love

Love is special
Love is sweet,
Everyone loves
Everyone hates,
People are lovely
People are sweet
So please love
But, never HATE!

Erica Taylor, Grade 4
East Marion Elementary School, MS

Dolphins

Dolphins leap out of the water,
Like a tiger jumping for its prey.
Then landing with a crash,
Disappearing into the sea
Like a shooting star dancing across the sky.
Finally speeding up towards the clouds like a rocket
They come from the water until the fun fades away,
And the dolphins
Are Deep
Deep
Out
Of
Sight.

Drew Nelson, Grade 4
Crestwood Elementary School, KY

The Way We Are

We are extraordinary in every way,
some big, small we're just made this way.
We're black we're white, we're mixed and yellow.
If you don't want to be judged, don't be judgmental.

Like the saying goes don't judge a book by its cover.

Carolan Charles, Grade 5
Parker Road Elementary School, MO

The Bass

Pulling back,
Casting plump the bait falls into the water,
Starting to reel in slowly,
My fishing pole tugging,
Jerking back my pole,
Reeling in as a fast horse galloping,
Seeing a fin pop out of the water,
Being so happy I'm fishing for my first time and got a fish,
Never forgetting that day!

Jalen Manor, Grade 4
Goshen Elementary School at Hillcrest, KY

Todd

He's a little boy that loves to run.
Even when he's punished, he always has some fun.
He's sweet, he's crazy
Please never call him lazy
He always acts like a spoiled brat
My little Todd is my brother cat.

Cheyenne Nicole Winstead, Grade 5
Contentnea Elementary School, NC

The Pies

Twelve redberry pies came falling from heaven,
When they landed I only saw seven,
The other ones hit my head,
Now my neck is red.

Michael Nabil Azar, Grade 5
Our Lady of Fatima School, MS

A Prayer for Michelle

In the late afternoon sun, I heard
My brother praying in the woods saying
DEAR my Lord I pray for my sister Michelle
I don't want her to die because of pneumonia
Nor my mom because she had cancer.
Give them strength and courage
To go through day and night.
AMEN.

Michelle Brooksher, Grade 6
Temple Hill Elementary School, KY

Are You Talking

One man said are you talking,
I said I'm walking and talking,
The man said you're talking but the dog is still barking.
The man was walking and I was talking.

Jacques Arnaud, Grade 5
Arnaudville Elementary School, LA

I Am

I am somebody who will make it in life.
I am a man who will take care of his children and wife.
I am a doctor, lawyer, and fireman.
I am the minister who lends a helping hand.
I am the chief of police who chase thieves.
I am the one who prays and believes.

I am a leader, teacher, and guide.
I am a successful black man with pride.
I am proud of myself and who I have become.
I am creative and I know where I came from.

So when people look at you in doubt.
Say, "I am!" with a confident shout.

Calvin Payne, Grade 6
Danforth Intermediate Academy, MO

That Awesome Beach

Watch the waves there, there…
HUMUNGUS!!!!!'
Hey I know what what we can do!
go walking on the beach!,
LOOK OUT!!!!
It's, it's, it's
a jelly fish!
Hey I'll go jump off these huge sandunes while ya watch O.K.!!
DASHING, LEAPING, JUMPING, SPLASHING
Then I jump one last time…
GERONIMO!!!
Jumping an amazing jump
yelling while swishing in the wind
then crushing a shell into threes!!!
I love the beach!

Luke Ross, Grade 4
Alvaton Elementary School, KY

Blue

Blue looks like the dark, deep blue sky at night when you fall asleep.
Blue feels like water splashing against my face on a hot summer day.
Blue tastes like a soft, delicious, squishy blueberry in my mouth.
Blue smells like a steamy blueberry pie baking in the oven on a cold winter day.
Blue sounds like the cold ocean waves crashing against a sandy beach on a hot summer day.
Blue is the color of the world!

Bailey Turnbo, Grade 5
Geggie Elementary School, MO

Ode to Autumn

Autumn is here, but Santa is not. The leaves are falling, but presents are not. Hot cocoa fills the air, but eggnog does not. Autumn is here, but Santa is not. Autumn is here, but Santa is not. People are in their cars below the cool air overhead. In autumn the kids play outside while reindeer fly up and down till Christmas comes around. Autumn is here, but Santa is not.

Austin Heinz, Grade 5
Palmetto Christian Academy, SC

Dinner Tonight?

I walked into the kitchen, and guess what I said? "What's for dinner tonight Mom, please don't tell me it's that filthy slug beef and that old Aunt Jackie's bug bread?"

"Why no dear," she exclaimed with glee, "Just another bubble rubble dubble tubble bubble stew with some choco-jone black brew." I walked away in disgust and sat at the table and thought, why purple tomatoes with okra slime? Why oh why do we always have to eat foods that rhyme.

I sat down to eat, to see what was good, and asked my mean sister to pass the big, big, bowl. I then opened it and what did I see a beautiful bowl of plain potato salad looking at me. I looked at my mom and smiled with glee. I was then proud to see, a regular ordinary dinner looking at me.

Ivannah Campbell, Grade 5
Quail Run Elementary School, GA

I See...

I see the shiny, clear pool with a fence guarding it, watching every move I make
I hear the chirps of black birds blending in with the shadows of the tall wavy tree
Swoosh
I smell burgers on the grill and the smell of the lawn mower gas which makes my nose
Dance
I taste the juicy burgers on the soft brown buns
I feel the wet grass with the ants and other crawlers hiding in it

Landon Hopf, Grade 5
Bonaire Elementary School, GA

If I Were in Charge of the World!!!

If I were in charge of the world, nobody would wake me up on Christmas,
I would get a new outfit, shoes and purse once a week, and my room would be BIG.

If I were in charge of the world NONE would be bullied,
The whole school could watch me play Volleyball, We could do everything by the bell,
and I could spend 2 days a week in high school with my cousin.

If I were in charge of the world everything would be $1 with no taxes.
Nobody would have bad credit, NONE would do drugs, there would be no car wrecks
and there would be NO kidnapping.

If I were in charge of the world there would be a huge pool for Middle and High school,
NOBODY would starve, everybody would get along, and there would be NO problems at all.
If I were in charge of the world.

Chelsea Wright, Grade 6
Eminence Middle School, KY

What Is Love on Christmas?

What is love on Christmas?
It is when the love is spread because families
get together and open presents.

What is love on Christmas?
It is celebrating Jesus' birthday and why He
died on the cross.

What is love on Christmas?
It means giving and supporting others who don't
have much.

What is love on Christmas?
It is helping my family to get together and
celebrating Christmas with them.

Sheldon Graham, Grade 6
St Mark Elementary School, SC

Midnight Sky

Stars are vivid now
the moon glistens very bright
it is morning now

Forrest Dreher, Grade 4
Briarwood Christian Elementary School, AL

Feelings Are...

F eelings are compassion.
E veryone has them.
E ach one is different.
L ike invisible magic things.
I n your head.
N ice little thoughts.
G reat things.
S ad things.

A n ugly thing.
R esting.
E veryone has to have feelings.

Feelings Are...

Painful, sad, happy, great, magical, ignorant, nice, mean,
nerve wrecking, but mostly they are you.

Tyler Chu, Grade 5
Parker Road Elementary School, MO

Be Free

I love the world, its beauty and all.
Its wonderful meadows and its pretty falls.
My family is special, my friends are great,
my pets are cute, I have no reason to complain.
I love my life. It has been so good to me,
but I love my rights that let me be free.

Cecelia Mizelle, Grade 4
St Thomas More School, NC

Football and Gymnastics

Football
tough, disciplined
tackling, passing, running
brotherhood, class, leotards, balance beams
flipping, tumbling, jumping
flexible, strong
Gymnastics

Connor Smith, Grade 5
Briarwood Christian Elementary School, AL

If You Would Like To

If you would like to
come sit in my shade
to cool yourself
from the hot sun,
that would be okay.

If you would like to
come climb my branches
and swing on my limbs,
that would be okay.

If you would like to
gather my twigs
to use for your fire,
to keep you warm
on cold winter nights,
that would be okay.

For I am the oak tree
and I can help you in many ways.
But only if you would like me to.

Louisa Hopkins, Grade 6
Charleston County School of the Arts, SC

The Great War

There is a cry in the wind,
And then the war does begin.
The cries on the battlefield are so loud,
All you can hear are the soldier's shouts.

When the war is over there is relief.
Another war will come the townspeople believe.
I guess the town will be safe.
So they will have good mornings when they awake.

Seth Hendon, Grade 4
Stephens Elementary School, AL

Thanksgiving

eating a big turkey with all the trimmings
having family and friends over eating at the table
the laughter of family
the first cut of the turkey
thanksgiving

Cody Bishop, Grade 6
Guntown Middle School, MS

My Favorite Ornament

B efore I was born
A n ornament for me
B ecause my family loved me
Y ou see

I t is so beautiful
N one can compare

A vision of Jesus for

M ankind everywhere
A little part of my heart
N ow hangs on our tree
G od gave His Son
E ternal life for me
R eminds me I'm part of God's family

Morgan Coley, Grade 6
North Iredell Middle School, NC

Dogs

Dogs spotted big ears
Small, big, fast, slow, tall, short, fat
Droopy ears short legs.

Ross Balkman, Grade 5
Shirley Elementary School, AR

Butterfly

With eyes on your wings
Oh, butterfly beautiful
You have pretty wings

Ethan Hodge, Grade 4
East Jones Elementary School, MS

My Dog

My dog Buddy he is man's best friend
His fur as white as snow
His nose is pug and black
He loves to run and to play sometimes
He forgets to come back
He is a great listener but can't talk
Bud my man he loves the mud
The more he can roll and jump
The more the fun

Dylan Montgomery, Grade 5
Zalma Elementary School, MO

Christmas

Christmas
Glowing lights
Candy cane candle
Bells and Christmas carols
Cheese balls and Christmas cookies
Feeling and ripping Christmas presents
Christmas

Miranda Justus, Grade 4
Tamassee-Salem Elementary School, SC

The Owl and the Mouse

The owl flew from
Tree to tree
In search of a mouse
to fill its belly
The mouse scampered from
Root to root
In the forest to find a home
for the winter's snow
The owl heard the mouse,
The mouse heard the owl…
Down went the owl
Swooping, swaying, plummeting
To the ground
Trying to catch the mouse to
Fill its belly
Fast went the mouse
Running, sprinting, scared
Like a small, brown,
Furry rocket
Now looking for a
Hiding place

Hannah Ellis, Grade 6
Eminence Middle School, KY

The Mix Up

"Hello, hello, how are you today."
"What? What did you say?"
"Did you say that it is Monday?"
"Oh I'm sorry I thought it was Friday."
"There must of been a mix up."
"Awh man I have to wake up."

Jamie McLeary, Grade 5
Zalma Elementary School, MO

Football

I would be a running back,
And kill them with my speed,
Just like Edgerrin James,
But I know that will never be.

I would like to be a quarterback,
So everyone could see me,
Just like Peyton Manning,
But I know that will never be.

I would like to be a wide receiver,
And look like the lion king,
Just like Michael Ivirin,
But I know that will never be.

I would like to be a defensive end,
And sack me two or three,
Just like the great Reggie White,
But I know that will never be.

Jacolby Darr, Grade 5
Providence Academy, TN

Tigers

Tigers are peaceful
They fill my heart with such joy
They're gorgeous to me

Devan Vernold, Grade 5
Sycamore Elementary School, GA

James' Lame Name

There once was a kid named James
Everyone hated his name
They threw him at the walls
Tripped him in the halls
Nobody likes James
But one day something changed
James changed his name to fame
The school went wild
They talked to him for a while
Now everyone loves James
Because of his new name

Devin Delcambre, Grade 6
St Cecilia School, LA

Veteran

V ery brave and courageous
E xcellent soldiers are
T rained to fight
E ager to help us. They are
R unning from the enemies
A merican soldiers are
N ever going to give up.

Brina Rae Welch, Grade 4
Cherokee Elementary School, AR

Books

Some books are really great.
Some books I really hate.

Most of the books I read are cool.
Some books help out in school.

Robin Hood is one to read.
I think that book is a need.

Now my poem's almost done,
Read a book and have some fun!

Mark O'Neal, Grade 6
Community Christian School, NC

War

War is red
It tastes like rotten meat and sour milk
It sounds like nuclear bombs exploding
It smells like gun powder blasting
It looks like blood
It makes me fill with fear

Austin Abshure, Grade 4
Cleveland Elementary School, OK

I Am a Military Brat

I am a Military Brat supportive of my dad.
I wonder if he will go to Iraq.
I hear my heart pounding fast.
I see him coming home soon.
I want my mom to be happy.
I am a Military Brat supportive of my dad.

I pretend that he is still here.
I feel the hugs he gives me.
I touch the picture of him every day.
I worry that he won't come home for a very long time.
I cry when he leaves.
I am a Military Brat supportive of my dad.

I understand when he says he has to go.
I say good-bye to him.
I dream he is coming home very soon.
I try not to cry in my room.
I hope he comes home soon.
I am a Military Brat supportive of my dad.

Victoria Weiser, Grade 6
Walker Intermediate School, KY

I, Chocolate

I smile, beaming at you.
I'll make you happy when you're blue.
For a few pennies I'll fill you with happiness.
I'll light your eyes with joy and bliss.
I can bring sunshine on the gloomiest days.
No matter how sad you are, I have my ways.
I jump for joy when you reach for my bowl,
I'll warm your insides and refresh your soul.
Hidden in my wrapper lies a wonderful treasure,
Designed to bring you untold pleasure.
Priceless moments I can give,
Adding new highs to the life you live.

Arush Lal, Grade 6
River Trail Middle School, GA

Fall

Colorful leaves falling down,
Red, orange, and brown covering the ground.
Cool and windy weather filling the air,
But some people don't even care.

I look around
There isn't even a sound
But the leaves crushing beneath my feet,
And the wind rushing through the trees.

This proves to me that God is great,
The seasons change and are never late.
He paints each tree with love and care,
He shows His goodness everywhere.

Kyndal Ellzey, Grade 4
Evangelical Christian School, TN

The Ocean Waves

Waves roaring about
Splashing against the hard rock
Very calm and still

Eliza Graham, Grade 4
Briarwood Christian Elementary School, AL

Firework Show

The Firework Show is a show you can't miss
From the bottom of my heart you'll want to see this
They fly and show in the sky
This is a sight you can't deny

Fireworks, fly, fireworks pop
I'll guarantee you, you won't want it to stop
It shows in designs, and flies so far
If you look close, it looks like a star

It's the Fourth of July, fireworks fly
You won't be scared, but you won't be shy
I like to see fireworks, I like to see them glow
But all it is, is just a show

Tyrelle Broadwater, Grade 6
St Mark Elementary School, SC

Easter

Easter is the time for bunnies to hop
And the time for Parents to shop
We play soccer while my mother is a big talker
Parents buy candy and tuck it away
While children get it all through the way
They get what they get wherever they go
They follow the way that gets them the most
All through the day they do all sorts of things
Like run and scream the whole day
And that's what happens on Easter day

Aaruran Chandrasekhar, Grade 5
St Michael Parish School, WV

Black

Black is beauty as beauty can be,
Black is charcoal, metallic, ebony,
Midnight's the night that will come and the day that'll fade,
Or it can be anger and hate,
Pitch is the feeling of scales on my snake,
Black is the hisses of my angry black cat,
Jet is the feeling of a velvet tall hat,
Black is oil leaking out of a car, bloop, bloop, bloop,
Black is the smell of sticky gross tar,
Crow is like tires screeching in my ear,
Black is the color of startling fear,
Black is the taste of power and might,
Black is a very unusual sight,
BLACK

Alicia Hope, Grade 6
Alvaton Elementary School, KY

Lollipops
I like lollipops,
They're nothing like soda pops.

They're so sticky,
They'll make you icky.

I hate soda pops,
But I love LOLLIPOPS!
Kaitlyn Thomas, Grade 4
West Elementary School, MO

Chickens
Chickens, so soft, so sweet,
Always hungry!

Chickens, roosters, hens,
I love them all,
But always hungry!

Chickens, I have three.
They're always soft and always sweet.
Chickens, always hungry!
Clay Jacks, Grade 4
Hayes Elementary School, OK

Outsiders
They are unique,
but why, I'm not sure
for it's all a big blur.
The farther it goes on and on,
the more it's unclear,
for I just don't know
what makes them unique.
Ryan Powers, Grade 5
Immanuel Lutheran School, MO

Books
Potion for the heart
Medicine for the brain
Open – give it a start
Promises to entertain
Prescription runs low
Want to stay merry
Tells you where to go
Refill at the library
Brandi Hongell, Grade 4
Krebs Elementary School, OK

Cats
Cats are white
black and even colorblind
but cats die just like people.
But they are furry and cuddle
so enjoy your cat before it dies.
Maverick Anderson, Grade 6
Dyer Elementary & Jr High School, TN

Christmas Is…
C elebrating with your family
H anging colorful stockings above the fireplace
R ipping paper off of your gifts that are piled high under the tree
I cicles hanging from your house
S now days, getting us out of school
T insel on your tree
M istletoe above all of the doorways
A plate of gingerbread men
S inging Christmas carols
T rying to sleep, but too excited
I cy winds bringing down pearly white snow
M erry days bringing lots of presents
E very color imaginable, hung up in trees
Jessica Boyer, Grade 6
Alvaton Elementary School, KY

Waterfalls
The water speeding down like a race car on a track
Underneath is a lake, beside it is a forest of trees.
You could hear millions of frogs in the field, singing their lungs out
Splashed water hits the lake like a ball
hitting the floor like a basketball only to come back up again
The air filled with water, a rainbow of colors around the masterpiece
Crisp leaves falling into the water
The water so cold I was about to freeze into an ice cube
The warm towel hit my skin after a good swim,
Felt like a heavy blanket in a summer day
How I love waterfalls.
Jessica Honadle, Grade 6
College View Middle School, KY

Christmas
C heer and laughter fill the home.
H omes are filled with family and friends.
R eindeer prance through the yard and up to the chimney.
I see Santa coming.
S ounds of presents opening fill the room.
T earing paper, shredding ribbon and sounds of joy.
M ade gifts for mom and dad, make them proud.
A ll of the children have lots of presents.
S eason's over, tree is down, and lights are put up until next year we begin again.
Emily Ledbetter, Grade 4
Stephens Elementary School, AL

911
On September 11th something went bad
Our school got out early when I got home my mom was sad
My mom said a terrorist must have got mad
And my mom was not the only one sad so was my dad

A teacher said to a boy whose dad got killed cheer up lad
My parents set me down, said an airplane hit a big building a lot more than a tad

I hope 911 doesn't become a fad
Harley Moore, Grade 6
Qulin Middle School, MO

Time: Day and Night

Time: It goes so fast,
It flies when it's night,
It goes so fast.
When I wake up in the day it starts again.
Sometimes I wish I could stop time!
I could sleep more in the morning;
Or play longer before bed.
I wait for school to end.
Why does time fly when you're having fun?
Oh, why time doesn't fly when you're bored?
I don't know why!

Matthew Sparks, Grade 5
Paint Lick Elementary School, KY

The Pot

The black soil,
The tiny seed,
The cool water giving birth to a sprout.
The bright green sprout,
To the tiny stalk,
All the time growing into a bud.
As the bud opens slowly,
All that matters then is the flower.
But nobody remembers that the seed would have
No place to put its roots
Without the little red flower pot.

Maggie McKenzie, Grade 4
Atkinson Elementary School, NC

Christmastime

C old and snowy night
H aving a great time with your family
R ed fire warming the whole room
I cy feeling of snow in snowball fights
S melling the heavenly aroma of cookies baking
T rimming the huge tree with sparkling ornaments
M aking holiday cards for relatives
A ll the presents you could ever want
S nowy roof tops where Santa can land

John DeLancey, Grade 5
Sullivan Elementary School, TN

A Thought

A thought, so clean, pristine and clear,
Ringing true for all to hear.
Pure and calm, whole and torn,
Stronger than a gale force storm.
A thought shows the right and wrong,
Echoing louder than a gong.
Shedding light for all to see,
A thought is taller than a tree.
Divine and perfect majesty.
A thought is bigger than a sea.

Justin Brown-Gnarra, Grade 6
Haynes Academy for Advanced Studies, LA

The Little Lost Dog

I once had a little dog
that got lost in the heavy fog.

He was chasing a big green toad frog.
He then came across a wild hog.

The wild hog started chasing my dog.
Then my little dog got stuck in a log
while hiding from the wild hog.

I went out into the heavy fog
to look for my little dog.

Who got chased by a wild hog.
I found him stuck inside a log.

Now my little dog never goes into the heavy fog
for he is afraid he will get chased by a wild hog.

Hunter Norton, Grade 4
Friendship Christian Academy, MS

Riding Skateboards

I like to ride my skateboard
And then I pray to the Lord
That when I do my jumps,
I don't hit any bumps.

Sometimes I go on ramps,
And I could get leg cramps.

I should wear kneepads and a helmet
And I'll be pretty safe.
Then I'll go home
And put my board away.
I'll eat supper
And go to bed.

Ryan Davis, Grade 4
St Mary Cathedral Elementary School, MO

The Flag

I love the flag,
    The great old flag;
To the land I love,
    The grand old flag;

When I see the flag,
    The great old flag;
I put my hand over my heart,
    For respect to the grand old flag;

I love the beautiful flag,
    The high flying flag;
The flag I know,
    Stands for the freedom I show.

Meranda Prince, Grade 4
Heartland High School and Academy, MO

Dingo

Intense eyes you can buy
if you will…
you'll have a high bill,
but you'll always love
your Dingo
Jackie McCall, Grade 5
John Will Elementary School, AL

Beautiful Ocean

As I come near you,
I get so excited.

I feel your waves splash on my feet,
I smell the fishy salt water.

But I have to say goodbye
Every once in a while.

Bye,
Beautiful Ocean.
Shianna Williams, Grade 4
Cool Spring Elementary School, NC

If I Could Build a Snowman

If I could build a snowman,
I'd dress him in bright red.
I'd put socks upon his feet
and a top hat on his head.
I'd put a scarf around his neck
and mittens on his hands.
I'd find a carrot for his nose,
now that would look so grand.
I'd find some nice big buttons
to put upon his chest,
I'd hope the weather would stay cold,
or he would be a mess.
But since I live in the south
where there's never any snow.
My dream will have to stay a dream,
That's all you need to know.
Shiloh Stampley, Grade 5
East Marion Elementary School, MS

Gann

Gann is annoying,
And he never stops destroying.
He is my brother,
But he acts like my mother.
Gann can be astonishing,
But he never quits admonishing.
He thinks he's the best,
But we think he is a pest.
There is no other,
Like my brother.
Mary Fran Wright, Grade 5
Mountain Brook Elementary School, AL

The Earth

Oh, how sweet it feels
Under my feet.

As I walk under the trees,
There's a nice sudden breeze.

Everything is so fresh and clean.
I'm so happy nothing is mean.

For everything to feel so nice and calm,
It truly is a dream.
Tristan Duvall, Grade 5
Arnaudville Elementary School, LA

Bad and Good Day

Once upon a time
There was a boy named
Juan. He had a
Frog in his
Throat he never
Took his eyes off
A girl. Her name
Is Madson W.
She swept Juan
Off his feet.
Juan Mijo Trujillo, Grade 6
Armorel Elementary School, AR

Cars

Cars can go fast
Cars can take you places
Cars are good for driving
Cars have special pieces
Cars have different kinds of gas
Cars can help you learn
Vehicles
Jacob Buchanan, Grade 5
Sullivan Elementary School, TN

Twix

There once was a cat named Twix,
Who did such daring tricks.
She landed on her four feet,
She really wanted her kitty treats,
Oh my, how she licked, licked, licked.
Michael Ledbetter, Grade 5
American Heritage Academy, GA

Cats

Cats
Frisky, playful
Jumping, licking, frolicking,
An animal that cuddles with you.
Kittens
Millie Price, Grade 6
River Trail Middle School, GA

Opera

A wful at singing
B reaks glass
C lapping hands
D ark room
No more opera!
Kendra Lickteig, Grade 5
Trenton Middle School, MO

Basketball

We dribbled down the court
We do drills and try to be a good sport
I like to dribble the ball,
Sometimes I dribble into the wall.
Cassie Poole, Grade 4
Horace Mann Elementary School, OK

Puppy/Dog

Puppy
Cute, smelly
Playing, jumping, sleeping
Funny, playful — running, chasing
Eating, swimming, fighting
Big, prettier
Dog
Jessica McKibben, Grade 5
Trenton Middle School, MO

Autumn Leaves

Autumn leaves are like roller coasters
twisting and turning through the breeze.
Up, then down, then up,
then peacefully to the ground.
Landon Harkey, Grade 4
First Wesleyan Christian School, NC

Snowflakes

Snowflake
Very soft, white,
It's falling from the sky.
On Christmas Day I look outside,
There's snow.
Michelle Teus, Grade 4
Cleveland Elementary School, OK

People

Some people try and try
and some people scream and shout
Some people sleep 'til noon
and some get up and about

Some people talk and talk
and some people dance and prance
Some people eat and eat
and some people never get a chance.
Logan Piper, Grade 6
Central Arkansas Christian School, AR

October

October begins the early fall
And it is when everybody plays ball.

October is when people get candy at night
And on Halloween, we dress up as knights.

October is the third month of school
And we probably won't swim in the pool.

October is when the leaves fall
And it makes the trees look very tall.

October is when it turns cold
And makes us feel frisky and bold.

Turner Shane Butler, Grade 4
Contentnea Elementary School, NC

Dogs

Dogs are so much fun
when you play with them outside
and give them a bone

Baret Steed, Grade 4
Briarwood Christian Elementary School, AL

Red

Red looks like an apple that had just been picked from a tree.
Red feels like hot, fiery flames from a volcano.
Red tastes like a juicy fruit from an extraordinary island.
Red smells like sauce being put on a new delicious pizza.
Red sounds like fall leaves being stepped on into tiny bits.
Red is an awesome color.

Nick Emmenegger, Grade 5
Geggie Elementary School, MO

What Is in My Room

A twin size bed with flower power sheets
Five large buckets of candy
And a sheet of tempos and beats

Four baseball tickets from three months ago
Math and multiplication
And a tourist brochure for a major vacation

A batty headband to scare all of the kids
My Halloween costume
That used to be Great Uncle Sid's

A map of the United States
Especially one of Georgia
And I also have a lot of sketches of all the Golden Gates

I will wrap this up
And guess what?
I have to go clean this big mess up!

Nicole Daniell, Grade 5
American Heritage Academy, GA

The Ocean

The ocean is blue,
It will spray you in the face.
It's beautiful.

Abby Muir, Grade 4
Briarwood Christian Elementary School, AL

My Story

Lamont
Exciting, playful, smart, computer geek
Son of Patrick and Gwendolyn Tompkins
I like pizza, hot wings, and Tabasco hot sauce
I feel happy, mad, and sad
I need new shoes, new clothes, and good reports home
I give toys, games, and love to my little cousin
I fear Domino Harvey, Nemesis, and Jason
I would like to see Young Jac, The Game, and Nelly
Resident of University City
Tompkins

Lamont Tompkins, Grade 5
Nathaniel Hawthorne Elementary School, MO

Sad or Happy

Expressed love fills the air as kisses are adorned
Out the door flows joy that fills the air
Smiles approach as the time has neared
With excitement they strongly pulled me down the stairs
The rest lingered to arrive
Melted cheese fills the air as we walk through the door
Happiness appeared as we sat down to watch
Anger filled the atmosphere as a quarrel broke out
Comfortable and cozy my body felt as I laid down to rest
Laughter fills the room as our eyes are amazed
Sadness spread through as we depart

Mackenzie See, Grade 5
Cline Elementary School, KY

9/11 World Crisis

In the middle of a lazy afternoon,
Little did people know they would be in shock soon.
In the Big Apple there were planes up about,
But one of the planes had a particular route.
With an earsplitting boom it crashed into the tower,
With all of its might and all of its power
People were screaming with panic and fear,
While families at home were crying with tears.
And the plane had left a hole in the tower,
And the building collapsed like a wilting flower.
Then police and firefighters came near and far,
To prove what valiant heroes they are.
They saved many lives and lit out the fires,
And to this today their courage still inspires.
Many people have died and passed away,
Everyone should look back to the sadness of this day.

David Kim, Grade 6
River Trail Middle School, GA

Me

I am a ball player,
I practice my hardest.
I run with all my might,
I volunteer in everything.
I work out,
I am a ball player.
I train,
I do push-ups,
I run laps,
I do sit-ups,
I do jumping jacks.
I am a ball player.
I practice my skills.
I shoot,
I dribble,
I throw,
I tackle.
I am a ball player.

DaVeè Layton, Grade 6
Desoto Central School, MS

Martin Elementary

M artin
A lphabet
R ams
T eachers
I mportant
N ice

E quity
L unch
E very day
M ath
E ducation
N eat
T alented
A ll right
R eading
Y ou'll like it

John Duff, Grade 6
Martin Elementary School, WV

My Brother

My brother,
Man-eating monster,
coming after me.
I run!
Where do I go?
He's right behind me!
I'm trapped!
He asks a question.
What will it be?
He asks,
"Will you be friends with me?"

Kevin Mattingly, Grade 5
St Vincent Elementary School, MO

Men and Women Who Are Fighting for My Freedom

I am proud to be an American,
at least I know I'm free.
I want to thank the men and women who died and gave their lives for us.
When I go to sleep at night I could
hear the gunfire and bullets
hitting the ground.
Looking at the moon and stars,
I always think about you.
I want God to protect
the men and women
who are fighting for my freedom.

Ross Prejean, Grade 6
Leonville Elementary School, LA

Opa

My Opa was a great man,
He lived a long life,
He died on November 4th 2006.

My Opa took my mama and me deer scouting for a place to hunt deer.
I remember one time my Opa took us squirrel hunting,
We never saw a squirrel in those woods!

In his house he had 5 stuffed deer heads,
Mounted on the walls he also had a stuffed turkey in his home office.
I will never forget him I will always love him!

Ciara Plants, Grade 5
Paint Lick Elementary School, KY

The Brightest Hope

In the night sky, I'm a single star.
Watching over Earth as it sleeps.
I would be feeble without the help of others,
To light up the universe with me alone would never be possible.
Working as part of the team instead of alone,
All the praise isn't mine,

But still leave my mark long after I've gone out.
Mother moon our symbol of wisdom,
Gone, far away, to the other side.
All is dim, all hope gone, except for our weaker light which shines on.
But bravery, unity, and hope can be found in the darkest of times,
So we shine on in many formations,
Millions and millions of us,
Stars in the endless heavens.

Christina Hansen, Grade 6
River Trail Middle School, GA

Flowers of Spring

Have you ever known about the unique types of flowers?
Have you ever noticed water lilies flowing with the current?
Have you ever sighted a daisy swaying in the breeze?
Have you ever wanted to smell the sweet smell of a magnolia?
If you have never done any of these things go now before the season ends.

Ashton Wright, Grade 5
Orange Grove Elementary School, MS

My Walk

When I was walking in the park
the sun was glaring at me
like I have let my kite go and hit it
I walked under my favorite tree
it seemed to wrap its branches around me
then I see bees around in a circle chatting
soon the wind howled at me and picked up my hat
I love to go and talk to my pals, sun, tree,
bees and the wind

Holly Burns, Grade 6
Armorel Elementary School, AR

Love

Roses are red.
Violets are blue.
Nothing in the world is as pretty as you.
God must have sent you from heaven above
Because you are so lovely
And so filled with love.

Danzel Bailey, Grade 6
Mount Zion Christian School, SC

Basketball

I love baseball, I love football.
I love basketball most of all.
Basketball season is in the fall.
It's time to get tickets from the mall.
Sometimes the ball crashes in to the wall!
On the court, players are very tall.
"Play #1 play #1," I call.
It's time to play basketball.

Jace Capps, Grade 4
Nesbit Elementary School, GA

Colors

Colors, colors, colors
there's so many
gold, silver, green, and white
but there's only three that support our country
those colors are red, white, and blue
God bless America!

Clemarion Yarborough, Grade 6
Brogden Middle School, NC

Rainbows

R eally beautiful thing
A colorful arch in the sky.
I wish I could find a pot of gold,
N ear the end of the rainbow.
B eware of the Leprechauns, they won't share.
O ne piece of gold I beware.
W ow, I'm at the end of the rainbow.
S oon my dream will come true!

Cara Milyn Channell, Grade 4
Stephens Elementary School, AL

My Best Friend

I got the news he was leaving.
Tears running down my cheeks.
My best friend was going to be leaving
If I didn't buy him.
Forte. Soon to be my horse.
At the barn the very day,
My mom gave the old owners the check.
He has been mine ever since.
We've had good times and bad.
He'll always love me. I'll always love him.
My best friend. He isn't just a sport.
You have to love and care for him.
He has to eat, sleep, and drink a bunch of water.
He has to be worked so he doesn't get fat.
He also has to be well cared for. Groomed.
No rock in the hooves. Stuff like that.
Forte is my best friend 'til death do us part.

Blythe Daniel, Grade 6
Beck Academy, SC

Flowers

F ragrance that smells good.
L oving attention to grow.
O pen and bloom in spring and summer.
W ater to have once they get dry.
E asy to plant in a garden or land mass.
R oses, daisies, and dandelions are my favorite.
S tems, leaves, seeds, and roots are the parts.

Candice Parker, Grade 5
Colerain Elementary School, NC

Pink

Pink looks like a bouquet of beautiful carnations.
Pink feels like a relaxing, soothing bubble bath.
Pink tastes like bundles of cotton candy.
Pink smells like blossoms in full bloom.
Pink sounds like humming birds drinking nectar from a flower.
Pink is an attitude.

Katherine Shelton, Grade 5
Geggie Elementary School, MO

Friends

They're always there for you
To cheer you up they know what to do
They always greet you with a smile
They'll make you happy for quite a while
They're with you during hardships and fun
Your friendship with them is never done
They help you when you're in trouble
They will come on the double
When you're sad and down
They will bring you around
Friends are always true
Again they're always there for you.

Ryann Bryant, Grade 6
Southwestern Middle School, NC

My Last Wishes

I found out some bad news today.
I found out I might die.
I only have a limited time left.
I will live my life to the fullest.
I will go bungee jumping.
I will go skydiving.
In fact, I think I will just start running.
I know, I will go to Hawaii.
No, I will go to Germany.
In fact, I don't need to do these things.
There is just one thing I want to do.
That is to spend the time I have left
with the person I love the most.
That person is my dad.
Yeah, that's all I want to do.

Jacob Whitmore, Grade 6
Kitty Stone Elementary School, AL

Books

Books
Long, good
Interesting, wondering, entering
Story, tale, news, poems
Entertaining, gossiping, writing
Short, fun
Magazine

Jessica Myers, Grade 4
Cleveland Elementary School, OK

The Hurricane

A hurricane is dark blue.
It sounds like crashing buildings.
It tastes like a lot of salt.
It smells like the ocean.
It looks like a wasteland of destruction.
It makes you feel terrified.

Kale Wehmeyer, Grade 6
St Vincent Elementary School, MO

Autumn Is Coming

Autumn is coming
So be hummin'
All those great songs and hymns.
Jump on a limb
Make sure it's not slim;
Or else you'll fall in.

Carving pumpkins, baking pies
Come on! Don't be shy.
Rakin' leaves
From under the trees.
Thanksgiving dinner
Won't make me slimmer.
So I'd better leave out the pie.

Paige Gottesman, Grade 5
Palmetto Christian Academy, SC

Differences

Some people murder and kill
and others help each other.
Some people eat their fill
while others sadly starve together.

Some people live their life
and other people throw it away.
Some people have no wife
and others marry her today.

Michaela Carter, Grade 6
Central Arkansas Christian School, AR

Life Around Me

The brook rushing past me,
I stand upon the majestic mountains;
I spot an eagle, proud and free,
Scanning the horizon;
The sun disappears;
Darkness surrounds my body,
While the serene sounds soothe my soul.

Nicki Lee, Grade 6
St Anne Catholic School, SC

Autumn Leaves

Like snow, autumn leaves are flying,
soaring,
swaying.
Then they tenderly fall to the ground.

Madison Lynch, Grade 4
First Wesleyan Christian School, NC

Ron

My uncle's name is Ron
He has a very nice mom
He has a pet cat
Who likes to sleep on a mat

Brittany Parker, Grade 5
Faith Christian School, SC

Takes and Gives

As I lie there thinking of him
It comes to me as it comes to them
In a dream, he is here with me
In this world he is not
I now know he is gone,
And he is not coming back
This place we call the world
Takes the people dear to us
Just as they took him
But as life goes on
These new people come in
And take a place
But will never replace
What is gone.

Marissa Gutierrez, Grade 6
Pleasants County Middle School, WV

Jesus

Jesus was a kind and gentle man
He never did anything wrong
He wanted the children to come to Him
Believe Him

If you just believe Him
I know you really will
Then you will go to Heaven
Believe Him

Jesus is like a rosebud
Blooming in the spring
He is open to everyone's hearts
Believe Him

Is he not good?
From what you have heard?
He is Jesus!
Believe Him

Abigail Brewer, Grade 5
Providence Academy, TN

Bad Day

The clouds are gray
My friend moved away.
It's a very bad day.
There was no more light
when I got into a fight,
It was a very bad day.
When I finally awoke,
I got a cut from some mutt.
It was a very bad day.
I can't believe my friend hit me,
and his dog bit me.
But, now he's gone
and I have to move on.

Cody Elliott, Grade 5
Franklin Elementary School, OK

Hot/Cold

Hot
Steaming, burning
Chilling, heating, melting
Sun, bubble, ice, water
Freezing, shivering, huffing
Icy, frosty
cold

Maurchel Brown, Grade 5
Sycamore Elementary School, GA

Hope

Hope is like the kudzu plant,
Spreading constantly,
Finding every tree

Alyssa Parbhoo, Grade 5
American Heritage Academy, GA

Skies

The stars are so pretty in the sky.
They are so pretty it stays in my eyes.
Oh how I wish one day I can fly
High in the sky.

When I look at the sky in the dark,
It always makes my eyes spark.
In the sky I see the stars.
Going through the night I see cars.

The stars are so pretty at night.
I can see them from a very good sight.
Also when it gets day and the sun gets down.
When it gets down my foot goes to the ground.

When the night comes I get so glad.
My mom tells me to come in the house and I get so mad.
So tonight was the night for me to see the sky.
I just want to say goodbye.

Latoya Denese Smith, Grade 6
St Mark Elementary School, SC

I Am a Military Child

I am a girl supportive of my father.
I wonder if my father will retire from the Navy.
I hear my father saying he will be home soon.
I see my father leaving.
I want my father to retire.
I am a girl supportive of my father.

I pretend to go on one of my father's trips.
I feel my father hug me when he gets back.
I touch my father's picture when he is gone.
I worry about having to meet new friends.
I cry when my father leaves.
I am a girl supportive of my father.

I understand that my father has to leave.
I say that we have troops gone.
I dream that we will have world peace.
I try not to cry when my father leaves.
I hope for the war to be over.
I am a girl supportive of my father.

Sarah George, Grade 6
Walker Intermediate School, KY

Christmas

Christmas
Christmas trees with a shining star
Cookies in the kitchen for Santa
Christmas carols sung by little children
Christmas meals being eaten by happy families
Presents being opened by excited families
Christmas

Dylan Knox, Grade 4
Tamassee-Salem Elementary School, SC

Our Gracious God

I give praise to the Lord above
    He gave us His patience, He gave us His love,
He gave me His mercy, He gave me my life,
    He is with me through all my strife,
He helps me fight my fight,
    Against Satan who leads me from right.

Will Brown, Grade 6
Community Christian School, NC

When I Go Deer Hunting

one day I went deer hunting with my dad.
we had to wake up at 4:00 in the morning.
we went to the deer stand and we waited.
seeing squirrels jump through the tree was funny.
we didn't see another thing then we went to go get
something to eat
we went back and then we went to go hunt somewhere else
we did not still shoot anything.
then we went home and we went to bed.

Julius Allen, Grade 4
Alvaton Elementary School, KY

Supersonic

I am a strong, bad, and you don't want any of me
because I will knock your house down.

I am fast as lightning.

If the Hulk tries to stop me I will spin
supersonic winds at him and take his powers.
Spiderman and Iceman don't stand a chance either.

You may see me at night or day
You better look out because I am a tornado.

I am your worst nightmare

Roman M. Baldwin, Grade 5
Pembroke Elementary School, NC

The Meaning of Baseball

What's the meaning of baseball?
Energized, electrified, jittery kids
Hoping to hammer in a home run.
Anxiously waiting for the pitcher to hurl the ball.
Watching it travel like an explosion from a gun shot.
Blasting the ball like a laser beam,
Dashing to first base.
Flashing like lightning to second,
Sliding onto third base,
Triumphantly sailing over home plate.
Doing a "home run dance" with a grin as wide as Antarctica.
Hearing roaring crows rooting for their kids.
That's the meaning of baseball!!!

Jacob Atwell, Grade 4
Price Elementary School, KY

My X-Box

This is my X-Box
It lets me play Sonic.
Even though it can easily break,
I love it because it's electronic.

This is my X-Box
To me it really rocks.
When I play it,
My fingers move like a fox.

This is my X-Box
Of course, it's shaped like a box.
I scream when it freezes!
Then, on my door my mom knocks.

Eli Thompson, Grade 5
Heber Springs Elementary School, AR

What's Up and What's Down

```
        sky       down
         the        is
          in         on
        high          earth
         is             but
         up               wait…
       floating!
     I'm
```

am I on earth or
in the sky?

Anna Setzer, Grade 4
St Thomas More School, NC

Tractors

I like John Deere tractors.
I think they are great.
But if you drove them to town,
You'd be terribly late.

I don't know about you
But I would not drive a tractor.
And I would not be on
the show of Fear Factor!

I like John Deere tractors.
I don't know about you,
But if you throw this poem away
I won't like you.

Lauren Kois, Grade 4
Brilliant Elementary School, AL

The Wrath of Fall

Cold at day and night,
Owls hooting and plants drooping,
Then all the leaves fall.

Jared Kanatzar, Grade 4
Cleveland Elementary School, OK

My Sister

My sister is this ditsy chick.
In sports she's always the last one picked.
In the morning she looks so goofy.
Her make-up is smeared, and her hair's all poofy.
Even with all those mishaps I love her anyway.
'Cause she's my sister, even if sometimes she feels more like a blister.

Kaitlyn Hawk, Grade 6
Cottonwood Public School, OK

The Crucifixion of Christ

Jesus died on the cross for you and me
He saved our souls, the world rejoices you see.

He rose on the third day with all power in His hands
God the father, the Son and the Holy spirit forever will reign.

Give thanks to Him for the Crucifixion Sacrifice
For a life filled with God's love.

Give thanks to Him for the Crucifixion Sacrifice
For the Holy Spirit pouring in our hearts from above.

Give thanks to Him for the Crucifixion Sacrifice
For saving our souls; salvation is free.

Give thanks to Him for the Crucifixion Sacrifice
We can now live eternally.

Rejoice, and be glad Christ has risen and lives
In His rising we are justified and freed forever
What a blessing; see how God gives
Give thanks to Him for the Crucifixion Sacrifice what a glorious day.
Without it; how can we pray?

Gabrielle Griffin, Grade 5
Holy Rosary Academy, LA

On the Other Side of the World

What a great day

What a great night
I will see the sun soon
in my sight

I will see the moon soon in my sight

How I will be hungry

How I will be tired
I hope I will have a good sleep tonight

Tomorrow I will not be
so sorrowful

I wonder what it is like on the other
side of the world

I wonder what it is like on the other
side of the world

Sarah Abney, Grade 6
Daniell Middle School, GA

Old Saint Nick

Silver bells were ringing, old church bells were dinging
at the time of midnight when old Saint Nick
snuck up to the top of a certain house.
This house bright with lights
to show this family's love for Jesus's birthday, Christmas.
Old Saint Nicholas thought very hard for a moment or two
before he delivered the presents to this faithful family,
"How am I a part of this overexciting occasion?"
After a while he thought,
I represent God's loving and glorious spirit
to all the world by giving out presents for all to love and enjoy.
From then on Old Saint Nick knew his place
on this joyous occasion we call Christmas.

Michael Johnson, Grade 5
Landmark Christian School, GA

Rainfall

I watch a raindrop
as it suddenly pours to the ground in sheets of rain.
The peaceful noise calmly clears my mind.
The rain beats on the window,
almost like it wants to come in.
I walk outside with no shelter to keep me dry.
Right above me a shower occurs,
letting me know it will storm tonight.
The rain seems to sing a graceful song.
As I was walking back inside trying to dry,
the water won't leave me.
I looked back outside, and the rain was gone,
a beautiful rainbow has appeared.
The rainfall is over…

Amanda McDonald, Grade 5
Saffell Street Elementary School, KY

My Garden

Bright cherry red tulips.
Brilliant divine triangular shapes.
Bleeding-hearts hanging like a bat.
Green green ivy growing and multiplying.
Orange lilies waiting for a drop of water.
Emerald ivy spreading through the garden.
Miniature concrete statues going through all the weather.
Blossoming, blooming, sprouting flowers.
Oddly shaped ruby red flowers waving in the wind.
Chirp, Chirp, Chirp
Little birds waking up the four o'clocks.

Sabrina Dawn Stice, Grade 6
Alvaton Elementary School, KY

Waves

I ran to the beach,
waves came by to say hi,
they knock me down.

Jane Walsh, Grade 4
Briarwood Christian Elementary School, AL

A Colorful Tree

Leaves yellow and red
It's a big, beautiful plant
Reaches to the sky

AnnaClaire Benes, Grade 4
Briarwood Christian Elementary School, AL

Volleyball

I hear the roar of the crowd as I'm standing on the court,
And I think to myself…I love this sport.

I love when we spike it,
That's the way Coach likes it.

I hear the whistle blow,
Then my serve has to go.

We scored another point,
The effort was joint.

We pulled out the win,
I can't wait to play again.

We hit hands under the net,
A worthy opponent we met.

Hannah Underwood, Grade 6
LeBlanc Middle School, LA

Merry Christmas

Christmas is just not about getting presents.
It's a joyful holiday when Jesus was born.
It's a tradition, you sit down with your family and talk,
open presents, and sing carols.
There are all kinds of decorations to celebrate.
Like colorful lights, put on Santa suits,
and sometimes it snows for Christmas.
This is what you do when Christmas arrives.

Jamie Noble, Grade 5
Western Hills Elementary School, AR

Poisonous Spider

Poisonous spider
Spinning web, catches his prey
Black, tiny spider.

Joseph Cash, Grade 4
Briarwood Christian Elementary School, AL

I Wish I Could Fly

I wish I could fly up to the sky.
So far up I would look like a duck.
If I could fly I would reach the moon.
If I could I would act like a baboon.
If I could fly I would look like a flying star.
Maybe people will think I am a chocolate bar.
Oh how I wish I could fly.

Ashley Harrison, Grade 4
Ode Maddox Elementary School, AR

Wonderful Winter

Winter makes snowmen
cold weather and snowball fights
friends and family
Troy High, Grade 6
Tomlinson Jr High School, OK

Daytona

Daytona Gaudet
fun, friendly
jump, play, run
I love to care for animals.
Daytona Gaudet
Daytona Gaudet, Grade 4
East Jones Elementary School, MS

School

I love school
Because its really cool
Do you like it to
I bet you do
Math, science, language, and history
Sometimes there's so much it's a mystery
I love my teachers
Because they have good features
All in all my school is great
So don't be late
Gabby Easterwood, Grade 5
Graham Elementary School, AL

Uncertain Future

I once was full of happiness
That was all around.
But, now there are only memories
That will never be
My halls were so beautiful
If only you could see
I sheltered all the little ones
When there was a storm
Now all there is to do
Is sit around and mourn
If only my walls were painted
And if children roamed about
Maybe I would be happier
But the future is untold
Beth Comstock, Grade 6
Pleasants County Middle School, WV

Springtime

Flowers blooming.
Butterflies awaking.
Bees humming.
Deer galloping.
Bears roaring.
Babies coming.
Vanessa Burns, Grade 4
Cave City Elementary School, AR

Life

Life is easy, life is hard
Life is fun, life is boring
Life is long, life is short
Life is big, life is little
Sometimes life makes you mad
Sometimes you wish you could live again
Life has many adventures
Life has many consequences
Life is bright, life is dull
Life is smart, life is dumb
But most of all life is life.
Josh Less, Grade 6
Woodland Presbyterian School, TN

Oak Leaf

I am a leaf from the great oak tree.
I feel a tickle, and what do I see?
A wise old man painting on me,
He dips his brush in scarlet red,
Fall is here; no more is said.
Draven Slane, Grade 4
Cool Spring Elementary School, NC

Kittens

Kittens chasing prey
Chasing mice and mother's tail
Having fun all day
Rebecca Cruey, Grade 5
Sycamore Elementary School, GA

Lions

Lions are large, lions are fierce,
lions have sharp teeth that can pierce!

Lions can run, lions can play, but
they can also pounce on prey!

Lions are cuddly when they're small, but
no so cuddly when they're tall!
I love lions!
Lane Lawe, Grade 5
St Thomas More School, NC

Tennessee

T ennessee is cool
E ducated people
N ice people live here
N ew people like it here
E njoyable
S uper fun
S ee the mountains
E ntertaining places
E ncourage
Spencer Sams, Grade 5
Debusk Elementary School, TN

Fall

The colors so bright
Sounds of fallen crackling leaves
Then shimmering rain.
Samantha Dennington, Grade 4
Cleveland Elementary School, OK

Moonbeam Path

Moonbeam path shines so bright,
Moonbeam path lights the night.
Over, under, there it goes,
Moonbeam path no longer shows.
Everything does seem to end,
But tomorrow…Moonbeam path
Is waiting 'round the bend.
Ciara Pink, Grade 4
Moyock Elementary School, NC

Jesus

Nice, our Saviour
Caring, loving, giving
Born on Christmas
Christ
Megan Menzel, Grade 4
Wohlwend Elementary School, MO

Traditions

F or a time, families can bond
A round the fireplace.
V ery small children dancing and singing
O ver and over again
R ipping present wrappings to see
I nside.
T elling about how Christmas began.
E verybody setting up Christmas trees.

T raditional carolers come a —
R ound, singing at your door.
A ll the elves making gifts,
D azzled by the lights and music.
I nto a wonderful
T ime eating a dinner with my family.
I n the malls buying presents
O n Christmas
N ativity scenes everywhere.
Alyssa Williams, Grade 5
Sullivan Elementary School, TN

Marvin the Martian

Marvin
greenish, smallish
blasting, banging, crashing
angry, upset, crazy, prepared
Martian
Tessa Black, Grade 4
Cleveland Elementary School, OK

The Fall

The fall is the best, I love the fall,
It's my favorite season of all
There are so many things to be seen,
Like the leaves of orange, yellow, and green

Vincent Contrevo, Grade 4
South Topsail Elementary School, NC

Dreams

Dreams are very special to me.
They mean a lot to some of us.
Once I had one where I broke my knee.
After that I missed the bus.
You know how they say "If you work hard they may come true."
Some people think that's not right,
Well if you ask me I think that's true I hope you do, too.

Christa Watson, Grade 5
Lula Elementary School, GA

Where Did the Dragons Go?

Whenever you look in the sky,
You won't see any dragons fly by.
Nobody knows quite where they went,
Do you know?

Maybe they all died out from no food,
Maybe one day they just all went ka-boom!
Scientists don't really know for sure,
Do you know?

They could have died from indigestion,
A lot of people have other suggestions.
Don't ask me how, I wouldn't know!
Do you know?

Do you know where the dragons have gone?
Did they vanish like the wind o'er the sea?
I don't think you know, nor anyone else,
Do you know?

Jonathan Boccarossa, Grade 5
Providence Academy, TN

Mice

You put out traps and catch us.
Doesn't anyone care?
You have cats that catch us like lightning.
Doesn't anyone care?
We are cute and cuddly so
Doesn't anyone care?
We are mammals like you humans.
Doesn't anyone care?
We wild mice only live for about 3 months.
Doesn't anyone care?
We live a life…
Doesn't anyone care???

Jay Hicks, Grade 5
Bellwood Discovery School, TN

My Mom

My mom loves me very much!
When I need someone to hold.
She is always there for me.
She's the very very best the best mom alive.
I love her very very much and she is really kind.
She has a very pretty name it is one of a kind.
I love it very very much and she is super cute!
I hope she never ever dies because I love her so very much
and then I will cry all the time!

Alesce Kimble, Grade 4
Lewis Vincent Elementary School, LA

I'm an Army Brat

I'm an army brat who is supportive of my father.
I wonder if he will be ok.
I hear airplanes and bombs going off.
I see lots of movers.
I want my father to come back.
I cry went he has to go to Iraq.
I'm an army brat who is supportive of my father.

I pretend that I was right beside him.
I feel sadness because he is gone.
I touch his picture.
I worry if he will be ok.
I cry when he leaves.
I'm an army brat who is supportive of my father.

I understand that he has to leave.
I say he is my hero.
I dream that I am right beside him fighting.
I try not to cry.
I hope that the war will be over.
I'm an army brat who is supportive of my father.

Diamond Holloman, Grade 6
Walker Intermediate School, KY

The Ocean

Waves crashing on rocks.
Refreshing cool mist and sweet scent.
With white waves, blue sky.

Kathryn Jason, Grade 4
Briarwood Christian Elementary School, AL

I Hate

I hate listening. It hurts my ears.
I hate walking. It hurts my feet.
I hate writing. It hurts my hands.
I hate thinking. It hurts my brain.

I hate waking up in the morning.
It hurts my eyes, but the one thing that
I don't hate is me.

Josh Hunley, Grade 4
Tazewell/New Tazewell Elementary School, TN

The Quiet Frog

Little quiet frog
Always behind the flowers
In the summertime.
Summer Thomas, Grade 4
Hillcrest Elementary School, TN

Fall

Back and forth,
Here it goes.
Fall is going,
Like a popsicle melting in the sun.
The leaves are falling
Crashing
Hitting the ground.
They fall and fall,
Waiting for winter to come
By the cold winter snow,
snuggling in the soft white snow
sinking,
sinking,
down,
down,
and alone.
Grace Kittle, Grade 4
Crestwood Elementary School, KY

Animals

Deer, rabbits and mice
Animals big and little
They live in the world.
Kate Elizabeth Zecher, Grade 5
Crossville Christian School, TN

Your Soul in Misery

Then you know
hate and
can't ignore it
Your
life is
now dark
There's no
way to
control it
but to ride
the wave
of misery
to the heart
and seize
a strong and
powerful
sense of
love to
free your
soul
Jessica Smith, Grade 5
American Heritage Academy, GA

The Day I Become Famous

So many things in life pass you by,
but that's okay because sometimes it will do that.
One day I would love to become famous.
I would get all the fame, fortune, and I'll have the nicest clothes ever.
As I get older, I may change my mind,
because sometimes becoming famous can be a serious thing.
One day you might lose everything you've got, like the people that got hit
by hurricane Katrina.
You never know so be careful what you wish for.

Andrea Poteat, Grade 5
Drayton Hall Elementary School, SC

My Family

My family is a lion's pack:
Dad is the lion, king of the jungle,
Big, powerful, and not always smart.

Mom is the lioness,
small, but smart and quick.

Mollie and Fido, the dogs,
are the half year-old cubs.
Who are young, becoming smart and quick.

Cowgirl, Garfield, Huewy, Dewy, Lewy, Hannah, Lily and Pumpkin, the cats
are the newborn cubs;
they don't have a clue about their world.

Connor, my brother, is the lioness' cub
Lovingly he follows her all the way.

I am the older cub
smarter, the one who holds this pack together.

Riley McCormick, Grade 6
College View Middle School, KY

The Destroyer

I can come at you without much notice.
I will destroy anything in my path.
My winds are strong and swift.
I'll come from any direction and you won't even know it.
I'm tall, wide and strong.
I'll put your house on another acre or make it as flat as a pancake.
 So if you see me coming get out of my way!
Because I don't have a conscious at all!!!

Amber R. Locklear, Grade 5
Pembroke Elementary School, NC

White

White looks like diamonds on a gold necklace.
White feels like a nice knit cotton sweater on a snowy day.
White tastes like a crisp brown marshmallow roasted over a warm pit fire.
White sounds like a lovely seagull flying over the bay.
White is the color of life.

Gannon Joyner, Grade 5
Geggie Elementary School, MO

Ode to PlayStation

I Love PlayStation!

L ive action, lasers, labyrinth;
O nly the best will survive.
V ictory or death!
E ndangered lives in perilous missions.

P rofessional sports,
L ost memories, and friends,
A ll players must face the test.
Y es, it is hard but it pays off in the end.
S afely complete the mission.
T here is no try, do or do not.
A bandon what you know and use your imagination.
T ranscend the boundaries of the real world.
I llusions can distract.
O vercome the forces of evil.
N ow, do you think you've got what it takes?

André M. Johnson Jr., Grade 6
Haynes Academy for Advanced Studies, LA

My Life

My life is complicated
My life is sad
Sometimes my life is really bad
Every day there is something new

Some of my life's past memories are sad…
Some can be glad
But all through my troubles…
I can see how wonderful my life can be.

Elizabeth Markham, Grade 6
Brogden Middle School, NC

Thank You for Fighting for Our Country

America is the place for me to be.
The soldiers protect us
from being killed.
Angels watch over them
as they fight for freedom.
There is barely grass
on their battlefield.
Many fires are noticed as they fight.
Even after the sun sets
soldiers still fight for freedom.
Looking at the lily pads
with flowers in the pond,
playing with my grandma's dog
thinking about the weather
above the battlefield and
leaves falling off trees as they fight.
Thank you for fighting
for our country.

Jarred Lanclos, Grade 6
Leonville Elementary School, LA

The Cat "Baby" and the Fish

The cat sits by the fish tank all day.
His name is Baby and he's a scary stray.
He hopes to find a way to play
The paws at the tank chasing the fish away!
The fish swim and swim all day.

The fish enter the rocks for a safe place to stay.
But the cat's paw finds a way.
Baby paws the tank and thinks of dinner
Oh those fish are getting thinner!

Baby dreams of fish in his sleep.
He really wants a fish to keep.
If only the top were not there
Baby might give the fish a scare.

Taylor Dane Piatt, Grade 5
Midway Covenant Christian School, GA

Hope

Will hope remain for Katrina survivors?
   I hope so!
It is a "squabble" for Katrina rebuilding.
   I pray for hope!
Hope sparkles like diamonds…
   It drips into the heart.
Hope is like a bee in a honey factory.
Hope is as lovely as a rose.

Hope lifts Katrina victims' spirits…
   As bright as moonlight!
Hope is a rainbow of dreams.
Hope is like a flame spreading and spreading.

Hope is a waterfall of faith for Katrina victims,
   It pours faith across the land.
   It teaches the inner soul.
   It rains love everywhere.
Hope is all that matters.

Kelsey Jordan, Grade 5
Breitling Elementary School, AL

The Sea

It roars like thunder.
It crashes hard like lightning.
That is my warning.

Hamp Briley, Grade 4
Briarwood Christian Elementary School, AL

Books

Looks like words big and bold
Sounds like pages rustling softly
Tastes like an appetite never filled
Feels like pages worn with age
Smells like forests long gone

Annabelle Neville, Grade 5
Briarwood Christian Elementary School, AL

Elves

Elves,
Elves,
Elves,
Skinny elves,
Fat elves,
Neat fancy smart elves,
Dumb lazy messy elves,
These are just a few.
Funny elves,
Crazy elves,
Happy jolly helpful elves,
Traditional loving busy elves,
Young elves, too.
Old elves,
Sleepy elves,
Don't forget hardworking elves,
Last of all, best of all,
I like creative elves.

Autumn Williams, Grade 5
Tates Creek Elementary School, KY

God's Love

God's love is special
It is true
His love is shining
Over you.

God's love is grateful
just like a fair
His love will always
be right there.

God's love is powerful
just like hard wood
His love will always
be so, so good.

God's love is awesome
and that is so
His love is like a broken car
it will never go.

God's love is wonderful
and that you will trust
God's love is the reason
He made us.

Deion Jamison, Grade 6
Holly Hill Middle School, SC

Rainbows

Colorful sky art
Patterns of hues splash above
Clouds smile floating by

Adam Alston, Grade 4
Broadway Elementary School, NC

Santa Claus

S pends time with his elves
A nother name is St. Nick
N ine reindeer
T ravels a lot
A sks for cookies and milk

C hecks his list twice
L ooks for nice children
A nother Christmas, another trip
U nder a roof
S ome say he's not real

Grant VonderHaar, Grade 4
Wohlwend Elementary School, MO

Aurora

Aurora
Fast, ruthless
Flying, cutting, earsplitting
So fast it's scary —
Shocking, astonishing, aspiring
Elite, venomous
Aurora

Dustin K. White, Grade 6
Pulaski County Middle School, GA

Music

Let it play, let it free
Let it say I can be
Let it soar, let it out
Sing more, dance it out
Let the music take control
Release your soul
Be yourself, release yourself
Create the music, play the music
Let it play, let it free
Let it say I am me.

Kaelyn Maness, Grade 6
Greenville Montessori School, NC

About My Teacher

I have the greatest teacher in school.
And she's really fun and cool.
Her favorite fur is wool.
But even though she's always nice to me.
I am still bad in school.

William Elliott, Grade 4
Magnolia Springs Baptist Academy, AL

Winter

Winter is as cold as ice
My friend thinks it is very nice
When the sun shines on the snow
It makes a wintery glow.

Baylee Webster, Grade 4
Horace Mann Elementary School, OK

Rain

Rain
Dark, lovely
Sleeping, snoring, weeping
A day to kick back and relax
Cold

Kaitlyn Keenom, Grade 5
Bayyari Elementary School, AR

Alexandria Marie Houser!

Don't lie
Don't kill
Don't talk back
Don't hit your sister
Don't throw parties
Don't go with strangers
Don't slide down the banister
And never, never, never sneak anywhere!

Alexandria Houser, Grade 5
Landmark Christian School, GA

Do You Like Me for Me

Do you like me for what I wear?
Do you like me for what I got?
Do you like me, or do you like her?
Do you like me for who I am?
I just want to know,
do you want to know?
Do you want to buy me,
or do you want to get to know me?
Do you like me for me?

Robyn James, Grade 5
Parker Road Elementary School, MO

I Am From:

I'm from Lexington, KY
  the bluegrass
    state.
I'm from Pam my mom
  and Marty my
    dad.
I'm from Gary my brother
  and Marty J.R. too.
I'm from home cooked
  meals during
    Thanksgiving.
I'm from sunny days
  in the summer.
I'm from sledding down
  hills behind TC
    High School.
I'm from the Kentucky
  River cold and
    blue.

Willy Lynch, Grade 5
Tates Creek Elementary School, KY

9/11

It started out a normal day
Until something happened that blew our skyscrapers away
The planes hit the towers
With such great power
They fell to the ground
With a horrifying sound
Oh what a devastating sight
All the people running in fright
The news channels were on all day
People were so shocked they didn't know what to say
The policeman and fireman were so brave
That led some of them to their early grave
We will always remember those who died
And their families' tears that they cried
We did nothing wrong
We have nothing to regret
For nine eleven we will never forget

Dylan Yancey, Grade 6
J D Meisler Middle School, LA

Beautiful Day!

Beautiful, beautiful oh, what a beautiful day!
Shouldn't we start shouting Hooray!
Today is a beautiful day
And everybody is happy this way.
The weather is beautiful like everybody else.
But we all come out like a bundle of elves.
Today, today
Oh, what a beautiful day
My life, oh, so good
Not like the people of wood.
Yes, and everybody shouts, hooray, hooray!

Hoby Quebedeaux, Grade 5
Arnaudville Elementary School, LA

Drawings

My drawings will be my legacy.
Some people will use them as recipes,
As they draw pictures of their own.

I might use a pencil, I might use a brush.
I take my time, I'm not in a rush.
And my best work is done when I'm alone.

The colors I use are happy and gay,
And are bright as a sunny day.
But what my drawings are, is unknown.

Ian Smith, Grade 6
North Iredell Middle School, NC

The Ocean Waves

The ocean waves crash
And mash into the rocks and
They are beautiful

John Hayden, Grade 4
Briarwood Christian Elementary School, AL

Wanting to Escape

You are the jail, I'm the prisoner
My chains are filled with all your memories
My bars are filled with your kisses
My bed is filled with all the cheats and lies
My mirror is filled with your 'in my eyes' perfectness

All I want to do is escape from this dark, daring, dooming place
I say when my serving will be over?
Then I remember I have a lifetime sentence
You are the jail, I'm the prisoner

Morgan Smith, Grade 6
Eminence Middle School, KY

My Fat Cat Abbey

A bbey is a fat cat,
B ut she eats like a gnat!
B ehind her head she has a nice back —
E veryone says she's flabby, so
Y ou could say she's my flabby Abbey!

Paul Budz, Grade 5
Our Lady of Fatima School, MS

Apples

Apples may be crunchy,
Apples may be sweet,
Apples may be munchy,
But candy is my treat.
Apples may be red,
And maybe some bright greens.
But when I'm in my bed,
I eat a bag of jelly beans.
Apples may be juicy,
Apples maybe be smooth.
But me and my friend Lucy,
Would rather take a snooze.

Elizabeth Curcuru, Grade 6
Haynes Academy for Advanced Studies, LA

Thanksgiving

Thanksgiving, Thanksgiving, Oh how I love,
The warmth you bring,
Your beauty so much like a dove,
That it makes me want to sing.

It's not your food,
It's not your name,
It's everyone's mood,
It's everyone playing a game.

But what I love most cannot be touched,
It's the love that you bring,
That is what I love so much,
That is what makes me want to sing.

Elizabeth Raines, Grade 6
Guntown Middle School, MS

Santa

S atisfied
A wesome
N ifty
T riumphant
A mazing

Preston Davis, Grade 4
Landmark Christian School, GA

Mommy and Daddy

M arvelous
O n the go
M any problems
M ust become a teacher
Y et still works

A lways lovely
N ot always happy
D oes not yell a lot

D aring
A nd
D oes love Mommy
D oes like to yell
Y et is always loving

Molly Myers, Grade 5
Zalma Elementary School, MO

Autumn: My Favorite Season

Tired autumn nights,
Falling leaves, colorful trees,
Not hot, not too cold.

Molly Dodson, Grade 6
Tomlinson Jr High School, OK

My Little Pet

My little pet is friendly,
I bought him from a store.
He is as slow as molasses,
So he can be a bore.

He crawls on the ground
And eats all the dust.
His hard green shell,
Look at it, I must!

He is a quiet one,
A grunt is his only sound.
If I leave him outside,
Who will get him? The hound!

I love him so much,
A million times more
Than all the other turtles
In that calmly-hectic pet store.

Mary Margaret Bryan, Grade 5
Providence Academy, TN

Every Stitch of Love

My grandmother use to sew quilts.
She was an expert at it.
Her quilts had very cool designs!
They are very comfortable.
She sewed quite a few.
My grandmother is up in Heaven now.
She is up in a much better place.
Come to think of it, she probably is making much better quilts, too.
Well, I sure do miss her.
The quilts are the only big thing that I have left of her.
Every time I sleep with the quilts that she made
I feel like she is right there sleeping with me.
My grandmother made her quilts with every stitch of love.

Susannah Smith, Grade 4
Sequoyah Elementary School, TN

Woods

smelling
freshly dug dirt,
ancient musty leaves,
decaying wood of fallen giants,
cool breezes hitting me in the face
like a lookout tower over every strip of land,
smell of caves filling the air,
twigs cracking at every step,
birds singing the longest song, never stopping for a breath,
small chittering chipmunks scurrying on the ground,
never quiet, an animal scurrying on the ground or tree limb falling,
shaded by all the towering trees overhead,
frogs and katydids, croaking all through the
night

Forrest Edward Beane, Grade 6
Alvaton Elementary School, KY

What Happens Between Brothers

Parties
What's my girlfriend doing?
Nick, get out of my room!
Nick, stop. What are you taking?
A CD
Which one?
Why do you care?
Because it's mine
Slam! He made it out the door
I'll get him
I'll get him good
I know, I'll put a sign
"Put CD here"
Then when he comes in he will see the sign, and put it by the open window
I will hide, then he will knock on the door and come in
Then I will push him out the window.

Knock, knock. Tommy.

Nicholas Bloom, Grade 5
South Nodaway Elementary School, MO

Hunting

As I saw the sun coming through the clouds
I put in several rounds.
As I saw a deer on the run,
I said to myself, "This is going to be fun!"
As I lined up the eye of my gun
I thought to myself, "Tonight we'll eat a ton!"
BOOM!!

Troy Taylor, Grade 4
Evangelical Christian School, TN

Rescue, the Saint Bernard

He's the color of toast that's been browned.
When we talked,
He never made a sound.
I threw him up in the air,
But he sometimes touched the ground.
He got washed in the washing machine,
And he went pound, pound, pound.
If you're talking about trips,
He's been all around,
When we slept,
In my arms he was wound.

Annabelle Bright, Grade 6
Woodland Presbyterian School, TN

Nature in the Morning

On this breezy morning
I see leaves
Falling off empty trees
I see birds flying in the air
Looking lonely and in despair.

Sounds are mixing in the sky
Also cars are passing by
Birds chirping make mornings bright
The flag waving brings morning to light
People are talking up the street
These are sounds that make mornings meet.

Feeling the wind on this autumn day
Leaves you happy with nothing to say
Coolness makes mornings all but peaceless
Making my day full of happiness.

Hunter Shelton Harlow, Grade 6
Temple Hill Elementary School, KY

My Game

On NFL Street you use your feet,
You have to pass when you're on the grass,
When on the roof just like a poof.
You can have the ball first or pick first,
On what is called a pickup game,
on my Playstation 2 video game.

Dustin Wood, Grade 4
Brilliant Elementary School, AL

Giving Thanks

On one special day we sailed away
Away to a place
Where giving was for thanks
There was more fun in giving thanks
Than to hop around and say hooray

For we bundled down for winter awaits
In the freezing cold till we met our fate
When all of a sudden came out of the fog
The good old friendly Wampanoags
For all we knew they were friendly
But later we found out that they were deadly.

They taught us to plant
They taught us to fish
They taught us to hunt
And put food on our dish

On one fine day
We went our ways
When someone said lets feast today
We gathered up turkey and cornbread, too
We ate for thanks just like you

Jordan Christopher, Grade 6
All Saints' Episcopal School, TN

The Ice Skater

It was a crisp cold winter day,
and through the park I made my way.
But when the beauty came into sight,
the pond twas just a layer of ice.
I stared at the pond (of course) in awe,
as the snow from the clouds started to fall.
I glanced fast across this pretty sight,
and sure enough to my surprise,
a small figure came across the ice.
The girl was dressed in a skirt and tights,
she wore a leotard.
A pair of blades accompanied her shoes upon her.
Her hair was tied up in a bun.
Jumping gracefully upon the ice,
she seemed to flutter in the sky,
with the birds up so high.
And the memory still lives today,
and I shall not tell you later,
I still remember every move of the graceful ice skater.

Jamie Stalfort, Grade 5
Stokesdale Elementary School, NC

What I Saw

I saw a little kitty cat walking past my house.
I asked where he was going, he said to find a mouse.
I asked what he would do with it, he said they would play.
Then he would say goodbye to it, until another day!

Madison Leigh Dodd, Grade 4
Brilliant Elementary School, AL

In the Pool

My brother is gone
I'm alone
Reached for water
And fell in
At the bottom
Of my pool
Scared
Air bubbling out
My mouth
Dying dying I say
I see someone is here
Come to get me
Wanting
Wanting
I'm out
Finally out
C.P.R.
I will be
All right

Najah Underwood, Grade 6
The Mountain Community School, NC

Elizabeth

Elizabeth
Smart, sweet, beautiful
Daughter of Cindy
Who loves God, Mom, and writing
Who feels good about knowledge
Who needs education, love, and care
Who gives love, care, and happiness
Who fears snakes, bugs, and crocodiles
Who'd like to see Australia
Who dreams of being an author
A student of Windsor Elementary
Lee Lee

Elizabeth Skinner, Grade 5
Windsor Elementary School, NC

Winter Sickness

In the winter if you get a big chill,
You will get very ill,
And when you get a runny nose,
People will hear a lot of blows.

Kassie LaBree, Grade 4
South Topsail Elementary School, NC

Mall

Come one, come all,
see the magnificent mall
with candy and treats
and sweets to eat
toys to buy
how I love the mall!

Jaimie Grammer, Grade 4
Cave City Elementary School, AR

Legend of the Dogwood

Dogwood tree plain and tall,
I see your berries every fall.
I see your blossoms every spring,
They almost make me want to sing.

To sing about your past,
How it changed oh so fast.
I know you have been treated rough,
But you are so very tough.

You held the Lord,
You were the cross.
Oh what a cost!
God All Mighty was so mad,
He made you lean and look so sad.

DeForest Tuggle, Grade 4
Stephens Elementary School, AL

Veteran

V ery helpful
E nd in sight
T hank you
E veryone's hero
R espect you
A rmed forces love you
N egotiate for peace

LeAlyson Bailey, Grade 4
Cherokee Elementary School, AR

LothLorien

In a land far beyond
past a mountain
there is a wood
like a golden fountain

Ho! The land of LothLorien
The Mellyrn trees
their boughs so bright
bathing in a golden light

Ho! The land of LothLorien
Here the Lady rules in peace
her silken gowns with a crease
and the elves that live so well
upon the banks of Nimrodel

Ho! The Land of LothLorien
O Lorien! O Lorien!
hear my woeful cry.
O Lorien! O Lorien!
I leave you with a sigh.

Ho! The land of LothLorien.

Josh Arend, Grade 6
College View Middle School, KY

A Boy Playing His Flute

A boy was playing his flute.
He had a crimson red hat made of velvet.
The boy is engaged in his music.
He is focused.
There is movement in his hands.
He has a ruffled silk collar.
He is gazing towards the light.
The boy has a violin and a recorder,
but today he chose the flute.
The room is shaded.
So is the boy's coat.
His hand, face and his collar are tinted.
He is calmly sitting in an ornate chair.

Alex Brogan, Grade 5
Saffell Street Elementary School, KY

Summer

Summertime is fun.
Swimming all day in the sun.
Playing basketball.

Jaron Faulkner, Grade 6
Tomlinson Jr High School, OK

Don't Even Talk to Yesterday

Don't talk to yesterday
It won't respond
It's sleeping
It has moved on
So start speaking to today
And you won't feel so much regret
So don't bother to talk to yesterday
You decide what happens now
Not what happened the day before

Ryann Poe, Grade 4
Landmark Christian School, GA

Veteran

V eterans are cool.
E verlasting love.
T ough and hardworking.
E ager to fight for us.
R un them away.
A nd fight for us.
N ever stop 'til it is done.

Bryce Trivitt, Grade 4
Cherokee Elementary School, AR

The Girl Named Jane

There once was a girl named Jane,
who wanted to live in Maine.
But then the phone rang,
and the door bell rang,
and at the door was John Wayne.

Kurtis Chandler, Grade 4
Judsonia Elementary School, AR

Green

Green looks like grass after a heavy rainfall.
Green feels like a sunny summer's day at the beach.
Green tastes like an apple just picked from a tree.
Green smells like a fresh apple pie right out of the oven.
Green sounds like birds singing on a spring day.
Green is the color of the world.

Eleanor Conley, Grade 5
Geggie Elementary School, MO

The Ocean

The sea is wavy
Aqua colors green and blue
It's so beautiful

Bentley King, Grade 4
Briarwood Christian Elementary School, AL

The Sky

The sky is blue and beautiful
It looks like an enormous painting.
The sky is a road for birds.
Clouds move in and out of it.
The sky can be happy or sad.
It can be as calm as a farm in the country.
Or it can be as hectic as a big city.
It is the window for spirits to look down.
The sky is always with us.

Clark Freeman, Grade 6
Woodland Presbyterian School, TN

I Wish I Were Sam Gribley

I wish I were Sam Gribley
And this is what I'd do
I'd go to the beach, and take you too
I'd swim in the water till the sun gets hotter

I wish I were Sam Gribley
And this is what I'd do
I'd have a great big family
And that's how we will do

I wish I were Sam Gribley
I'd run away from home
And go to the Catskill Mountain
To see the deer herd roam

I wish I were Sam Gribley
I'd trap some giant fish
And make it into dinner
A delicious, juicy dish

I wish I were Sam Gribley
And this is what I'd do
I'd build a home for me
And also one for you

Katia Caballero, Grade 4
Nesbit Elementary School, GA

My Old House

My old house is the place to be.
It is cozy as you see.
It has windows and doors so neat
Keeping them closed keeps in the heat.
Its walls and floors are so warm.
They protect me from the storms.
That's why this old house is so neat
Because it protects me and keeps in the heat.

Jamie Davis, Grade 6
Pleasants County Middle School, WV

Nature

As I scan clear blue sky
I can see an eagle pass by
Oh, how I wish I could soar
Wow! Look, there's a boar
The animals know that my presence is here
I think I can hear them wildly cheer
Here I walk as a fall forest girl
I happily make a beautiful twirl
The soft green grass I feel with my feet
As I dance to the soft forest beat
My healthy blood-pumping heart
Had completely fallen apart
And I hadn't had the groove
To make the longest move
Well goodbye my dear animal friends
I never thought that it should end

Anissa Armaly, Grade 5
Prince of Peace Catholic School, SC

Although You're Dead

Although you're dead you're still a friend.
Although you're dead you'll still be loved.
Although you're dead you're still in my heart.
Although you're dead you're still in our family.
Although you're dead you're still my cat that I will never forget.

Sam Switzer, Grade 5
Parker Road Elementary School, MO

The Furious Tornado

I am the indestructible monster.
You or anybody else can't stop me.
I will rip your house to shreds.
I will kill you or put you in the hospital.
I am the worst thing you or anybody else has been in.
They call me the thing.
I can go as fast as a cheetah.
My wind speed is 300 mph.
I am as powerful as a locomotive.
I am as deadly as a black widow.
I can throw you more than 5 miles.
I am the furious tornado.

Adam Tharp, Grade 5
Pembroke Elementary School, NC

Rainbow Lorikeet

Tropical colors
Charming while it's upside down
Rainbow Lorikeet
Dealexus Lockett, Grade 4
Orchard Elementary School, AL

Shining Pond

The pond outside my window,
Shines in the sunlight
Sending a warm glow.
Chandler Massengale, Grade 6
Beck Academy, SC

About the Sun

A small little sun
Playing behind the high cloud
In the summertime.
Talia Payne, Grade 4
Hillcrest Elementary School, TN

Hearts

Hearts are like puzzles,
All from the start.
People put them together,
Then break them apart.
Then someone comes along,
Maybe weak, maybe strong,
They put glue on the puzzle,
So it will last long.
Nichole Patterson, Grade 5
Chester County Middle School, TN

Basketball

Ball
Shoot
Pass
Dribble
Fast
Score
Time-outs
Uniforms
Foul
Sweatbands
Shoes
Whistle
Ref
Cheerleader
People
Team
Get ball
Game
Practice
Now that is
BASKETBALL!
Kitt Rogers, Grade 6
Armorel Elementary School, AR

If I Were a Tear Drop

If I were a tear drop I would hear crying of the person creating me,
If they were crying for joy I would hear a laugh
that fills the night with happiness.
But if they were not I would hear a scream
that pierces the night with eternal sadness.
If I were a tear drop I would see a red puffy face
of the person crying me out,
With nose so runny and eyes so sad or happy.
If I were a tear drop I would smell the sweat
from the person being hot from crying so much,
And the smell would be a heck of a horrible smell
That smelled like fresh garbage
With a hint of rotten eggs added.
If I were a tear drop I would taste the salty after taste of me
And nasty, horrid, disgusting taste of the dirt of the floor,
As I fall down, down, down.
Shaleigh McCarthy, Grade 6
Eminence Middle School, KY

Twelve Very Sweet Days of Christmas

On the first day of Christmas the candy man gave to me a whole string of Laffy Taffy
On the second day of Christmas the candy man gave to me two gumballs…
On the third day of Christmas the candy man gave to me three jaw breakers…
On the fourth day of Christmas the candy man gave to me four Snicker bars…
On the fifth day of Christmas the candy man gave to me five Reese cups…
On the sixth day of Christmas the candy man gave to me six pixi sticks…
On the seventh day of Christmas the candy man gave to me seven fruit roll ups…
On the eighth day of Christmas the candy man gave to me eight Nestle Crunches…
On the ninth day of Christmas the candy man gave to me nine Nerd ropes…
On the tenth day of Christmas the candy man gave to me ten gummi worms…
On the eleventh day of Christmas the candy man gave to me eleven salt water taffies…
On the twelfth day of Christmas the candy man gave to me twelve 3 Musketeers…
Eleven salt water taffies Ten gummi worms
Eight Nestle Crunches Seven fruit roll-ups
Six pixi sticks Five Reese cups
Four Snicker bars Three jaw breakers
Two gum balls and a whole string of …Laffy Taffy
Tyler Burkhart, Grade 5
East Bernstadt Elementary School, KY

A Rapid River

Speeding over the land like a galloping horse,
Yet at the same time soaring as gracefully as a bird,
The river races around like a racecar,
Rushing over rocks like waves washing up on shore,
The river is like a passage leading to a mystical place,
The river dives into the water at a waterfall like a dolphin lunging in,
A waterfall is like a geyser that has exploded,
The river roars as loud as a lion,
Turning side to side like skiing downhill left to right,
Connecting two bodies of water like a bridge,
Refreshment for animals for the water is as cold as ice,
As blue as the morning sky,
A roaring, rapid river!
Vidisha Holsambre, Grade 6
River Trail Middle School, GA

War

War is a death not a life.
War is your doom, if you are in it.
You've heard on the news, about these terrorists attacks.
Also on the news, about murders and other cruel things.
DON'T throw your life away, war is your terror every day!!

Kevin Meyer, Grade 5
Parker Road Elementary School, MO

Fly

I'm on a balance beam,
Or so it seems,
And I'm about to fall.
I just can't stay tall!
Something is wrong.
I just can't stay strong.
But I know there is a place,
I will eventually have to face,
And when it comes in sight,
I know it will definitely be right.
I haven't grown my wings yet and I don't know how to fly,
But I'll keep on pushing 'till I reach the sky.
And I know I'm not that good and I'm probably a fool,
But I'll keep on pushing,
And I'm telling you,
I am going to reach that,
Once I finally learn how to fly.

Erin Shealy, Grade 6
Mount Zion Christian School, SC

Brown's Wonderful Life

Brown sounds like the crispy leaves on a wonderful fall day
as they crack under my feet as I walk.

Brown tastes like KFC's crispy chicken that crunches
through my teeth.

Brown feels like a rock that stayed in the scorching hot sun
in the middle of the day.

Brown smells like the brown chocolate that I left
on the scalding hot cement, melted.

Brown looks like the dirt after a hard day of football practice.
Brown.
Brown feels like the dirt running through my fingers
as I gather up juicy worms for fishing.

Brown smells like the mud on the side of a swamp after a rain.
Brown tastes like hot chocolate on a freezing winter's night.
Brown sounds like peanuts getting switched into peanut butter.
Brown looks like the bark of a tree as a woodpecker shreds
it into a home...
Brown.

Dylan Dishman, Grade 5
Cool Spring Elementary School, NC

Spiders

Spiders are blackish
and tarantulas are brown.
They are both awesome.

David Salchert, Grade 4
Briarwood Christian Elementary School, AL

My God

My God is an awesome God,
When you are truly happy
Is when you follow Him.
You rely on Him to keep you from sin,
By going to church and praying to Him.
You should treat others the way you want them to treat you
And God is there to help you and me.
I love to share the wonders of God,
And to learn right from wrong,
That's one promise I have with Him,
Together, our journey is not long.

Brittney Mosby, Grade 6
Friendship Christian Academy, MS

The Jack-o'-lantern and the Scarecrow*

I am a scarecrow; I am stuffed.
I am a jack-o'-lantern; I was carved.
WE WERE MADE BY A HUMAN.

I am a scarecrow; I am multi-colored.
I am a jack-o'-lantern; I am orange.
WE ARE BOTH WARM INSIDE.

I am a scarecrow; I am made from hay.
I am a jack-o'-lantern; I used to be a pumpkin.
WE BOTH HAVE A PURPOSE.

I am a scarecrow; I keep crows from eating crops.
I am a jack-o'-lantern; I am a decoration.
WE ARE BOTH OFTEN SEEN IN THE FALL.

I am a scarecrow; I see many animals.
I am a jack-o'-lantern; I see many kids.
WE BOTH HAVE FUNNY FACES.

Joshua Eager, Grade 4
Vanoss Elementary School, OK
*A poem for two voices.

The Perfect Charm

Mom you are like a charm from heaven.
Before you were born God picked you up in his hands.
Then just made you beautiful as you could be.
Then gently put your beautiful body perfectly back.

When you were born you were sparkling like a diamond!
Most people thought you were made of diamonds.
But we knew you were a charm from God.

Christian Dodd, Grade 4
Magnolia Springs Baptist Academy, AL

Just Plain Gross!

"That is just plain gross!" I say
when I see what I have for lunch today.

A can full of green bean soup,
A cup full of blueberry goop.

A moldy apple with little green spots,
A squishy banana with brown polka-dots.

An expired fruity juice box,
A cookie that smells like old socks.

And so I had to say,
"I guess I won't have lunch today!"

Julianne Vance, Grade 5
St Thomas More School, NC

Soccer

Soccer
Fun, physical
Running, kicking, slide tackling
A rugged tough game
Football

Walter Hix, Grade 5
Landmark Christian School, GA

Christianity

C hristlike attitude
H umble
R ead your Bible
I nformed and ready to spread the Word
S teady pace with Christ
T ruthful about your Christian life
I nner peace
A ppetite for Christ
N ice to others
I ndividuality
T ight with Christ
Y ell and praise Jesus' name

Rachel Johnson, Grade 6
Desoto Central School, MS

My Treasure

My cats cuddle up with me at night.
They make me happy when I'm blue.
When they play with me
They jump and soar like birds in the air.
When I hold them they're soft like my
Grandmother stroking my cheek.
I can tell them my secrets,
And they never tell them away.
My cats are my treasure,
Shining in my heart.

Kendrick Farley, Grade 4
Crestwood Elementary School, KY

The Lost Mountain Frog

A lost mountain frog
Creeping behind the mountain
In the autumn time

Marcus McMillan, Grade 4
Hillcrest Elementary School, TN

Frog

I had a frog,
and it jumped.
When it jumped,
it landed on my sister.
And when it did,
she screamed so-o-o loud,
I thought I was deaf.
I couldn't hear for an hour.

Josh Mattingly, Grade 5
St Vincent Elementary School, MO

Brave Knight

A knight in shining armor
watches the land.
Fighting off giants
until the queen returns.
When she is back
he rests.
His mission complete,
for now.
A once lush brown coat
now a scruffy mess.
He has been almost eaten.
His back has been stitched up.
His nose is long gone.
He has traveled
from Hawaii to Nova Scotia.
"Who is this brave knight?"
You ask.
He's a chocolate brown bear
named Teddy.
The protector
of my bed.

April Fowler, Grade 6
South Oldham Middle School, KY

Christmas

C aroling around the neighborhood
H olly berries being picked
R eading by the fire
I nviting family in out of the cold
S aying thanks around the table
T elling funny stories
M aking blueberry pie
A ctive children playing
S aying "good bye!"

Kayla Pierson, Grade 5
Sullivan Elementary School, TN

Snow

Don't you like snow
Falling down from the sky?
When there is no snow
I usually cry.

The feeling of happiness instantly comes.
The ground is all white.
Everyone is out.
It's a beautiful sight.

The shape of each snowflake
Is never the same
Each child is running
Or playing a game.

The wonderful and amazing snow
Doesn't always last.
So please go out there
And have a blast!

So, is you see snow out the window
Do not let it go.
Go outside
And play in the snow!

Baylee Carter, Grade 5
American Heritage Academy, GA

My Attitude

My attitude
Determines how I feel,
My attitude
Determines what I do,
My attitude
Determines what I say,
My attitude
Determines how others feel,
My attitude
Determines my success in life,
My attitude
Reflects my walk with God,
What does my ATTITUDE say to you?
Is my ATTITUDE what it should be?

Jared Thompson, Grade 6
Pulaski County Middle School, GA

Summer Fun!

Summer is here today,
let's all go out and play.
In the outdoors we all have,
a great great day!
We all have fun in the beginning,
but sadly know,
soon to come is the ending.

Kim Williams, Grade 6
Graham Elementary School, AL

White Is

White is a diamond out of the ground,
You asleep without a sound.
White is the snow freshly fallen,
A new sidewalk ready for walkin'.
White is an angel's wings ready to fly
Up to the clouds in the sky.
White is a new born's pureness ready to call.
The spray of water off the fall.
White is clean cars that zoom on by.
It is also your rolled eye.
White is the hope that is inside of you.
The milk from the cows that go moo.
White is the letter that I send,
To tell you it is the end.

Emily Maulden, Grade 6
Lost River Elementary School, KY

People

Variations are in our lives.
People are as varied as the weather.
People are in our lives as much as the sun.

Kyle Beyard, Grade 5
Salem Elementary School, AR

My Pony

My pony is sweet,
My pony is cute,
My pony is very, very meek,
I love my pony.

When I got out to ride,
He comes up to my side,
And speaks to me with his eyes, "I love you"
I love my pony.

We gallop the fields,
Like eagles in flight,
Soaring so fast, free and light,
I love my pony.

We go back to the barn,
I feed him and groom him,
I would die if I did not have him,
I love my pony.

Billie Henard, Grade 5
Providence Academy, TN

Feast

F amily
E njoys one
A nother's company while we
S imply sit and
T alk at Grandmother's
　　dining room table.

Taylr-Lace Chisum, Grade 6
Nathaniel Hawthorne Elementary School, MO

Christmas Eve

It was very snowy,
The wind was very blowy,
And there are cookies that were very doughy.

Jordan Abney, Grade 5
Midway Covenant Christian School, GA

Clouds

Clouds are puffy, white and soft
And almost every shape
They can be pointy, round, or even like a picture
They are fun to look at when you are bored
I love clouds

Nick Genereaux, Grade 4
Evangelical Christian School, TN

Brothers

B othering you all the time
R acing to eat the most candy
O ften scaring you
T hrowing candy at you
H aving fun, sometimes
E ating hot dogs, candy, and s'mores
R acing door to door for candy
S creaming at their sisters

O ften getting me in trouble
N ever quit teasing me

H appy Halloween, Jonathan and Frederick
A fraid of spiders
L aughing all the time
L osers all the time
O n the ball to get candy
W in or lose they are always good brothers
E ven one is in college
E nough candy for the night
N ot listening to them

Jessica Schindler, Grade 5
Frankford Elementary School, MO

Two Skies

One dark, one brighter,
They both are very gorgeous.
They are shades of blue.

Emily Atkins, Grade 4
Briarwood Christian Elementary School, AL

At Bat

I put on my batting gloves, ready to hit.
I step out to the on deck circle, thinking…will I get a hit?
With all my faith in my bat,
I walk up to the plate…taking one deep breath.
The pitcher throws the ball and the ball went to the fence.

Nick Debo, Grade 6
Brogden Middle School, NC

The No Sleep Sleepover

Tonight is my sleepover
The best kind
I'm not going to close an eye
But maybe just to blink
But I will never fall asleep!
We'll play Truth or Dare
We'll drink sodas and eat
But I will never ever fall asleep!
We'll watch movies
And play lots of fun games
But I will never ever go to sleep!
It's late now
And I'm willing to wait for dawn
But I will never ever fall asle-z-z-z-z-z-z.

Elizabeth Sheffield, Grade 4
Landmark Christian School, GA

The Fifth Grade Bus

The fifth grade school bus,
Is such a fuss,
People fighting and people missing,
Is that Jane and Ricky kissing?
Paper and erasers zoom by my head,
Even lunches and that's what I said.
My head always hurts from the noise,
Whiney girls and cranky boys.
Monica and Janice telling tales,
The boys are snorting just like whales!
The fifth grade bus is not very thriving,
But, guess what?

I'm driving!

Sarah Grammar, Grade 5
Our Lady of Fatima School, MS

People

Some people run and play
and some just watch TV
Some people punch and kick
and some just go have tea

Some people knit and sew
and others would rather die
Some people drive and drive
and some never reach the sky

Taylor Suffridge, Grade 6
Central Arkansas Christian School, AR

Monkey

Monkey
Brown, wild
Hanging, climbing, swinging
Monkeys like to climb
Ape

Ashley Manek, Grade 4
Russell Babb Elementary School, OK

The Morning Breeze

When I go out each morning, I feel the morning breeze.
This breeze makes me feel spunky, and makes the leaves rustle on the trees.
This breeze blows the birds who are singing to me.
I hurry to the bus stop, for late I would be.
Slowly, the sun comes out, and the bus roars over.
I sense something fresh, the smell of green clover.
I arrive at my school which is so busy.
All this commotion makes me feel really dizzy.
But something unknown comforts me, please tell me what, just please.
Then I realize, it is the comforting morning breeze.

Yinan Zheng, Grade 4
Brookwood Elementary School, GA

My Mean Brothers

A cting sweet around Mom
B eing big bullies
C ackling about something!
D on't you dare!
E ating everything here.
F ood is in my bed, EEW!
G oof balls running around.
H urtful and mean
I 'm telling Mom!
J ust leave me alone!
K ind of annoying.
L iar, liar pants on fire!
M y brothers ate my homework!
N ot caring what they break.
O h, no! Not my hair!
P ractical jokes.
R ampaging through the house.
S top right there!
T orn curtains,
U tter destruction!
V ampires I tell you, that's what they are!
W hy me?
Y ou did this?
Z ooming out of my room.

Julia L. Vaughn, Grade 5
Sullivan Elementary School, TN

Kew's Royal Gardens

Kew has branded its stamp in botanical history.
For a long 45 years it saw its renaissance and its glory.
The building of Palm and Temperate houses,
Lying of Arboretum and herbarium was founded.

Under Queen Victoria's patronage,
The garden flourished and was unique in its age.
All this took place under two directors, Sir William and Joseph Hooker.
Nesfield was the artist and landscape designer.

The Arboretum at Kew
Is home to many plant species rare and few.
It traveled from the entire world
With leaves straight, rigid, and curled.
The leaves of Corsican and Stone Pine
In the sun, they glisten and shine
In the herbarium, it created and developed seed plants
It presented plants with life's grant.

Royal Gardens' vastness and enormity surpasses its 300 acres.
It is the fruit of their labors over countless and unimaginable years.
Gardens, landscapes, flowers, and foliage
Created Kew's fabulous and fantastic heritage.

Sharon Roy, Grade 6
River Trail Middle School, GA

Everybody Loves the Soldiers

I'm glad to be in America,
the best place for me.
The soldiers are fighting for us.
The soldiers should have many
things for helping us.
In America you can go everywhere
because of the soldiers.
You can buy many things in America,
I want to thank the soldiers.
Soldiers are blessings for everybody for helping the USA.
The air is what we need on Earth.
Everybody loves the soldiers
who are helping America.

Edward Edmond, Grade 6
Leonville Elementary School, LA

Seasons

When the flowers bloom you know it's spring.
Baby animals play, and the birds sing.
The time is near for school to be out.
The kids are happy, but their parents pout.

Summer's here we're out on break.
I can go on vacation; I can camp at the lake
We go to Grandma's and swim in the pool
Man, I'm glad I'm out of school.

I raked and I raked all the leaves in a pile.
I jump in the leaves and come up with a big smile.
I get to go hunting and watch football,
Since fall has started, I've had a ball.

In winter the cold wind will blow,
And kids can go out and play in the snow.
We decorate our tree with lights and a bow.
The fire place is lit and gives off a big glow.

Jake Tollett, Grade 5
Joann Walters Elementary School, AR

Dalton Stroup

D etermined to work hard all the time
A thletic and fast
L oves my family and friends
T o swim and play games are my favorite things
O zzie is my dog I love to play with
N ow you are going to learn more about me

S uite Life of Zack and Cody is my favorite show
T ara and Alan are my mom and dad
R ock and Roll is my favorite music
O utside is where I like to play
U sually I get my homework done
P izza is my favorite food to eat

Dalton Michael Stroup, Grade 4
St Mary Cathedral Elementary School, MO

When I Go to My House

I went to my house and what did I see?
I saw a little dog walking, a little cat sitting.
Jill, Bob, and Gerrit went up, went up, to the attic.
When I got to my room and what did I see?
I saw a little elf laughing, a super hero flying.
Jill, Bob, and Gerrit went down, went down, to the basement.
When I got to the basement what did I see?
I saw a big fat man eating, a little, girl dancing.
Jill, Bob, and Gerrit went out, went out, of the basement.
When I got out of the basement what did I see?
I saw a little boy dialing, an upset stomach smiling.
Jill, Bob, and Gerrit went out, went out, of the house.

Darron Morehead, Grade 5
Franklin Elementary School, OK

Trees

I like to gaze at the trees.
They are the subject for nature to play free.
Colors are displayed so very well.
Just how it's done I can't really tell
Greens, red, yellows, and browns
blend together so well — I can't frown.

Trees are an expression of nature's beauty
no pens or brush can capture — not even by duty.
Trees can swing — did you know —
the breeze and leaves swish to and fro.
Even are strong to catch and hold the snow.

Kennedy Ransom, Grade 5
Pembroke Elementary School, NC

Leaves, Leaves Everywhere

It is fall time at last —
My sister and I are having a blast!
There are piles of leaves everywhere —
Just for my sister and me to share!

Colorful leaves falling in my hair —
Though I really don't care!
Some are red and some are green —
A very strange color I never seen!

Two leaves are having some tea —
They are talking about their family tree!
Soon the trees will be boney, brown and bare —
I hope the leaves don't care.

Stacey Borchert, Grade 4
North Elementary School, NC

Kickball

Kickball,
Kick, steal, goal, run, black,
Think, score, play, win games, cool game
Hit, fall, pass, out, shoes

Juwan Twillie, Grade 4
East Jones Elementary School, MS

Oh Brother!

Kind brothers
Mean brothers
Smart, dumb, weird brothers
Short, cool, tall brothers
Those are just a few!

Older brothers
Younger brothers
Happy, sad, lonely brothers
Skinny, fat, funny brothers
Scary brothers too!

Helpful brothers
Crazy brothers
And don't forget cute brothers!

Last of all
Best of all
I like sweet brothers!

Hannah Crouch, Grade 5
Salem Elementary School, AR

The Drop Zone

The Drop Zone is like when
the world falls.
Drop Zone is like a short
person falling off a cliff.
That is why I don't want
want to ride the Drop Zone.
I like to ride the Drop Zone,
but I am scared.
It feels like we are jumping
from a cliff.
That is why I don't want
to ride the Drop Zone.

Desiree Singleton, Grade 5
Drayton Hall Elementary School, SC

Thanksgiving

Thanksgiving is the time of year
When all our family meets,
To celebrate and give our thanks,
And eat our favorite treats.

Turkey, dressing and pumpkin pie,
And mashed potatoes, too.
We'll be lucky if we can breathe,
Whenever we get through.

We laugh and talk and eat some more,
Until at the end of the day,
When looking forward to next year
We send them on their way.

Seth Kamphaus, Grade 5
Canute Elementary School, OK

Autumn Is Here

Autumn is here,
But not the reindeer.
It's cold at night,
Sometimes just right.
I can't wear flip flops,
'Cause its not hot.
Autumn is here,
But not the reindeer –

Thanksgiving is coming up,
And we have a cup, full of hot cocoa –
The bears are hibernating,
The birds have stopped singing –
Autumn is here,
But not the reindeer.

Gabriel Botero, Grade 5
Palmetto Christian Academy, SC

Night and Day

Night
dark, nocturnal
sleeping, stalking, prowling
moon, stars, sun, sky
playing, running, skipping
bright, diurnal
Day.

Jonathan Galloway, Grade 5
Harahan Elementary School, LA

Thanksgiving Day

Thanksgiving is the time to eat —
It's also time for my mother's meat.
All the turkey with lots of dressing —
Is a marvelous blessing!

Every year the turkey talks —
It also does funny walks.
We overlap our plates with food —
Then the baby boy booed!

Brittney Tarbush, Grade 4
North Elementary School, NC

Basketball

Hearts are racing
Breaths taken
The clock is ticking
We need one shot to win
I know we can, I know we can
Take the SHOT!
Oh I think it's getting hot,
The ball is rolling off my finger
Everyone lingers...
Brogden Middle are national champs.

Cory Hargrove, Grade 6
Brogden Middle School, NC

Everything Is Nothing

Everything is here
Everything is there
Everything is everywhere
But nothing is here
And nothing is there
So I quietly climb up the stairs
Then someone whispered in my ear
"Go back downstairs my sweet dear."
Although it gives me fear
Of who it was that whispered in my ear
I quietly creeped down the stairs
Without a whisper or a glare
I slowly climbed into my bed
With all of this running through my head
Could this all be a dream
So I pinch myself to see
I fell nothing because everything is here
Everything is there
Everything is everywhere
But nothing is here
And nothing is there

Khadijah Blackman, Grade 6
Bellwood Discovery School, TN

If I Were...

Hello!

My name is Maleake

If I were a color,
I'd be orange like fire.

If I were an animal,
I'd be something strong
Like a leopard or tiger.

My favorite place is at school,
Where you learn.
And peaceful.

I love listening to hip hop
When I am going to sleep.

Maleake Burris, Grade 4
Pine Tree Hill Elementary School, SC

Friends

Friends can make you happy
Friends could make you sad
You have fun with them every day
Even though you want your way
They help you whenever you need them
So, you don't have trouble
I have a friend. Do you?

Shonesty Hannah, Grade 6
Brogden Middle School, NC

Thanksgiving

Thanksgiving is a special time.
We have cranberry sauce and pumpkin pie.
A lot of things we can be thankful for,
Is love all around us and more.

The settlers had an adventure and landed on Plymouth Rock
The Indians helped us grow crops.
We grow an abundance of food each year.
That is why we observe Thanksgiving and
Celebrate everything so dear.

Leah Husong, Grade 5
Trenton Middle School, MO

Thanksgiving Fun

Thanksgiving is very fun to me,
It makes me fill up with lots of glee.
After we sit down and say the blessing,
I ask if I can have some dressing.

Thanksgiving is the time of year,
The time of year to hunt for deer.
I like to dance in the jumping leaves,
But sometimes they stick in my sleeves.

This holiday is the time to eat,
Especially my father's fantastic fried turkey meat.
This time of year won't make me frown,
At least not till the sun goes down.

Katelin Cunningham, Grade 4
North Elementary School, NC

Stop and Think

Stop and think about what you do,
Stop and think about how you do it,
Maybe you might make a mistake,
So learn from it and don't take it for granted.

Mylea McKenith, Grade 6
Brogden Middle School, NC

I Am Glad to Be an American

I am glad to be an American.
Frogs are jumping on lily pads,
crickets are chirping in the yard.
People from Iraq dreaming of living in the USA.
Maybe when the war is over
they can come here.
Thank God there are
angels watching over us.
The weather is so nice
with green grass.
We would not enjoy any of this
if it was not for our soldiers.
I thank our soldiers
for everything they do.

Dylan Vasseur, Grade 6
Leonville Elementary School, LA

A Ride on My Horse

The sun is setting.
Time is short.
I don't want to go home.
I'm in the woods with my horse Trotter.
My mom comes out on her horse Travis.
She says it's time for dinner but I don't listen.
After she leaves I turn around and trot after her.
We were right near his stall when I jumped off Trotter
And gave him a hug like I'm never going to let him go.

Jamie Castellow, Grade 4
Moyock Elementary School, NC

My Life

I learned to swim at age four,
Now I want to do it more and more.

I started school and made my way to sixth,
My mistakes I learned how to fix.

My friends will come and they will go,
But my best friends stay with me like so.

I have been blessed, my teachers have been good,
My parents have set a good example as they should.

School, family, sports, and friends; My life has been fun,
As I look ahead to the future, I realize that it has only begun.

Daniel Sharpe, Grade 6
Tyro Middle School, NC

The Game

Running down the field
Not ready to yield.
They run, run, run
With the fans watching people are stunned.
Through the whole night and the day light.
Catching the ball and not giving up without a fight
With the pressure on them during the game
They are trying to claim the victory fame.

Timmy Saunders, Grade 6
Queen of Angels Catholic School, GA

Thanksgiving

Today is Thanksgiving.
I thank the Lord that my fish is still living.

I ate some apple pie,
and my fish, well he died.
I really wanted to cry.

I went outside, climbed a tree
and scraped my knee.
Oh! how horrible could it be.

Anna Green, Grade 5
Midway Covenant Christian School, GA

Christmas

The angels sang the merry bells rang, carolers are caroling and everyone bought out the store,
you guessed the time yell it out, it ain't a crime, go see your friends, go see your family,
everyone is dandy, gift wrap is handy, but remember don't eat too much candy!

Patrick Merritt, Grade 5
Evangel Christian Academy, AL

New England Patriot Blue

New England Patriot Blue looks like fans at a home football game, doing the wave
New England Patriot Blue sounds like the coach cheering on the players when they sack the opposing quarterback.
New England Patriot Blue smells like the spray paint in the cheering fans hair.
New England Patriot Blue tastes like the blue raspberry starbursts I was eating during the game.
New England Patriot Blue feels like the fans jumping off my shoulders onto the field when they win the Super Bowl
New England Patriot Blue is the color of the logo on the middle of the field.
New England Patriot Blue is the sound of foghorns blowing when they get a touchdown.
New England Patriot Blue is the smell of chalk that fans use to write stuff on the windows of their cars.
New England Patriot Blue tastes like the cotton candy I was eating at half-time.
New England Patriot Blue is the feeling of confetti falling over me when they won the game.

Cody Overcash, Grade 5
Cool Spring Elementary School, NC

Friends

I have friends; do you?
Do you have the kind of friends I do?
The kind who are caring, trustworthy, and nice
The kind who'll care to help you in school when you don't understand stuff
The kind who'll help you when you make a bad grade, or the kind who'll congratulate you when you make a good grade
I hope you have friends like I do
They don't have to be popular, or punkish, or rockish, or nerdish, or geekish, or brainish, or anything
They just have to be friends
They don't have to live across the street, or down the block or two miles away
They can live anywhere
They just like you for you
Do you have friends like I do?

Kristina Kremer, Grade 6
Smyrna Middle School, TN

The Unknown

The world was meaningless as if a black velvet curtain had stained a clear glass surface. The pulse of what was and what would
never be was as still as night. Her face portrayed a little tear meant to be hidden. Hidden inside her internal veil of the
unknown. Until she realized. Only she could discover the door hidden in the haze to set her free from the life she never chose.

Ronnisha Lewis, Grade 6
Savannah Middle School, NC

I Remember Boston

I remember Boston…
Watching a Red Sox game, Grandma's fresh butterscotch pie, feeling the nice cool water

I remember Boston…
Smelling the freshly cut grass, seeing the big city, tasting the franks at Fenway Park

I remember Boston…
Playing, running, laughing

I remember Boston.

Bryan Gropp, Grade 5
Sycamore Elementary School, GA

Flags of Our Fathers

Once there was a flag,
Whose stars and stripes gleamed.

Our fathers carried this valuable flag,
And made it stand tall.

Don't ever burn nor step on the flag,
For it shows disrespect.

Always love and cherish it,
To keep our nation proud.

Always remember,
Respect the flag.

And love Jesus Christ
The Lord.

Bradley Slaubaugh, Grade 4
Heartland High School and Academy, MO

Bells

Jingle, Jingle the church bells ring
Jingle, Jingle we begin to sing

Jingle, Jingle the Christmas Bells ring
Jingle; Jingle what a celebration it brings.

Jingle, Jingle Christmas a spectacular time of the year.
A Christmas celebration is almost here.

Jingle, Jingle lets have some fun
Jingle, Jingle and worship God's son.

Toree Elliott-Mize, Grade 5
Hatfield Elementary School, AR

All About Me

If I were a color,
I'd be green.
Like the dark green pine trees
If I were an animal,
I'd be a dog.
Like a very smart and fast lab.
My favorite place is at home on the river,
When it is on a hot and sunny day.
And when I get to go fishing.
My favorite snack is cheeze-its,
The kind that has extra cheese
From Wal-Mart
I really get upset,
When I get in trouble and it is my brother's fault.
And I have to go to bed at 8:00.
I love to listen to country music
When I am in my car.

Brian Prewitt, Grade 4
Pine Tree Hill Elementary School, SC

Summer Days

Summer is here now.
Daisies sit in the sweet sun.
The birds sing a song.

Caroline Logan, Grade 4
Briarwood Christian Elementary School, AL

My Bed

Small television playing quietly
Warm sheets rustling delicately
Same silent sounds approaching slowly
Tiny whispers awakening creepily
Fine firm fluffy pillows like cotton sitting calmly
White light switch as bright as the sun flickering lightly
Vanilla air fresheners spreading rapidly
Watermelon gummy bears melting quickly
Chocolate M&M's crunching noisily
Fire engine red Gatorade streaming swiftly
I feel relaxed and tranquil

Brad Worrell, Grade 4
Bailey Elementary School, NC

Mother and Brother

M y sweet loving mother
O ur mother is nice to people
T he things that makes me happy
H er hugs are soft and sweet
E nough love. never, I'll love you more and more
R emember I love you.

A nd brother or mother I choose both
N ever say I hate my mom you'll hurt her heart
D ear mom and brother I love you

B rothers are mean but sometimes he's nice
R ough or kind we never know
O ur heads go crazy
T hought he was mean but I know he's nice
H e will play sometimes maybe not.
E nough tall he's very tall
R ough or soft will always be loved

Jennifer Luque, Grade 6
Brogden Middle School, NC

My Mom

My mom is outgoing.
She is out standing as a hairdresser.
She is a person who you can agree to.
She is a person who will never leave your side.
She is a person who will be kind if you are.
She is a person who it takes a lot to get mad.
She is a person who likes to read.
She is a person who likes to help people.
More than anything she loves her kids.
What can I say she is my fantastic mom.

Zachary Ty Harrell, Grade 6
Armorel Elementary School, AR

Proud to Be in America

I am proud to be in America
with a sky so clear and bright.
I sit on the side of a big oak tree
wanting to find a bright gold stone
to give to soldiers for protecting us.
We need God to wake us up
and do other things.
The soldiers have to fight
in big green tanks to protect us.
The moon brightens
the dark black sky.
The short grass has a moist feeling
as the sun rises.
A candy painted Chevy zoomed by
on 26 inch rims.
A family dog waits
for his master to
come back from Iraq!

Kaleb Thomas, Grade 6
Leonville Elementary School, LA

Fall

Let's ride on a carriage ride in the fall.
Riding through the leaves,
That will be a ball!
All of the colors — aren't they wonders?
The red and the yellow like the sun…
jump in the leaves, isn't it fun?

Tasting pumpkin pie with whipped
cream on top, maybe a little
maybe a lot.
Turkey and dressing oh so good,
with ham and yam. Fall is the best!
Oh, I have to go get some rest.

Ani Patenaude, Grade 5
Palmetto Christian Academy, SC

Monsters

Creatures and monsters
Ghosts and ghouls
Tonight's the night
They all come out

The full moon rises
A wolf's howl is heard
The sun is down
Leathery wings flapping around now

Beasts come out
But they don't come in
Stay in your house
And lock your doors

Alexis Martin, Grade 6
Alexandria Middle Magnet School, LA

Cats

Cats, cats, everywhere.
On my hats and in my chair,
On the pillows and the floor,
On the tables and out the door.

In they come,
Sly as a fly,
Looking for a piece of pie.

"Down, Kitty," I said.
"Go away,
But come back another day."

"I'm too tired to play,
Hear me now.
I love you so,
But please remember you have to GO!"

Dakota Daugherty, Grade 5
North Shelby Elementary School, MO

Pretty, Blue Shell

Aquamarine in color
Rough insides
Smooth outsides
Big or huge
Marvelous,
Exciting,
Amazing
Soft as a feather
Put it to your ear
You will hear the laughter of kids
Wish you had it
Wish you could hear it
So awesome
So neat
So beautiful
So blue
So unique
Like me and you

Myleka Jefferson, Grade 6
Alexandria Middle Magnet School, LA

Spring

The rain falling down
How beautiful and humid
Peaceful and quiet

Dominique Burnett, Grade 6
Tomlinson Jr High School, OK

Holiday

Jingle bells are up
Pine trees aromas in town
Pinning tree ornaments

Christian Serrano, Grade 6
Pulaski County Middle School, GA

Verbs

Verbs, verbs, they get on my nerves,
Nouns are much better,
So are describing words.
They give me a headache
And make me sick.
I want to punch 'em,
And sock 'em, and give
'em a kick.

I'm trying to be nice,
But they're not cool.
I really don't like
To study them in school.

I would rather do chores
And wash the dishes,
A noun like cake
Is just delicious.
The verbs jump and play
Are just OK,
But, nouns I can enjoy
All day.

Christopher Morgan, Grade 5
Nesbit Elementary School, GA

The Sun Is Glaring in My Face

The sun is glaring in my face,
I'm hot and sweaty,
and out of breath,
running
playing
with my friends.
Laughing
singing
and having fun.
We are going swimming
to get
cooled down,
goggles and swimsuits
and don't forget the sunscreen,
I have a smile on my face because,
the sun is glaring in my face.

Brittani Schadler, Grade 5
Walton Verona Elementary School, KY

Veteran

V eterans fighting for victory
E ager to fight
T raining for values
E nemies ready to serve the
R ed, white, and blue
A nd America's home
N ever give up!

Tarah Earle, Grade 4
Cherokee Elementary School, AR

My Pets

I love my pets oh yes I do.
There's Larry and Shelby who I love oh so,
And Harry the fish who I had to let go.
Harry was 9 when my cousin killed him,
Harry was not very fat at all actually he was very thin.
We always played, his favorite games was colors of flames.
I love my pets as you can tell,
They're something I'll never sell.
I hope you love my pets as much as I do,
Because to me they are just like me and you.

Mary Margaret Anderson, Grade 4
St Ann School, TN

Amazing Love

Amazing love…Amazing Grace!
My Lord, My Savior, puts a smile on my face!

From the tomb he arose on the third day!
He came back to show the way!

My Lord, my Savior, his amazing love!
Will get me to the great place above!

Amazing love… Amazing Grace!
Let it put a smile on your face!

Mitchell McCrary, Grade 5
Etowah Elementary School, NC

Veteran

V igilant where they watch over us
E mbraced in the world's hope
T riumphant fighting for the good of our country
E agle-eyed fighters
R eady to serve our country
A merican freedom is ours
N avigating to save our Nation

Matthew Garner, Grade 4
Cherokee Elementary School, AR

Nana

My Nana, as alive as fire.
Energy flowing, like an electric wire.

Caring for others, like a protecting mother.
Treating all, as her little brother.

Her laugh is shrill, yet is music to ears.
The happiness with it, takes away fears.

Solemn and graceful, electric and chatty.
Yet not like most people, she won't drive you batty.

Calm and unique, experienced and poised.
In her heart, is nothing but joy.

Matthew Furlong, Grade 6
Charleston County School of the Arts, SC

Shoe

Sally Sue lost her shoe
Oh no! Oh gee! Could this be true
It's pink and green quite so bright
Come over here we need some light
Look over your head
Look under that bed
Look in that cart
If it's playing hide and seek it's smart
Sally Sue please don't frown
"Come on," look side to side up and down
She's got to go to school
If she doesn't have a shoe she won't be cool
Oh look it's under that stool
Oh yeah! We rule!
Ye ha scream and shout
Hurry put it on you've got to get out!

Mallory Whitaker, Grade 6
Briarwood Christian Elementary School, AL

Morning

See all the cabinets in the big kitchen
Hear the microwave when it goes off
Smell the bacon and eggs cooking in the morning
Taste the bacon and eggs we just cooked
Touch the plates, forks, pots, and pans

Jordan Zwitch, Grade 5
Bonaire Elementary School, GA

Egyptian Pyramids

Tall
tombs for
the Egyptian Pharaohs
and many dead ends to confuse
robbers who might try to steal the body
And keep them wandering in there for a very
long time and were also very large like the Great
Pyramid which was the largest one of all the pyramids and
was the largest building until the Eiffel Tower was built in
Paris, France which makes me think the Egyptians were very
advanced for the time period to construct such a huge Pyramid.

Michael Avossa, Grade 6
Beck Academy, SC

A Picture

A picture is worth a thousand words
at least that is what I have come to understand
from everybody's uncivil demands.
I see two pictures; what does that mean?
2000 words or does it depend on their quality?
What if three I come to see?
What do I do or how about you tell me.
I only know a picture is worth a thousand words,
and that is all that matters you see.

Libby Strickland, Grade 5
Drayton Hall Elementary School, SC

Halloween

Creepy, spooky
You see costumes.
Some are
scary.
Some are
hairy.
Some are
funny.
Look, there's one that's a
bunny.
Dark, full moon, foggy
come to mind
Candy!
Lot's of candy!
Tons of candy!

Andrew Smith, Grade 5
Walton Verona Elementary School, KY

Grandfather's Garden

In my grandfather's
garden there are
tomatoes on vines
green and yellow
Red — the juicy ones
That my
grandfather
loves.

Logan Beach, Grade 4
Alvaton Elementary School, KY

Thankful

I'm thankful for God's great love.
I'm thankful for heaven above.
I'm thankful for the moon that glows.
I'm thankful for the stream that flows.
I'm thankful for my glee.
I'm thankful to be me.
I'm thankful for Thanksgiving.
But most of all I'm thankful for Jesus
That Jesus is still living.

Kenneth W. Armstrong, Grade 4
Ode Maddox Elementary School, AR

School

To me school is a bore
Personally, I don't know what it's for.
I would much rather run and play
until it's time to hit the hay
Homework is so long and dreadful
it always give me quite a headful
School will last all the day.
but now my teacher is in the hallway
So for now,
let the students play!

Osborne Brown, Grade 5
Shannon Forest Christian School, SC

Where the Towers Once Stood

Once they were there now they are gone
Once they stood there proud and tall
'til they came to a fall.
Now what is left is nothing,
but broken hearts and lives.
People all over the nation cried. What, the Pentagon?
It stood white and pretty. Many people feel pity.
September 11, 2001 a day we will not forget. But a day many people will regret.
U.S.A. so strong and proud we'll grind those people to the ground.
Freedom does not come free, but in the home of the brave
and the land of the free, will always be a WE not an I.
We will win our fight. September 11, 2001 where the towers once stood.

Jordan Hensley, Grade 6
William Blount Middle School, TN

Battle of Britain

Only did Britain stand, facing the wrath of Hitler's might.
An air battle did commence.
Britain fielded a world wide air force with the sturdy Hurricane and the Spitfire,
that spat bullets from six guns, to save the day!
For Germany only Aryan pilots did fly.
"For Germany" they cried then they died.

Hank Massaro, Grade 6
Bellwood Discovery School, TN

Fall

Fall is a wave of pure cold sweeping the country
Leaves tumbling from trees creating enormous pools of brown and brown-red
Hay scattering the ground wafting in the air
It's pumpkins filling yards with light in shapes of scary faces from the candle inside
Red and orange painting the sky in afternoons and mornings

Taylor Ray Tinsley, Grade 6
Alvaton Elementary School, KY

The Best Dog

My old dog Missy was a chocolate lab
She was a very nice dog sweet, too.
I loved her more than anything.
She's very playful so every time I saw her I wanted to play with her.
Missy had smooth brown fur.
One day my papa took her to the animal shelter.

Missy was the best dog I ever had!!
It was too long ago to remember why he did.
I loved that dog! I always will!
I've had a lot of other dogs after I had Missy!
The German Shepherd (Brakkus) that I have
right now isn't anything like Missy.

Missy was different from other dogs.
There are all kinds of different dogs in the world,
I would choose Missy for the best one.
It will be really hard to forget about a dog like her.
I will always love her and that's coming from my heart!

Lauren Bird, Grade 4
Alvaton Elementary School, KY

Halloween Orange

Halloween Orange looks like a jagged teeth sitting on the front porch. Halloween Orange feels like digging into wet, slimy pumpkin seeds. Halloween Orange tastes like pumpkin pie with whipped cream on Thanksgiving Day. Halloween Orange sounds like the Fall Festival people screaming their lungs out. Halloween Orange smells like fresh pumpkin bread coming out of the oven.

Halloween Orange is dry mud on a hot day. Halloween Orange is a three pointer basket going through the hoop. Halloween Orange is a sweet candy corn taste in your mouth. Halloween Orange is the smell of a cinnamon pumpkin candle. But most of all it is a Halloween color.

Megan Privette, Grade 5
Cool Spring Elementary School, NC

Medieval Man*

A long, long time ago, I can still remember how that victory used to make me smile.
And I knew if I had a lance, I could make my people dance and maybe they'd rejoice for a while.
My adversaries made me shiver, with every siege that they delivered.
Scoffing on the mote's edge, I couldn't abandon my pledge
And I was baffled when they screamed, the news they told of his sinister scheme.
And I was woeful deep inside, the day the king died. So bye, bye Mr. Medieval Man.
Hauled my charger to the battle and the battle was won
And the colossal knights overpowered the foes
Singing this'll be the day that they lose. This'll be the day that they lose.
Now for ten years other sentinels, detect and blunder other foes
And that's just how it use to be. And they'll be sing'n
Bye, bye Mr. Medieval Man, hauled my charger to the battle
And the battle was won, And the colossal knights overpowered the foes
Singing this'll be the day that they lose. This'll be the day that they lose.

Colt Pennino, Grade 6
Lake Castle School, LA
*Adapted from the song "American Pie" by Don McLean

Penguin

I know the ice like the back of my flipper. I know my enemies and they know me. You are the seal, sea lion, and killer whale. I am a flightless bird, but I still have wings. I can swim as fast as a race car. I have thick feathers that keep me warm, warm like a waterproof coat. I have friends, you probably do too. My friends are the Chinstrap, Gentoo, King, and Macaroni. Every year I find a mate, and lay an egg smoother than a stone. Then the egg hatches and there are more.

Maggie Newman, Grade 4
Bellwood Discovery School, TN

About Me

I want to be a lawyer and doctor that is good, giving, and graceful. I need love and peace in the world. I have a home with my mom. I want you to know I love God and peace. I want you to know that I am a playful person. I know that I love Jesus and God. I gave my life to Jesus my Savior. I want to go to the South and North Pole which is freezing and frigid.

Angelica White, Grade 5
Evangel Christian Academy, AL

Joy*

J is for *jewel* sparkling in the light, and oh what a beautiful sight!
O is for *one* who is the one grandma for me, and how you hated getting stung by little bees
Y is for *yard* work your favorite hobby, and it looked so much better than a hotel lobby

Grandma, oh grandma, I wish you were still here with us on the Earth,
But we know you're up there where life has more worth.
I guess it's ok to say that you have gone away,
to a much better place where you can stay.

Tory Hogg, Grade 6
Haynes Academy for Advanced Studies, LA
*Dedicated to my Grandma Joy

Animals

Animals are cute,
Animals are funny.
Some go quack,
Some go moo.
Some jump up and down,
others slither on their bellies.
Little lions lurk sometimes,
and others like rabbits run rapidly.
Some depend on Mother Nature,
others depend on their habitat.
Some are big,
Some are small.
But most of all,
Animals are cute,
Animals are funny.
Karsen Hicks, Grade 5
St Teresa's School, GA

Thankful for Thanksgiving

Thankful for Thanksgiving
Let's show thanks for all.

Let's tell how we feel once and for all
happy, thankful, forgiving, joyous.

We give and take
as we thank everyone.

Now it's time for the dinner.
Please come and join
love and play.
Finally have a happy day.
Jackie Willis, Grade 6
Guntown Middle School, MS

I Saw a Deer

Running down the road at night,
I saw a deer in the light.
It ran so far away,
I hoped to see it another day.

So there I stood,
Wondering if it was gone for good.
When I started to run away,
The deer came back to play.
Joshua Lumpkin, Grade 4
Stephens Elementary School, AL

Nature

Nature is the soft wind and the warm air
Leaves hit the ground lifeless in despair
Sun beats down on trees today
And soon the cycle starts again
Allison McIntare, Grade 6
Harrisburg Middle School, AR

Slaves

We are the slaves
We came across the waves
Life in America is hard
Most slaves work in the yard
Some work in homes and towns
All work from sunup to sundown
We all pray
That one day
Our debt will be paid.
Brittany McConnell, Grade 5
Alvaton Elementary School, KY

Thanksgiving

Gathered all around
Big, fat turkeys everywhere
Mashed potatoes on every plate
Cream corn, gravy, iced tea
Make sure everyone has enough
Of these tasteful items yet to come
Beth Crowder, Grade 6
Guntown Middle School, MS

Fall

Leaves shining like sun
Shivering from the fall breeze
Leaves falling like snow
Ivy Lee, Grade 6
Livingston Middle School, TN

My Room

My room is my favorite place.
That is where all my dreams are.
In my room…
It is peaceful.
In my room…
It is comfy.
In my room…
Yes, I love my room.
It's my favorite place to be in!
Stephanie Hatton, Grade 5
Stokesdale Elementary School, NC

The Jawbreaker

Finally
Something sweet I can eat
I waited so long
I unwrap the jawbreaker
Berry, lemon, cherry
Blue, yellow, red
It's changing
But it melted away
Bye-bye jawbreaker
Tomorrow I shall buy a new one
Ally Turner, Grade 5
Walton Verona Elementary School, KY

Deer

Deer are fun to hunt.
I like to eat deer jerky.
Bucks have big antlers.
Jonah McCulley, Grade 5
Shirley Elementary School, AR

Take a Trip

There are many places I want to go.
But I can't go.
So I dream about them day and night.
I dreamed that I could take a flight
Over to a distant land.
If you'd like to go, just take my hand.
We'll fly away to Paris, France.
We'll go to Paris, we'll dance a dance.
So, if you would like to go,
Take my hand; we'll go, go, go!
Montressa Jorice Gray, Grade 5
Contentnea Elementary School, NC

Fall

Fall is cool.
Fall is breezy.
Saying goodbye to the pool
is not easy.

Fall brings holidays,
excitement in many ways:
family to see,
food to eat and
we even get to trick-or-treat.

Next thing you know
the leaves are yellow, orange and brown,
lying on the ground.

So peaceful and quiet,
a lot of silence
and not much violence.
Meagan Mulcahey, Grade 6
Madisonville Middle School, TN

Myself

I love to play games.
In the yard all by myself.
Just having cool fun.
Jasper Blackwell, Grade 4
Indian Springs Elementary School, AL

Bees

Bees buzz by honey
for the pollen and nectar
to support their queen
Austin Learo, Grade 5
Etowah Elementary School, NC

Friendship*

Friendship —

Among special others,
deep in our hearts and souls.
An everlasting effect,
from love, care, and a bond
like no other,

From pre-k, or just this past year,
all your friends, new or old,
are like no other.

Though some may grow apart from us,
though you never thought it to be,
you will never forget the past friendships,
the ones like no other.

Morgan Carrico, Grade 6
College View Middle School, KY
*Dedicated to Vixie Greco

Unknown

When I first looked into your brown eyes
You seemed like you would tell nothing but lies.
Now that I have gotten to know you better
I promise to love you forever.
You always know how to make me smile.
For you and I would walk a thousand miles.
Every time we hug I feel all warm inside.
Together there are no secrets we have to hide.
I hope that we will always be friends.
From now on and until the end.
I hope I never have to tell you goodbye.
And if I do I will definitely cry.
There are so many things I like about you
But the most important thing is that I love you!!!

Katelynn Lassalle, Grade 6
Haynes Academy for Advanced Studies, LA

Very Peaceful

This young man is playing the flute.
The sun is shining brightly in the room.
He is just sitting in a hand carved chair.
I can see the value of his hat.
He is just sitting glancing out the window.
I tell the boy loves his music.
It is just the boy and his lovely music.
He is engaged in his playing.
His fingers move smoothly across the rough flute.
The boy is very serious about his music.
In the foreground is the boy.
In the background is the recorder and the violin.
His collar tells me his family is very wealthy.
I can tell his mind is very peaceful.

Lauren Edwards, Grade 5
Saffell Street Elementary School, KY

Friends

F is for friendship.
R is for rough times.
I is for issues.
E is for everlasting.
N is for never a problem.
D is for dying for each other.
S is for special people.

When I think of this word, it reminds me of my FRIENDS.

Lela Flowers, Grade 5
East Marion Elementary School, MS

Hunting

Fall is in the air,
    And that means hunting.
You go into the woods,
    And you come out with a big black bear!
You take it home,
    And you cut the fur right off the bear.
You take it to the tanner,
    And he makes it into a rug.
You set it on the ground
    And let it dry for a day or two.
Then you have a good rug!
Now it's time to sell it to a friend,
    Or maybe a family member
    For less than fifteen dollars.
You mail it to them.
They call you back and tell you "thank you."

Then you go back in the woods
    And you come out with an elk…

Dakota Lane Burrell, Grade 6
Scotts Creek Elementary School, NC

Peace

Peace is what our earth is aching for.
Little creatures are having their habitats destroyed.
War is what countries are going through.
Soldiers killed every day.
Peace is what they need.

Isabella Gross, Grade 5
Saul Mirowitz Day School - Reform Jewish Academy, MO

Fences for Sale

Fences for sale, fences for sale
They're two dollars, they're one dollar
Come buy them for target
Come buy them for rent,
But buy them here or buy them nowhere.
When buying these fences
For how much you want
Then buy these fences
For a whole lot.

JaiDé Webber, Grade 5
Elkhorn Elementary School, MO

I'm Allergic to My Sister

I'm allergic to my sister,
She gives me bumps and sores,
I'm allergic to my sister,
I hate it when she snores,
SO when you see her coming,
You really better run,
Cause getting bumps and sores,
Is not a lot of fun!

Ryan Metcalf, Grade 4
Brilliant Elementary School, AL

My Dog

My dog has long red hair
He loves to sit in his green chair

He wags his tail non-stop
I don't clean up after him with a mop

My mom cleans up after him all the time
I just comfort him when he wines

He loves to play tug-of-war
Then I'm always sore

Domenica Sutherland, Grade 5
St Thomas More School, NC

Instruments

Guitar
Loud, musical
Strumming, plucking, humming
Strings, pick, keys, pedals
Striking, tapping, playing
Soothing, soft
Piano.

Kara Thomas, Grade 5
Harahan Elementary School, LA

Frogs

Frogs
Slimy animals
Jumping, swimming, singing
Beautiful songs of joy
Amphibians

Zach Vance, Grade 6
Lost River Elementary School, KY

Mrs. Sellers

S weet
E verything
L ifelike
L ovely
E njoyable
R eady
S eptember

Amber DeHaan, Grade 4
East Jones Elementary School, MS

If I Were in Charge of the World

If I were in charge of the world
you would get $50 each day
there would be no more orphans
each kid would have their own house.
If I were in charge of the world
there would be no science classes
no oil shortage or chores and everything would be free
there would also be free lunch and you would not have any teachers
all adults would be really nice you would have no bosses
you can play with friends all day long there would be no grades,
all movies are rated pg you can date whoever you want and whenever you want.
You pass all of your classes no matter what
You would have no taxes there would be no moms or dads
there would be no physicals no shots
you would have 24 hours on the playground (hot or cold)
you would be perfectly healthy
ice cream is breakfast no school no Mondays
AND MOST OF ALL YOU WOULD BE PERFECT
IF I WERE IN CHARGE OF THE WORLD!!!

Kaitlyn Eades, Grade 6
Eminence Middle School, KY

Don't Judge a Person

Don't judge a person 'till you've walked in their shoes,
'till you listen with their ears and you've spoken with their tongue

'till you know what they're thinking,
know how they feel, you never can know,
you never can tell, what they'll be like inside.

because a person is unique, not like anyone else…
so don't judge a person 'till you've been in their shoes,
'till you've seen their life, and know how they feel.

because a person's unique, not like anyone else.

Caralyn Evans, Grade 6
Brogden Middle School, NC

I Am Haunted

I am haunted by what's in the dark.
What I think is in the dark is coyotes crawling through the crops.
Bears hiding behind the barn.
I am haunted.

I am haunted by my teacher.
I don't like when they give me as much homework because
I am afraid I won't be able to do it.
Teachers teach and try to give as much homework as possible.
I am haunted.

I am haunted by robots ruling the world.
Humans being destroyed.
I am haunted.

Bobby Brewer, Grade 5
Eminence Middle School, KY

Nature's Beauty

Seasons greetings come to me —
Colors changing, choice is free.
Leaves are falling on rooftops —
I hear the raindrops go plop, plop, plop!

The wind is talking in the air —
Nature's showing a beauty affair.
Squirrels hide acorns they have found —
As leaves fall to the ground.

Big, black balls of smoke go in the air —
Bears have many berries to share.
Beauty shows its majesty —
Or does nature show its beauty?

Ivette Fernandez, Grade 4
North Elementary School, NC

Water

I am energetic like the waves that crash upon the sands.
I am as pure as the water before pollution.
I love to watch what you do on lands.
I can be wild or calm like chemical solutions.
Unpredictable like the weather is something I am.
I love all animals, like the water loves fish.
To be free and wild is one thing I wish,
With open arms I will wit for you and even open hands.
Energetic like the waves that crash upon the sands.

Janice He, Grade 6
River Trail Middle School, GA

Games at School

There are a lot of ways to play at school,
But some are not so very cool.
You can play outside.
You can watch birds fly high in the sky.
You can play with the printers.
But stick with the scissors.

You can play bouncy ball,
But watch out it could go in the hall.
There is a beanie bag bed,
And Mr. Potato Head.
You can play on a desk,
But don't leave a mess.
Then it's time to go home,
But don't go alone.

Kyle Manning, Grade 4
Tazewell/New Tazewell Elementary School, TN

Sunflowers

Sunflowers are bright yellow.
Their attitude is very mellow.
Planting them is so much fun.
Right in the middle of the hot summer sun.

Miranda Hanc, Grade 4
South Topsail Elementary School, NC

Austin's Fireworks

I do not like fireworks
when they pop they hurt my ears.

When they blow up
the light hurts my eyes and they are not cool.

But when I light them, it is so much fun.
Oops I threw some in a fire.

Austin Sprinkle, Grade 4
Brilliant Elementary School, AL

I Saw a Very Odd Thing Today

I was walking home with my dog on a fall day.
I saw a cat chewing on a bone
then in the woods I saw a rabbit fighting a deer.
Then I saw another deer eating meat.
Then I saw a cat barking
and a dog meowing,
a cow neighing and a horse mooing.

Shianne Niederworder, Grade 5
Drayton Hall Elementary School, SC

Santa Is So Big!

Santa is so big.
People leave him porkchops instead of milk and cookies.
Santa is so big.
He doesn't say ho, ho, ho.
He says mo, mo, mo.
No one knows why Santa is so big.
If you see him he might have a wig.

Darian Lindsey, Grade 5
Western Hills Elementary School, AR

Man's Best Friend

I have a dog his name is Ace,
He's brown and white with black on his face,
His legs are long and his nose is short,
When he runs a lot he breathes with a snort.

He's got a friend her name is Priss,
She's Mom's dog and she's a mess,
They run, and play, and bark, and growl,
Till she goes in he starts to howl.

When I go riding on my ATV,
He runs beside of me,
Barking and biting at all four wheels,
He acts like he's having them for his very next meal.

He's my best bud there is no doubt,
Because when I leave for school he sits in a pout,
He awaits my arrival every day after school,
He's waiting by the road with a mouth full of drool.

Tatum Stuard, Grade 5
Joann Walters Elementary School, AR

Proud to Be in America

I am proud to be in America
sitting down under the stars.
When the cool windy breeze comes,
I have a vision in my head
about the soldiers.
Every star reminds me about a soldier.
I hope my friends and relatives
feel the same way.
I hope the soldiers
come back soon.
I want to thank you
with all my heart.

Brooke Artigue, Grade 6
Leonville Elementary School, LA

Veteran

V ictory for veterans
E verybody tried
T ogether they stand by each other's side
E veryone is trying to help
R ights are what they have to help
A nybody could die
N ot all will stay alive

Candace Seward, Grade 4
Cherokee Elementary School, AR

Masks

They are so mysterious
They hide our faces
So many kinds
Lions, tigers, and bears
With a mask you could be anyone

Lacey Cantrell, Grade 6
Dyer Elementary & Jr High School, TN

Fall

leaves, rotten, rakes, long sleeves
warm, colorful, squirrels, play
songbird, puddles, rain

Audrey Paige, Grade 4
East Jones Elementary School, MS

Black Grimalkins

Black grimalkins,
Like cheese,
Spooky cats,
At Halloween,
Fuzzy fur,
Despises dogs,
Loves mice,
Pounces around,
Sometimes pets,
Usually wild.

Aspen Howard, Grade 4
Russell Babb Elementary School, OK

Different Colors

Green is grass.
Green is a chair.
Red is a fire truck.
Blue is the sky.
Yellow is the sun.
White is the cloud
formed in a shape.
Gray is a thundercloud.
Brown is the tree in fall.
Orange is a cheetah.
Pink is a shirt.
Silver can be a desk.
Black can be a sheep
sitting on the lawn.
Pink can be a
fat pig sleeping.
Red can be an apple
on the floor
just sitting there
getting stepped on by people.

Logan Elmore, Grade 4
Cool Spring Elementary School, NC

Seasons

Summer
warm, dry
traveling, swimming, running
picnic, vacation, cocoa, fireplace
skiing, skating, snow boarding
cold, wet
Winter

Elaine Smith, Grade 5
St Dominic School, TN

Who Am I?

I'm wild and clever and silly.
I play and draw and swim.
I'm a boy and student and reader.

I sound like a lion,
I feel like a pirate,
I move like a rabbit,
And look like a Super Hero!

I'm as wild as a lion,
And fast as a hare.

I wait for my plane to leave.
I long for a pirate ship.
I hope for a cool Game-Boy.
I dream of being a Jedi Knight.

My name is Alex.

Alex Shapiro, Grade 6
St Joseph Institute for the Deaf, MO

Fall

Leaves are trembling.
Trees are swaying in the wind.
The season is here.

Jessica Holler, Grade 6
Queen of Angels Catholic School, GA

The Sun

A star in the sky,
A light in the day.
It shines up in space,
and gives off a big ray.
It is here in the day
But not in the night,
That is the sun
That gives off so much light.
The star for the Earth,
and for the Milky Way.
It is constantly moving,
No time to sit and lay.
I've told you the story,
And so I must say,
If you look in the sky,
You'll see it by day.

Eric Baylot, Grade 5
Nesbit Elementary School, GA

Christmas Morning

Seeing the
snow falling.
knowing that it's
Christmas morning
dashing to the tree
kneeling down
shredding open
the presents for me.
noticing a little
present
is for me
SILVER LOCKET!
I was shocked
beautiful and amazing.

Sam Wilson, Grade 4
Alvaton Elementary School, KY

Valentines

Valentines, oh Valentines,
It's the best time of year.
It's Valentines, it's Valentines,
I love this holiday.
It's Valentines, it's Valentines,
You get chocolates shaped like hearts.
It's Valentines, it's valentines,
What a wonderful time of year!

Devin Conley, Grade 5
Paint Lick Elementary School, KY

Football Is Life

Before the big game
You have fans cheering as if they won the lottery
You are sitting there still
But you take the time to smell the fresh-cut grass and hotdogs
And your heart beats faster than a dragster race
But you are still isolated in the game
The number 88 on your jersey
It defines you
Only you
Everything about you…
But maybe it defines life

Mayme Covey, Grade 6
Christ Episcopal School - Middle School, LA

Fun, Fun, Fun in the Sun, Sun, Sun

Lying down on the beach getting some sun,
Once I got up and had some fun.
Where's the water?
I feel it getting hotter.

Gwynn Waters, Grade 4
South Topsail Elementary School, NC

In My Garden

Abundant, brilliant flowers in my garden
Blooming, maturing, growing up to be adults
Bronze soil helping my flowers grow to perfection
Blossoms of blue, aqua, tangerine, lime, and teal
Soft, gentle, and tender vulnerable to anything
Curling up to go to sleep at night
Fuzzy with dew in the morning from Mother Nature

Michael Dalton Cassady, Grade 6
Alvaton Elementary School, KY

Waves

Flowing, calm, blue waves
They are crashing to the shore,
Waves, waves, gorgeous waves.

Nikki Sullivan, Grade 4
Briarwood Christian Elementary School, AL

Thanksgiving

Looks like leaves falling everywhere
Sounds like laughs
Feels like winter
Tastes like Turkey and pie
Smells like rolls baking in the oven

Patrick Lewis, Grade 5
Briarwood Christian Elementary School, AL

The Ocean

The salty ocean
It looks like white, fluffy clouds
Splashing against rocks

Tyler Harris, Grade 4
Briarwood Christian Elementary School, AL

Love Is

Love is a very special thing.
It is a smile on your face,
A light in your heart,
Your soul will shine.
Love means your family, a guy, your friends, your pets,
But all together it means the same,
No matter what or where.
Love is a passion,
For you're near and your soul love will come together
No matter who you are.
God and love are the same.
They both are strong, they both are bright.
Love is a special thing.

Logan Gates, Grade 6
Desoto Central School, MS

My Favorite Teacher

My favorite teacher yes indeed
is Mrs. Corbitt yes siree
She laughs, she smiles, she teaches with style
She makes our day all worthwhile
She likes pink and green
and watching froggies on her big flat screen
Mrs. Corbitt, so sweet
gives us a treat
She lets us have fun
while learning a ton
She's not a fright, but a delight
and so you see why the Mrs. Corbitt is my favorite teacher

Meda Jordan and Amelia Walley, Grade 5
Montana Elementary Academic Magnet School, AL

The Gift of Your Pretty Face

Once I saw your pretty face,
My life fell into place.
Your true blue eyes looked into mine,
And in them I could see the sunshine.
In a terrific face such as yours,
I can see so much more.
In your face I see my life,
Wonder if I'll be your wife?
You're the best thing that's happened to me,
Only if you could be,
The person that I want to know,
The person that says cool instead of so.
When I look in your face,
I see who you are,
You aren't like a shooting star.
Looking in your eyes,
I know you're clever.
Your face is most beautiful ever.
I sit here and wonder every day,
Am I in love or in the way?
Just hope to see your face another day!

Brianna Smith, Grade 5
Deyton Elementary School, NC

Anticipation

Hearts and feet pound
Pulses and girls race
Charging down the court
With determination on each face.

The ball in my hand
And the sweat on my lip
Only two minutes left
In the championship.

Bending my knees
As I hold my breath
Pray for the perfect shot
And my team's success.

It rises and arches
The score is now 11 to 10
We get a big trophy
And now I can't wait to do it again.

Emily Loup, Grade 4
Lewis Vincent Elementary School, LA

In the Park Homer

Here's the wind-up and the pitch
SWING…it's going
The crowd cheers
The glove misses
Over his head
Past first
Rounding second…to third
I'm heading for home
The ball is coming
The dive _____ head first
Under the tag by an inch
S-S-S-A-A-A-F-F-F-E-E-E!!!
The biggest cheer
The winning run!

Vinnie Piantanida, Grade 6
Bernard Middle School, MO

West Virginia

W ild and wonderful
E lks in mountains
S o beautiful
T rout fishing every day

V ultures in the sky
I nsects on the ground
R abbits hopping
G rizzly bears in the woods
I chthvosuar in the lakes
N ice place to live
I bey running on mountains
A pples to eat

Wesley Ellis, Grade 6
Martin Elementary School, WV

Fall

F all is my favorite season.
A ll of the leaves are different colors,
L ike orange, red, yellow, and brown.
L eaves are sometimes crunchy, which means they are dead leaves.

Laurel Morgan, Grade 4
Stephens Elementary School, AL

Lavender

Lavender looks like the beautiful lavender plants in the forest.
Lavender sounds like the graceful chirp of a bird in the fall breeze.
Lavender smells like the sweet smell of the lavender leaves
Lavender tastes like my grandma's sweet apple pie.
Lavender feels like taking off your shoes and relaxing in the fall breeze.
Lavender is the color of my sister's new shoes
Lavender is the sound of the tree leaves ruffling in the wind
Lavender is the sound of the fall flowers in the air
Lavender is my mom's sweet potato pie on Thanksgiving day.
Lavender is the feeling of my family's love on Thanksgiving day

Tatyana Allison, Grade 5
Cool Spring Elementary School, NC

Brandon

When I heard you passed away, my life became incomplete.
There is no more seeing you laugh or your beautiful smile.
It was almost like you went to sleep,
But there was no one who could wake you up.

God had left your body, but took your soul for him to keep.
Now you're in heaven looking down,
And never will you wear a frown.

For now you are in heaven where there is no heartache, no hurt, no crime.
For you are mine.

My own blood, my own heart, my own soul,
For you are always with me,
No matter where we go.
And one day we will meet again.

Rachel Green, Grade 6
Haynes Academy for Advanced Studies, LA

Books

Books can give you knowledge.
Books can help you spell and write.
Books can help you study.
Books can give you good grades.
Books are helpful in so many ways.
Books can give information, yet books can have stories too.
Books aren't stationary and you can move them around.
Books don't take up a lot of space, yet books have so much to teach kids.
Books can have poems and sentences too.
There are books for novices too.
If you become daunting about something, grab a book and they will help you.
Books can have happy endings too.

Chris Pelikan, Grade 5
Parker Road Elementary School, MO

Coach and Teammate*

Coach	Teammate
I push them	They push me so hard so
hard so they know	I will get it right.
what to do.	
If they are hurt	Sometimes it feels like
we will let you	they don't care if we're
sit out and rest	hurt.
for a while.	
Sometimes I get	Sometimes I get so
so mad at them!	mad at my coach!
Sometimes they	Sometimes I'm glad
make me proud!	he is my coach!

Amanda Kapuscinski, Grade 6
Beck Academy, SC
*A 2 voice poem

The Way I Live?

Izaac
animal lover, marbles, Legos, models
James S. and Deja T.
hamster, babies, and my Grandmother
mad, mad, mad
Science item, trains, and Legos
pencils, paper, friendship
dogs, cats, and snakes
Grandmother, Father, and an Ecologist
Florida
Tobias

Izaac Tobias, Grade 5
Nathaniel Hawthorne Elementary School, MO

My Room

My favorite place to be
As everyone can see.
Is my room,
Where I dress up and groom.

I play with and talk to my friends
over the weekends.
I like to read and write,
It gives me great delight.

I have many books and toys,
Playing with them gives me joy.
I like my bed and the canopy
and all the things in the room there can be!

No wonder I love all the things in my room that there are,
Anytime I play with them I think I have gone very far.
I love my computer, my books, my clothes and my games.
That is why my room is my "hall of fame."

Rishika Singh, Grade 5
Crosswind Elementary School, TN

Pencils

They just sit on your desk and do nothing at all
Different shapes, colors, and sizes
Pencils just lay there like stone
Until somebody wants to use them
Use them to write or even to draw
That's why I use them.

Samantha Macchi, Grade 5
Salem Elementary School, AR

Dogs

Dogs are furry dogs are nice
they've got big ears and drool all the time
they like to play and they like to sleep
they're better than cats and
they're awesome pets for you and me
and guess who that's my dog Chole

Ashley Springfield, Grade 4
Duncan Chapel Elementary School, SC

Notice

A quiet beating
The waves are telling you to hush
To notice the beauty of their domain.

Small children laughing and splashing in the blue black sea
As the radiant sun shines down on everything.
Illuminating every sparkling grain of sand.

The sun is reaching for you
Touching you and warming
Every single ounce.

In the distance, seagulls squawk
Longing for stale pretzel crumbs
Like toddlers whining to get what they want.
And while caught up in their cry,
A soft breeze blows carrying sand with it.

Everything together is a symphony

Mary Efird, Grade 6
Chapin Middle School, SC

Bugs

Bugs are small,
but I don't like them all.
I like beetles, ladybugs, caterpillars, and worms.
I don't like ants, mosquitoes or bumblebees.
Bugs are neat,
but not good to eat.
Bugs are cool,
and you might find some at school.
I like bugs they're awesome, too
do you like bugs I know I do.

Casey Allemond, Grade 6
Arnaudville Elementary School, LA

Paintball

Paintball
Messy, swift
Communicating, running, destroying
It is really challenging
Shooting.
Shane Washburn, Grade 4
Russell Babb Elementary School, OK

Little 'Ol Me

Short and skinny,
Who could it be
They have little legs,
That make them short to a tea

She likes to dance
Although she can't
When she moves her legs
It looks as if she had to prance

Now hmm I'm looking but I cannot see
Her feet are as small as they can be
She has no problem
Not at all
Because she isn't even tall

But when she stands
Although she is short
They look as if they were
Standing next to a cork!
Adriana White, Grade 6
St Mark Elementary School, SC

All About Me

Hello!
My name is Mackenzie
If I were a color,
I'd be pink
like a cats nose
If I were an animal,
I'd be graceful and colorful
like a butterfly
My favorite place is, in the pasture
When I ride my horses
and groom them.
My favorite snack is smores.
The chocolatey ones
from camping on the river.
I really get upset,
When I have to get up in the
morning and I have to go to school.
I love listening to music
and singing
when I am in the car.
Mackenzie Higgins, Grade 4
Pine Tree Hill Elementary School, SC

Winter

The snow is falling,
Grandpa is hauling,
Grandma is calling,
Her dog named Walling.
Blake Anderson, Grade 4
Cave City Elementary School, AR

Puppies

Cuddly and sweet
I would like for you to meet
My little puppy
Whose name is Pete
He's fat and round
A cuddly little hound
Who jumped on my bed
Then fell to the ground
Jake McVey, Grade 5
Graham Elementary School, AL

11 of September

In two thousand and one
It wasn't that fun.

On the eleventh of September
Everyone felt tender.

The smoke in the air
Looked like a black bear.

Then the towers fell down
Straight to the ground.

Everybody tried
But most of them cried.

Fourteen men in suicide
Crashed and died

Iraq will go down
Straight to the ground.
Thomas Wilson, Grade 6
Edmonton Elementary School, KY

Alabama Football Great, or Not?

A labama football has the
B est tradition in
C ollege football.
D o you think it is?
E SPN says we do.
F ine with me if you say no, but I would
G reatly appreciate it if you said yes.
H owever, you've got your opinion and
I 've got mine.
Robert Howard, Grade 4
Stephens Elementary School, AL

The Future

Wondering, wondering,
What will be.
Looking back in twenty years,
Will I still look like me?

I wonder day in and day out,
What life is all about.
Is it just for fun,
Or for getting something on Earth done?

Just wondering, wondering,
All the time.
What the future will bring?

In time I will know.
Only time will tell.
Twenty years from now,
I guess it will show.
Janine Nowak, Grade 6
Orange Grove Elementary School, MS

Fall

Fall is here.
The air is cold and crisp.
Hear the rush of the wind
and the crackling leaves
as people walk on them
without a care.
Temperatures jump from warm to cold.
Leaves display amazing hues
of orange and red and yellow.
But as soon as it begins,
the breathtaking fall
comes to a close
as winter settles in.
Josh Thomas, Grade 6
Immanuel Lutheran School, MO

Zac's Best Friend

He wakes me up early,
By licking my feet,
I better getup,
Or he'll pull off my sheet.

He gives me kisses,
and I'll give him a hug,
I'll give him a toy,
and he'll give it a tug.

This little dog.
I'm going to keep.
He shares my life,
And makes it complete.
Zac Walker, Grade 5
Joann Walters Elementary School, AR

The Battle Castle

I fight, I fight, I fight all night long
I saw a knight fling a kite
I saw a knight singing a song

That knight had the golden sword
He hit his opponent with a cord
And he had a nice big Ford

He had a big bad black horse
It acted free, wild, and it was very furious
The knight was very curious

But no one didn't know I was the king
And I have a lot of bats, with big wings

Lacarvia Toussaint, Grade 6
St Mark Elementary School, SC

Friends

Friends are always there for you
even when you have the flu
they might not be there through your life
but sometimes when you get in little fights
that make you just want to pull out your hair —
but just remember…friends are always there

Kintessa Wagner, Grade 6
Leland Middle School, NC

Figgaro

One late November night.
I went to visit a friend.
I saw a pretty sight.
It was their cat who made my troubles seem to end.
His name was Figgaro,
He was a nice cat.
He sat by the window,
I wished he could chat.
I played with the boys,
But nothing seemed as fun,
As giving Figgy some joy.
And being his favorite one.
When it was time to go.
I was a little sad.
I already missed Figgaro.
But I was glad for time we had.

Jessica Thorne, Grade 6
Community Christian School, NC

The Man and the Long Nose

There once was a man who had a long nose,
Which in that nose sat some crows,
There were rows of toes in that nose,
And that was all he smelled all day,
His nose was all he dealt with until May.

Zack Robichaux, Grade 6
St Cecilia School, LA

A Flower

Seed in the dirt,
Ready to pop out,
Sprouting a new life,
Into the world,

Growing more and more,
Its beautiful colors,
Wonder smells,
Attracting insects,

Insects of every shape,
Every size,
Every color,
Sucking the nectar,

Carrying the pollen,
Just like a doorman,
At a hotel carrying your luggage,
Up to your room.

Seed in the dirt,
Ready to pop out,
Sprouting a new life,
Into the world.

Kelsey Hall, Grade 4
Goshen Elementary School at Hillcrest, KY

Otters

Brown and furry, wet
dive deep under water at
the aquarium.

Anna Hornsby, Grade 4
Briarwood Christian Elementary School, AL

My Cat Scamper

Scamper,
Scamper,
You are the queen,
Though sometimes you can be very mean.

Your tail is long,
Your ears are small,
When you see a dog,
You start a brawl.

You beat up Spot,
Happy too,
I'd hate to be a dog,
If I were you.

Your claws are sharp,
Your meow is fierce,
You're like this every day,
But I love you anyway.

Katelyn Coffman, Grade 5
Joann Walters Elementary School, AR

Over There

Over there, over there,
Our soldiers fight
With might.

As the hand of death comes
And plucks
People from the Earth
As a farmer picks weeds
From his crops.

And many fall dead
As boats sink,
Tanks explode,
And planes fall
From the skies.

Over there, over there
Our soldiers fight
With might.

Joseph Cosentino, Grade 6
Fayetteville Christian School, NC

Woods

When you walk through the woods
You hear birds chirping
You see squirrels jump from tree to tree.
Chipmunks run through the leaves.
Under your feet you hear sticks cracking
A deer jumping through the woods.
The leaves falling out of trees.
It is really fun to be in the woods.

Samantha Kimball, Grade 6
Pleasants County Middle School, WV

Who Cares

Roses are red
Violets are blue
My hair is black
And I am too
But who cares
The color of you

Kellie Simpson, Grade 6
Harrisburg Middle School, AR

Angels

I wish I could
be with them,
looking down
on my friends.

To spread my
wing up and fly
like and angel
In the sky.

Faith Samala Robinson, Grade 5
Laurence J Daly Elementary School, MO

Time

Long ago it was destined to begin, no one ever figured out when.
It will never stop, it'll never break, and it will definitely never end.
You can always kill it, you can always save it.
Relish, remember, spend, or savor it.
It's a thing we all share, anyone can take it.
Thinner than paper, more flexible than clay.
Comes in years, months, weeks, and days.
Buy, stall for, give, or keep track of it.
You will always need it but never have lack of it.
A clock, an hourglass, or even a sundial.
Not believing in time would make you be in denial.
They say it's an illusion, and that it was only manmade.
Closer it will come, and away it will fade.

Hayden Lam, Grade 6
Orange Grove Elementary School, MS

My Best Friend, Brandy

A lways there to cheer you up.
B est dog I've ever had.
C uddly and soft.
D idn't ever leave your side.
E verybody loved her.
F riendly and nice.
G od takes care of her now.
H ow we all loved her very much.
I will never forget the way we played
J ust never stopped playing.
K ids loved her, too.
L oved to eat leftovers.
M y best friend forever.
N obody could turn her down.
O wner of our hearts
P recious and adorable.
Q ueen of the house.
R an as quick as lightning.
S weet and loveable.
T houghtful of people.
U nder your feet all day.
V ery loving
W hitney's best friend.

Whitney Reed, Grade 5
Sullivan Elementary School, TN

I Am Haunted

I am haunted in the past by bad guys breaking in my house
They might steal me away and put me in a small silver suitcase
They might throw me in the rough rocky river and I would die

I am haunted in the present that I might get cruel cancer
I am terrified that I might never see my family again

I am haunted in the future that I might be in a crunching car crash
I might get paralyzed
And I will never walk or play again.

Ben Willhite, Grade 5
Eminence Middle School, KY

Purple

Purple looks like fresh grape jelly on my crunchy toast.
Purple feels like a happy spring day.
Purple tastes like a plump juicy plum watering in my mouth.
Purple smells like the burning of a scrumptious lavender candle.
Purple sounds like a quiet night as I lay soundless, asleep in my dark room.
Purple is the color of joy.

Abby Schlueter, Grade 5
Geggie Elementary School, MO

Youth
Young people all around,
Running and falling on the ground.

Oh! what a little bundle of joy,
Every last girl and boy.

Watch them run, play, and skip,
Look at the little ones playing in the yard.

Time seems to just fly by,
Watching the little ones' kites fly so high.

Freedom is an ordinary thing,
For these kids with such zing.

They will run, they will frown, they will hang upside down.
The young and restless, no kidding!

At the end of the day all they have is enough energy to say
"What fun I had today!"

Alexis McKinney, Grade 6
Orange Grove Elementary School, MS

Green Is…
Green is the leaves in spring
And the stems of a flower that it brings
Green is the feeling of envy
The color of poison ivy
Green is the smell of fresh cut grass
A church's stained window glass
Green is a grasshopper playing around
The leaves in a pumpkin patch hanging upside down
Green is the broccoli you just can't stand
Or a butterfly landing on your hand
Green is a rotten sandwich sitting out over night
A frog being held right
Green is a lime without its slime
A green painted sea for me to look at
Green is a candle anyone can handle
And moss that grow on trees
Green is the color of a pickle
Don't forget cucumber
Green is so much
I can't think anymore, wait don't forget
The little green line on the computer

Ciera Jayne Wilk, Grade 6
Lost River Elementary School, KY

What Does Thanksgiving Mean to Me?
Thanksgiving is when you get together
you and your family and pray for thanks.
Then you eat and spend time with your family.
Be blessed you have a family who loves you
and a roof over your head.

Clay Robison, Grade 6
Guntown Middle School, MS

Future Divide
There is a future divide between East and West
I just can't decide which is the best
I settle in the middle
And watch a little
For I can see the war
Very soon it will be June
And the East will have won

Bree Kirkland, Grade 6
Bellwood Discovery School, TN

Dads
Do you remember when
Your dad told you those
Princess and prince stories?
Do you remember when
He rinsed you in the bath,
or so I have heard?

Were you ever afraid
Of what might happen once you get older?
Like, if he would leave you
And never see you again,
Or would he just stop loving you anymore.
Some people do.
Do you?

Zoe Terrell, Grade 6
Harrisburg Middle School, AR

Seven Little Monkeys
There were seven little monkeys swinging from trees
The first one fell off a vine onto her knees
The second one fell asleep
The third one started to eat
The fourth one jumped a big leap
The fifth one hid under a sheet
The sixth one started to scream
The seventh one kept on swinging vine to vine

Taylor Kelty, Grade 5
Ascension Elementary School, KY

The Closest Thing to Flying
Sliding down a mountain,
Hitting small bumps, swerving
Hit a big one and flew,
A rush of color,
White,
Green,
Blue,
Powder flying like
Out-of-control helicopters
Behind me, then, a crash, a flood of cold,
Surrounded by a cloud of snow, and back to the top,
To do it all over again

Jenson Rawlings, Grade 5
Big Creek Elementary School, GA

Mom

Today's the day
I have to say
I love you a bunch
You make me lunch
You give me money
You also call me honey
Today's the day I have say
You are a special woman.

Samantha Michelle Dellinger, Grade 5
Zalma Elementary School, MO

I Need

I need to comb my hair
I need to brush my teeth
I need to make myself neat
I need a book bag
I need a ruler
I need my pencil,
I need my paper
I need my teacher to be nice
and smart for me to go to school today,
I need,
I need,
I need to do homework when I get home
so I need you to leave.

Vanessa Beard, Grade 4
Lewis Vincent Elementary School, LA

My Teacher

My teacher's name is Ms. Taylor,
She is my favorite one,
She has a cool way of teaching,
She is also very fun.

On the way to school,
I look forward to the day,
I don't want school to end,
But that's all the way in May.

I am glad she is my teacher,
It's too bad it has to end,
We are getting very close,
She is like my best friend.

Aleaka Cooper, Grade 5
Sycamore Elementary School, GA

My Daddy

Magnificent and joyful
loves the way I sing
Goes to see my soccer games
takes me to the mall sometimes
Loves my smile
I LOVE MY DADDY!

Madison Rose, Grade 4
Alvaton Elementary School, KY

Rain

Rain rain what a wonderful thing
but how could I like it if it
ruins my day
I know it helps
but why can't I play
I don't care if it's wet or dry
please just let me play
it's just drops of water
what could it possibly do
I'll tell you what it ruins my day

Tyler Pentz, Grade 5
Drayton Hall Elementary School, SC

Fairy Penguin

Cute fairy penguin
Expert in climbing mountains
Lovable creature

Nicole Iida, Grade 5
John Will Elementary School, AL

Drama Queens

Drama queens can be mean
And sometimes lean.
Some may even make a big scene.
Their conditions will worsen
When acting like sick persons.
I wish I were a drama queen,
Making people believe
I'm a superstar
Driving a fancy sports car
With all the paparazzi
On the drama queen, Me!

Lindsay Young, Grade 4
Cleveland Elementary School, OK

Fall

Leaves falling to the ground.
Trying not to make a sound.
All the colors in the night.
When I wake up in the morning,
They really make a sight
When fall is gone,
I'm really sad.
So I sing a song.
I can't wait till next year.

Rebecca Saige Boyette, Grade 5
Contentnea Elementary School, NC

Light and Dark

Light sheds one way,
through a cave.
As darkness stops the night,
from going away.

Irhad Sehovic, Grade 5
Bayless Intermediate School, MO

Summer

I see flowers bloom
While dirt is on my hands
Seeing cute bugs go

Shelby Sanders, Grade 6
Tomlinson Jr High School, OK

Fruit

Fruit,
Fruit,
Fruit,
Sweet fruit,
Sour fruit,
Big huge ripe fruit
Small crunchy tangy fruit,
Those are just a few.
Yellow fruit,
Red fruit,
Green juicy round fruit,
Pink fruit too,
Red cherries
Orange oranges
Don't forget the purple fruit.
Last of all best of all,
I like juicy fruit.

Morgan Mendenhall, Grade 6
Hayes Elementary School, OK

Jesus

Jesus died for my sins.
Yes, I know He did.
He chose us over Himself.
He was thinking about us.
He's in heaven right now,
Thinking of us when He looks down.
He rose from the dead,
It has been said.
Our prayers are with Him all the time,
We need our praises to make Him shine.
Jesus has made everything in sight,
He wants us to take it with delight.
Jesus is cool, Jesus is great.
He will love you anyway.

Steven Cannon, Grade 6
Desoto Central School, MS

My Room

Purple with sparkles,
dolphins everywhere,
Tinkerbell beads hanging from the door,
doll palace,
a huge sliding bed,
my big doubled window…
My room!

Maggie Caton, Grade 6
Dyer Elementary & Jr High School, TN

Katrina

Nervousness all around
People watching
People waiting
People packing
People leaving

The storm bears down
Destruction all around
Lives forever changed
Our town will never be the same
Katrina

Olivia Mayeaux, Grade 6
Haynes Academy for Advanced Studies, LA

I Am a Military Brat

I am a military brat who was born in Texarkana, Texas.
I wonder if soldiers will come home safe and alive.
I hear gun fire and planes every day.
I see buses and planes leave with soldiers.
I want them to come home safe and alive.
I am a military brat who was born in Texarkana, Texas.

I pretend that the war is over
I feel sad for my friend and when her dad leaves.
I touch my friend's hand when she is sad about her dad leaving.
I worry about her dad in the war.
I cry when she cries about her dad in war.
I am a military brat who was born in Texarkana, Texas.

I understand that they need to go.
I say no when they go.
I dream about them coming home safe and alive.
I try to help my friend when her dad is in war.
I hope they come home safe and alive.
I am a military brat who was born in Texarkana, Texas.

Maison Gennings, Grade 5
Walker Intermediate School, KY

Poets Poets

Poets poets everywhere,
poets poets here and there.
The words they use are rhyming
like timing, miming, and chiming.
If their poems are written well,
they'll be published and ready to sell.
With silly words and words so untrue
the books of poems will be sold out by the afternoon.
All the people will read the phrases
about silly people and silly places.
Some poets write sad poetry too,
about great disasters or a friend they once knew.
Poets poets across the miles,
write their best poems on things that make others smile.

Cathleen Banks, Grade 5
St Michael Parish School, WV

Jumping Rope

Jumping rope is fun
We can count from 100 to 1
We can play Sky Blue, Double Dutch, or just by ourselves
We can jump rope wherever we dwell
We can jump rope inside and out
When we jump rope we're always about
So go ahead and try it three times the charm
Jumping rope will do you no harm
Whirling, Twirling and Swirling about
If you love jump rope just give a little shout
Rain, Hail, Sunshine, or Snow
We can jump rope wherever we go

Alexandra Stadler, Grade 6
Haynes Academy for Advanced Studies, LA

Smiles

Smiles are meant to share
Smiles are very different in many ways
Smiles are great
Share them with a friend
Cherish the smiles you get from everyone
Smiles you give make people's days a lot better
When you just smile
They make you feel better.

Gabby Crossnoe, Grade 6
Dyer Elementary & Jr High School, TN

The Last Person on Earth

If I was the last person on Earth,
I don't know what I would do.
I'd probably just lie around
And eat candy all day long!
That would be fun
But then I'd have to go to the candy store.
I can hear the chocolate screaming my name.
Oh, what a joy that would be,
But we know this is all a dream.

Alexis Bloodworth, Grade 5
Bonaire Elementary School, GA

The Despairing Story of "Pearl Queen"

There was a ship called Pearl Queen
A bigger ship you've never seen
The vessel's crew was very mean

The Pearl Queen wasn't a place to give birth
It was a ship of black-hearted mirth
No more treacherous boat was there in all the earth
The Peal Queen came to be deserted

The Queen eventually came to an end
By a relatively bad makeshift mend
To a watery grave the sea had to send
The Peal Queen's story is over

Sterling Conyers, Grade 5
Landmark Christian School, GA

To a New Baby

Little kicking, cuddling thing,
You don't cry, you only sing!
Blinking eyes and stubby nose,
Mouth that mocks the budding rose,
Down for hair, peach blows for hands
A-h-h-h of all the "baby grand"
Anyone could wish to see,
You're the finest one for me.

Skin as soft as velvet is:
God touched you on the cheek and chin
Where he touched are dimples in.
Creases on your wrists, as though
Strings were fastened round them so
We could tie you tight and keep
You from leaving at night.
Do you know, you flawless pearl
How much we love our baby girl

Cassia Harris, Grade 5
Laurence J Daly Elementary School, MO

Veteran

V ictorious soldiers are enduring
E xcruciating pain. They are
T errified, but
E quipped to fight. They are
R evolutionary
A larmed soldiers who are
N ever going to give up for our nation.

D.J. Adams, Grade 4
Cherokee Elementary School, AR

A Memory That Will Last Forever

"You read to me Shelbi!"
A wish from my brother —
to read *The Foot Book*,
a rhyming book by Dr. Seuss.
Digging through the books,
I finally found it laying right beside
The Three Little Pigs.
Covering him with a blanket,
scooting up next to him,
and opening the book.
Avery loves this book.
He yells out the words
he knows:
left foot,
right foot,
up,
down.
He loves reading.
I enjoy reading to him.
This is why he likes it so much.
This memory will last forever.

Shelbi Pace, Grade 5
Etowah Elementary School, NC

Autumn Leaves

Autumn leaves are like birds in the sky.
They are floating and flying and soaring in the air.
Soon they gently fall and land peacefully on the ground without a sound.

Allie Smith, Grade 4
First Wesleyan Christian School, NC

Prayers of the People

People pray for many different reasons
But here's one very important reason I can never forget
9-11-01
"God, help us through" "God, keep us safe"
"God, let them be alive" "God, don't send us to war"
"God, what's happening?" "Jesus I pray amen"
Mothers, wives, sisters, and grandmothers hoping their
kids, husbands, brothers, and sons are okay
"Lord, let me live" "Lord, save me"
"Lord, don't let them do this"
"Lord, why are they doing this?"
"Lord, why do they hate us?"
"Jesus I pray amen"
People scared to death
People dead, people shocked
People don't understand
People are just sitting doing nothing with their eyes closed
No one knows what they're doing
But I know what they're doing, they're praying to God and saying
GOD BLESS AMERICA

Stephanie Pimental, Grade 5
Toccoa Elementary School, GA

Father and Daughter

I love my daughter

    I love my dad

She is so sweet

    He can be so embarrassing

She makes me laugh
I love meeting her friends

    He makes me laugh

    He asks my friends too many questions
    He cooks the best meals

I cook the best meals
She is the best daughter

    He is the best dad

I'll always be there for my
daughter

    My dad will always be there for me.

Chandler Dew, Grade 6
Beck Academy, SC

You Can Write Anything About Puppies

New puppies are like getting a new toy.
They bounce around on their little big feet.
They chew on everything that gets close to their nose.
Their puppy breath smells, and they go when you don't want them to go.
The thing that I don't like is that they grow up to be big.

Faith Abbott, Grade 6
Dyer Elementary & Jr High School, TN

Out of the Ashes

The animal I've chosen you may not know;
It's a mythical bird from long ago.
For it lived in a time of Egyptian Pharaohs;
Where it is today, nobody knows.

I've chosen this bird for what it symbolizes;
For out of the ashes it arises.
It's been compared to Jesus Christ;
Showing that after death comes life.

The bird has wings of red and gold;
It heals itself when wounded by foe.
This bird is said to be really old;
Death on this bird has no hold.

As we come to the end of my rhyme;
We are almost out of time.
I'll tell you its name in the next line;
It's a Phoenix bird, and it's a favorite of mine.

Andy Tedder, Grade 5
Joann Walters Elementary School, AR

The Terrible Tornado

I am terrible and horrible
If you get into my path this will happen.

I will throw you for miles and maybe tear you all to pieces.
I will destroy homes and buildings and land wherever I go

I can get high winds up to 100 M.P.H.
I can bring rain also.
I can spread as wide as 5 miles and I look like a monster

I smell like garbage and I am your worst nightmare.
What am I.

I am a tornado

Briana Ransom, Grade 5
Pembroke Elementary School, NC

Santa's Little Helper

I am a little elf and I work for Santa Claus.
And I've seen reindeer because,
Every Christmas Eve, Santa goes for a ride.
When children try to see him,
He has to run and hide.

I've talked to the man myself.
He says I'm really kind,
Because I'm an elf.

Elves make toys,
For all of the girls and boys.
We know it brings them joys.

Maria Layton, Grade 4
St Mary Cathedral Elementary School, MO

Cycling

I learned to ride my bike this summer
it took quite a while…
you have to learn to balance
then have to learn to shift your weight
learn to steer
peddle
so these are all the steps you need to know
to ride a bike

Leslie Hicks, Grade 5
Walton Verona Elementary School, KY

Yellow Lilies

Lovely and yellow,
sways gracefully in the sun
fun to pick and smell.

Christie Robertson, Grade 4
Briarwood Christian Elementary School, AL

Seasons

There are four seasons that I know of
they all sing their own song
all sing with peace and love
and none of it is wrong.

Summer sings with beauty
it is as hot as the sun
fall sings with joy
with a trillion orange leaves of love.

Winter sings with comfort
it is very cold outside
spring sings with sudden hope
with lovely peaceful flowers on each side.

I have told you about all the seasons
they are long but yet they're short
God made each one for a pleasant reason
they all have a beautiful purpose on His Earth.

Meredith Tallent, Grade 5
Providence Academy, TN

Life

Life is hard
life is strong,
but for some
life is long
Life has a big purpose,
but some may think life is worthless
The purpose is to live and love
and give praise to the Lord
He listens from above
That's what I think life is about
now give me your opinion I'll hear you out

Christopher Ross, Grade 6
Douglass Elementary School, TN

Missing You

I feel so bad.
I stay so sad.
Oh, how I miss my dad.

Been gone a year.
Wish he were here.
I hold him dear,
And try not to fear.

He's not a soldier
But still in harm's way.
Wish he were here,
So we could play.

I pray each night,
To end this fight.
Let our boys come home,
Where they all belong.

Santa's on his way,
With toys and treats,
Will not be the same,
Till soldiers walk American streets.

Erika McBride, Grade 5
Joann Walters Elementary School, AR

Valentines

Valentines, a good time of year
To show love to your dear!
It's a holiday not to fear
'Cause everyone will cheer!
A time to show love
To see a flying dove!
'Cause happiness comes from above
So give a valentine to someone you love.

Alexis Everitt, Grade 6
Graham Elementary School, AL

Long-Footed Potoroo

There standing I see…
a long footed potoroo
starts to look at me

Christina Rosaun Pace, Grade 4
John Will Elementary School, AL

Veteran

V ery brave
E ager to fight
T ogether they stand in the war
E ndanger the lives of our soldiers
R eady to fight in the war
A bility to fight to the end
N ever give up.

Austin Eli Himschoot, Grade 4
Cherokee Elementary School, AR

Feeling Fall

Fall brings good feelings
the weather is getting cold
the leaves change colors

Renee Franklin, Grade 6
Tomlinson Jr High School, OK

Super Spy

I stalk about
Never in doubt
A bug on the wall — a fly.
It's me, a spy!
I stalk my prey,
A criminal astray.
Justice is here,
I want to sneer
At the criminal's pout
When I am about.
In jail they go
Not a friend, but a foe
Until they're all gone.
No more cons!
The world will be safe
For little waifs.

Veronica Clark, Grade 4
Cleveland Elementary School, OK

My Friend, the Cardinal

The Cardinal is my crested friend.
He is very playful.
My friend sings cheerful, beautiful songs.
He is nice and joyful.
A Cardinal is red and likes to eat seeds.
That is my friend, the Cardinal.

Christian Lawrence Rogers, Grade 4
Northeast Baptist School, LA

America the Beautiful

America the Beautiful,
shines with goodness and light.
America the Beautiful,
all day and all night.
America the Beautiful,
a country that is free.
America the Beautiful,
it's what we shall always be.
America the Beautiful,
has an army that fights with pride.
America the Beautiful,
they fought until they died.
America the Beautiful,
it shines from shore to shore.
America the Beautiful,
we shall be forever more.

Brendon Ryan, Grade 5
Spring Branch Elementary School, MO

Life

L ove is a part of life.
I nvincible
F orever
E verlasting

Jermaine Riley, Grade 6
Leland Middle School, NC

My Mom Is the Best Because…

She is like a refreshing drink
on a scorching summer day
She is the color yellow because she
is a bright, gleaming person
She is pure like an angel
and as sweet as sugar
She is a warm blanket of joy
She has a very sincere, forgiving heart
She is full of humor
She is overflowing with love
She has an everlasting spirit
She is a really open person and
will talk to anyone
She is always encouraging me to
shoot for my dreams
My mom is a unique person and
she is the best!

Katie Waters, Grade 6
Chapin Middle School, SC

Boundaries

Boundaries, Boundaries,
Holding me back.
Nowhere to run,
Nowhere to go.

These ropes forcing me to stay,
Like this bar attached.
This thing on me,
It won't let me run!

Boundaries, Boundaries,
Capturing me.
There was a time,
That I ran free.

Now I'm trapped,
In this wooden jail.
This fence restricting me,
I can't move!

Boundaries, Boundaries,
Let me out!
I want to run,
On the open range.

Harley Matthews, Grade 6
Bellwood Discovery School, TN

You Died for Me!

They thought you were viscous
because you worshipped someone different.

While you were getting hurt
the guards were gambling on your shirt.

You had to wear the crown of thorns
if you imagined you can see them wearing horns.

And you died on the cross for me
because you thought it will set me free.

I think you died on the cross
for a very rich and thankful cause.

Jasmine Vongphakdy, Grade 5
Magnolia Springs Baptist Academy, AL

Water Waves

When I was swimming
in the water I could see
waves hitting on me

Travis Hightower, Grade 4
Briarwood Christian Elementary School, AL

Family

When you think of family,
you think of love.
When you think of love,
you think of kindness.
These are all things that your family should have.
Pleasing your family is an important characteristic
which makes a family great.
Every day, please someone in your family.
If you think about it, this only takes a little time out of your day.
Remember, this is your one and only family.
They take you to the ice cream parlor,
and take you to the barber.
Your family often takes you to church and school,
even though, sometimes, you may not think this is cool.
The important thing to remember,
is to love one another,
especially when it comes to your father and your mother.

Elizabeth Griffith, Grade 6
Queen of Angels Catholic School, GA

Oranges

Oranges are orange
so sweet and sometimes sour
their tangy taste runs through your taste buds
and makes them jump for joy
they're sometimes sour for even an hour
but the goodness of an orange
will last forever

Mallarie Riffe, Grade 6
Dyer Elementary & Jr High School, TN

My Big Black Dog

I have a big black dog,
I wrote about him in my blog,
He isn't as ugly as a hog,
But he still doesn't look much like a dog.

Logan Acton, Grade 5
Midway Covenant Christian School, GA

Weekends

Weekends, weekends, I watch TV.
Weekends, weekends, when I am free.
Weekends, weekends, when I can play.
Weekends, weekends, tomorrow is the day.
Weekends, weekends, I will have fun.
Weekends, weekends, my poem is done!

Jim Breland, Grade 4
East Jones Elementary School, MS

5th Grade

We're big kids, strong and tough,
We laugh, we play, and do fun stuff.
Playing kickball, soccer, and frisby too,
In 5th grade there's plenty of sports to do!
The teacher we have is quite tricky
At trying to get us to do our work quickly.
She uses all her skills and talents too,
To help us learn many things that are new.
In 5th grade they expect you to do your best,
As shown in reading, writing, and lots of tests.
We work, we play, we study hard,
So in the end we'll all go far.

Katelyn Jones, Grade 5
Stokesdale Elementary School, NC

Fishing with My Father

I sat by the pond
My father next to me
I bait my hook
Then toss out my line
I wait for a while
Then I feel a very hard tug
I pull the rod to set my hook
Then slowly and carefully reel it in
Finally I see it
A very large fish
It looks like a white bass
In excitement I take it off the hook
When I show my father he exclaims, "Good job!"
I put it in the ice box
My father and I
Are grinning from ear to ear
As we walk home
We have joy in our hearts
I long to come back
Hopefully by tomorrow

Ashley Bryant, Grade 6
Carmel Elementary School, GA

May Prayers

He took the wind,
And He took my heart,
Just to let me know,
We'll never be apart!

I'll always be in His dreams,
And I'll always be in His thoughts,
He said He will forgive me,
Every time that we fought!

I spoke to Him,
As if He were my dad,
He would always cheer me up,
Even when I was sad!

Although, I've never seen Him,
On these foggy days of May,
At least I know I'll see Him,
Well, maybe someday.

Rachel Foster, Grade 6
Orange Grove Elementary School, MS

May

There was a day in May
which was an awesome holiday
I went outside to play
and it was hot all that day
I went inside to get a drink
but there was water in the sink
I went back out to play again
and there they were, all my friends!

Stephanie Morgan, Grade 6
Graham Elementary School, AL

Freedom

Freedom
Endless Possibilities
Hopeful, Grateful and Thankful
God Bless the U.S.A.
Free!

Jeremy Gann, Grade 4
West Elementary School, MO

May God Bless America!

America
I want to thank them,
the soldiers,
for fighting for us.
Fighting for our country
where the flag flies free.
The bald eagle flies proudly
through the wind and the rain.
Our country still stands powerfully.
May God bless America!

Bailey Richard, Grade 6
Leonville Elementary School, LA

Yellow

Yellow looks like the stars up in the sky at night shinning
Yellow sounds like chicks chirping while following their mother
Yellow smells like the cheese on a sandwich people are eating
Yellow tastes like the hot melting cheese in my mouth
Yellow feels like the flower all over my yard rubbing on my leg as I'm walking
Yellow is the sun shining on a sunny day at the beach.
Yellow is the sound of the yellow gum you're chewing in your mouth
Yellow is the taste of the soda mountain dew
Yellow is the smell of bananas people are eating
Yellow is the feel of a toy in a little kid's hands

Moises Morales, Grade 5
Cool Spring Elementary School, NC

I'm Haunted

I'm haunted of the green monster under my bed
because I thought he would reach out and pull me into his liar!
I'm haunted of the clown who comes out at night and
tries to kill me because of the movie *It!*

I'm haunted of the creepy crawly spiders who hang on my window
because of the movie *Eight Legged Freaks!*
I'm haunted of the snakes that are outside trying to bite me
because I have been bit before!

I'm haunted of getting killed because
I think I'm going to go to war someday!
I'm haunted of being homeless when I grow up
because there is a 50% chance I will be.

I'M HAUNTED!!!

Chris Wells, Grade 5
Eminence Middle School, KY

I Am Haunted

I am haunted,
By the crack in my creepy closet where the big bad boogieman once lived,
He would grab me with his pointy pale fingers,
Take me in the dark dreaded closet,
And I would never come back again!

I am haunted,
By the night noises that I hear upon my closet door,
A screech here and a scratch there,
Is it a horrible human that is going to take me?
I just turn up my radio one notch louder,
Then I go back to bed!

I am haunted,
That my family will die a dreary death,
That I will be all alone,
That I will cry and cry until there is no water left in me!

I am haunted!!!

Brianna M. Prewitt, Grade 5
Eminence Middle School, KY

Rudolph the Red-Nose Reindeer

One snowy night in the North Pole,
A reindeer named Rudolph was born for a role.
He had a bright red nose,
That dazzled like a scarlet rose.
All the other reindeers would leave him out,
Making poor Rudolph pout.
Sometimes Rudolph would cover the light,
But it still glowed and they found him at night.
One foggy Christmas Eve,
Santa Claus was ready — but they couldn't leave.
The fog was too thick to ride,
"We'll never get the presents out in time," he cried.
Then he noticed Rudolph's nose aglow,
He told Rudolph, "You be the leader and we'll follow."
They made an amazing sight,
Flying house to house delivering presents all night.
Christmas was saved that day,
Santa was overjoyed and all the reindeers screamed "Hooray!"
After that all the reindeers showed respect to him,
And Rudolph was filled with pride to the brim.

Arshiya Lal, Grade 6
River Trail Middle School, GA

Thanksgiving

Sounds like families greeting one another
Looks like family and friends thanking God
Smells like all the yummy food…including the pies
Tastes like the delicious turkey and stuffing we have each year
Feels like full stomachs and love.

Anna Byers, Grade 5
Briarwood Christian Elementary School, AL

Nature

You look,
You sigh,
While you see nature beginning to die,
You think,
You know,
That nature will always grow,
You look,
You see,
How wonderful nature can be,
You watch,
You glare,
While the wind goes through your hair,
You look high,
You look low,
And you see things that seem to glow,
You watch,
And you cry,
When you see things that seemed to have died,
You look,
And you glare,
And just wish you could go there.

Virginia Stewart, Grade 5
Christ Episcopal School - Middle School, LA

Pizza Attack

Looking at the pizza
With glaring eye
On the hunt for food.

Sniffing the pizza
With a wiggling nose
Liking the aroma.

Pouncing at the pizza
With sharp claws
To grip tight!

Biting the pizza
With sharp teeth
To chow down.

Running to the living room
With fast feet
To hide.

J.P. Middleton, Grade 4
Goshen Elementary School at Hillcrest, KY

Noah and the Ark

Noah put into the ark two animals of each kind.
He wanted to save them and all of mankind.

The flood waters rose as the storm raged on and on.
Then everything became calm.
They left the ark two by two at the break of dawn.
They made a brand new life in a brand new world.
And their lives went on and on.

Noah's story and ours are the same.
After Katrina, the flood waters came.
The storm raged on and on.
Then everything became calm.
We left our safe place like the animals too.
We made a brand new life in a brand new world.
And our lives go on and on.

Bianca Gonzales, Grade 5
Holy Rosary Academy, LA

Walker's Ways

Walker is my friendly dog that
I hold very dearly.
All he cares about is
toys
family
walks
and he loves his food morning and night.
He always greets you with a big doggy smile
and a wet sloppy lick wherever he can get his tongue.
These are Walker's ways.

Preston Knibbe, Grade 5
Walton Verona Elementary School, KY

Seasons

Icicles melt, Blue Jays sing.
My favorite time of year is spring.

I love summer
Because it's not a bummer.

I like fall
That's when I grow tall.

I enjoy winter,
Because into school you cannot enter.

I love the seasons
For a few unclear reasons.

Landon Lynch, Grade 5
Cottonwood Public School, OK

Football

football, touchdown, red
fun, shot, helmet, pads, pants, white
safety, touchback, team

Caleb Schubert, Grade 4
East Jones Elementary School, MS

Seasons

Winter is cold and lonely,
and I was thinking if only,
the sun would come out today,
so I could go and play.
It would be a lovely day.

Spring is warm and bright,
it's even warmer at night.
It's a good time to play outside,
wish I had a horse to ride.

As summer comes there is no school,
and I wish my parents had fewer rules.
The sun gleams high up in the sky,
makes me wish that I could fly.

But Autumn comes way to soon,
as I stare into the moon.
I wish that I could fall asleep,
A cup of hot chocolate would be neat,
and a pair of socks to put on my feet.

Taylor Marynn Still, Grade 5
Macedonia Elementary School, SC

Snow

White snow on the ground
Kids drinking hot chocolate
Shoe prints in the snow

Joe Whitaker, Grade 5
Sycamore Elementary School, GA

My Favorite Place

It's my sun room you see.
With a ping pong table and everything!
It may be hot in there.
But look at me do you think I care?

We have fun all the time.
Sometimes I even beat my dad!
When I win sometimes he gets mad.
Have you ever beaten your dad?

Mikala Lowry, Grade 5
Pembroke Elementary School, NC

Me and My Dog

My name is Lorna Bryce
My favorite book is Lorna Doone
I'm a dancer
I explore like Daniel Boone

I am an energetic girl
I do good in school
I make all A's
I am cool and I rule

I like animals
I have a dog, her name is Puddles
She is four years old
She is a cuddles

I am funny
And witty
I have a great smile
Also, I am pretty

Lorna Bryce, Grade 5
American Heritage Academy, GA

Snow

Snow is really near
Snow is finally here
Roll in into a ball
It doesn't matter if it crumbles and falls
Slide on it with a sled
Slide on it with your head
Hurry before the snow will go
Before it's time for the snow to go

Hannah Desenberg, Grade 5
Tates Creek Elementary School, KY

Clumsy

There once was a boy named Tad,
who went to get his fat dad.
Because someone fell,
he wanted to tell.
Next time he'll wear a knee pad.

Joshua Harris, Grade 4
Judsonia Elementary School, AR

My Nature Body

My hair is as
wispy as the
wide stratus clouds

My eyes as open
as the morning sky

My neck as pale and
white as the clear blue
water's sand

My ears and hearing are
as open as the sound of the wind

All of this is what
I see…
Nature's an important part of me.

Deborah Cuellar, Grade 5
Drayton Hall Elementary School, SC

Veteran

V ery sad day in war
E yes on the enemies
T anks echoing as they fire
E veryone running not to get shot
R ight to fight for America
A mmo blowing out our guns
N obody can stand their family dying.

Eddie Felton, Grade 4
Cherokee Elementary School, AR

Rumors

A rumor is like a rash
That spreads among everyone
When you catch it, it'll spread
How long will it stay on you?
Will you pass it on?

Elsa Meyners, Grade 5
Herbert J Dexter Elementary School, GA

My Daddy and I

My Daddy is my hero,
My Daddy is my friend.
No matter what happens
I'll love him until the end.
My Daddy will always protect me,
My Daddy helps me when I am down.
If I am crying and I am lonely,
My Daddy will come around.
When I weep
My Daddy will hug me asleep.
But he will always be my Daddy
And I will never want to change that!

Lauren Martinsen, Grade 6
Lake Castle Private School, LA

The Legend of the Petoskey Stone

Long, long ago, there was a huge mountain.
Water sprung out of the top like a fountain.
It towered over Lake Michigan
And provided shelter for the animals again and again.
One night, lightning struck its tip.
It cracked, it crumbled, it slipped.
All of its majestic power
Was drained from its tall tower.
The rock that once stood so high,
Fell into the lake as it waved good-bye.
Today this rock is called the Petoskey stone,
And if you find one do not groan.
Instead keep it in your clutch.
For it is worth so, very much.

Abigail Baudry, Grade 6
Queen of Angels Catholic School, GA

Autumn

Birds chirping happily in the colorful trees
Copper, gold, scarlet, and violet leaves painting the landscape,
Listening to the crows cawing, knowing fall is here,
Thanksgiving feasting, tasting the turkey and dressing,
Day and night having even times,
Raking the painted leaves, then hurdling into them,
Crops getting picked to sell to buyers,
Autumn winds etching frost on the grass,
Pumpkins being carved for Halloween,
Autumn is a painting filled with many colors that soothe me.

Tanner Lane Kirby, Grade 6
Alvaton Elementary School, KY

Ocean Blue

Surged water, foamy
Look! Dark water is crashing
Ocean is so cool

Ethan Mosko, Grade 4
Briarwood Christian Elementary School, AL

If I Were in Charge of the World

If I could change the world,
there wouldn't be any mess to clean.
Brussel sprouts wouldn't be seen.
There wouldn't be any limitations on reading,
and no one would be leading a group.
There wouldn't be any drugs,
and all you ever gave were hugs.
There wouldn't be any grades,
and nobody would have to be a maid.
We'd just do our own thing,
dance, play, and sing.
It would only be a happy world.
and the world would be called,
"Haley World!"

Haley Jordan, Grade 6
Eminence Middle School, KY

Pumpkins

Are orange and fat,
Large and taste horrible raw,
Being used as food.

Luke McKay, Grade 4
Briarwood Christian Elementary School, AL

The Empty Schoolhouse

As I walk to the empty schoolhouse,
Only the janitor remains.
I come to school this night
In need of my difficult homework.

No sounds are made,
Except for the squeaky floor.
As I walk up the stairs,
A sudden rain comes and stays.

When I got up to my homeroom,
I found my desk so suddenly.
Soon my difficult homework was found,
And I headed back to the front of the school.

Then the rain cleared,
So I was able to walk home.
But something came to me so soon,
Did I forget my reading book?

Austin Morse, Grade 5
Etowah Elementary School, NC

The Last Journey

I crouch down in the corner, my doll cradled in my arms,
I don't know where we're going but I'm guessing it's quite far.
Mama sits right next to me, her head between her knees;
I know that she's been crying by the way she looked at me.
Papa's standing in the corner, his eyes sunken to the floor;
by looking at his face, I know he hates this even more.
The cart we are riding in is crowded and it smells,
and the man standing in front of me keeps bursting out in yells.

"My son!" he screams, his face bright red.
I close my eyes in knowing that his son has been long dead.
A baby starts to cry, and a woman begins to shriek,
we know that she's gone crazy, looking at her clenching teeth.
It is very dark and murky and I'm growing full with fear,
and Mama's shining eyes are once again brimmed with tears.
But then the moment comes, the cart screeching to a stop,
the small door is thrown open, revealing quite a shock.

After adjusting to the light, we saw what filled us with such fear;
we see a tall fence, enclosing us in here.
We slowly lift our heads, reading the large sign,
the words filled us with horror; it read

AUSCHWITZ

Katie Joyce, Grade 6
St Jude School, TN

Holocaust

The Holocaust was bad for everybody;
Especially the Jews.
Now that I see the pictures,
It puts me in despair.
I see Jews in the pictures,
And what they had to wear.
When I look
It makes me cry,
Who deserved that
And why oh why?
Why did the Nazi soldiers do that,
And just to the Jews?
Which kid to die and which to live,
Who would want to choose?

Laura Ball, Grade 5
Heber Springs Elementary School, AR

Volcano

V iolent eruptions
O utbursts of hot gases
L ayers of lava
C one shaped mountains
A ctivates earthquakes
N ature's disasters
O utrageous clouds of smoke

Hunter Alston, Grade 5
West Bertie Elementary School, NC

My Senses

I love my eyes
They help me see
My ears
They hear so beautifully

My tongue it tastes
Everything I eat
My nose it smells things
Like the smell of sweaty feet

I feel the metal of our door
The wood of our cow field fence
But Mom says there is one sense I lack
And that's my common sense

Hannah Rodgers, Grade 5
Walton Verona Elementary School, KY

Veteran

V ictorious soldiers who are
E ager to fight. They are
T rained well
E mbracing their strength, you hear
R umbling foot steps.
A merica's soldiers, will
N ever give up!

Savannah Birdsell, Grade 4
Cherokee Elementary School, AR

Feelings

Some people read the Bible
and never put it into their lives.
Some people talk and talk
and never understand the reason why.

Some people make fun of others
and never care how that person feels.
Some people sleep in anxiety
and always wonder about where they're going to get their next meal.

Dylan Sherrill, Grade 6
Central Arkansas Christian School, AR

Childhood Is

Childhood is loving to play soccer.
Childhood is being at my favorite place, Grandma's house.
Childhood is watching scary movies.
Childhood is playing with toy cars.
Childhood is being the best on the team.
Childhood is living in New York.
Childhood is my sister holding a rock in one hand
    and bread in the other, and accidentally biting the wrong one.
Childhood is dreaming to be a doctor.

Aybek Korachayev, Grade 6
Lost River Elementary School, KY

Oh Winter

Time to put away the scary things and get out the Christmas things
You know when Christmas is coming,
It gets cold every day and starts to snow.
Then we start to get out the Christmas tree,
And put the ornaments on.
Then we put the stockings up and put the presents under the tree.
The next morning you wake up and eat your candy,
open the presents and thank God for Christmas.

Jamie Gregory, Grade 5
Paint Lick Elementary School, KY

Autumn Madness

I see trees that are bare
Once with leaves full of life.
I see the moon in the early morn
Looking down in delight.
I see the flag blowing in the wind.
Meaning peace to our country once again.
I see birds in a tree making music for our ears.
I see trees stiff with fear.
But some sway in the wind.
I see a cedar tree standing tall and green.
I see an old tree holding many secrets.
If only I could know what secrets it holds.
I see a cat watching its prey, thinking: oh! What a lucky day.
I see birds fluttering in the air as graceful as can be.
I see leaves on the ground with some twirling around.
Autumn madness is in the air just stop and you'll find it everywhere.

Cole Michael Mutter, Grade 6
Temple Hill Elementary School, KY

Lovely Ocean

Wet and beautiful
water splashing on the rocks
sun shining on me.

Alauna Elizabeth Glass, Grade 4
Briarwood Christian Elementary School, AL

My Other Sister

Once I had two sisters.
    One of them was healthy.
    One of them was not.
Their names were Caroline and Rachel.

One day Rachel got sick.
    She had a disease.
    She had no heart beat.
The doctors sent us home from the hospital.

Someday I'll see her in Heaven.

Joshua Thompson, Grade 4
Northeast Baptist School, LA

God

God is always there
for you if you ever need
him forever more.

Madeline Smith, Grade 4
Briarwood Christian Elementary School, AL

Thanksgiving

T his holiday is for families
H aving each other on this day
A day for being with friends, and eating with them
N o one should be left out
K ind people made this day
S o we could have one whole day of being family
G iving thought to the pilgrims and
I ndians, for putting aside their differences.
V alue what they gave us.
I nside we all enjoy and give thanks on this
N ice day, eating great food, and
G iving thanks for everything we have.

Zackary Daugherty, Grade 5
Sullivan Elementary School, TN

My Favorite Place

Is in the woods
In a hole
I think that it could be deeper
I don't go in the summer because of snakes
But in the fall it is sweet
Where water falls
Not so far down
It's so beautiful
That's why I go

Trevor Ford, Grade 5
Stokesdale Elementary School, NC

Deral

We are gathered here today to pay our dues
To the one and only Deral, the hairdryer.

Deral, the hairdryer, would always make time for fun
Even if you were on the run.

He would get real hot and burn your hand
But then get sad and turn on his cool button.

He worked very hard to dry hair
He would sort of "recycle" the air.

And when he used too much power
He would flip a breaker to keep the house safer.

He would put up with getting thrown around
And with humans yanking his plug out the socket.

He would make your hair smooth and sleek
And gosh darn it, he never gave up.

Poor, poor, Deral
He was laid to rest.

Tayler McMurtrey, Grade 6
Edmonton Elementary School, KY

Something's Out There

Something's out there and I know it,
Something's out there no doubt about it.
It watches me every single night,
Something's out there, all right.
And as I sit here talking to you,
It might jump out and yell, "Boo!"
I think I am crazy,
Somebody save me.
It's coming, it's coming,
I can feel myself shaking.
I see two eyes glowing red,
Maybe I should hide in bed.
I see fangs flashing white,
Suddenly, I open my eyes,
Into day which is so nice.
My mom opens the door and says,
"Good morning sleepyhead, you've slept for days!"
Hey, wow! It's just a dream!

Tiffany Jih, Grade 6
Bellwood Discovery School, TN

Thanksgiving

Thanksgiving is a time to stuff your mouth,
With turkey, rice, and food from the south,
Then you cry with a stomachache,
Before you eat the red-velvet cake.

Jordan Hebert, Grade 6
St Cecilia School, LA

Dursun

D og lover
U nderstanding the English language
R ussian immigrant
S kateboard rider
U SA is fun
N ineteenth of May is my birthday
Dursun Fayzulov, Grade 6
Lost River Elementary School, KY

Heath Goanna

Goanna
fierce, strong,
climbs, bites, attacks
muscular, slender, quiet, shy
Lizard
Johnathan C. Watson-Smith, Grade 4
Orchard Elementary School, AL

Dragonfly

The dragonfly flies
He lands on my right shoulder
He is pink and gold
Lacey Wilson, Grade 5
Etowah Elementary School, NC

Thanksgiving

T asteful food on the table
H appy to be with family
A dvice being given
N eighbors coming to eat with us
K nowing we have a loving family
S melling turkey, ham, and stuffing
G iving joy to everyone
I nviting family over
V ideos being watched
I ce skating on the frozen pond
N esting in our beds
G iving thanks.

D reaming of that savory turkey we had
A lot of noise as our family leaves
Y elling goodnight to mom and dad
Vanessa Housewright, Grade 5
Sullivan Elementary School, TN

Hurricane Katrina

Buildings getting taken,
Houses getting flooded,
Winds are blowing hard,
Windows are shattering,
No electricity and very hot nights,
The levee systems breaking,
Hurricane Katrina in Louisiana.
Tyler Fleming, Grade 4
Lewis Vincent Elementary School, LA

Mistakes

We used to be so close
You were the shoulder I would cry on
I never thought of the end
Then you made a mistake

I thought you'd always be there
Just like how you used to
Having fun never stopped
Until you made the same mistake

I don't even care anymore
About which road you take
You're out of the picture
Because you make the same mistakes
Elizabeth Lamb, Grade 6
Bellwood Discovery School, TN

Autumn Leaves

Autumn leaves are like dancers.
They soar across the stage
And sway back and forth.
Mary Elizabeth Pardo, Grade 4
First Wesleyan Christian School, NC

Polka

When I was small and very young
Polka and I would laugh and run.
She slept with me
Almost every night
And would guard me when shadows
Would give me a fright.
We would lie in the grass
And count stars in the sky.
We were always together,
My stuffed dog Polka and I.
Now that I'm older
She sits in my chair
Loyal and faithful,
My friend's always there.
I'll keep her forever
Oh, the fun we have had
Right there to hug if ever I'm sad.
Olivia Mills, Grade 6
Woodland Presbyterian School, TN

Veteran

V ictory, hope it comes
E yes on the enemy
T hey use their tanks
"**E** mergency," the enemies say
"**R** ights are ours"
A mbulance come and go
N ow we're done with these men's pain
Hope Isaacs, Grade 4
Cherokee Elementary School, AR

A Frog's Life

Frogs, frogs so smooth, so green
They're very cool, their senses are keen
Smelling, hearing, they see things unseen

But when they die, they're not the same
They're dull, boring, and very lame
But that was just life, when death came.
Zachary Breathwaite, Grade 4
Moyock Elementary School, NC

I Still Feel Like a Little Kid

I still feel like a little kid as you know,
I sleep with a flashlight and a lamp also.
I need my pillow fluffed
and think why am I doing this stuff?
I get tucked in at night.
I don't think this is right!!!
I need my music on as you can see.
Just what is happening to me!!!
I still feel like a little kid as you know,
but the only good part is,
I get a kiss that fills me up head to toe.
Annie Zigman, Grade 4
Center for Creative Learning, MO

Me

Justin, 11
Happy, hyper, friendly
Son of Miriah and Happy
Brother of Sara and Makayla
Best friend of many
Owner of flea
Enjoys fun
Happy, hyper, helpful
Who needs time
Who feels like losing it
Who would like to go to Arkansas
Who feels strong about family
Who would spend the summer in my tent
Born in North Kansas City
Sharp
Justin Sharp, Grade 5
Trenton Middle School, MO

Birdy Birdy

Birdy, birdy, in the sky
oh how I wish I could fly
If I could I wouldn't mind
oh me, oh my, I wish I could fly
If I could I would fly
faster than the speed of light.
Birdy, birdy, how I wish to be like you
But I'll just leave flying up to you.
Lauren Tucker, Grade 5
Franklin Elementary School, OK

I Am Haunted

I AM HAUNTED by the pretty people that dress up as
Wicked witches that have green, slithering, slimy
Fingers with blood coming down the body
I am haunted.

I AM HAUNTED by Chucky with those
Snake scars on his face
I really hate scary spiders and snakes
They are really scary.
I am haunted.

I AM HAUNTED by the thought of creepy cancer
I don't want my mom, my dad, or me to get
Creepy cancer
I am haunted.

Sabrina Sample, Grade 5
Eminence Middle School, KY

Friends

I love my dear friends.
I love their cheery ways.
I know they're always there for me in the night or day.
So now you know my friends
and their loving, cheering, and dearing ways.

Morgan Cagle, Grade 4
Brilliant Elementary School, AL

Land of the Free

America is my country.
I was born here you see.
It has always been strong and something to see.
I'm so proud it is my country.

We have mountains and rivers and much beauty you see.
Many struggle to get here from over the sea.
Our soldiers fight for freedom for me.
So I can live in America the land of the free.

Madasan Muse, Grade 6
Joann Walters Elementary School, AR

My Fat Cat

I've got a fat cat
that likes to nap.

He's fat like my dog,
and gets a squeaky mouse toy from Santa Claus.
My fat cat's name is Paws.

He enjoys food,
and is very rude.

My dog and Paws
both love eggnog.

Stephen Kukura, Grade 5
St Dominic School, TN

The Wind Feels...

The wind feels so good
running through my hair
as I am driving down the road.
And when it's hot outside
and the wind blows it feels so good.
I like going outside when the wind is blowing
because it feels so good.
Wind wind wind that sounds so good.
So go outside and have some fun.

Melviena Hayes, Grade 6
Dyer Elementary & Jr High School, TN

Seven Friends

Seven friends eating a pie
The first one ate too much and got sick
The second one dropped his plate
The third one wanted more
The fourth one didn't like pie
The fifth one threw up
The sixth one crammed his pie in his mouth
The seventh one forgot how to eat
    so he threw it to start a food fight.

Ramsey Mayne, Grade 5
Ascension Elementary School, KY

Dancing

Dancing is my dream.
Dancing helps me to overcome my fears.
It makes me feel whole again when I am sad or
overwhelmed.
Dancing is my power.
Dancing makes my shoes move to the rhythm of the beat.

Symone Tripp, Grade 5
Bonaire Elementary School, GA

Candy

Candy is sweet.
Candy is sour.
Candy goes by like every hour.
Candy is hard.
Candy is soft.
Candy is irresistible stuff.
Candy is bitter.
Candy is tough.
But we love candy ever so much.
Tootsie Rolls, lollipops, candy bars and so much more.
Oh how much candy people adore.

Jessica Jolin, Grade 5
Stokesdale Elementary School, NC

The Ocean

The ocean is blue.
Is a cheerful, calming place.
Is a home for fish.

Alexis Pate, Grade 4
Briarwood Christian Elementary School, AL

Outside

I wish people wouldn't judge me from the outside.
They say they don't and they never will, but I know they have just lied.
I know this because, they see someone good looking and then they are obsessed with them.
They don't know that that good looking person has a heart of stone and just looks like a gem.
On the inside of us, is like we're living in a whole different place.
In that place we are judged by our insides and not our face.
People need to start judging other people for what's on the inside.
If one person started judging the inside of people, everyone else would follow and not be judged from the outside.

Cortney E. Hays, Grade 6
J D Meisler Middle School, LA

Books

One of my favorite things to do is to read books all afternoon.
Some books are about pirates with hooks under their sleeves.
Whereas some books are about animals that say moo or bark or whatever they may be.
But my favorite book of all is the one about my Lord my God for always and eternity.

Jamie Roberts, Grade 5
St Teresa's School, GA

Mr. McGyver

Mr. McGyver lives across the street, and every day he comes and goes from his house without a peep. I've never met him, and they say he's a creep, but I really think he would be very sweet. One day after I got home from school I decided to do something really quite cool, so I told my mom, sister and dad, my mom and dad said "Not bad son, not bad" I looked both ways and crossed the street to see this so called creep. I knocked on the door and rang the doorbell, it chimed and chimed and worked very well. He opened the door and said "Hello" he looked like a very kind and gentle fellow. I replied "Hello" and "How do you do" he said "Come in, I welcome you" he asked "Would you like some candy?" I replied and said "That would be dandy." He said "Is it all right for you to have candy before dinner?" I said "Yes it is my mom's a winner." As the clock struck seven I said "I must go for I must be asleep by eleven." As he begged me not to go I said "I will come back tomorrow." I went home to tell my mom and dad of the best day I have ever had. The next day I went to school and told everybody "that Mr. McGyver was cool" they said "No way, he's a creep," and I replied "He really is sweet." And I said "Don't believe a rumor that someone tells you, get the person that it's about's side of it too."

Lexy Ellis, Grade 5
Our Lady of Fatima School, MS

Christmastime

Christmastime is the best time of the year.
When Christmas comes around there is deer.
One thing we do for Christmas is decorate our whole property.
We are always boppy.
Usually we put Christmas lights on my grandmother's house.
Every year I see the same exact mouse.
We always put our tree up a day after December first.
I think it gives us a curse.
My mom and I put up the tree every year.
We ask my dad if he wants to help and he just snares.
Then we go in my room and put my tree up and top it with a cup.
The year of 05 we bought some plastic candy canes and stuck them down our driveway.
They got blown away and did not stay.
We stood them back up and strung them with lights.
We were tired and went in and drunk some Sprite.
Last year, my mom bought a blow up Santa that lights up, then my dog shed on it and my sister thought it was yuck!
It took an hour to get it up, but we did, even though it looked like a flat squid.
Our whole Christmas turned out bright and beautiful.

Mary Miller, Grade 4
Hatfield Elementary School, AR

The Revolutionary War

Look, look at this picture right here.
I think it was painted by Paul Revere.
The colonist wanted to vote.
Since they couldn't they threw tea off the boat.
Paul Revere made his big ride.
He made that ride with a lot of pride.
At Bunker Hill militia built a fort.
The British had to retreat and abort.

Sorrell Dunn, Grade 6
Graham Elementary School, AL

Camping at Kerr Lake

Steel docks shaking heavily
Huge boats and bass speeding rapidly
Greasy bacon spitting resoundingly
Tiny crickets are violins chirping repeatedly
Dead fish floating lifelessly
Enormous tree like statues disintegrating slowly
Tasty hamburgers cooking properly
Sweet chocolate dissolving quickly
Appetizing hamburgers grilling swiftly
I feel full and grateful.

Jordan DeCosse, Grade 5
Bailey Elementary School, NC

Free Animals

Animals wild, animals free,
Animals willing to be free.
Animals love to run and love to be free.
Animals love to be petted by people like me.

Animals wild, animals free,
They love to run wild and eat willingly.
So would you like to be an animal?
I know that I would.

Animals wild, animals free,
So let them be free.
They just might love you,
Just as they do me.

Dillon Magallanez, Grade 4
Hayes Elementary School, OK

My Dream About Texas

I like to go to Texas because of BBQ,
And the sweet smell of hay running through,
I ride with the cowboys and do you know what they say?
Let's go to the rodeo and smell the sweet smell of hay.
The cowboys say "Giddy up" and the cowgirls say "Oh my"
'Cause when I get on that horse, it feels like I'm going to fly.
My horse and I go really fast,
And that's not fun because we are coming in last,
So we get to the gate and I jump so high,
I went over the hill and jumped into the sky!

Emily Laxson, Grade 4
Elizabeth Traditional Elementary School, NC

Art

Art is like a picture you can jump into.
You can,
Sketch your thought of what's in your mind.
You can,
Draw the impossible, show the world what you can do.
This is no competition of who can draw the
Best…
Most creative…
Or Most artistic…
You win in that competition by you, and the people that
cheer you on.

Art is important and that's what art is all about…
No one is against you…it's only
You.

Wynne Huo, Grade 5
Big Creek Elementary School, GA

White

White looks like the blankness of clouds.
White feels like cold snow in the winter.
White tastes like powdered sugar in a factory.
White sounds like the beautiful fresh air in the morning.
White sounds like the ringing in my ears when I hit my head.
White is most colors of the world.

Hunter Blunt, Grade 5
Geggie Elementary School, MO

The First Day of School

School is here, we're over with summer,
Time to greet a new friend, time to learn a new number.

The kids wave hi, as they walk to class,
A smell drifts by of the newly cut grass.

Grab a worksheet and head to your seat,
The first day of school just can't be beat.

The last bell rings, the children pile out,
The chatter begins, there's lots to talk about.

The students depart and the teachers, too.
I can't wait 'till tomorrow, how about you?

Elizabeth Balch-Crystal, Grade 4
Wrights Mill Road Elementary School, AL

I Wish I Weren't So Famous

I wish I weren't so famous
I wish photographers would stop taking my picture
I wish the TITANS would stop asking me to sing at the ball game
I wish Jeopardy would stop giving me so much money
Maybe if I weren't so famous I'd be able to see
how it feels to be a normal kid!

Ciara McKenzie, Grade 5
Sullivan Elementary School, TN

Fall

Fall is a time
A time of changing leaves
Red, yellow, and orange

The weather is cool
Rainy, cold, and snowy

It is a fun season
You can jump in the leaves
Play game with your friends
And have hot chocolate
Eddie Hoffa, Grade 5
Walton Verona Elementary School, KY

The Battle

The battle is raging,
Guns are going off,
How I wish all of this would stop!

Fog of gunpowder,
The wind in the air,
It blows about the people's hair.

Rain that falls to the ground,
Echoes of screaming from all around,

I cannot see through the mist and fog,
With no sign that it will end,
I wish that it never happens again.
Dana Bombe, Grade 6
Clarksburg School, TN

All About Me

Hello
My name is Chase
If I were a color,
I'd be dark blue
Like the summer sea
If I were an animal,
I'd be small and gray
Like a koala
My favorite place is the beach
When it is summer
and the seagulls are flying
My favorite snack is graham crackers
The large type
That you get from Kroger
I really get upset
When I have to get up at six o'clock
to get on the bus
I love listening to hard rock
When my friends are there
to listen to it with me
Chase Poore, Grade 4
Pine Tree Hill Elementary School, SC

What You Find in a Jewelry Store

A few gold rings, some bling bling
A silver watch without a blotch
A cross charm that means no harm
That's what you find in a jewelry store
It's all just jewelry galore
Hunter Robertson, Grade 5
American Heritage Academy, GA

Flower Blossom

Flower blossom,
Oscillating petals,
Elegant stem,
Neon center,
Sleek corolla,
Luminous pistil,
Vivid butterfly weed,
Effloresce blossom,
Charming receptacle,
Lavish leaves,
Graceful stigma,
Vibrant stamen,
Delightful seedling.
Chelsey Hoch, Grade 4
Russell Babb Elementary School, OK

The Dame School

Girls were no fools
When it came to schools
The colonial chick
Was quick to pick
A Dame School

These were in friend's homes
The girls were never alone
Learning to pour tea
Sewing in quilting bees
A Dame School

They learned the alphabet
They would never play with a net
They learned their prayers
Some would say "Who cares?"
But not in a Dame School
Leah Greene, Grade 5
Alvaton Elementary School, KY

Christmas

Holly hanging,
People praying,
Presents being passed;
Kids laughing,
Cameras snapping;
Everyone's having a blast.
Madeline Hurley, Grade 6
Blessed Teresa of Calcutta School, MO

Brandon Brown

Brandon
Smart, nice, strong
Sibling of Jon and Chris
Lover of dogs, sea monkeys, and fish
Who feels generosity and
understanding
Who needs love, friendship, and support
Who gives love and friendship
Who fears darkness
Who would like to see how spiders
make their webs, a real moon rock
Brown
Brandon Brown, Grade 5
Ascension Elementary School, KY

Thanksgiving

Thanksgiving
Thanksgiving
Thanksgiving

Happy Thanksgiving
Fun Thanksgiving
Freaky, cool, funny Thanksgiving
Colorful, big, warm Thanksgiving

These are just a few

Restful Thanksgiving
Loving Thanksgiving
Parades, loud, bad Thanksgiving
Cold, snowy, cuddly Thanksgiving
Spooky Thanksgiving, too
Slow Thanksgiving
Gold Thanksgiving
Don't forget healthy Thanksgiving
Last of all, best of all,
I like family Thanksgiving.
Chelsea Sanford, Grade 5
Tates Creek Elementary School, KY

We Come to School

We come to school
We play and drool
We also have lots of fun
We dance and sing
We play and laugh oh boy
I think you should come
We sleep during class
We play during break
Oh wait we can't be late
So come to school
To play and drool
Come on we can't be late.
Ashley Goodwin, Grade 6
St Cecilia School, LA

The Poor Family

There they lie,
A boy, a girl, a mom, and a dad.
Sometimes they just have to cry.

They don't have money for food;
And sometimes people can be rude.
But they are a strong family;
And they will always live happily.

Their spirits will never die down.
They won't be treated as clowns.
People should not treat each of them as if he or she were
wearing an ugly gown.

They are human.
So they should be treated with respect.
Still they don't have a house with a den;
They having feelings!

Karlos Lopez, Grade 6
Haynes Academy for Advanced Studies, LA

Just Here

Just sitting here trying to find the words to say
everything has its day.
Just crying here watching time float away
I'm just a'dying here living life day to day.
I don't know what's next
or what to expect.
I should just face the facts
and get life back on track.
It's been ten months maybe a year
so now its time to face my fears.
I'm always hiding the feelings inside
trying not to collide with my past.
I can't let go I can't even try
because every time I do it brings tears to my eyes.
But I wish I could let it go just float away.
Never return ever to see the day
it all comes back to haunt me again.
I just wish I could put it all to an end.
But until then I'll just forget what I can
and move on to live yet again!

JUST HERE
Lauren Burroughs, Grade 6
Thompson Middle School, AL

Football Game

Smell the cow manure on the sidelines.
See the ball soaring in the air at you.
Feel the ball in your hands when you catch it.
Hear the pads pop when you get tackled.
Taste the dirt in your mouth after the play.

Slade Biles, Grade 5
Briarwood Christian Elementary School, AL

A Dragon Who Developed Strep Throat

There once was a dragon who developed strep throat
Who lived in a nearby moat
He couldn't breathe fire
Without his fever getting higher
So he fell asleep wearing a coat.

Travis Richards, Grade 6
Martin Elementary School, WV

Snow

When I looked out, I used to see snow.
So white,
So vivid,
So fun to look at.
Now I only see dull dying grass.
How boring!
I used to put on my snow pants, jacket, hat, gloves, and scarf.
I could build a snowman,
Throw a snowball,
And make snow angels.
I would wear my boots to school
And carry along my shoes for inside.
It was so much fun to ride on my sled with my sister in my lap.
I felt so happy and joyful, so free.
Now I just feel gloomy.
I miss the snow.
Oh, snow, when will you come see me again?

Allison Stanley, Grade 5
Kiroli Elementary School, LA

Football Game

Smells like buttery popcorn
Tastes like a hotdog and pizza
Feels like cheering
Looks like an enormous yardstick
Sounds like an announcer

Taylor Mitchell, Grade 5
Briarwood Christian Elementary School, AL

My Dad

I really love my awesome Dad
Fighting fires is his fad
He goes into a burning house
It makes me nervous as I wait
Because sometimes he is really late
He is my very best friend
If I am in danger
He is there to defend
He went out with no one in sight
Right on this very night
Just to try and save a soul
Even if it is in a manhole
We will always be best buds; side by side
Even until the very end
Because I know he is my most awesome friend.

Kristin Grose, Grade 6
Pleasants County Middle School, WV

Picking Up Seashells

I love going to the beach,
But I do not like the water.
My favorite thing to do is
Picking up seashells.

Grabbing my red bucket,
I ran to the shore
Scouting my choices.

There were,
Round oyster shells,
Sharp seashells,
White, black, and pink seashells.
So many choices.

I put them in a jar
To remind me of what
I did on my trip.

Kacie Bates, Grade 5
Etowah Elementary School, NC

The Gate of Pity

Off he rides,
Into the night.
Fighting off the fright,
His dapple gray,
Joins the Fray.

His dapple gray,
Gets a bite,
A bite that can only come from spite.
Yes, fright knew spite,
The one who gave the bite.

The dapple gray,
Lost the fight.
He gained his way to Pity.
The long forgotten city,
Though the rider now had
To trod the ground himself.

He continued on his way,
Passing through the Fray,
From night,
To become day,
Ever gaining his way to Pity.

Jordan Nease, Grade 6
Greenville Montessori School, NC

If I Were a Kite

If I were a kite I'd fly so high;
I'd fly so high, I'd reach the sky.
I'd fly all day, I'd fly all night.
And that's what I do…if I were a kite.

Allison Ashworth, Grade 5
Midway Covenant Christian School, GA

What's the Point?

What's the point in doing, if you don't care what you have done?
What's the point in being, if you don't care who you have been?
What's the point in living, if you don't care about the life you have lived?
So when you go outside today, put on a happy smile…
Because what's the point of living a life that's very sad?

Margaret Shull, Grade 5
St Dominic School, TN

The Theater

What a magical place.
It will beckon to those with talent to come and perform.
The theater changes expressions like the heart of a human.
With feelings of happiness, sadness and rage the theater is real.
People come and watch the show of a human just like a theater.
The theater releases joy to the lucky public who fall upon a happy thing.
People inside it have a special place in their hearts especially for the theater.
It has many parts like the heart, stomach and the brain as the stage, seats, and wings.
The theater is so special, so we'd better hang on to it!

Kelsey McNeely, Grade 6
River Trail Middle School, GA

I Want a Horse

I want a horse well of course everybody knows.
If I tried to get on it I would have to stand on my toes.
If I got a girl horse I would name her Bessy,
and I would clean her stall once a week, so it wouldn't get too messy.
When I heard my friend got a horse I kind of felt left out,
and I sat on my chair, and I began to pout.
I know if God wanted me to have a horse He would have put it there,
so I really shouldn't care.

Katie Roxanne Clapp, Grade 4
Tri-County Christian School, MO

Musical Stairs

There is a beautiful house with beautiful stairs;
In fact these stairs are musical stairs.
They click and clatter they ding and they dong
Each step you take is a musical song.

Those stairs they're long one thousand miles long the biggest I've eve seen
And the children play a cheerful song, with lovely melody.
They run so fast up and down, very exhausting indeed.
They get tired fast; they take a seat, that's all they really need.

The musicians teach their kids on these wonderful stairs,
They teach one by one, but sometimes in pairs.
But one day the stairs said "I'm tired" and stopped,
So we just sat there on those non-musical stairs and thought.

When those terribly wonderful stairs awoke we played many wonderful songs,
We danced and sang, marched and cheered was very, very loud.
When the party was over and everyone left you still hear them play,
Do you, do you hear those beautiful, wonderful stairs play today?

John O'Roark, Grade 5
Providence Academy, TN

What Does Thanksgiving Mean to You

Thanksgiving is a time of joy.
Not the time you get a toy.
Helping and sharing are things for this day.
It's a time for the youngsters to play.
Families get together to eat.
This is what Thanksgiving is meant to be.

Matthew Dahlke, Grade 6
Guntown Middle School, MS

I Scribbled on My Face

I scribbled on my face
I don't know why I did
I scribbled on my face
Also on my chin

On my nose there is a rainbow
On my cheeks are blue and pink
Of course I colored in crayon
Because I have no marker ink

I scribbled on my face
I cannot wash it off
And I wrote my name on Sue,
but the only thing I did not scribble on is you

Natasha Popkin, Grade 5
Etowah Elementary School, NC

Horses, Horses

Horses, horses, cantering, trotting,
Muscles rippling, head held high,
No other animal can compete,
Horses, horses, jumping 3 foot 4,
Galloping out of breath,
Make great companions for those who love…
Horses, horses, running free,
I wish I had one, don't you?

Kristen Sorensen, Grade 6
Brogden Middle School, NC

The Woman and the Man

Across the way and over the dark,
Three skips toward the sky and
Six leaps through the clouds, and
Stop at the one lined with gold.

A lady sits perched on her chair in the clouds.
A man watches her with a smile on his face.
He approaches with care not to scare her away.
He stops at the girl wearing gold.

She looks at the man with a dream in her eyes.
She tilts her sweet face to the heavens above.
She quietly rose to her feet, showing grace,
And they danced 'til the sea turned to gold.

Sally Burgess, Grade 6
Bellwood Discovery School, TN

Blue

Blue is calm, quiet, and peaceful
Blue is turquoise, light blue,
Dark blue, and navy blue
Blue is blue jays singing,
Blue is dreaming and thinking,
Blue is blooming flowers,
Blue is the wavy ocean,
Blue is the bright blue sky
Blue

Ahmia Feaster, Grade 4
Chester Park Elementary School of Fine Arts, SC

Leaves

Losing their color,
lovely to look at and stare,
they drop to the ground.

Marianne Akins, Grade 4
Briarwood Christian Elementary School, AL

Horses

Horses, horses throw your mane,
Stomp your feet to the funky beat.
Gallop, gallop everywhere,
The air flowing through your hair,
Your ears twitching as you gallop through the forest.

Crystal Mandel, Grade 4
Moyock Elementary School, NC

Gymnastics

I used to take gymnastics
A few years ago
I just couldn't get past this one trick
Another level I wouldn't go

I tried and tried and tried
But I just couldn't get it
I fell on my back a few times
But I went right back up to that bar again
And again and again

A few months it took me
Because I only went once a week
But that didn't stop me
From what I used to seek

Finally the day had come
I could feel pride
Instead of pain
I could now do it again and again

Another level I would go
And this only happened
A few years ago

Amber Delperdang, Grade 6
Beck Academy, SC

Roses

Roses bloom shyly
Growing in size
As they reach
With their petals
Up to the skies
Brooke Blackwell, Grade 5
Bonaire Elementary School, GA

Veteran

V ictory is ours
E mbracing our loved ones
T ired from all the wars
E nduring through hard times
R evolutionary soldiers will receive
A wards
N ever stop our troops.
Genevieve Rogers, Grade 4
Cherokee Elementary School, AR

Merry Christmas

M om makes cookies for Saint Nick
E veryone is happy
R eading Christmas cards
R ight turns into the driveway
Y oung kids playing

C hristmas is here
H appy holidays
R ocky under our feet when we walk
I s very special to us
S aint Nicholas eating cookies
T urkey and ham we eat
M erry Christmas Saint Nicholas
A wesome Saint Nicholas
S aint Nick coming down the chimney
Nikki Carter, Grade 4
Tamassee-Salem Elementary School, SC

My Mom

Lisa McAdoo
Gracious and helpful
Rapidly cleaning
I always know she's there.
Bethany McAdoo, Grade 5
Salem Elementary School, AR

Number 1 Mom

She laughs, I play
I cry, she mocks me.
When I ride the four wheeler
She drives, I ride.
She cooks, I watch.
She talks, I don't listen.
Christopher Lane, Grade 6
Edmonton Elementary School, KY

A Man from Peru

There once was a man from Peru
Who dreamed he was eating his shoe
He woke from a clatter
To see what's the matter
How silly that man from Peru
Jordan Murphy, Grade 6
Livingston Middle School, TN

My Best Friend

My best friend has dark brown hair
He also has deep brown eyes
He likes to run and jump
And be one of the guys
His favorite sport is just like mine
The difference between he and I
Are four legs and a tail
And his name ends in "Y."
His name is Buddy
He is my buddy forever and ever.
That is why.
Derek Barnhart, Grade 6
Pleasants County Middle School, WV

Fog

Thin and thick
Different shapes and sizes.
White that rolls
across the ground
and disappears
Into the day.
Tristan Geile, Grade 5
St Vincent Elementary School, MO

Dreams

There is a land of peace and joy;
There is no destruction or evil.
Lands full of girl and boy;
No strong nor feeble.
Where fantasies are true,
Where creatures roam free,
Where everything is new;
And it is only you and me.
Where is this you would ask.
It would seem
It would be a task,
Because you must dream.
Hayden Songy, Grade 6
Lake Castle Private School, LA

The Turtle

The turtle swims fast
He sits on a rock all day
He is brown and gold
Savannah Givens, Grade 5
Etowah Elementary School, NC

Winter

Winter is the time
for snowball fights and snowmen
fire warms my cold toes
Braydon Albert, Grade 6
Tomlinson Jr High School, OK

The Raindrop Man

He dances across the street,
up the alley, and onto me.

He hits my roof with a
pitter-patter, pitter-patter,
into the gutter and down the shoot.

He runs through the grass,
playing tag with his friends,
then jumps down the curb landing
SPLAT!! before he starts again.
Alex Buck, Grade 6
Brogden Middle School, NC

Spring/Fall

Spring
Warm, cold
Walking, jogging, running
Park, pool, backyard, friends
Play, playground, house, outside
Jumping, raking, falling
Cool, peaceful
Fall
Hannah San Miguel, Grade 5
Sycamore Elementary School, GA

A Good Day

Buck and Doe both like the grass.
He walks up to the stand,
With a huge mass.
Then he spots us and is gone.
He stops because he sees a fawn.
We get another look,
But it's too far away.
Then we spot another one,
And say, "Man, what a day"
This one isn't a buck, but a young doe.
I say, "Should I take it?"
And then I think, "No."
Dalton Mettes, Grade 5
North Shelby Elementary School, MO

Clown Fish

In a vast ocean
A clown fish swims in a reef
At the break of dawn
Evan Benjamin, Grade 4
Robert E Lee Elementary School, TN

A Burrowing Owl

With its gleaming eyes,
Seeing in the night,
Swooping down and snatching its prey,
Consuming it with its slicing beak,
Taking mouthfuls of it.

With its cunning claws,
Landing on a skinny branch,
And holding itself there,
Flying from limb to limb,
Leaving claw marks.

Its bony feet,
Tucking under itself,
When soaring in the cool air,
Its toenails sharp,
All of them glowing in the moonlight.

With its feathered wings,
Dropping down,
Landing in its underground burrow,
To lay its eggs,
And to hide from the sunrise.

Katie Posto, Grade 4
Goshen Elementary School at Hillcrest, KY

Our Big Trip

One summer day in the month past May,
we got in the car and went very far.
Our first stop was Tennessee,
where we saw the Grand Ole Opry.
Then our next stop was Cincinnati,
to have fun with Mom and Daddy.
We then dropped off Dad at Ohio State,
while Mom and three boys made a great escape.
We were Canada bound across the border,
where we got a Canadian quarter.
The final treat was better than any ball,
when we saw Niagara Falls!

Bennett Bice, Grade 4
Stephens Elementary School, AL

Fred's Friends

Here is Fred.
His friend is Ted.
When Ted and Fred go out to play.
They meet Betty and say say say.

"Hey Betty!
Come out to play with me and Ted all day."
"Ok," said Betty.
"I'll come out to play,
But maybe not all day, Ok?"

Ali Davidson, Grade 4
Tazewell/New Tazewell Elementary School, TN

My Sister

I couldn't wait 'til my little sister was here!
She was so cute,
she slept all the time.
She never caused trouble,
Not even one time!

I couldn't wait 'til my sister was six months old!
She was so cute,
She smiled all the time.
She wasn't much trouble,
Just a little bit, though.

I couldn't wait 'til my sister was one!
She was so cute,
She walked and talked,
And I heard what she said,
But I didn't understand all of it.

I couldn't wait 'til my sister was 2!
She was so cute,
She walks and talks and follows me around.
She causes so much trouble
Getting into MY stuff!
I CAN WAIT 'TIL SHE IS 5!

Cierra Wall, Grade 6
Alpena Elementary School, AR

Love

Trapped in the darkness of fear
Waiting for my love to appear.
Hoping he will save me
Over the sea, that's where I will be.

He turns the darkness of fear
into happy music that I can hear.
I love him so and would hate to see him go.
My love is true and that's all I can do.

My thoughts are about him
inspite that I used to doubt him.
But my love is still true
There's nothing else I'd rather do.

Haley Dawkins, Grade 4
Stephens Elementary School, AL

Snakes

Cold-blooded reptiles, snakes may be.
Lots of snakes live in trees.
Some snakes live on the ground,
It causes lots of people to frown.
Snakes are a reptile that don't really stink.
Some snakes live in a garden, I think.
Snakes are reptiles that should be respected, you see,
Because snakes live in the wild were they are free.

Randell Lainhart, Grade 5
Paint Lick Elementary School, KY

The Last Person

The last person on the Earth
Would be a drag
No one would be there
Except the trees whistling about
And the lovely ladybug and butterflies
Whispering in your ear
The wild animals would be sneaking
To find their food
I would walk into the jungle
Hearing owls hoot, and seeing
The wonderful tree frogs hopping about
Maybe I am the last person on the Earth
So it wouldn't be such a drag

Haley Benson, Grade 5
Bonaire Elementary School, GA

Tornadoes

Hurry
Run, it's here now
I hear a whistle sound
Mommy, Daddy, help me
Is it safe now?
It's ok it's over.

Madison Hunter, Grade 5
Broadway Elementary School, NC

Love

Love is in the air
I feel it everywhere
Even when I'm doing my hair
This passion everyone calls love
Just a simple little hug
Is love

Brianna Barnes, Grade 6
Brogden Middle School, NC

My Dog, Sadie

My dog, Sadie,
Is sweet.
She makes me happy.
She makes me leap.

My dog, Sadie,
Is brown and white.
She makes me happy,
When I'm blue.
I bet she'd make you happy, too.

Jessica Martin, Grade 4
Hayes Elementary School, OK

Winter

Cold wind brushes my cheeks
Cold snow piling in my boots
Snowball fights never end.

Kali Turner, Grade 4
Lula Elementary School, GA

My Horse

My name is Hunter, and I want you to know
about my horse I had a year ago.
We had lots of fun she was so smart.
We were best of friends right from the start.
She had long blonde mane.
Her eyes would shimmer with sparkling blue.
I loved her a lot, she loved me too.
I would ride her through the pond
and through the pasture and down the hills.
I often wonder if she was watching her weight.
She didn't care for sugar cubes but for apples she couldn't wait.
I would ride her bare back or with a saddle.
I'm sure it didn't matter with Twister that's a fact.
Her mane would blow softly as she ran on the grass.
To her as she galloped it was just the present with no future or past.

Hunter Garrard, Grade 4
Brilliant Elementary School, AL

This Little Girl

This little girl dances gracefully in the sun with her heart heaped with fun.
Pirouettes, splits, and leaps make her move so upbeat.
Outside in the rain or even on a snowy day.
This little girl loves to dance.
She doesn't worry if she sweats or hurts. Just so she dances.

Kendi Wyatt, Grade 6
Arnaudville Elementary School, LA

I'm From

I'm from Dolly Parton cassette tapes, and week-long baseball games.
I'm from an old guitar, and that race car, shotgun shells, and cow bells.
Kentucky, Arkansas, and Texas is where I'm from,
and the old oak tree with the initials carved in it.
I'm from an old scar, and that wrecked car.
I'm the crow on top of the fence guarding your sweet memories.

Jameson T. Reddin, Grade 6
College View Middle School, KY

Wyoming

Have you ever smelled sweet hay or seen the brightest stars?
I have, only in Wyoming.

Have you ever gazed upon emerald eyes as big as coins
Or rode bareback on your favorite horse?
I have, only in Wyoming.

Have you ever seen waves of grass and painted mountains?
I have, only in Wyoming.

Have you ever seen snow fall sideways and pile up as high as the sky?
I have, only in Wyoming.

My heart is in Wyoming.
My breath is in Wyoming.
I will be whole again, only in Wyoming.

Maisy Brichetto, Grade 4
Sequoyah Elementary School, TN

Tico the Terrible Tornado

I am a huge big gust of wind
My speed is 300 mph
I am indestructible
I cause bad injuries
My name is Tico the Terrible
I am the biggest and largest of them all
I roar through cornfields and forest
I toss houses, cars, animals, and anything in my path
I AM A TORNADO
You will NEVER FORGET ME!!!

Nicholas W. Locklear, Grade 5
Pembroke Elementary School, NC

My Teacher's Mind

Why is my class so loud?
They laugh too much.
Can I make them quieter?
They're going to kill me.
Will they outgrow me?
Will they have their homework done?
How good are they at stories?
How hard are they working?
What excuse will I get today?
Will something happen if I leave the room?
I need some chocolate!
Is someone going to get hurt?
I'm tired!
My new class is scaring me!
Stop annoying me!
I need to go home!
Should I move the desks around?
Be quiet!
I'm hungry.
Great, I have to grade papers!

Scout Miller, Grade 5
South Nodaway Elementary School, MO

Homework

Homework is hard,
Homework is time consuming.
Homework is confusing and annoying,
Homework, "Why do we do it?"
Homework means: Practice Makes Perfect

Jeremiah Morgan, Grade 5
Paint Lick Elementary School, KY

Veteran

V ery sad
E very soldier tries
T rue some die
E very person needs to call more soldiers
R un from the enemies' tank
A ttacked by enemies
N ever give up

Simon Decker, Grade 4
Cherokee Elementary School, AR

Fire and Ice

fire
hot, destructive
burning, smoking, hurting
sticks, sparks, snow, haze
freezing, melting, numbing
cold, slick
ice

Colin Smith, Grade 5
Briarwood Christian Elementary School, AL

Clouds

Cumulus
White, fluffy
Soaring, flying, floating
Making children all around the world wonder
Cloud

Jennifer Lynn Perry, Grade 5
Contentnea Elementary School, NC

To Follow Your Dream

If you have a dream
Don't let it go;
Don't forget it,
Just reach for your goal.

No matter what people might tell you,
No matter what they say,
If it's your dream,
Don't let it stray.

Practice makes perfect,
It's all up to you;
There is nothing that anyone can do, except you.

Through hardship and turmoil,
through times that are rough;
Only you can achieve it
If you can stay tough.

So no matter how far away
Your accomplishment may seem;
If you want it enough,
Just follow your dream.
This is the hardest adventure there is.

Ezra Sheffield, Grade 5
Bostian Elementary School, NC

Moon

I am whom?
I'm but a shiny object in the sky.
When you are in darkness, I bring out the light.
When you want me, don't take flight.
I'll be with you all through the night.

Samuel Raines, Grade 4
St Thomas More School, NC

Zoo Family

My mom, my dad, and my sister too.
They are all part of my family in the zoo.

Wild dogs, cats, monkeys too.
They all live with me and you.
We have breakfast at eight, lunch at two.
Dinner at ten in the very fine zoo.
Wake up at seven, go to bed at eleven.

It's all part of the very fun zoo.
Tori Lampkin, Grade 5
Cottonwood Public School, OK

Spring

Spring is a time of fun and joy
Almost everybody loves it, girl or boy
Flowers bloom, ice melts
And birds begin to sing
Squirrels and chipmunks wake up
And hear the lovely ring
Water flows down to the bay
Cows wake up and eat the hay
Run outside and feel the warm
New baby animals are being born
Shed your winter coats today
So you can run outside and play
Spring is a time of fun and joy
Almost everybody loves it, girl or boy
Erin Anderson, Grade 4
Sequoyah Elementary School, TN

My Uncle

M eet my uncle
Y ou will love him

U ncle John
N othing is better
C ool stories to tell us
L oving
E nergetic
Dakota Trauco, Grade 4
St Thomas More School, NC

Thanksgiving

Thanksgiving
is the time of year
when everyone you love is near…

You have a feast
where you can eat like a beast…

Be thankful for what you've been given
thank goodness for THANKSGIVING!
Aubrey Haire, Grade 6
Guntown Middle School, MS

One True Friend

A friend to trust,
A friend to love,
One true friend

A friend who cares,
A friend who listens,
Your emotions to bear

A touch of life
that makes you smile,
That is one true friend.
Abby Myers, Grade 6
Dyer Elementary & Jr High School, TN

The Dead Grass

I'm that piece of grass that hates its life,
because I grew up on the street.
Flat then fine again and again I say,
"STOP YOU CRAZY PEOPLE!"
but, it never works.
Michael Barnes, Grade 4
Lula Elementary School, GA

Hear the World Whisper

Hear the world whisper
In the dark night sky.
See the world slightly move a budge.
Feel the world stop
When it goes to sleep at the sunset.
Hear the clock,
The world's alarm,
Yelling at the morning.
Hear the world's cheering on Earth Day.
See the Earth partying
With the moon and Pluto.
Susannah Oder, Grade 5
Bonaire Elementary School, GA

Thanksgiving

Thanksgiving is very cool
All the food makes you drool
It's time for family together
No matter what the weather

You may love the food
You may love the mood
There's turkey and pie
Set on the table high

Pass it all around
There's fun abound
Even if you're not a queen or king
You should give thanks for everything
Garrett Lyons, Grade 6
Victory Christian School, OK

Ray

R emember the water fights
A n amazing horse trainer
Y oung at heart!
Haley Purkapile, Grade 5
Trenton Middle School, MO

Grizzly

Big, growling grizzly
Walking among the oak trees
Smelling the forest
Austin Millwood, Grade 5
Bonaire Elementary School, GA

My Stuffed Animal Fluffy

When I was just a baby
I had a little friend.
I'll tell you all about it, maybe
It'll make you grin.

Fluffy was its name,
Brown and black was its color.
We would play games,
It was a gift from grandmother.

When I was really sad,
Fluffy's tail would catch my tears.
When I was really mad,
I'd kick Fluffy in the rear.

Fluffy was not put up for safekeeping,
And not stuck in a box.
Saying goodbye forever caused weeping,
I'll truly miss him lots.
Alexander Karr, Grade 6
Woodland Presbyterian School, TN

Spunky

Usually caged,
Until I come and uncage him,
Intelligent,
For his species,
This little guy,
Chirps when I whistle
Stays on my shoulder, finger,
And climbs up my shirt,
Feathered,
Often quiet,
Sometimes noisy,
Full name,
Spunky Pierre Alexander Sopovic,
The birthday present I'll never,
Ever,
Forget.
Ben Sopovic, Grade 6
Bernard Middle School, MO

A Magical Place

Deep in the mountains
Are fountains.
Flowing springs of blue and white haze
A sight so beautiful it filled my gaze.

The soft cool air
Tickled my hair.
The river that follows this gorgeous fall
The trees that surround are very tall.

This land is filled with pink and blue fairies
With orange and green magical berries.
They appear in the pale moonlight
And their dancing is a merry sight.

The fragrance in the air is so sweet
It made my heart skip a beat.
This is all the time we can spend
So I'm sorry to say our journey must end.

Ashley Marter, Grade 6
St Cecilia School, LA

Dogs

Dogs are people's best friends.

They love to run and play every day with you,
My dog's smile can make me smile too.

When I am sad, they can make me cheery,
If a burglar tries to break in, my dog is leery.

A knock on the door and my dog starts to bark,
It's great when you're home alone in the dark.

I think dogs are people's best friends.

Jacob Mayer, Grade 6
St Joseph Institute for the Deaf, MO

All About a School and a Mall

School
small, tiresome
learning, boring, teaching
books, cafeteria, stores, food court
shopping, spending, buying
big, awesome
Mall

Elizabeth M. Polhill, Grade 5
Briarwood Christian Elementary School, AL

1-2-3 Here Comes Fall

Leaves are red and green.
Leaves fall off in the spring yes.
Here they come count them.

Rachel Nix, Grade 4
Briarwood Christian Elementary School, AL

Billy's Sad Story

There was a little boy
His name was Billy
He woke up from his nap
He thought "Where am I."

He walked outside "Where am I."
He thought "Have I been kidnapped."
then his Grandma walked in
He remembered he was in Ohio

He started crying
He was in Ohio
He was there because his parents died
They died in a car accident

He was sad
Then his Grandma said "It will be all right."
Then she gave him some cookies and milk
He felt a little better

Janae Hancock, Grade 6
Qulin Middle School, MO

Sunrise

Appears at morning
This beautiful thing it is
God's majestic hue

Davis Moers, Grade 4
Briarwood Christian Elementary School, AL

The Seashore

Seashore winds blow,
as the tides come and go,
Coming off the sea,
and the fish swim with great glee.
The waves hit the sand,
seeming soft as a baby's hand,
The water is so clear,
I can tell sharp rocks are nowhere near, and
The beautiful shells, I can tell,
were placed here by God.

Rania S. Glass, Grade 5
Midway Covenant Christian School, GA

Potato Peeler

I am a potato peeler.
My outsides shine with glee,
but in I am rusty and rough.
I can be noisy with frustration.
I am sharp in mind. I am smooth all over.
I am scratched with age.
My outsides curl.
I am dirty with fingerprints. I can be loose.
I am a sturdy potato peeler
waiting to be held with love again.

Dana Beck, Grade 4
Lynn Fanning Elementary School, AL

Little Sister

Little sister,
So annoying
Anytime I leave,
She thinks she has to come.
She just,
and I say, just,
Has to act like me.
I want to scream!

But sometimes…
She becomes so precious
Like a little butterfly.

Olivia Garris, Grade 5
St Vincent Elementary School, MO

Horse

Horses
Soft, fast, tall
Running, galloping, trotting
I love to ride horses.
Filly

Allison Ferrell, Grade 5
Shirley Elementary School, AR

Dog/Cat

Dog
Cute, cuddly
Running, jumping, barking
Doghouse, dog toy, litter box, cat bed
Playing, meowing, licking
Fluffy, pretty
Cat

Kelsie Lewis, Grade 5
Sycamore Elementary School, GA

Candy

Candy,
Candy,
Candy,
Sweet candy,
Sour candy,
Big fat Hershey's candy,
Long thin Kit Kat candy,
Those are just a few.

Brown candy,
White candy,
Big fat tootsie roll candy,
Chewy bubble gum too.
Reese's candy,
Crunch candy,
Don't forget Snickers' candy,
Last of all best of all,
I like Butterfinger candy!

Brittany Marie Mullenix, Grade 6
Hayes Elementary School, OK

I Am a Military Child

I am a military child and part Korean.
I wonder about the people in the army.
I hear a lot of shooting outside when they are practicing.
I see a lot of old army buildings.
I want my step father out of the army.
I am a middle child and part Korean.

I pretend I'm a soldier in the army sometimes.
I feel scared when I hear the loud noises on the base.
I touch my hands together to pray for all those fighting the war.
I worry about my stepfather when he is away.
I cry when he leaves for war.
I am a middle child and part Korean.

I understand that they work really hard and sometimes all night long.
I say being in the army is one of the proudest jobs anyone could do.
I dream about the day my stepfather comes home.
I try to help my mom more when he is gone.
I hope there will be a day when no ones dad or mom has to leave for the war.
I am a middle child and part Korean.

Christina Mitchell, Grade 5
Walker Intermediate School, KY

Oklahoma's Oil and Natural Gas:
A Celebration of Oklahoma

Our state called Oklahoma,
Where oil and gas abounds,
Wildcatters drilled the Mary Sudik,
A new industry was found.
The industry grew at such a rate,
Wealth was brought to the Sooner State,
Tulsa became the leading town,
Where oil and gas was richly found.
Oklahoma the Sooner State.
Oil and gas has made us great.

Sarah Cloyd, Grade 5
Canute Elementary School, OK

Military Child

I am a military child who likes to play like an army man.
I wish that my dad will come back from Texas so we can go places and have fun.
I hear gun shots and tanks firing.
I hope my dad comes back.
I am a military child who likes to play like an army man.

I cry because it is the third time my dad has left.
I know my dad is in Texas working on tanks and is sending me gifts.
I talk to him on the phone.
I want to send him gifts, but I can't.
I am a military child who likes to play like an army man.

I know my dad is a good dad and treats me right.
I know he likes to live in places that I can go to, but I can't miss a day of school
I am a military child who likes to play like an army man.

Lamichael Johnson, Grade 4
Walker Intermediate School, KY

Let It Rain

I'm sitting on my bed
Looking at the rain fall down
Well, I better enjoy it while I can because
Tomorrow it will be gone
I go put my rain coat on and shoes
Run out the door and start to dance
I keep on dancing and dancing and dancing
While the rain keeps fading away
So I go back inside and wait for another day like today.

Natasha Beck, Grade 6
Scotts Creek Elementary School, NC

Love

To that special someone.
I'm waiting here for that someone every day and night.
Needing someone to hold me tight.
To cheer me up when I'm sad.
To make me smile when I'm mad.

To that special someone.
I'm waiting here
For that someone every day and night
Needing someone to hold me tight
To cheer me up when I'm sad.
To make me smile when I'm mad.
I need that someone who will always care.
Someone that will always be there.

Jose Yanez, Grade 6
Brogden Middle School, NC

Autumn Leaves

Autumn leaves are like dancers. The leaves jump
    on the clouds like a dance floor,
        singing, bringing music to my ears,
            twisting and turning with the other partners,
                loving every minute of it.

Mara Woods, Grade 4
First Wesleyan Christian School, NC

Moonlight Thinking

Lying in the moonlight
Looking at the stars
Wondering how my life has come this far.

Thinking what my life truly means to me
Thinking how my soul has come to find me.

As I lie there I think,
And think, and think
Who I'm supposed to be.

I think why I am here
Why do I finally see
What my life truly means to me.

Joseph Sorrentino, Grade 6
Woodland Presbyterian School, TN

Oh, Winter, You Are So Cold!

Oh, Winter, you are so cool,
    Your lake looks like a frozen pool.

Oh, Winter, you remind me of Christmas snow,
    This year it's going to be a great show.

Oh, winter, how bright your sun,
    We love to play outside and have fun.

Oh, winter, you are so white,
    When I look in the mirror I don't know what to do.

Winter, you make my cheeks red,
    And the cold wind goes through my head.

Oh, Winter, you are my favorite of the seasons,
    And these are all of my reasons!

Lauren Rogerson, Grade 4
Pines Elementary School, NC

The Night

In the night,
The black bat night,
The moon shines as a flashlight.
Little stars twinkle in the grass.
Owls hoot like a train in the distance.
Trees stand like statues in the light breeze.
My eyes close as the sky gets darker and quieter.

Taylor Roberts, Grade 4
Chester Park Elementary School of Fine Arts, SC

Strawberry and Blueberry

The strawberry is cleaned
but the strawberry seeds are planted to grow.
Some drop on poison ivy and are choked.
Some drop on good soil
and grow from the ground
and to feed a person
to them I say strawberries are good
but they are great for health.
Blueberries are great too
Because people love their great taste.

Brody Barnes, Grade 5
St Teresa's School, GA

Why Am I So Little?

Why am I so little?
Why am I so small?
Why can't I be really big and very tall?

My sister says I'll grow,
But what I really want to know is
Why am I so little and why am I so small?

Alexis LeBlanc, Grade 5
Oberlin Elementary School, LA

The Moon

The moon is dark
The moon is bright
Why can you see that
Shine so bright like the sunset
Going down like this moon let it
Shine so bright, bright, bright

Jeremy Tackett, Grade 5
Zalma Elementary School, MO

Veteran

V ictory they had
E ach of them were brave
T ogether they help
E ach other and telling us not to
R un away
A rmies standing up for us and the
N avys also did that.

Colby McGuire, Grade 4
Cherokee Elementary School, AR

Soccer

Soccer is filled with fun and joy
It is played by either girl or boy
All coaches are very nice
They always give advice
You can do tricks on the other team
That makes them really steam
Don't ever get sad
Or the coaches will be mad
There is always time to play
Either play night or day
When you help a friend
It will pay off with a goal again and again
You have time
So don't be a lime
All you have to do is have fun
And that is the meaning of soccer.

Christian Kenvin, Grade 6
Queen of Angels Catholic School, GA

Tornado

When I was just a little boy
The sky was always green
Like the grass below our feet
It got really, really windy
Then an alarm sounded
And we went into the cellar
Woo, Woo
The wind rang in our ears
The wind made the trees dance
Upon the storm
Then at last the tornado
Twisted through the trees of Lonoke

Austin Cowart, Grade 5
Bonaire Elementary School, GA

Colorful Butterflies

Colorful butterflies
Pretty colors,
Blue eyes,
Red wings,
Purple antenna,
Beautiful butterflies,
Fly away.

Catarina Bell, Grade 4
Russell Babb Elementary School, OK

God's Love

God's love for us is never-ending
He died for all our sins upon the cross
Does anybody else love you that much?
No, because it's only God's love
If we could only comprehend
What He was put through
He was hung on the cross
He was beat like crazy
He rose from the dead
Would anybody do that for you?
No, because it's only God's love
It's only God's love

Jesse Hinson, Grade 6
North Iredell Middle School, NC

Veteran

V itality important to us
E xplore justice
T erritory protected
E merge winners of truth
R esolve conflict
A lways dedicated
N oble and humble

Michaela Young, Grade 4
Cherokee Elementary School, AR

So Cold!!

So cold, so cold,
So cold I'm getting frost bite,
So cold, so cold, I want my mommy,
So cold, so cold, I won't go to sleep!

So warm, so warm,
So warm I'm getting blisters,
So warm, so warm I want my daddy,
So warm, so warm, I'll go to sleep!

So happy, so happy,
So happy I'm getting butterflies
So happy, so happy, I want them both,
So happy, so happy, I burst out with
   Laughter!

Jayden Clark, Grade 5
Canute Elementary School, OK

Mechanical Doll

Mechanical doll
Sweet and sour
Weeping and chatting
Always around
Baby sister

Jacob Irby, Grade 5
Salem Elementary School, AR

Sandy Beaches

The water rushes to your feet,
Music moving to the beat,
Fish swimming through the waves,
Clams digging to be safe,
Splashing, kicking, having fun,
At the beach, in the sun.

Ashley Howard, Grade 5
Evangel Christian Academy, AL

Veteran

V iolence goes on
E veryone cries
T ogether as a team, they work
E yes see things that hurt
R unning right and left
A merica is saved
N ervously they arrive

Shaina Manning, Grade 4
Cherokee Elementary School, AR

Within the Darkness

Hope could be gone
Light may never break
The way is lost
But there are many paths to take
All in shadow
Through desolate shade
Time stretches on
All seems to fade
Through cloud and storm
The dawn will sever
Through pain-filled night
And shine bright as ever
Even if life gets trying
Never stop the fight
For always remember
Within the darkness, there is a light

Emily Pounds, Grade 6
Riverwood Middle School, NC

Elephant Boy

My favorite super hero is Elephant Boy.
He uses his mumbo-jumbo.
Elephant Boy is actually a toy.

Kurdt Foy, Grade 5
Oark Elementary School, AR

The Frog

Look, there, everywhere
jump, jump, all around, green, red
every head of frogs

Dani Karcher, Grade 4
Briarwood Christian Elementary School, AL

Another Autumn

Autumn leaves fall on my head,
And they fly away as they go to bed.
Their colors are yellow, red, and brown,
In the trees all through the town.

When fall comes, it gets real cold,
Jackets and jeans start to get sold.
Halloween will come, and it will go,
After that, it's time for sweet, sweet snow.

Jack Pearson, Grade 4
North Elementary School, NC

My Garden

Flowers growing high to the sky
Multiplying place to place
Yellow, glamorous sunflowers
Blooming orchids
Bright sun shining on flowers
Curved leaning towards the sun
Tall blooming flowers rising to the top
Sweet smelling flowers blossoming one by one
Colorful flowers growing from the ground
Ruby red roses blooming for the day.

Tyree Lancaster, Grade 6
Alvaton Elementary School, KY

The News

Going to the hospital.
Waiting there with my family.
Watching mom lay,
In a relaxing tan bed.

Knowing she was in pain.
Cheeks flushing,
With a cherry red color.
My dad saying, "You can do it."

The doctors talking loudly.
What could it be?
Is it a boy?
Or could it be a girl?

My heart filling with love.
Waiting for him to come,
Into our world.
Now my new baby brother is born!

Tyler Lolla, Grade 4
Goshen Elementary School at Hillcrest, KY

Wolves

Wolves, wolves in the woods.
Wolves chasing Little Red Riding Hoods.
There's wolves here, there's wolves there,
There's wolves running everywhere.

Wolves, wolves jumping all around.
Wolves pouncing to the ground.
There's wolves here, there's wolves there,
There's wolves running everywhere.

Wolves, wolves laying on the ground.
Wolves love jumping all around.
Invisible wolves in your hair,
Invisible wolves everywhere.

Wolves, wolves on the go.
Wolves, wolves never slow.
Wolves, wolves here and there,
Wolves, wolves everywhere.

Christian Hill, Grade 4
Stephens Elementary School, AL

God

God is my Redeemer, God is my Faith,
God is all, he will not faint, God is the one
I can trust. He's the creator of all,
God is my King He will die for me.
God is my everything, my trust in Him will
Keep us together. Blessed be His name
He's the Holy One. Let us dance and
praise His name for He is good.
But here I am to worship Him, the almighty.
God's love is deep and high, when I am
in pain and sick I'll lay it down for
the joy of the Lord. Every move I make
I make in Him. Forever God is
faithful forever God is strong and His
love endures forever. I'll jump in
the light of Jesus all the way, For
There is no one like our God I'm
alive and well, because He died and rose again.

Ayanna Tillman, Grade 5
Landmark Christian School, GA

Peace Hero

Through the darkness, through the night,
I see a bright figure with a dark light,
There comes your hero, so brave and bold,
To save from what the future brings,
You're stuck in a battle, the north and the south,
Both sides tugging on you to join their beliefs,
When my beliefs are beliefs of peace,
The hero comes to me and says,
"Welcome to a new land, where peace will always stand."

Allison Thompson, Grade 5
Bonneville Elementary School, AR

Summer Days

Sleeping in one day
I'm outside on the next day
Swimming after that

Ebony Jackson, Grade 6
Tomlinson Jr High School, OK

Little Pixy

Little Pixy,
Nymph fairy,
Grants wishes,
Flies high,
Pretty hair,
Short gnome.

Shanna Hall, Grade 4
Russell Babb Elementary School, OK

Come to the Movies

See the people playing on the screen
Hear the people whispering behind you
Touch the sticky floor with your feet
Smell the buttery popcorn
Taste the juicy gummy worms

Jordan Kushinka, Grade 5
Bonaire Elementary School, GA

Robert

Robert Stevens
sad, mean
run, jump, kick
I like games — lots of games
Robert Stevens

Robert Stevens, Grade 4
East Jones Elementary School, MS

Computer Technology

C ategories
O utstanding
M ind taking
P ersonal
U nexpected sites
T echnology
E xciting
R eally cool

T otally awesome
E xcellent
C an do almost anything
H elpful with tons of things in the world
N ew every year
O ut of the box thinking
L ikable
O n the job
G reat for learning
Y early improved

Neil Vernon, Grade 4
Islands Elementary School, GA

A Blessing for Guitarists

May you have as much success as Van Halen
May you be able to play the guitar as fast as Angus Young
May you be able to give the crowd a great show like Jimi Hendrix
May you be able to hit cords like Jimmy Page
And may God help you to get a great guitar

Taylor Schiffman, Grade 6
St Francis Xavier School, AL

I Am From

I am from Nicholasville, where I grew up…
To moving from there to Burgin at age 6.

I am from living in a large white house with many trees in the front yard
And has a green tin-roof accompanied by a bricked chimney.

I am from "Go get your bike to ride to the store for some milk…"
From "Don't you eat that in the living room!"
To getting up early in the morning with my stepdad to take Mom to work…
And returning home in time to mow the yard.

I am from hitting and fighting with my 3 brothers
To having parents who smoke a lot!

I am also from my grandparents, Nanny and Pa,
Who like a clean car and house…
To going with my grandpa to work at Bob Allen's farm
And then going fishing with Pa on his BIG boat
That sits on Herrington Lake.

That's where I'm from…

Mike Aubrey, Grade 5
Burgin Independent School, KY

Army Son

I am an Army son who loves his family and tries to help when Dad is away.
I wonder when my Dad will go away again.
I hear Bradley tanks firing.
I see Soldiers marching.
I want the war to end so Dad doesn't have to leave again.
I am an Army son who loves his family and tries to help when Dad is away.

I pretend Dad is here even when he is gone.
I feel proud that my Dad is in the Army.
I touch the flag to remind me of my Dad.
I worry about something bad happening to Dad when he is away.
I cry when he has to leave.
I am an Army son who loves his family and tries to help when Dad is away.

I understand that Dad has to do his duty.
I say that everyone deserves respect.
I dream about my friend who died in the war.
I try to be good in school and do the right thing.
I hope all Soldiers come home safe.
I am an Army son who loves his family and tries to help when Dad is away.

Dakota Everett, Grade 4
Walker Intermediate School, KY

What Thanksgiving Means to Me

To me Thanksgiving means a time to spend time with your family and give thanks to others and to God for a good family, a house, and other things. It is a time to eat a whole lot, and a time to get out of school for a week. It is a time to play with my friends. A time to watch TV and the Thanksgiving Day parade.

Luke Huddleston, Grade 6
Guntown Middle School, MS

Flowers for Mom

So many flowers don't know which to pick. It's so hard to choose. When you find the right kind you get some more of the ones you like. Just pick them. Dandelions, sunflowers, red tulips, pink tulips, and yellow tulips. Then you skip home and hide them behind your back. Then show them to your mom. If she loves them get a pot and put soil and the flowers in the pot and water them. And she always *loves* them!

Bailey Coleman, Grade 4
West Elementary School, MO

Spiderman

The preschool children play and shout warning me that I should watch out
But I ask them if me, Spiderman, cares? Nope, because I'm almost to the top of the jungle gym

I'm just a few feet away the children now have stopped their play
Turning their heads to Spiderman in the parking lot, out jumps doctors from the ambulance van

Finally, I make it to the top and raise my special magic mop
I flex a muscle, wave my hand blowing kisses to my fans

I lose my balance and accidentally trip my hands fall backwards and my feet slip
And I'm falling…falling through the air and then I realize that I should have cared

I hit the ground with a crack and a thump landing on an uncomfortable lump
My arm is broke, my mouth is bleeding my heart is rapidly beating

The doctors come and pick me up load me in the ambulance trunk
I cry in fright but they shut the doors and lock them tight

So my children, that is what happened to Spiderman yes, that's right, I broke my arm without a fan
15 stitches in my mouth and hand next time, I'll just settle for Superman

Baheya Malaty, Grade 6
The Mountain Community School, NC

Great Horses

Great horses are horses that neigh and play.
No horse means bad, well maybe just a tad,
What makes them sad is when you're glad with something that will hurt you, not just a tad.
You should trust your horse, even if YOU don't know the course.
Every horse has a source to make you, of course, happy.
Horses weren't meant to be shown, or sold when they get too old, they are all worth pure gold.

Saskia Lindsay, Grade 5
Mountain Road Elementary School, GA

Thanksgiving Day

Thanksgiving means a lot to me. Family, friends, wonderful food like turkey and dressing and pecan pies. My grandma's house is where I'm at on Thanksgiving day, gathered around the table with my wonderful family. We all give thanks for our many blessings which is what Thanksgiving is all about, appreciating the little things that we don't seem to notice. But those things that we don't notice can be the things that matter the most, like a simple hug or a small bug on the sidewalk. These are why Thanksgiving means the most to me.

Claire Cash, Grade 6
Guntown Middle School, MS

Untitled

Blood is splattered on the ground.
Mist floats softly all around.
The moon rises, the sun falls
Darkness covers home and hall.
From abyss come unearthly sounds.
Eyes grow on shapeless mounds.
Tonight the fiends
Are crowned as kings.
Fear and darkness abound.

Austin Stollhaus, Grade 4
Montessori School of Louisville, KY

Flag Football

F un to play
L ike to win
A lmost everybody likes it
G ood to win

F unny
O ver-achieved sport
O n Thursday and Friday we play
T errific
B est sport ever
A lot of subbing in and out
L osing is hard
L ike the game

Logan Tweed, Grade 5
Debusk Elementary School, TN

Veteran

V ery good
E very second of war
T ake off the war
E arth
R ecieve to us
A ll America loves you
N ice to the world.

Debra George, Grade 4
Cherokee Elementary School, AR

Flowers

Flowers
Calming, peaceful
Beautiful, warm colors
You give them water and they'll grow
Soundless

Grace Hawkins, Grade 4
Cleveland Elementary School, OK

Beautiful Spring

Springtime is so cool
full of flowers that will grow
but soon they will go

Michael Mullennix, Grade 6
Tomlinson Jr High School, OK

On Top of My Doggy

On top of my doggy
All covered in fleas.
Tried to give her a flea bath
And she tried to kill me.
She ran onto the table
And onto the floor.
She ran into the bathtub
And out the back door.

Jasmyne Hester, Grade 4
Islands Elementary School, GA

Love

Love is a hand
Held fast in your own
Love is a kiss
The sweetest you've known
Love is a joy
You feel from the start
Love is a dream
You keep in your heart
Love is a world that's enjoyed by two
Love is wonderful
Love is you

Keira Ronetta Wilson, Grade 6
Douglass Elementary School, TN

The Gift of Food

Food is important
for us to survive
but the gift that I would give
is not just food
it's important to my family
it keeps the history alive
on my father's side
it's to make carnitas
and although the recipe
has developed over the years
it leaves a little part of family history
in its very taste

Evelyn Espinoza, Grade 6
North Iredell Middle School, NC

My Best Friend

I have a friend
So I'm never alone
We don't fuss
We don't fight
When I need her she's in sight
Maybe she's different
Maybe she's not
She love to eat ice cream cones
What it all comes down to is
My best friend is Ally-Cat Jones.

Yasmine Alston, Grade 6
Brogden Middle School, NC

Tornado

A fearsome vacuum
Sucking up nervous nature carelessly.
heaving,
ripping,
tearing…
It reaches farther and farther
along the Earth.

Then someone pulls the plug
Everything stops,
and nature
tires to
pull itself back together.

Kristen Sutterer, Grade 5
St Vincent Elementary School, MO

Veteran

V ery brave,
E xcluded for a larger cause,
T ogether united,
E ncountering the enemy,
R evolutionary,
A s nice as can be,
N oticeable to others.

JR Copeland, Grade 4
Cherokee Elementary School, AR

Ode to My Teachers

Thank you
All
Of my
Fifth grade teachers
For keeping me well
Educated
For if it wasn't for
You I wouldn't even get a
Job
And have to live a
Terrible life
On the street

Jamie Mittelstaedt, Grade 5
Walton Verona Elementary School, KY

The Light

Some people like and love,
and hold secrets very tight.
Some people think they are immortal,
and their future isn't that bright.

Some people hear and say,
and spread rumors of spite.
Some people wish and wait,
and are hidden from the light.

Brady Hibbs, Grade 6
Central Arkansas Christian School, AR

Getting Sophie

As my family pulled up the driveway,
I was shaking and my hands sweating.
Today I was getting a kitten.
My Nana said it was half Siamese.

I was excited to see my kitten.
I thought of a name in the car,
Sophie!

Everyone seemed to glide to the barn,
Except I seemed to jog.
When I saw her with her mom,
I thought she was the cutest thing ever!

Her eyes were as blue as the ocean.
She had tiny paws and a little button nose.
Her ears so small,
But able to hear.
Sophie had a black tail,
That looked like a black snake in the hay.

A faint meow came from the little kitten.
She is Sophie,
I love her and she's all I want.

Caroline Hauss, Grade 5
Etowah Elementary School, NC

Sports

I love to play sports every day,
the only thing I like to do is go out and play.
I like soccer and basketball the most…
the only thing I hate to do is hit the post.
Luke Deacon, Grade 5
St Thomas More School, NC

Houdini Meets the Genie

One day Houdini
Summoned a magical genie.
Being a magician
Houdini followed the tradition
And wished a wish
That he had a goldfish.
As Houdini watched it swim,
He named the goldfish Jim.
That's when the genie became unrealistic,
And Houdini thought he was antagonistic.
So, he challenged the genie
To a game of "eenie menie"
To see whom would get the wish
And who would get squished.
When Houdini won
The genie was done.
So Houdini put him back in the lamp
And became a worldwide champ.

Taylor Fitzsimmons, Grade 4
Cleveland Elementary School, OK

My God

In the start
God created all
Everything was great
You should have seen it all
I wish I could have been there
To watch His mighty hands
You could not possibly imagine
The pride He must have felt
This is my God and I love Him very much.

Kendall Powell, Grade 5
Columbus Christian Academy, NC

Blue

Blue looks like the big blue sea.
Blue feels like a waterfall hitting me.
Blue tastes like a juicy blueberry popping in my mouth.
Blue sounds like a stream of water flowing down a stream.
Blue is a very smoothing color.

Ashley Bequette, Grade 5
Geggie Elementary School, MO

Christmas

I wake up hearing nothing but silence, until I hear
My brother walking around as anxious as a horse ready
to get out of the gate;
He hears me walking out of my room as happy as can be
Because it's Christmas Morning!
We go to wake our parents
They turn to see the clock
It's ONLY 6 o' clock!
We read the Bible story
Just like every year
It comes alive this time and whispers in my ear,
"Hooray, hooray, it's this time of year!"
We walk out of the bedroom
And go down the stairs
There they are, the presents
Piled up to the ceiling
Just waiting for us to open
Just waiting, just waiting.
It's finally over and everyone says
"I can't wait 'til this time next year
And we'll do the same thing again!"

Kellie Upton, Grade 6
Eminence Middle School, KY

Math

School makes you smarter
It can also be harder
You can learn math
Whole, part, or even half
School isn't always fun
Because you can start back where you begun
Ashley Xiong, Grade 6
Albemarle Middle School, NC

Sun

The sun streaks across the sky
Rising higher and higher.
Waiting to sink to the ground
And disappear
Casey Unterreiner, Grade 5
St Vincent Elementary School, MO

Three Knombs

There were people of three.
And they were knombs.
They loved to cook.
And read a book
They live in trees.
Atlanta Humble, Grade 5
Oark Elementary School, AR

Holidays

I love all holidays
wish they were here every day
Easter is full of eggs
and bunnies hopping on their legs
Halloween is full of candy
with witches and goblins handy
Thanksgiving is full of turkey
and some homemade jerky
Christmas is full of gifts
with snow and Santa all in a lift.
Madison Roberts, Grade 5
Walton Verona Elementary School, KY

I Like to Play

I like to play soccer,
on a rainy day in September,
on a Saturday.

I like to play baseball,
on a sunny day in May,
on a Saturday.

I like to fly a kite,
on a windy day in March,
on a Saturday.

I like to make snowballs,
on a snowy day in December,
on a Saturday.
Isaiah Norris, Grade 5
Etowah Elementary School, NC

Spring

In the spring,
My dad bought me a diamond ring.
It was very spiffy,
But my mom took it off in a jiffy!
Sara Lucas, Grade 4
South Topsail Elementary School, NC

Ice Bully

He shows up when you least expect it.
The stomp of his feet sends icy, blinding, horrifying winds
covering everything it touches with ice.
You can't stop him from pushing you down.
If you are caught in his presence he will give you a stunning punch
that will make your whole body numb.
No one can tell when he is near or far away.
His spine-chilling voice prevents you from hearing anyone.
When he gets extremely mad he will even shut down schools.
You always have to be ready to get in a safe place.
He will steal the joy and fun out of your day.
His kick will freeze your flesh. Even the principal is afraid of him.
So be on your guard
for the icy, horrifying, blinding, stunning, spine chilling,
joy and fun-stealing Ice Bully.
Jacob Carlton, Grade 4
Big Creek Elementary School, GA

The Rush of Speed

It rushes by like light, without much of a sight.
You know its power, being able to pass everybody
With a roar of the engines and the rush of painted lines.
On the road, you feel invincible!

Everybody waits for the moment, being able to
Floor it, going 0mph-60mph in seconds; it's amazing!
Put down the top and ride low and slow or high and fine; it doesn't
Matter. Just go the long way and you'll make it to the best place
Ever, the race track.

The race track, the smell of burnt rubber. The best
Part — you're not watching, you're flying in your leather throne.
The one place that speed limits don't matter. As fast as
You can go is the limit. It's your time to take control, on the
Race track, highway, or better — my way, both.
Christopher Stone, Grade 6
Statesville Middle School, NC

Adam

I have a friend who's name is Adam,
he is a boy from Indiana
He is not a man. My feelings for him are pure.
This is one thing I know for sure.
I go to my dad's house to visit,
sometimes I guess my heart begins to miss it.
The fun times we all have together,
inside my stomach I feel as light as a feather.
His brown hair and his big smile,
even though he is shorter than I just seeing him is worth the while.
While we are so far apart
the feelings I have are still in my heart.
Though my feelings may one day end,
Adam will always remain my friend.
Branna Conrad, Grade 6
Edmonton Elementary School, KY

Red Is…

Red is the color of your heart,
Red is your furry winter scarf,
Red is an apple as you take a bite,
Red is a bloody nightmare when you get in a fright,
Red is a rose from your true love, who always fights,
Red is forest fire when it says goodnight,
Red is the American flag as it flows,
Or your lava lamp that always glows.
Red is a cherry that people always mistake for a berry,
Red is a parrot that always eats carrots,
Red is the color of Rudolph's nose, or Santa Claus' clothes.
Red is a cardinal when it chirps good-bye.

Jasmine Cardenas, Grade 6
Lost River Elementary School, KY

One Final Warning

The sun takes a rest about midday.
Then the clouds all shout "Hurray!"

The church bells ring — 12 for noon,
Telling that a storm's coming soon.

Only the quiet caws of birds,
Now the sirens can be heard.

Sirens wailing, screaming, to a giant sound.
That was the final warning,
The tornado has touched down.

Natalie King, Grade 5
St Vincent Elementary School, MO

Baby Blue

Baby Blue looks like sky on a summer day.
Baby Blue sounds like the wind rustling through my hair.
Baby Blue smells like a baby after a bath.
Baby Blue tastes like sweet cotton candy.
Baby Blue feels like a baby's blue coat.
Baby Blue is the color of my jeans.
Baby Blue is the sound of the thunder.
Baby Blue is the baby crying
Baby Blue is the sweet cotton candy in my mouth.
Baby Blue is my soft coat

Jackie Taylor, Grade 5
Cool Spring Elementary School, NC

Hot/Cold

hot
warm, red
burning, warming, scorching
fire, flames, ice, iceberg
freezing, thickening, frosting
frozen, iced
cold

Daniel Scott, Grade 5
Briarwood Christian Elementary School, AL

Thanksgiving Means

Thanksgiving means…
It means a time of thankfulness,
family, friends, love, caring, and doing favors.

Thanksgiving is a time
of happiness, joyfulness, and being giving.

And most of all
Thanksgiving is about being thankful.

Thanksgiving only comes once a year
so make it the best time of the year!

Britton Wright, Grade 6
Guntown Middle School, MS

Wind

A storm is brewing,
The gale is ready,
Feel the strength of the storm.

Destructive force,
Awesome power,
On the hour.

Hurricane come,
Tornado blow,
Against all will the storm shall grow.

Randomly comes the strike,
Day or night,
Confusion and chaos ensue the forceful might.

A new day is dawning,
The sky is clearing,
Less are fearing,
All are cheering,
The Dark Storm is gone.

Dallton Frick, Grade 6
Curtis Inge Middle School, OK

Thanksgiving Food

Thanksgiving to me means food.
All you can eat food.
Food, food, food, food, and of course food.
And also the most important thing is giving thanks.
That's why it's called "Thanksgiving."
And don't forget FOOD!
I mean food like
Turkey
Sweet potato casserole
Green beans
And rolls, lots and
Lots of rolls.
That's what Thanksgiving means to me.

Cory Scribner, Grade 6
Guntown Middle School, MS

Australian Fur Seal
Seal
fat, hairy
slide, slither, swim
whiskers, loves to play
Mammal
Cadavia Sledge, Grade 5
John Will Elementary School, AL

I'm a Tree
I'm a tree whose life is ruined.
I lived a good life until now.
Tall, happy, and beautiful I stood.
Then, I was on the ground.
I ask why they did it.
They chopped me up.
I didn't feel a thing.
I was shipped off on a truck
Into a factory I went.
Saw dust flying, all kinds of machines.
Where am I now?
I am right here.
This paper is a part of me.
Jocie Butler, Grade 6
Pleasants County Middle School, WV

A Rose
Here is a rose for you
A yellow rose indeed
As bright as the sun
As colorful as a rainbow
Kimberley Copeland, Grade 4
Ava Victory Academy, MO

Christmas Is Here
Christmas,
Christmas,
Christmas,
Fun Christmas,
Boring Christmas,
Stupid cool ugly Christmas
Awesome weird little Christmas
These are just a few.
Family Christmas
Santa Christmas
Big huge tiny Christmas,
Crazy funny silly Christmas,
Hilarious Christmas
Sad Christmas, too.
Spooky Christmas,
Enormous Christmas,
Don't forget long Christmas,
Last of all, best of all,
I like good Christmas.
Deion Webb, Grade 5
Tates Creek Elementary School, KY

Summer
Summer brings the sun
so that means go play football
with your family
Christian Morales, Grade 6
Tomlinson Jr High School, OK

The Way Trees Grow
Trees grow in summer.
Some die in the wintertime.
In the spring they bloom.
Emma Stamps, Grade 6
Livingston Middle School, TN

The Ocean
The ocean is so far away
Yet so close to me
I hear it night and day
Wherever I may be
The sound just won't go away
Like it is knocking at my door
Every night when I pray
I pray it will stay forever more
Anna Fink, Grade 6
Queen of Angels Catholic School, GA

School
Math, Reading, Language, Bible,
You will have them all at school.

P.E., Music, Art, Computer,
Things cannot get any better.

It is time for recess now,
This is where we run and play.

Now we have to go inside;
Wow! I had a great day!
Savannah Stewart, Grade 4
Evangelical Christian School, TN

Christmas Wonder
There was a baby born in Bethlehem
As precious as a gem.
Like his father, he was a king
Of every single thing.
He was born on Christmas Day
In a manger full of hay.
Shepherds came to meet him.
Kings came to greet him.
The shepherds were led by a star,
But the kings came from afar.
I believe this story is true.
I wonder if you do, too.
Samantha Hamann, Grade 6
Fayetteville Christian School, NC

Test
I like doing test
When I am doing a test
I do my very best
also when I take a test
I wear a special vest
when I am doing a test
I do it on a desk
when I get a test
I go at it with zest
when we did a map test
I had to look in the west
Christopher Cousin, Grade 4
Lewis Vincent Elementary School, LA

Like the Wind
Horses are like the wind
So wild and free
Horses can steal your heart
With their big trusting eyes
And sweet soft nose
They are gentle giants
And the right animal for me
Alex Jones, Grade 6
Desoto Central School, MS

Beagles
Beagles are gentle
Beagles are kind
Beagles like to bark all the time
Some like to hunt
Some like to play
Some like to bark all night and day
Some like to hunt rabbits
Some like to hunt deer
But most of all they will love you all year
Brittany Johnson, Grade 5
Qulin Middle School, MO

Summertime Days
Buzz, Buzz goes the bees,
Swoosh, goes the trees,
As they blow ever so softly,
In the summertime breeze.

As I sit here on my door step,
Singing praise,
I thank the great Lord,
For all the summertime days.

As the sun beams bright,
The flowers amaze you at sight,
That's why I pray, oh Lord I thank You,
For this summertime day.
Addison Love, Grade 4
Trinity Christian School, SC

The Darkness and the Light

I'm dark, musty, and cold.
I smell damp and old.
You'll find the water strong enough to make a hole.
No chance of finding light in my moldy self.
I would probably give you a fright, without the light.
I call myself a dingy, stingy cave.

I'm bright, warm and so very light.
Don't look at me or else you'll see as if it's night.
You'll think I'm pretty and witty.
No chance on finding night in my sight.
I'll give you the warmth of my core.
I rise and set before the morn.
I say don't look at me, but I'll see thee.
I'm the bright, yellow, mellow, cool guy, the sun.

Leigha Stahl, Grade 6
Mount Zion Christian School, SC

Labor Day

Labor Day is a day off from school.
It is a day to relax and be cool.
No school that day we just have fun.
Go outside play and run.

Labor Day is a day for shopping.
You can get ice cream with sprinkle topping.
On this day you can go to the park.
While you're there watch the dogs bark.

I like this day it only comes once a year.
I'm so glad Labor Day is here.
You spend money here and there.
But in the end you really don't care.

We celebrate this day outside.
It is so fun on the water slide.
We fry chicken and fish.
We grill hot dogs and cheese burgers as we wish.

This is what we do for Labor Day.
We usually don't have fun this way.
Goodbye for now rather than tomorrow.
I hope this poem doesn't bring any sorrow.

Tra'Saun Rush, Grade 6
St Mark Elementary School, SC

Veteran

V ery many people lose loved ones
E veryone is very sad
T hey fought for our freedom
E veryone runs out to battle
R ecruits are dying
A rmymen were sent away from their families
N urses run to help hurt soldiers

Britney Reding, Grade 4
Cherokee Elementary School, AR

Funny Foam

Funny foam, funny foam
Even smells good on a garden gnome.
Funny foam, funny foam
I talk about it on the telefoam.
Funny foam, funny foam
Is made in a big round dome.
Funny foam, funny foam
It fits very well in your home.
Funny foam, funny foam
Makes your smells enhancement go KABOME!!!
Funny foam, funny foam
It's not real it's just my imaginatome.

Eric Magyar, Grade 5
Stokesdale Elementary School, NC

Christmas

One night after Thanksgiving
We put up our Christmas tree.
We hung up our ornaments,
And giggled with glee.

Our house smelled like gingerbread,
The lights twinkled so bright.
We were waiting for Santa,
Late one cold winter night.

We have no chimney,
So he came through the door,
For when we awoke,
There were gifts on the floor.

This is the season,
For love, giving and cheer.
Christmas is by far,
The best time of the year.

Kelly Schaubhut, Grade 6
Haynes Academy for Advanced Studies, LA

I Am Haunted

I am haunted by the space under my bed.
Scared that some creepy, crawly monster
will grab me and pull me under.
I am haunted.

I am haunted by Waverly Hills it gives me the chills.
Dried lungs on the elevator wall.
On the rooftop balls roll and bounce.
I am haunted.

I am haunted by cancer.
Afraid I will be like my great grandfather and
never see my great grandchildren.
I am haunted.

Austin Stivers, Grade 5
Eminence Middle School, KY

Ode to My Emotions

Anger, frustration
sadness, embarrassment,
all of these are what
I am
I am angry when
my teachers yell,
I am frustrated when
my dad screams,
I am sad when I
think about death,
and I am embarrassed
when my mom talks
about my childhood
anger, frustration,
sadness, embarrassment,
all of these are what
I am.

Julia Paige Jones, Grade 5
Walton Verona Elementary School, KY

Courtney

C ares about people
O ften helping others
U nique in many ways
R eading wizard
T houghtful friend
N eat hand writer
E ats and plays all the time
Y oung author

Courtney Silvio, Grade 4
Moyock Elementary School, NC

People

Some people work and work
and some may lay around.
Some people sleep in beds
and some sleep on the ground.

Some people cry and cry
and many may work for food.
Some people may ask nicely
and some may be very rude.

Ally Van Enk, Grade 6
Central Arkansas Christian School, AR

November

N uts
O ak trees
Lea **V** es
B **E** autiful colors
M agnificent
B reezy
Pr **E** tty
R elax

April Rudolph, Grade 4
East Jones Elementary School, MS

My School Morning

Got out of bed French toast, I was fed
Went to wash my face combed my hair in place
Turned the TV on to check the weather then got my school books all together
Stood on the corner to catch the bus that is when my mom likes to fuss
Did you wash your hands? Brush your teeth?
Is all your homework done? Yes, yes, yes! Now can we have some fun?
Played with my puppy Zach picked up my back pack
The bus showed up and I got inside I braced myself for a long, long ride
Finally I made it to school my friends and teachers are so cool
The bell rang for classes to start my favorite class is art
Went to lunch drank fruit punch
Now more classes in the afternoon!

Kalika Groaning, Grade 4
Trautwein Elementary School, MO

Just a Dream

It is one to one; a tied up game
And we have the ball.
Everyone is shouting; the other team is pouting,
'Cause we have the ball.

Oh no! Here comes a defender.
If I can only get by him swift as lightning I'll fly.
Yes! I nutmeg him!
The other team is shouting "No!"

OK, here comes the sweeper,
With twelve seconds left to go.
If I get by him, if I can only get by him,
I can score the winning goal.

Yes! Bam! I did the Maridona!
One kick, one strike, and I can score the goal!
With three seconds left, here it goes…I shoot and…what happened?
I wake up very upset, because I find out it was…just a dream.

Kyler Williams, Grade 5
Providence Academy, TN

The All Time Present

My parents are hiding something.
They are not telling me anything.
My hands are covered in sweat like the pouring water of rainfall.
My parents tell me it's a surprise.
I only wonder what this is all about.
We pull to a house.
I hear puppies yelping inside.
I stare at my parents and they smile happily.
Now I know what this is about.
I received my Christmas pup that night.
I always will remember my feeling.
Sitting there with a smile as wide as can be.
Thinking of all the things I could do with him.
I felt as though I was lifted to my feet from all the misery.
I love him to this very day!

Samantha Tindal, Grade 6
Beck Academy, SC

Camping

I love to go camping with my whole family.
A walk down the long nature trail is relaxing.
We feel as if nobody is around us.
Here we are in our special place.
Our special place is beautiful and peaceful.
Everywhere I look I see big trees,
And I feel the cool breeze on my hot face.
My dad builds a fire for us to sit around.
My mom says our worries don't exist here,
Our special place is where we can clear our mind.

Danny Robin, Grade 6
Arnaudville Elementary School, LA

Poetry

I don't like writing poetry.
My words never seem to rhyme.
We've been writing them all week in class,
But not one's been in on time.

I don't know what to write about.
Teachers say, "Use your imagination!"
I've tried writing couplets and haikus,
And even personification.

Katie Mattingly, Grade 5
St Vincent Elementary School, MO

Snowflakes

Looks like tiny, white specks breezily floating down
Sounds like quiet, peaceful stillness
Tastes like frozen water droplets that barely stay on your tongue
Smells like damp earth
Feels like a soft, frigid blanket

Natalie Pugh, Grade 5
Briarwood Christian Elementary School, AL

On Christmas Day…

Waking up on Christmas Day,
Opening presents, ready to play,
Dolls, cars, clothes, and games
Not enough batteries, what a shame,
Wrapping paper all over the place,
Shoving candy canes in their face,
The day's almost over, say good-bye to our kin
I can't believe Christmas day is at the end.

Carmen Thomas, Grade 6
Graham Elementary School, AL

Fall

When it's fall, there's always something going on.
Someone is making pumpkin pie,
Or your brother is watching James Bond.
Sometimes it's a bad thing, like you have to eat peas,
Or it's a fun thing, like jumping in leaves.

Ian Romines, Grade 4
Evangelical Christian School, TN

Flowers

Flowers are pretty, flowers are great.
I've loved to pick them since I was eight.
There are so many colors,
I hate to choose
Which ones I love, which ones I refuse.
Flowers are pretty, flowers are great.
So many colors, so many names
So many styles, none of them lame.
I like to put them in my room, and in my house
So I won't feel gloom.

Mackenzie Beckham, Grade 6
Desoto Central School, MS

Thanksgiving Joy!

Thanksgiving is a time for food,
time for family, friends, and neighbors.
It's a wonderful time to eat, laugh,
and just plain talk to your family.
Thanksgiving is a time of love and enjoyment!

Lauren Ellis, Grade 6
Guntown Middle School, MS

The Test

I studied all night in my room alone
I stressed all day until the bell rung
I walked into the classroom fretting the test
Then the teacher said, "I'll give you a rest."

Maria Parker, Grade 6
Harrisburg Middle School, AR

Ye Old Gobbler

Ye old gobbler was old and tough
we knew he wasn't tender enough

So he was glad when we were sad
so no one killed him not even Dad

Around the barnyard he strutted his stuff
until all of us had enough

He knew he was safe 'cause he was old
he thought his stuff was pure gold

"Ye old gobbler" we said
we wish you were dead

But he was tough and Mom knew
he just would not do

So we had store bought Turk
as we watched ye old gobbler smirk

The end of this story is true
we all had Thanksgiving so don't be blue.

Trevor Scott, Grade 6
Edmonton Elementary School, KY

Friends

Friends are friends to the end.
Nothing can ever separate them.
They're there at every turn and bend.
That's why friends are friends
to the end.
Joey Gray, Grade 5
Immanuel Lutheran School, MO

Turquoise

Turquoise sounds like my blue
Kool-Aid getting all slurped up
Turquoise tastes like chewy,
Blue-raspberry bubble gum
Turquoise feels like my shiny
Jacket during a rainfall
Turquoise smells like the
Shimmering ocean
Turquoise looks like my sparkly
Blue pants in the beautiful sun
Turquoise is the color of my finger
When it's getting smashed by the door
Turquoise is the color of my mom's
Apron while making pancakes
Turquoise is the color of my hair
Being dressed like a crazy clown
Turquoise is the color of my dad's
Cologne bottle when we're going out
Turquoise is my grandma's shimmering
Eyes in the moonlight!
Ashley Cromie, Grade 5
Cool Spring Elementary School, NC

Harriet Tubman

Harriet Tubman
She took people to the north
She was amazing
Adam Giacomo, Grade 5
Sycamore Elementary School, GA

My Farm

My farm is the rainbow.
It sounds like chirping birds.
It tastes like juicy beef.
It smells like stinky cow manure.
It looks like beauty in nature.
It makes you feel happy and thankful.
Jacqueline Richardet, Grade 6
St Vincent Elementary School, MO

Autumn Leaves

Autumn leaves are like shooting stars
Setting off in the sky —
So bright they catch my eye.
Samantha Redden, Grade 4
First Wesleyan Christian School, NC

Howling Wolves

Howling wolves. Howling wolves.
Their harmony will live.
The chorus of three seem like fifty.
The same wolves that help me sleep.
Howling wolves. Howling wolves.
The song that will live forever.
The song that stays up all night.
The song that sleeps at day.
Devann Kirkpatrick, Grade 5
Holsenbeck Elementary School, GA

Will I Ever Change

He wonders
He wonders
will I ever
change
like my friends
will I ever
change
Sarah Vanvoorhis, Grade 6
Edmonton Elementary School, KY

Veteran

V ery
E agerly
T rained soldiers. Who are
E xtremely
R eady to
A ttack the enemies.
N ever stop protecting the country.
Trevor Nordstrom, Grade 4
Cherokee Elementary School, AR

Fun with Friends

The skate rink was fun,
We skated we didn't run.
It was Julia's first time to skate,
And she made a bunch of mistakes.

Carlee was super fast,
Compared to her we came in totally last,
It was fun for us all,
We had fun even if we did fall.

The music was great,
We met a girl named Kate.
Even if I can't skate,
It was so great.

The best part of that afternoon,
Was that it was June.
And sharing Holly's birthday,
Was fun even if she was born in May.
Lyndsay LeDoux, Grade 6
St Cecilia School, LA

Some Ways to Pop Popcorn

You can pop it on the stove
You can pop it on your nose
You can pop it on the fire
You can pop it even higher
Ginny Hearn, Grade 4
Landmark Christian School, GA

Thanksgiving

T urkey
H ugging family members
A time of thanks
N ational holiday
K ind people
S o good dressing
G ood food
An **I** mportant day
A lo **V** ing family
I mportant people
I **N** the month of November
G oing out to eat
Kayte Avera, Grade 4
East Jones Elementary School, MS

Dad

funny fantastic
running typing traveling
My dad is hilarious
daddy
Shay Bland, Grade 4
St Thomas More School, NC

Dogs

Dogs
Furry, funny
Growling, running, protecting
Pet from long ago
Buddy
Robert Young, Grade 4
Russell Babb Elementary School, OK

Christmas Day

Jolly Christmas day
We praise His son Jesus Christ
On this day His birth
Nicolette Hollowell, Grade 6
St Cecilia School, LA

Game Time

Helmet, pads and cleats,
fans cheering in the seats.
Hours and hours we practice in the heat,
to get ready to win and defeat.
Next week we will go back and repeat.
Jon Jon Yu, Grade 6
Queen of Angels Catholic School, GA

About Christmas

Once in little old Bethlehem there was a women name Mary.
She was so pretty and had a baby on Christmas night
And His name is Jesus and is the Son of God.

We serve God
He is so many things to us
He is a our Savior
He is our Lord.

God is awesome
He is so many things to me
He is cool.
I love Jesus, He is very cool.

Sydney Miller, Grade 4
Magnolia Springs Baptist Academy, AL

Best Friends

Best friends are the best, best friends
would help you when you're down
and they would turn your frown around,
they would always be by your side,
they would never lie,
they would always be there when you need them most,
and they sure would never boast,
they would always be honest and modest,
they will get you the best birthday present ever
without a doubt,
even in a drought,
and they would be your friend forever and ever.

Shelby Schepens, Grade 5
Our Lady of Fatima School, MS

Fall

Fall is short and sweet.
Hear the crunch under your feet.
Lovely to the look.

Rachel Heard, Grade 4
Briarwood Christian Elementary School, AL

Football in Fall

Football is very fun —
Football is where you run.
All the quarterbacks mumble —
Boy, do they make me want to rumble!

You don't want the ball to drive —
You want it to stay alive.
Pass it to him, them, and then me —
Man, am I glad this game is free!

You may want to race, rumble, or rob —
But maybe later eat some corn on the cob.
Sometimes you may want a ride —
But you have to pace yourself in a stride.

Hunter Lewis, Grade 4
North Elementary School, NC

What a Dream

Red and blue are the colors of my favorite team
I wish I would play for them, oh, what a dream
I would be the best in the sport
The game for the other team would be very short
Curve ball, fast ball, slider, strikeout
And when I go to the plate there will be no doubt
I won't strikeout and I will be the best clutch hitter
Oh, what a dream

Marcos Herrera, Grade 6
Brogden Middle School, NC

Ocean

Like a huge blue tub
Home for plants and animals
A fun place for kids

Sully Jeter, Grade 4
Briarwood Christian Elementary School, AL

The Nest

Little tiny eggs,
Lay peacefully in a nest.
They're safe in their home.

Audrey Wright, Grade 4
Briarwood Christian Elementary School, AL

Hank

He was born on the first of March,
he's adorable as white as starch.
There were twelve others in the bunch,
whenever he eats, it makes a crunch.

When he looks at me with those,
big, brown eyes, I want to fall apart.
Sometimes he's dumb.
Sometimes he's smart,
but all in all he has my heart.

He likes to chase after his toy,
how I love my little boy.
I know one day he'll pass away,
but I'll love him then, and I'll love him today!

Vixie Greco, Grade 6
College View Middle School, KY

Shooting Stars

Sparkle sparkle
Here we are
All alone on a shooting star
Twinkle twinkle
In the sky
God's fireworks flying by
It's so beautiful as you see
I'm glad it's just you and me

Olivia Head, Grade 4
St Elizabeth Ann Seton Catholic School, OK

Summer Time

Time with family.
Going to our reunion.
Playing with my friends.

Brittney Bell, Grade 6
Tomlinson Jr High School, OK

Bad Day

I get out of bed and brush my teeth
I get dressed from my head to my feet
I wash my hands I wash my hair
I even wash my underwear
I go to school
I do my work
I rule at reading my spelling book
I talk to Bob I talk to Kim
I even talk to the Siamese twin
Now the day is over
I walk home with my friend
Now my story is over
And now it's the end!

Tiffani Hendershot, Grade 6
Martin Elementary School, WV

Nature's Beat

Nature's beat
Makes the world go round.
It is where life is found.
When animals meet each other
One becomes the mother.
Their babies are small
They will grow tall.
They learn to live alone
They sometimes mate with a tone.
When they are older
They are bolder.
They will grow
And fight a foe.
They will mate
Their meeting is fate.
When a mother gives birth
A new life is on earth.
As you see,
This part of life is in you and me.

Daniel May-Rauchman, Grade 6
Solomon Schechter Day School, MO

Veteran

V eteran my grandpa was
E very day more die
T o you guys and girls we love you all
E nergy you guys must have
R eturn we hope you do
A round the world you go
N ot warriors but friends you are

Chad Cloninger, Grade 4
Cherokee Elementary School, AR

Global Warming

People are in their cars to go to work.
They are throwing trash outside their windows
in a rush to work to earn some cash.
The world is getting to be a dirty place.
I looked at a person's face and saw him litter.
Then he went to work to solve a case.
We all need to help Global Warming slow down.
Hurricanes, tornadoes make me hurl up potatoes.
So let's pick up trash on the ground and stop people from littering.
When you see someone doing something bad say,
"Hey, lad, don't do bad."
So the world can be a better place.

Ben Packman, Grade 5
Saul Mirowitz Day School - Reform Jewish Academy, MO

Family Matters

T hanksgiving gives me joy: I hate when it goes
H igh up in the sky; I see many people.
A person like me loves it when family gathers,
N obody is left out except my grandma who died —
K indly she comes down from the garden and sits down with us;
S oon she leaves after Thanksgiving Day
G oing to paradise — can't wait to go
I n the garden they have Thanksgiving the same way,
V ery many pilgrims gather in God's waterfall
I n peace land they sing; they dance, we miss them all;
N o Thanksgiving ever goes away in our hearts —
G o home to Heaven for Thanksgiving Day.

Oliver Regan, Grade 5
Robertsville Middle School, TN

If I Were in Charge of the World

If I were in charge of the world
I'd make brothers slaves,
Moms and dads would do anything you say,
and you could eat candy for breakfast, lunch, and dinner.
If I were in charge of the world
Teachers would be fun and nice,
We would play lots of games at school, we wouldn't have AR points,
and homework would be video games.
If I were in charge of the world
Everyone would have a home and money,
There would be no wars, there would be no littering,
and there would be no villains.
If I were in charge of the world
You'd get anything you wanted,
You wouldn't have to clean your room,
You wouldn't have to eat your vegetables,
and you wouldn't have to do chores.
If I were in charge of the world
There would be no principals,
There would be no library, and absolutely no bullies.
If I were in charge of the world.

Trey S. Paris, Grade 6
Eminence Middle School, KY

Lake Hopatcong

I love to go to Lake Hopatcong
The squishy sand stretches a whole mile long
I love the soft, squishy sand,
Slipping through my toes
On hot, summer days, I like to swim in the cool water
It's not crowded at the beach, not at all
EEEEEEKKKK!!! I think I stepped on a leech!
When I have to leave at the end of the day,
I feel really sad
So, good-bye Lake Hopatcong,
You will always be my favorite place.

Alana Pearson, Grade 5
Stokesdale Elementary School, NC

Roses

Roses, you are a beautiful sight.
You shine and glimmer like a diamond ring.
And you are like a star up in the sky.
You are a red Milky Way.
Bees buzz around you.
Insects wait their turns to look at you.

Megan Morrison, Grade 4
Ode Maddox Elementary School, AR

Earth

The trees look up at the sky,
The sun looks down at the earth
And warms the soul.
We look up at our heroes up in the sky.
They look down at us
And care for us on earth.
Oh, so pretty the earth might look,
But there is always something missing.
It looks to be perfect, but never.
We try to stop, but not, and never.
When something is wrong it will always be useful,
When fixed or not.
When things fall apart,
They can get better.
So keep on going and never stop.

Amy Hicks, Grade 4
Montessori Community School, NC

6:00 A.M. Every Morning

Mom wakes up,
Dad wakes up and makes the coffee,
Then Mom wakes me up,
Dad takes a shower,
I get ready while Mom is in the kitchen cooking breakfast,
Dad and I eat really fast,
Then Dad heads for work,
I head for the bus,
And Mom heads for bed.

Abigail Hoeft, Grade 5
West Elementary School, MO

Money

Jingle,
Jingle, in your pocket!
A girl may get a golden locket.
A boy may get a video game.
Some people use it for fame.
Jingle,
Jingle, in your pocket,
You can use it to get some chocolate.
You can buy a new T-shirt, candy, games and food.
If someone wanted it your response would be
No way, dude!

Jacob Crase, Grade 5
Walton Verona Elementary School, KY

Ocean Waves

The ocean waves
feel like tiny tadpoles
sticking to my feet
and between my toes.
It thrashes violently against
the mossy seawalls
and glides back into the ocean.
Ahh!
The cold, icy water
runs over my warm body
as I lay in the soft sand.
It makes me wonder
into my dreams
where the pastel green waves
carry me
across the ocean water.

Seo Hyun Lim, Grade 5
Forest Avenue Academic Magnet School, AL

Autumn Leaves

Autumn leaves are like snowflakes.
They fall slowly until they rest.
The wind picks them up and they are gentle again.

Dylan Bishop, Grade 4
First Wesleyan Christian School, NC

Dance

Arms positioned! Muscles tight!
Dancing is filled with many delights!
Leaping across the wooden floor,
Twirling 'til you can't spin no more!
A changement here, a pirouette there,
A grand battement up in the air!
Flexibility is the key
To a fantastic dance recipe.
A delicate figure moving gracefully
Feeling the music through your strong body.
Messages are sent with the dancer's face,
Dance is enjoyed throughout the human race!

Kaylin Chan, Grade 5
Lake Norman Charter School, NC

Falling Stars

Stars are falling,
falling into the frozen abyss
they feel cold, they taste like
water, they are never the same.
What are they?

Snowflakes.

Phillip Dunn, Grade 5
Walton Verona Elementary School, KY

Ocracoke Beaches

A beautiful place to be,
a wonderful dreamy scene.
The sound of the ocean
is music to my ears.
But the thunder and lightning
just brings out my fears.
The beach can be scary
if you are afraid to drown,
there is a sound that can
bring you very down.
You can bike,
you can run,
you can play under the sun.
It's the sea that I see,
It's the ocean that surrounds me.
Now the rain is gone,
the sun is back,
and now I'm heading to the shack.

Sarah Hamon, Grade 5
Montessori Community School, NC

Colors

Green is for the grass that grows.
Red is the color of my burnt toes.
Blue is the color of my shirt.
Gold is the color of my skirt.
White is for the clouds up so high.
Yellow is a color I see outside.
Black is for the end of the day
When I go to bed and pray.

Maggie Young, Grade 5
Ascension Elementary School, KY

Fences

Fences, fences all around.
Fences, fences big and brown...
Fences, fences chains and wood.
Fences for Native Americans.
Fences for English.
Fences for me and you.
Fences big and small, wide and skinny.
Fences for all!

Megan Guthrie, Grade 5
Elkhorn Elementary School, MO

Jack-O'-Lantern

Jack-o'-lanterns,
some emotional
sad, happy, mad
even glad
Jack-o'-lanterns
some made up creatures
witches, wizards, ghosts, goblins
Jack-o'-lanterns
some people
Elvis, hippies, old people
Jack-o'-lanterns
some creatures
cat, dinosaur, even frogs
Jack-o'-lanterns
aren't they fun?

Hannah Hicks, Grade 5
Walton Verona Elementary School, KY

The Sea

The waves rise up and roar
at the beach.
The dolphins sigh
and the sharks cry.
Lightning rips through the sky,
charging the Earth.
Hard as a nail,
the crab scuttles
across the sand.
The thunder booms
like hands clapping
after a show.
The sand moves
with each wave.
Truly, the beach is a beautiful place.

Brianna Garcia, Grade 5
St Teresa's School, GA

Thanksgiving

Thanksgiving is a time to share
Where people come together
They sit and eat and talk to others
Thanksgiving is a very
Special time to come in and enjoy
So enjoy it while it lasts because
Pretty soon it will be over.

Louisa Leister, Grade 6
Guntown Middle School, MS

Christmas

Christmas is a time to care
Christmas presents are hard to share
Snowflakes are fun and pretty
Sometimes they cover up the whole city

Sierra Miller, Grade 4
Horace Mann Elementary School, OK

Shark

Shark
Beast, carnivore
Biting, eating, swimming
Predator from the ocean
Fish

Collin Jaworski, Grade 4
Russell Babb Elementary School, OK

Moms

Moms are so funny
they make you laugh and giggle
they tickle you all over
and make you squirm and wiggle

Shelby Mullikin, Grade 5
Walton Verona Elementary School, KY

Hunting

A time where you are focused
like a horse in the Kentucky Derby.

Sometimes a time where there
is nothing to do but sleep and,
Hunting is like no other time
It is a time to hear.

It is a time to see.
It is a time to feel
your heart beat, as that
big buck comes in.

Greg Mackey, Grade 6
College View Middle School, KY

My Brothers and Sisters

They harass me.
They devour me.
And when I think it's over, it isn't.
And when I tell,
they jabber on, and on, and on
about how *they* didn't do it.
I did.
They don't do anything.
It's all just me.
They will drive anybody crazy
If they have the chance!

Alex Lipe, Grade 5
St Vincent Elementary School, MO

Christmas Tree

Christmas tree
big, small, ornaments, beautiful,
glowing, standing, lighting,
my Christmas tree glows
tree

Kiona Kuykendall, Grade 5
Shirley Elementary School, AR

How I Love Mary

Mary's smile is as gentle as the warm sun.
Mary smells as sweet as a thousand roses.
Mary's voice is as quiet as a lullaby.
Mary's touch is as soft as a baby's cheek.
Mary makes me feel as safe as I am in my warm soft bed.

Alex Boudloche, Grade 5
Holy Rosary Academy, LA

Rainbow

Blue is the color of the sky at night
Blue is the color of the flickering light
Blue is the color I think of when I cry
Blue is the color of the tears in my eye
Blue is the color of the waving sea
Blue is the color inside of me

Red is the color of the Cline Panthers spirit
Red is the color I wear when I cheer, "Let's hear it!"
Red is the color of my face when I'm mad
Red is the color of the hat on my dad
Red is the color of the eraser I use
Red is the color of my brother's running shoes

Black is the color of the black top in the road
Black is the color of the spots on a toad
Black is the color of a selfish one's heart
Black is the color of the midnight dark
Black is the color you always see
Black is the color of the monster you don't want to be

Danielle Plummer, Grade 5
Cline Elementary School, KY

Pretty Fall, Beautiful Fall, Peaceful Fall

Every night I ride my bike down by the creek.
I spy geese. Pretty geese. Pretty leaves.
I spot my dog Buster, and his reflection in the water.
It gradually gets dark. We head home.
Faster, faster. We slow down. Pretty geese. Pretty leaves.
Pretty fall, beautiful fall, peaceful fall.
I pedal home. I decide I should take my dog Bubba for a walk.
Come on Bubba. I run outside!
Almost pitch black. I turn on my flashlight.
Ruff, ruff! Bubba barks.
He spies three deer. Two does, one ferocious 8-pointer.
Beautiful deer.
Pretty fall, beautiful fall, peaceful fall.
We ride once more to the creek.
Another doe. Silence. Still. I am a mannequin.
She bounds off. Crunch! I hear as she leaves.
Pretty fall, beautiful fall, peaceful fall.
Turn. We head home.
Pitch black. Silence. Beautiful.
We pedal home again. I go to bed. I love Fall!
Pretty fall, beautiful fall, peaceful fall.

Clint Jones, Grade 4
Alvaton Elementary School, KY

Sea Turtle

During the night waves crash to the shore;
The turtles come to lay their eggs once more.
They waddle ashore leaving little tracks;
To dig a big hole as big as my back.
They do not do it for you or for me,
They do it for their babies, you see!
As they dig their hole, sand flies in the air;
Like snow falling everywhere.
As the waves crash on her shell;
Where she buried her eggs, she'll never tell.

Kaitlyn Hudson, Grade 6
Scotts Creek Elementary School, NC

Spider's Masterpiece

There was a spider
He's a one person builder
It's like sticky town

Kate Bowers, Grade 4
Briarwood Christian Elementary School, AL

My Best Friend Lucky

I love my dog, Lucky Cook
With the little wet nose
    And the big brown eyes
He brightens my day with a lick
Soft as silk
He loves to play
I think about him every hour of the day
With hugs and kisses
    He loves me so
Wagging his little tail
    The happiness that he spreads
    Makes me smile as big as I can
He loves to jump and run around
He is just like a brother to me
Lucky is my best friend and I will remember him forever
    In the years of my life

I love my dog, Lucky Cook

Haley Cook, Grade 6
Bernard Middle School, MO

Fall

When the leaves change colors they fall to the ground.
Crumble.
Crunch.
The leaves fall down.
In the town the children play around.
When mother says please,
the children rake the leaves.
Bright colors like green, orange, yellow and red.
But before you know it,
it's time for bed.

Kennedy Estvanko, Grade 5
Walton Verona Elementary School, KY

I Take It for Granted

I have a house that is warm in the winter and cool in the summer, I take it for granted.
I have clothes on my back, I take them for granted.
I have a family that loves me, I take them for granted.
I have food and am never starving, I take it for granted.
I have a good education, I take it for granted.
I have kind and generous friends, I take them for granted.
I have things that I can enjoy, I take them for granted.
I don't have to worry about where I'm going to live tomorrow, I take it for granted.
I have medicine when I'm sick, I take it for granted.
I have freedom, I take it for granted.
I have eyes that see and ears that hear, I take them for granted.
I have movies, books, and computers, I take them for granted.
I will be able to learn many things and go to college, I take it for granted.
I have electricity, cars to ride in, and many other modern inventions, I take them for granted.

I have so much that I take for granted, but God is helping me to be more thankful.

Laura Suddeath, Grade 6
Freedom Intermediate School, TN

Thanksgiving

Thanksgiving means to me a time to eat and talk to friends and family. Thanksgiving is a day that represents the finding of our country. It's a day like no other a day full of football and basketball the Egg Bowl Miss. State vs Ole Miss a day of fun and relaxation it's a day to spend time with your family to laugh and talk that's what Thanksgiving means to me.

Matthew Gumm, Grade 6
Guntown Middle School, MS

Springtime Changes You

Spring is here trees are changing so are you.
You're singing like a bird sitting in a tree and flying like an eagle.
You're standing like a tree all tall and brave and sitting like a flower straight and tall.

You're dancing in the rain like the leaves on a tree and swimming like a boat in the water.
You're grazing in the fields like some cattle and running free like wild horses.
You're like a dog about to scare off some birds and laughing like some kids.
You're playing like a cat and dog and swinging like a monkey.

You're blowing like the wind and sneezing like some sicklings.
You're buzzing like some bees and loving like a cat.
Let spring follow you like kids in love.

Kelsey Jones, Grade 5
East Marion Elementary School, MS

The First Day of School

"Wake up," my mom said. It was the first thing I heard on the busy, exciting morning. I could finally go to school and make new friends, and have lots of fun!! I jumped out of bed to slip my clothes on, swoosh went my shirt, zoop went my pants, zip went my jacket. By the time I knew it we were out the door and in the car. I had never been more excited in my whole life!! School
When I got there my teacher introduced me to the rest of the class. Then she called us up to the front of the room where she read us a story and we played some games. We had a snack then outside for recess…SWEET! I went straight to the swings and started swinging, the girl standing next to me asked what my name was, I answered, "Abby." She told me her name was Olivia. We played together for the rest of the day, it flew by! The bell rang and my teacher took us outside and my mom was there waiting. I couldn't wait until the next day so I could go back to school and play with my friends!

Abby Kissenberth, Grade 6
Beck Academy, SC

I Am the Light of Tomorrow

I am the light of tomorrow
I wonder about the people around me
I hear voices in my mind
I see people around me changing
I want to be all right so all of my fears are put behind me
I am the light of tomorrow

I pretend I am all right when I am really afraid
I feel sad when my family dies
I touch my heart and try to remember
I worry when I don't hear from my family and friends
I cry when I am lonely
I am the light of tomorrow

I understand that things can't always change
I say I feel good when I really feel bad
I dream of being an artist
I try my best at everything
I hope everything around me is all right
I am the light of tomorrow

Courtney Renee Armstrong, Grade 4
Walnut Grove Elementary School, AL

My First Breath

When I opened my curious little eyes,
I saw, then and there, my *life long* hero.
I wept for compassion,
and I wept for breath.
Wiggling my hands,
just searching for something, anything, to grasp on to.
Cradled in my mother's arm, feeling safe, secure, and loved.
I was picked up and rocked alarmed, but not afraid.
My first breath was a moment of *unforgettable* memories.

Waynie Lee, Grade 5
Big Creek Elementary School, GA

Basketball

A whistle blowing
A shot clock glowing
The score is 48-49
And we're that team that's behind
We only have time for one little shot
A 2 or 3 pointer, I'll give it what I've got…

Johnnie Tabron, Grade 6
Brogden Middle School, NC

The Christmas Tree

For some the Christmas tree is just a tree,
But it is much more than that to me.
It points its high point up to heaven,
It shows life through Jesus Christ.
With all the lights aglow, where else can you go?
For here is the Christmas tree at home.

Hannah Holstein, Grade 6
Apple Blossom Academy, AR

Veteran

V ictorious soldiers
E ager to win the war
T errified, but wise
E nergetic and ready to
R un home to their loved ones at the end
A lways admiring our soldiers and they will
N ever give up

Tessa Jackson, Grade 4
Cherokee Elementary School, AR

The Little Old Boat with White Sails

There once was a boat with great sails,
That blew in the wind "singing" to the whales,
And dancing to a song without words;
That little old boat with white sails.

The fishermen on board throw their hands in the air
Crying "Look at these find heads and tails!"
"There's millions and billions tonight we feast!"
On that little old boat with white sails.

Then, alas a storm threw the boat all around;
The men brought down the sails
That caught song of the whales,
Now, the poor little boat with downed sails.

The storm left them alone,
The crew let up the sails,
And the boat took them home;
That fine little boat with white sails.

Carrie Beth Williams, Grade 5
Providence Academy, TN

Summer

In the summer I drink a lot of cold water,
Because every day it gets a little bit hotter.
Sometimes I play Marco Polo in the pool,
And the day never seems to get cool.

Natalie Brown, Grade 4
South Topsail Elementary School, NC

I Am Haunted

I am haunted to go outside at nighttime
The big black dogs might get me
They might eat me or kill me

I am haunted by the big bad Big foot
He might get me or
Eat me or kill me

I am haunted in the future
That I might not have enough money
I might not have enough money to get food
I am haunted

Kevin Brewer, Grade 5
Eminence Middle School, KY

My Dog and Winter

It is cold outside
My dog does not like the snow
He hides in his home.

Rylan Boyer, Grade 4
Russell Babb Elementary School, OK

Rivers

Beautiful rivers
That flow through land, trees, and rocks
Treasure cool rivers.

Allie Martin, Grade 4
Cleveland Elementary School, OK

Help!

Help!
Where to go?
This way or that?

Help!
Can't find anything,
Where is anything at?

Help!
Don't know where to go,
Does anybody?

Bridgett Gibbons, Grade 5
North Shelby Elementary School, MO

Fred

Fred is red and small;
He can be feisty, but he's a doll.

His hooves are tiny,
But he is mighty.

Jumping is one thing he can do,
But he can do other things, too.

He jumps a course;
He is my horse!

Bailey Clark, Grade 4
Evangelical Christian School, TN

Birds and Fish

The clear blue sky.
Is as clear as the sea.
The birds fly high in the sky.
The fish swim fast in the sea.

You hunt birds that are in the sky.
You fish for fish that are in the sea.
They have another thing in common.
They're good to eat!

Gabriel Ballard, Grade 5
Etowah Elementary School, NC

Constitution

C lassic
O bedient
N ational
S aint
T alkative
I ntelligent
T each
U nfailing
T eacher
I mportant
h O nest
N ice

Alexis Starcher, Grade 4
East Jones Elementary School, MS

God Is the Best

God is the best
     He's great to all
He gives us time to rest
     For one and all
He's greater than any fear
     In the night
He hopes you hear
     That all is right
God is the best
     He loves us all
God is the best
     To one and all

Miranda Hallmark, Grade 6
Ava Victory Academy, MO

November Sun

The sun is setting
This November
The Harvest Moon is shining
This November
Happy relatives gather
Around the dinner table
Talking, laughing, passing food
All around the dinner table
Yes, Halloween has come and gone,
And Christmas is on its way
But for now let us enjoy
Thanksgiving Day.
Parents, siblings, aunts, and uncles
Even cousins are here
To celebrate and share
What is called "thanks"
For a joyous meal
Thanksgiving is about food and fun,
Yes, this is true
But even more important
Is the family all around you.

Kaitlyn Kornoely, Grade 6
Guntown Middle School, MS

The Sky

A wonderful shade of blue,
The beautiful sky is very cool.
With the clouds, it makes me sigh.
Oh, how I wish I could fly in the sky.
During the night, I can't say a word,
About the stars in the other worlds.
Don't forget the birds flying free,
In the endless sky, like the sea.

Jared Grogan, Grade 5
Russellville Intermediate School, TN

Bird/Dog

Bird
Bright, beautiful
Flying, perching, cawing
Eggs, nest, fur, paws
Running, biting, sleeping
Soft, cute
Dog

Spencer Nilsson, Grade 5
Sycamore Elementary School, GA

My Little Kitty

My little kitty,
Likes to leap and play.
My little kitty,
Really likes to lay.
My little kitty,
Killed a mouse last Tuesday.
My little kitty,
Likes to hit and run.
My little kitty,
Has loads of fun.
My little kitty,
Jumps with fear,
Every time a car comes near.
My little kitty,
Has a fear of dogs.
My little kitty,
Doesn't really jog.
My little kitty,
Is not a big liar.
My little kitty,
Is really a tiger!

Michelle Brown, Grade 6
Scotts Creek Elementary School, NC

The Trip to France

There once was a man called Dan,
who married a girl named Jan.
They moved to Paris, France.
They learned to ballroom dance.
Jan learned to do the can-can.

Sydney Brewer, Grade 4
Judsonia Elementary School, AR

Sorrow

Here I am, all alone
Here my sadness has been shown.
As I sit here, and I wonder
It pours down rain, and rolls out thunder.
If I had her, I'd not have to pay
I would have her if only I had protected her in some way.
My dreams turned to nightmares, my happiness to sorrow
No tomorrow, no tomorrow.
I awake in sorrow, sorrow neck deep
In all that sorrow, all I could do was weep.
As I wept, I heard someone yell
When I saw who it was, I turned very pale.
It was her, my long lost wife
There she was putting joy in my life.
We hugged, and we got reunited
The dark time in my life, she had just lighted.
It's okay now, everything is fine
It's okay now, at last she is mine.
And now, things are as they were before
Tomorrow, tomorrow, sorrow no more!

Matt Rau, Grade 5
Quail Run Elementary School, GA

When I Went to Disney World

Heart beating so fast,
Flying up and down hills,
Screams flying everywhere,
Twisting, turning, moving up and down hills,
Lasers flying through the air,
Water splashing moistening the air,
Smells getting in my nose,
Cool stuff stretches as far as I can see,
Cameras flashing as characters come to life.

Nicholas Sheanshang, Grade 5
Cline Elementary School, KY

Looking Over Mrs. Betty's Yard

The leaves are blowing in the winter breeze
Sounds of the delightful birds cheeping
Cheep, cheep.

The American Flag blowing in the wind
Whoosh, whoosh
The delightful mums blowing
Side to side.

The sound of a John Deere tractor
Vroom, vroom
The crackle of the leaves on the road when a vehicle goes by
The sound of the welding shop.

The sun shines on the damp grass
The sight of a cat waiting for a delightful meal
Looking over Mrs. Betty's yard.

Ashley Dawn Perkins, Grade 6
Temple Hill Elementary School, KY

Stars Are Bright

I like stars because they're bright,
And they float like a kite,
And they shine in the night.
What wonderful, wonderful stars.

They're great to see in the night.
So won't you come and see, all right?
When you go to bed at night
Remember the stars are watching over you, all right?

Brooklyn Buis, Grade 4
Tazewell-New Tazewell Elementary School, TN

Hail and Glory to the Orange and Black

All hail and glory to the orange and black
They show other teams
How they got each other's back
Can't wait till the game
We'll show them more of the same

Caleb Blansett, Grade 6
Harrisburg Middle School, AR

Fences

Fences, fences o' where are thou my fences
so big and tall,
you grew in the ground until someone chopped you down,
you can always keep secrets,
you have been through hot and cold,
So thank you for keeping in my hound dog.

Jacob Shirley, Grade 5
Elkhorn Elementary School, MO

A Secret Unsolved

Her smile is like the wind brushing the grassy green trees,
Like a girl giggling a secret,
A sorrowful bird soaring into the everlasting sky,
Or a petite flower blooming bright, big colors,
A soft hand sweeping away fresh-cut blood,
Or concealed anger bubbling beneath the surface.

Her smile is as white as an oyster's sparkling pearl,
As beautiful as the harmonious voices of nature,
The enchanted sunset at the end of the day,
The wish I have been waiting for.

A glowing moon that lights up the world when it's dark,
Or lightning that pierces and shatters the delicate heart.
A fairy tale with a happy ending,
Or an evil green witch cackling wildly.

Her smile is like the puzzle I strive to solve,
The code I cannot crack,
The lonely ghost haunting me,
The secret that remains unsolved.

Mattingly Shook, Grade 6
River Trail Middle School, GA

One Day

One day I woke up,
It was Sunday.
I was so happy
That tomorrow was Monday.

If it was Monday,
The week would be new.
I would have a lot of homework,
There is so much to do.

Since Sunday is over,
Today is a new day.
I am so excited
That today is Monday.

Allyson Parmer, Grade 4
Stephens Elementary School, AL

My Date

I'm going on a date
with a fine young mate
don't close the gate
when I leave for my date.

Alyssa Chappell, Grade 4
Home School, GA

Lydia

Lydia Myers
animal lover, pretty
swim, swing, dance
I like to play outside.
Lydia Myers

Lydia Myers, Grade 4
East Jones Elementary School, MS

Introduction to Autumn

The autumn leaves are falling,
there's been a change of air
With clues that fall is coming,
we feel it everywhere!

We all miss the summer season,
with hot, beach side fun
But that time has now ended,
and fall has now begun.

Winter is coming closer,
but everyone loves fall
The birds will soon stop singing,
with their sweet singsong call.

When the autumn leaves are falling,
there's been a change of air
With clues that fall is coming,
we feel it everywhere!

Tyler Hoover, Grade 5
Palmetto Christian Academy, SC

Christmas Is in the Air

Christmas, Christmas it is in the air.
People are shopping like millionaires.
We go window shopping and see
something we want
but in the end we don't.
People are singing Christmas carols.
People are decorating Christmas trees with snowmen and angel wings.
We are leaving cookies and milk for nice St. Nick, wow!
It's morning, and the cookies are gone but wait
He left me a note,
it said thank you for the cookies and milk they were great
if you are good next year you will get something good too.

Alexus Antia-Obong, Grade 5
Drayton Hall Elementary School, SC

Skating with Me

I like skateboarding you should too!
When I'm riding I'm not blue.
So many tricks I'm remembering are true
I hope they stick like glue.
I'll enter the game
I hope they call my name 'cause if they don't I'll never be the same.

Seth McKenzie, Grade 5
Graham Elementary School, AL

If I Were in Charge of the World

If I were in charge of the world
There would be no medicine, cleaning the house
Or vegetables, and you could have candy whenever you want
Have candy whenever you want. If I were in charge of the world
there would be no homework, recess for 2 hours, and no books.
If I were in charge of the world there would be no bullying,
no drugs, and no one dies.

Curtis Barrett, Grade 6
Eminence Middle School, KY

I Am Haunted

I was haunted,
By the slithery, slimy snakes that crawled around in my room YUCK!!!
I would step on them as I walked to my breakfast!
Could you imagine?

I am frightened,
That my Uncle Victor will have to go back to war in Iraq,
he's in Germany now, but who knows what'll happen,
he might have to go back, OH NO!!!

I am haunted,
By me growing up and being alone in a dusty dirty apartment
with no TV to watch, think about living life like that?
You're talking about horrible!!
I'M IN TROUBLE!!!

I'M HAUNTED

Tiffany Thomas, Grade 5
Eminence Middle School, KY

Pictures

Pictures, pictures, so long they last.
Until they become a thing of the past.
Pictures, pictures, hanging on the wall,
They are of people big and tall.
Pictures give us an eternal memory.
That is why pictures are important to me.

Jesse Walker, Grade 6
North Iredell Middle School, NC

Things Happen

Things happen that we can't control,
We go and do something bad.
Then we have to give up our souls,
And then we have to give up everything we had.

A couple of national disasters were not preferred,
And the U.S. has yet to recover.
But why must there be some deaths to occur
In order to love one another?

9/11 almost 3,000 or more lost their lives,
Then the whole U.S. was hurt and sad.
Now we're in Iraq and teens' lives are being sacrificed,
When people blamed Bush, everyone started getting mad.

Another national disaster had to unfold.
"Leave your home," the New Orleans residents were told.
After Katrina, getting back was everybody's goal,
But like I said before things happen that we can't control.

Jared Smith, Grade 6
Haynes Academy for Advanced Studies, LA

April 10th

I was scared…
My mom came into my room, she said that I shouldn't be mad
If my little brother is born on my birthday.

Hospital!
April 10.
Three days after my birthday!
Mom's going crazy, Dad's okay — I guess, Nonni's trying to
Get everything ready, I'm nervous.
Everybody's here — Aunt Tesa, Uncle Mike,
Aunt Bam, Sasa, Poppi.

Hallway.
Mom's getting epidural, go back in, baby's coming soon.
Hope he is nice.
Baby's here!
Carter McClain Blackwell, 7lb, 8 oz, 20 1/2 in.
Mom's ecstatic as ever, Nonni's cooing and oohing.
My turn to hold him, that little baby smell.
I HAVE A BROTHER!

Chandler Blackwell, Grade 6
Beck Academy, SC

School

Grasp the air, get a clue
Go to school and don't break the rule
Pay attention to what the teachers say
Think about what you do every day.
Do your lessons, do your test, do your best.
Grasp the air, get a clue
Do your best in whatever you do.

Anthony Rucker, Grade 5
Western Hills Elementary School, AR

Christmas

I can smell the big ham in the oven.
I can hear people laughing and talking.
I snuggle up to my horse's winter coat
as I brush him off.
I can feel the hot chocolate burning
my tongue a little.
I can hear the fire crackling as if it
was a human talking.
I can smell the Christmas tree in my living room.
Oh that wonderful pine smell.
I sat down at my family table and was
ready to eat with my family!
I love Christmas!!

Logan Stello, Grade 5
Drayton Hall Elementary School, SC

Foster Care

When I was two
My house smelled like poo
Then there was a knock on the door
When we were poor
I opened it up and guess what I saw
Two social workers standing tall
I was so scared
Because I found out my mom never cared
So then I went away
To a big blue bay
Now I am 12 and adopted
I guess what I'm trying to say
Is I have a new family today

Sara Ballard, Grade 6
Edmonton Elementary School, KY

School

School is full of books and learning,
Oh, help! My brain is burning!
Teachers are great at any rate,
They help you learn every state.
Math has every number,
It'll never be a bummer!
I like to put my eye in Science,
Reading, sure I love to read!
Wordly Wise, I like to use my words wisely!

Katie Taylor, Grade 6
Woodland Presbyterian School, TN

God Is Good

God is good to me.
God is good to you.
God is good to everyone,
No matter what they do.
He forgives their sins,
When they do something wrong.
And no other God can beat him,
Because He is the most strong.
You can be a saint,
Or you can be a sinner.
But if you follow God
You can be a winner!

Alisia Ortiz, Grade 4
Coleman Elementary School, OK

Pearly Whites

I am white and pearly
I am brushed morning and night,
I am stuck to your jaw.
All day and all night.
I am jagged sometimes,
And even crooked.
Then, when I get
Too out of control,
I get braces,
All over my faces.
And then my siblings,
Get taken away
By the hands of the humans.
And I make new friends,
Mostly adults.
And then I become an adult for life.
I am white and pearly teeth.

Holly Cissell, Grade 6
St Vincent Elementary School, MO

My Angel

I have my own angel,
he passed away long ago.
He watches over me.
When I am scared,
my angel comes,
and all the fear goes away.
When I cry, he comes,
and stops the tears from rolling
on with no end.
My angel watches over me carefully.
That's why I am so carefree.
My angel is watching over me now.
I may not be able to see or hear him,
but I know he is there.
He is the angel I call
my brother.

Alexa Guilliot, Grade 6
Arnaudville Elementary School, LA

The Animal in Me

There is a cheetah in me
With fur like a rug
And a tail like a snake
It swims like a dolphin
It meows like a small cat
It lives in my room
And makes me laugh
I wish people would laugh.

Kyle Wolf, Grade 5
South Nodaway Elementary School, MO

Football Fan

There once was a man named Dan,
He was a big football fan.
There is a reason why,
Basketball made him cry.
Dan Marino is the man!

Josh Moss, Grade 4
Judsonia Elementary School, AR

Rain, Rain

Rain, Rain, I watch it fall, I see
the raindrops I see them all.
Clear as a diamond, but soft
as a lullaby, I can't stop
staring as they drizzle by.
Rain, Rain, it's all very simple,
it makes the flowers popup like pimples.
Drips, drop, the beat
just doesn't stop. Some people don't
like rain, I don't know why,
because afterwards it leaves a beautiful
rainbow in the sky.
Rain, Rain, will it go away? Never.
I'm so glad that rain
will be here, forever.

Ayana Fennell, Grade 5
Landmark Christian School, GA

West Virginia

W ild
E ast coast
S tate
T oday

V ery nice place
I nsanely
R are
G overnor
I nteresting
N o
I llegal drugs
A llowed

Timothy Baker, Grade 6
Martin Elementary School, WV

Waves

Waves crashing by fast
Splashing against the strong shore
As they race with strength

Sam Gutierrez, Grade 5
Bonaire Elementary School, GA

Dog

Dog
Yorkshire Dachshund
Lives in a kennel
Waiting for me to pick it up
Loving

Gavin Crouch, Grade 5
American Heritage Academy, GA

Halloween

Halloween Halloween
Is where you get scared.
Ah! I think there is a spider on my head.
Ah! get it off get it off.

Emily Haynes, Grade 4
Cave City Elementary School, AR

Surfing

It's sort of hard
But it's worth the trouble
Paddle hard
Position yourself
And climb up quick
Or paddle back out and try again.
There was this wave I was riding
With my cousin Sara Morgan
We both saw and caught the wave.
I turned on the wave
And rode it all the way home.
What an awesome experience.

Will Fuqua, Grade 5
Shannon Forest Christian School, SC

Sick Pet

I got a sick pet.
So I took him to the vet.
The doctor said,
"He bumped his head."
So they tried to put him in a net.

Jared Hawley, Grade 5
Paint Lick Elementary School, KY

Animals

Lions, bears, and monkeys too
Like to show their feelings true.
Alligators, crocodiles like to show
Their big sharp teeth in a row.

Paige Mazurek, Grade 4
South Topsail Elementary School, NC

Sports

Football is fun,
even though you'll chew gum.
Basketball is a ball,
especially when you're tall.

Softball is fun,
although you play it in the sun.
Racquetball is such a call,
when the referee calls a time-out because your big fall.

Water skiing is not out,
because you can fish for trout.
Snow skiing is a ball,
even though you fall.

Tennis you can hit,
but not with a bit.
Golf is hard,
when you don't hit the ball far.

In hockey you can hit the hard puck,
that makes me pucker up.
Gymnastics is such a gravity halt,
on bars, beam floor, and vault.

Alexis Fender, Grade 5
Pleasant View R-VI School, MO

Benchwarmers

Benchwarmers warm the bench.
They never got on a field, not even an inch.
All the other people get to play,
But all benchwarmers want to do is play all day.
Then coach put the benchwarmers in.
Wouldn't you know it; the Blue Jays would actually win!

Trevor Hebert, Grade 6
St Cecilia School, LA

Blue

Blue looks like a perfectly juicy blueberry that just got picked.
Blue feels like a fluffy puffy pillow.
Blue tastes like a sweet raspberry pie.
Blue smells like a blue bell that just bloomed.
Blue sounds like a blue bird singing in the morning.
Blue is something you can see, feel, taste, smell, and hear.

Breena Patterson, Grade 5
Geggie Elementary School, MO

Nature

N ature is the feel
of the goodness of A n animal
and the T aste of the waters
in the pond. As nature U nravels
itself we R ethink what we
observe about the E nvironment.

JC Bradley, Grade 5
St Thomas More School, NC

I'm Worried

I'm worried that I'll forget how to
play the violin.
I'm worried that I'll die at an early age.
What if I get paralyzed somehow or
Bentonville might win.
I think I feel my hand cramping up,
so I think I'm going to have to stop right now.

Levi Pitts, Grade 6
Benton County School of the Arts, AR

Jack-o'-lanterns

Jack-o'-lantern jack-o'-lantern on the ground,
Jack-o'-lantern jack-o'-lantern fat and round,
Jack-o'-lantern jack-o'-lantern, please glow, glow, glow
Wind, wind, wind, please don't blow, blow, blow.

Kaitlyn Penn, Grade 4
Cave City Elementary School, AR

Rainbow

While I was reading a book one day,
The trees began to sway,
I heard a boom of thunder
I saw a streak of lightning
Then I saw a gorgeous thing,
A rainbow started to appear
Imagine that!

Divya Velury, Grade 5
Lawton Academy of Arts and Sciences, OK

Riding My Bike

The wind in my wild hair,
The familiarity of autumn's brisk mild air,
It all fits together like pieces of a puzzle.
I peddle my aching legs hurriedly making my clothing rustle.
I'm as free as a bird, for this all feels as if I could fly,
And forever I know that no creature can defy
The irreplaceable feeling that comes over me as I ride my bike.

Erin Patrick, Grade 6
Brogden Middle School, NC

I Am Thankful

I am thankful for having legs
to walk in school.
I am thankful to have a dog
To keep me company.
When my sister is not home,
I like to write letters
To my grandma and grandpa
If they are lonely.
I am thankful for having a teacher
Who is there if we have a problem.
When I grow up,
I want to be just like my teacher.

Cambrie Agee, Grade 4
Lee A Tolbert Community Academy, MO

Joe Manchin

J ust governor
O utstanding leader
E xcellent

M anners
A reasonable guy
N ot mean
C aring
H appy
I ntelligent
N ice

Ron Pickens, Grade 6
Martin Elementary School, WV

Homework

I stare at the paper,
I don't know what to write,
Somebody please help me,
Or I'll be up all night.

The project is due tomorrow,
I don't know what to do,
I've forgotten the assignment,
What should I do?

So I call my teacher,
To ask her what is due,
She puzzles at the question,
She doesn't have a clue!

She says look at the calendar,
What month is printed in red?
I say, "Wait a minute, it's July,
I should be in bed!"

Emma Willis, Grade 6
Brogden Middle School, NC

Proud to Be an American

I am proud to be an American
with great freedom.
The soldiers are fighting for us
You can hear the fire
of the guns in Iraq.
Spring is already here;
flowers are blooming everywhere.
The birds are flying peacefully
in the sky.
As I sit on a boulder,
I pray to God
that He is protecting the soldiers.
The wind begins to blow
then God lets me know
that the angels are watching over
everyone in the USA.

Emily Robin, Grade 6
Leonville Elementary School, LA

Christmas

Christmas is almost here.
People are as jolly as can be.
People are putting up Christmas trees.
The children are good, because they think Santa Claus is coming.

The grown-ups are saying that
Christmas is not about getting gifts.
It's about giving others gifts.
It's also Jesus's birthday.

Arlexia Newson, Grade 5
East Marion Elementary School, MS

Who Wants It Most

Batting practice, running bases, ground balls
It all comes down to who wants it most of all.
I tap my bat on the plate,
Then I tilt my head down as I sit and wait.

With a whirl of her arm, the pitcher tosses a fast one,
I swing too late, must have caught a glare of the sun.
Another wind up, and another hot one across the plate,
Like a tigress watching its prey, I sit and wait.

The next one will be changing up; that one is mine,
She floats it across the plate slowly and I send it down the line.
I'm rounding second and heading to third
The coaches are saying stop, but I'm not hearing a word.

I round third base, I have my eye on home,
No one can stop me when I'm in my zone.
The ball's coming to the catcher, I see out of the corner of my eye,
But I slide in safely, and watch the tears of joy that my teammates cry.

We've won this battle, we wanted it most,
With our Gatorade bottles, we all make a toast.
"To the coaches, parents, teammates,
as long as we want it the most, we'll be the ones to dominate."

Brook Bowen, Grade 6
Southwestern Middle School, NC

12 Days of Christmas

On the first day of Christmas my true love gave to me a signed Angus Young SG
On the second of Christmas my true love gave to me 2 guitar picks
On the third day of Christmas my true love gave to me 3 drum cymbals
On the fourth day of Christmas my true love gave to me 4 KISS action figures
On the fifth day of Christmas my true love gave to me 5 Marshall Amps
On the sixth day of Christmas my true love gave to me 6 guitar strings
On the seventh day of Christmas my true love gave to me 7 guitar straps
On the eighth day of Christmas my true love gave to me 8 guitar cords
On the ninth day of Christmas my true love gave to me 9 KISS albums
On the tenth day of Christmas my true love gave to me 10 AC-DC CD's
On the eleventh day of Christmas my true love gave to me 11 drummers drumming
On the twelfth day of Christmas my true love gave to me 12 guitar cases

Austin Sawyers, Grade 5
East Bernstadt Elementary School, KY

Math Test

The day has come once more
Where I walk through Mrs. Cook's classroom door.
I know I have a math test;
I did not study; hope to do my best!
Here she comes giving me the test;
Oh wow! She is looking her best!
I finish my test and turn it in;
I turn around, sit down, and think again.
I hope to pass this test with an 'A' or 'B'.
So my friends will see;
See how smart I can be?
With passing my test without an 'F', 'D', or 'C'.
Finally, came the time; I got my test.
I passed it! Thank God! I did do my best!

Kimberly Tucker, Grade 6
Scotts Creek Elementary School, NC

Frogs

They are very small
But yet they can jump so far
Their tongues are so long

Garrett Burks, Grade 4
Briarwood Christian Elementary School, AL

Spring

I love spring so very much.
Nature adds every touch.
I was walking down the street,
And guess who I meet?
It was a girl about my age,
And it wasn't pretty on stage.
She beat me in the "Winter Pageant."
The look on my dad's face you wouldn't imagine.
She beat me by one vote;
That's why I like spring the most.
So when winter comes, I lay down in my bed,
And I dream about spring and daisies in my head.

Emily McMullen, Grade 4
Stephens Elementary School, AL

Love

She looks at him he looks at her
To them the rest of the world is a blur
Strangely they already love each other
Like you just love to see a butterfly flutter
They stay there minutes hours days
Everyone thinks it's just a phase
A poet nearby writes about what he sees
Wondering when they will depart from this spell
Seeing as now it's starting to hail
Through the storm they're still in a gaze
Love has made them strong
And nothing can blow them away.

Katelynn Cheek, Grade 6
Harrisburg Middle School, AR

The New Kid

The laughter *and* humiliation
The feeling of a million *eyes* looking at YOU
Wishing You could go home
And hoping that you would fit in
Who are they looking at?
Are they looking at ME?
I do not like this feeling. I do not like it at all.
Do you know this feeling? I know this feeling.
I've been it.

Destinee Doom, Grade 6
Little Flock Christian Academy, KY

Dragons and Kitties

dragons
scary, deadly
flying, killing, eating
scales, fire, fur, milk
sleeping, meowing, playing
cuddly, friendly
kitties

Mac Macoy, Grade 5
Briarwood Christian Elementary School, AL

That Color

Purple sounds like victory at the end of a track race.
Purple tastes like grapes in the springtime.
Purple feels like soft velvet sheets.
Purple looks like love in the air.
Purple is royalty and royalty is the throne of God.

Victoria Turner, Grade 5
Cool Spring Elementary School, NC

Beautiful Day

The cool breeze blowing
The smell of nice warm fire
The smell of the sweet leaves blowing by
The feeling of dew soaking into your shoes
The sight of the warm sun shining down
The sound of birds chirping
The sound of the wind blowing
The sound of the flag waving against the pole
The sound of tractors zooming by
The sight of squirrels gathering up their nuts
For the winter season
All of these make up a Beautiful Day.

Christopher Daniel Stilts, Grade 6
Temple Hill Elementary School, KY

An Amazing Book

The book opens.
An amazing adventure pops out.
Characters laugh in the grass together.
The shadows fade upon the dark green grass.
The sun shines with a warm bright smile.

Evan Puckett, Grade 4
Unionville Elementary School, NC

Soccer

I kick the ball and make a goal
I run around as quick as a dog
I see the ball; it's like a sphere
I see the team feeling proud
When it ends
It's all good
We win. We win!
Then I see the team screaming loud
When we won the game, I felt happy
After all there was no shame.

Hunter Choi, Grade 5
St Teresa's School, GA

Dreaming of the Rainforest

She was in a mystical land
A land that seemed far away
There were plants all around
As far as the eye could see.
For she longed to live in this land
Of magical things
But, she lived in a city
No plants or animals,
Just cars and buildings
Imagine these things!

Alex Marshall, Grade 6
Woodland Presbyterian School, TN

Actions

Some people play sports
and other people don't
Some people go along
and other people won't

Some people sleep a lot
and other people work
Some people lay around
and others are alert.

Reagan Bennett, Grade 6
Central Arkansas Christian School, AR

Fall Time

In the fall the leaves drop,
falling down on me.
When I go outside to play,
I wonder if it will rain today.
Then I say it cannot rain,
'cause I will rake the leaves today.
I go outside to jump in leaves,
and get my sisters too.
Then we go inside the house,
to get some hot chocolate.
So we go by the fire place,
and then we finally go to sleep.

Megan Matson, Grade 6
All Saints' Episcopal School, TN

The Dark Park

I was at the park
at the darkest of nights.
It was so dark
I had four flashlights.

The place was too dark to see
the park filled me with fright.
The darkness frightened me
I knew something wasn't right.

In the dark park
something was going on.
I fell and hit a piece of tree bark
I was asleep until the crack of dawn.

Chance Richard, Grade 5
Arnaudville Elementary School, LA

Dogs

Dogs happily bark all day
Because of things they hear,
See,
Or answering what their owners say.
Maybe they just want to play.

I love dogs,
How about you?
They sleep like logs
And they love you, too!

Courtney Howard, Grade 5
Walton Verona Elementary School, KY

Halloween

Monsters everywhere.
Scary faces in your hair.
Giving you bad dreams.

Mikayla Marler, Grade 5
Zalma Elementary School, MO

I Was Walking

I was walking to the door
As I tripped on the floor
Then I couldn't see
After I got stung by a bee
And I was really sore.

Kayla Barron, Grade 5
Bonaire Elementary School, GA

Runaway

There was a young man of Belize,
Who said, "I will do as I please."
He ran from home,
Got scared all alone,
And was back at his house by three.

Rebecca Keipper, Grade 6
River Trail Middle School, GA

Trust

Trust is a thing you need.
Trust will help you succeed.
Trust is an emblem to give and care,
to meet a friend and trust your heart.
Trust is a thing to have.
Trust is a wonderful feeling.

Tyler Jones, Grade 5
Parker Road Elementary School, MO

Scared Turkeys

Thanksgiving, Thanksgiving
the turkeys are scared
they are hiding in camouflage
before we hunt them
for they know we will hunt them
raining, snowing, sunny, or cloudy
we will hunt them in any weather

Harley Rider, Grade 6
Guntown Middle School, MS

Midnight Shower

From a midnight shower,
dew was left upon each morning flower.
Above the grass floats a haze
that reflects the sun's gleaming rays.
Damp leaves shimmer on a tree
showing off its unique charm and beauty.
As the sun starts to rise
then each animal opens their eyes.
Joyful music sung by a bird
across the hill tops can be heard.
A softness is in the air
so sweet and warm as a blanket to wear.
A melody that a stream gives
makes it seem as if it really lives.
Skies change from gray to blue
as the storm goes passing through.
The air smells fresh and clean
with a light breeze of the new morning.
A rainbow forms within the sky
as colorful and as sweet as a lullaby.

Dakotah Price, Grade 5
Stokesdale Elementary School, NC

Lawmaker

L aw
A ble
W orthy
M ankind
A ppoint
K indhearted
agr **E** ement
wo **R** thy

Nicholas Mingo, Grade 4
East Jones Elementary School, MS

Christmas Eve

Sounds like carolers outside my window.
Smells like any and every kind of cookie.
Tastes like delicious eggnog.
Looks like stockings hanging over the fireplace.
Feels like a warm cozy fire on a cold winter day.

Claudia Day, Grade 5
Briarwood Christian Elementary School, AL

Christmas

C is for Christmas and Christmas Day
H is for the special holiday Christmas
R is for the reindeer that's what guides Santa's sleigh
I is for ice because of the icy weather
S is for a special day today
T is for thanks of Jesus
M is for Merry Christmas
A is for a silent prayer that we say to God for this day
S is for the Savior, Jesus Christ

Tameka McCullough, Grade 6
St Mark Elementary School, SC

Christmas Cheer

My family has a Christmas cheer
At the end of December every year
They have a tree and have a feast
So if they get hungry they can't be a beast
We have cakes and pies for dessert
Because if we don't we would go berserk
We open presents under the tree
So when we go home we can be free

Alyssa Williams, Grade 6
Graham Elementary School, AL

Without You

Roses are red
Violets are blue
How sweet they smell
When I'm with you!
But without you
I'm all alone
When you leave
It's not a home!
The air of sweet flavors go away
And the air of misery comes to stay.
I pout and shout
When you're not here
But I'm warm and comfortable
When you're near.
My heart breaks
My World quakes
When you're not here right now
But, when you're home
I'm not all alone
And all of this was worthwhile.

Danyel Poindexter, Grade 6
Nathaniel Hawthorne Elementary School, MO

The Question

I am sitting in the RV.
I am watching TV.
My sister is watching me.
She asked me where is the key.
I said I don't know.
Well how am I supposed to open the door.
Well find a way.
Looks like I won't be leaving the RV today.

Marcus Tandy, Grade 6
Graham Elementary School, AL

Number 21

Number 21 is the best running back in all of football.
He plays for the Chargers.
Just to watch him, and the way he runs with power,
That power is to win,
Is fun.
It is like one person trying to defeat seven.

This person is Ladamian Tomlinson
But people call him LT.
LT is just a regular guy
But with special gift.
This gift is the power to succeed
And to be all he can be.
Just like everyone should be…
All they can be.

Ross Ledoux, Grade 6
Christ Episcopal School - Middle School, LA

The Beach

The beach is a soothing place
to be. Splish Splash the sound
of kids playing at the beach.
The smell of sea pork on the ground.
The taste of salt water in the fresh sea.
The feeling of waves coming up to my feet.
The sound of seagulls singing all around.
The sight of people walking by peacefully.
The beach is a soothing place to be.

Dante Valtorta, Grade 6
Chapin Middle School, SC

Religion

Divine Mercy Novena
It is a very special group of prayers
That my mom and I read every night.
I will get special blessings if I have faith,
And trust in the Lord.
I pray every night for my family,
But I know that with these special prayers
Everyone will be all right.

Kameron Bailey, Grade 4
Holy Rosary Academy, LA

Summer

Playing on the beach.
Hot days with very good friends.
Swimming all day long!

Bailee Svoboda, Grade 6
Tomlinson Jr High School, OK

Beaver

Beaver,
kind and careful,
can chop wood with its teeth,
they are like a brother to me,
mammal.

Nathan Geeting, Grade 6
Community Christian School, NC

Technology

My sister loves her computer
But she loves her cell phone more.
No, maybe it's her iPod
I'm really not that sure.
Perhaps it's her new camera
That she favors most of all.
It could be the 360
That she plays with in the mall,
But all the time she does this
Dad's wallet is getting small.

Newt Cottrill, Grade 6
Pleasants County Middle School, WV

Lisa

My new puppy's name is Lisa.
She came home with my dad.
He had her and a slice of pizza,
I know Lisa was kind of scared.

She changed colors every season,
In the winter she's a little light.
But, in the summer she is dark,
I still love her in any color.

Lisa likes me to chase her.
She gets our shoes and runs away.
But we don't have anything to say,
Cause everything she does is AOK.

She lets me give her a shower
Without moving a bit.
Some shampoo and water
Will make her smell like a flower.

When I am somewhere far,
Her heart will be near.
Cause everything she does,
Is just so perfect to me.

Diana Dang, Grade 4
Nesbit Elementary School, GA

Hear No Weevil*

When you hear a buzzing in your ear, be aware that Weevil's here.
He flies around from here to there.
Spreading evil in the air.
He tries to tempt innocent children
And when they listen, his evil soul will glisten.
Hey Joey! You can make the whole class laugh. Just say that Jill looks like a giraffe.
Joey listens, and gets into trouble. His teacher sends him to the time out bubble.
As people sin Weevil grows. He'll get as big as you on your toes.
As weevil grows he gets more joy so, he tempts Reece to steal a toy. Reece wow!
Look at that. What a cute stuffed animal cat. It could be yours if you listen to me,
Just take that cat and you'll be happy. But Reece is not a silly fool.
She learned some things in Sunday school.
Reece prays to God and all is good.
She's glad she did what she should.
Weevil gets mad and starts to shrink. So he finds a way to win more strength.
He tries to tempt some little saints
But in their ears his voice is faint.
You can do the same thing too.
Just pay attention in Sunday school.
If you hear a buzzing in your ear.
Blur it out, because Weevil's buzzing near.

Lydia Drakeford, Grade 6
St Mark Catholic School, NC
*Based on the book "Hear No Weevil"

Williamsburg

W illiamsburg was home to 2,000 people
I s the capitol of Virginia
L istening to bells ring
L argest American colony
I magine people working, shopping, and speaking with British accents.
A ttending church on Sunday
M arried for life.
S ee chickens and sheep wandering through the streets.
B owls handmade and pots for other goods.
U nique crafts and games to do.
R eligion and government were not separated.
G ame of goose in Raleigh Tavern.

Mack Gilley, Grade 5
Alvaton Elementary School, KY

The First Day of Spring

Waking up at dawn's early light,
leaping to my window, "Oh how the sun's so bright!"
Grabbing my new spring dress I rush into the hall,
fly down the stairs and hear my mom call.
I tell her I'll be back by the end of the day,
as I slip through the door and pickup my diary on the way.
I grab my bike and pickup my helmet,
dashing down to the spring in my dress of velvet.
I watch the lily pads settle and the fireflies fly,
as I write in my diary and watch the time pass by.
As the sun begins to set and the sky turns pink,
I think about this day and how it was the first spring day this week.

Holly Wright, Grade 6
Bellwood Discovery School, TN

Love Is Not a Fairy Tale

Roses are Red Violets are blue
I can't wait to get next to you
You're so fine you can be mine,
You can be my little valentine.
I see you you don't see me
Let's not let that be
I see you walking in your school halls
I know your type, dark, black and tall
Sit down lets talk better yet lets take a walk
You drink a lot of protein
No wonder you always do the shoulder lean
I see your friends in the dark
Runnin around in the park
Don't laugh at my silly poem
You're just like me funny
Good and charming.

Jason D. DeWitt, Grade 6
Brogden Middle School, NC

The Wishbone

At Thanksgiving time
After the food and after the prayer
We draw two names from a hat that someone used to wear.
Those two people get to fight
For a wish they can make tonight.

It is Sis and me all ready to go
With one heave and one ho, it snapped.
I showed her the piece I got.
Hers was bigger than I thought.
I won't get that wish at midnight
How sad, it will be hers tonight.

Mikayla Hearn, Grade 6
Pleasants County Middle School, WV

Easter

Smells like chocolate and sweet candy
Sounds like wrappers being opened
Looks like the Easter Bunny
Feels like the wrapper in your hand
Tastes like the chocolate melting in your mouth

Joshua Thomas Reid, Grade 5
Briarwood Christian Elementary School, AL

Joy and Sorrow

joy
cheery, desired
dancing, skipping, singing
smile, laughter, depression, heartache
wailing, frowning, longing
painful, gloomy
sorrow

Caroline Carlisle, Grade 5
Briarwood Christian Elementary School, AL

Christmas Wishes

The holidays are here,
And the days are full of cheer.

I hope you've prepared a list,
And on it that one special wish.

Some people wish for lots of toys,
And others ask for Christmas joys.

Most teens want a brand new car,
But for a little kid a bike will go far.

Even though we all get a little greedy,
Don't forget those who are needy.

So try to help them with their wishes,
But still don't forget your own little wishes.

I still have my own,
But it's kind of at a big tone.

You see the one thing I wish for,
Is to see my cat Pepper run through the door.

Annie Smith, Grade 6
J E Holmes Middle School, NC

See

See me as one,
Of many a kind,
See me as a part,
Belonging in a whole.

Of many a kind,
Being popular isn't popularity,
Belonging in a whole,
Means you are on top of the popularity list.

Being popular isn't popularity,
Having true friends to share the laughs,
Means you are on top of the popularity list,
For life isn't a contest.

Having true friends to share the laughs,
Of many a kind,
For life isn't a contest,
See me as one.

Xinwei Zeng, Grade 6
River Trail Middle School, GA

Memories

Memories are good memories are bad
Sometimes they can make you come out really sad
I know what I see is just in the past
But sometimes I wonder how long it will last.

Yuri Jeter, Grade 6
Brogden Middle School, NC

Always Pray

There once was a day
when I didn't pray.
Everything turned upside-down
all around me
everything I could see.
There was an awful feeling
when I looked at the ceiling.
It made me feel like I was dead
although it was just in my head.
Then I sat down to pray.
This was an awful day.
I told Jesus how I felt.
The feeling was so warm I began to melt.
He told me how to handle everything.
I felt like a candle,
with Jesus as my fire.
That's my only desire.

Alex Eben, Grade 6
Desoto Central School, MS

An Ode to Merlin

A wizard, a mage,
A name known for ages.
Of a boy who had powers
To conjure up flowers.
He battled all sorts of creatures,
And to young Arthur was a teacher.
He was an extraordinary man,
Who traveled to mystical lands.
Used his magic for good and not evil,
For he, Merlin would always prevail.
But the day had come,
When the evil Nimue,
Imprisoned Merlin in a glass cocoon.
In that glass house,
He was trapped for years,
And there he will stay,
Until Arthur comes back,
And regains the throne once more.
I write this ode to this great sorcerer.
Because his magic and power,
Still exists.

Hareen Godthi, Grade 6
River Trail Middle School, GA

My Best Friend

H onorable
O utstanding
U nderstanding
S uitable
T ruthful
O ver the top
N ever not my friend

Griffin Teets, Grade 5
Our Lady of Fatima School, MS

Perfection

Perfection is a funny thing,
Spoken of so oft,
I wonder how nobody feels:
For everybody says, Nobody's perfect!

Elizabeth Jessup, Grade 4
St Thomas More School, NC

Fences

Fences, Fences
We love fences
They divide our land into halves
Blue ones
Yellow ones
Tie dyed ones
We love them all
Keep the little rascals in
Keep the silly old animals in
Don't you wish they had ones too
keep the kids locked in forever
They would be tall and colored from
The little kids coloring it
Parents would come from far and near
to let them demonstrate how it works
Just hope parents in your family
don't think about getting one
If they do you better run and hide!

Natasha Martinez, Grade 5
Elkhorn Elementary School, MO

Skateboarding

Skateboarding
Fun, painful
Jumping, flipping, rolling
Can you ollie well
Thrashing

Mikey Lee, Grade 4
Russell Babb Elementary School, OK

Storm

Cold rain is falling
Then comes the flashing lightning
Thunder adds a crash

Carter Jennings Holland, Grade 5
Etowah Elementary School, NC

My Sleeping Room

My room is a
night room with
stars and brownish
whitish walls.
It's very clean, it's my space.
No my place.
I feel like a falling star.

Alexis Rodgers, Grade 6
Dyer Elementary & Jr High School, TN

Constitution

C andidate
O rder
N ew
S uccessful
T alk
I ndependence
T ough
U nited
T ranquility
I nsure
O rdain
N ice

Justin Guthrie, Grade 4
East Jones Elementary School, MS

Ocean Night

The ocean's blue,
as blue as the sky.
When the sunset hits the ocean
It fills my heart with Happiness,
Until the sun goes completely down
and the stars fill the sky

Cassady Jones, Grade 4
Crestwood Elementary School, KY

Ornamental Snake

Slowly slithering
On the ground or in high trees
Happily hissing

Karley Richardson, Grade 4
Orchard Elementary School, AL

The Black Swan

The Black Swan is here
glides smoothly in the water
mystery in dark

Deidra Nicole Smiler, Grade 4
Indian Springs Elementary School, AL

When the Leaves Fall

I am the leaves,
I blow all around.
I fall off trees
when fall comes.
I see the cars go by,
I smell the pretty flowers,
I hear the storms explode,
When I am on the ground,
I can see the other trees.
The first day they are
green, yellow, orange,
brown, and red.
I am the leaves.

Reagan E. Patterson, Grade 4
Cool Spring Elementary School, NC

Tornadoes

Funnel
Much destruction
Neighbors' fearsome nightmare
Sweeping through darkened neighborhoods
Cyclones

Kholsi Tyner, Grade 5
Broadway Elementary School, NC

The Town at Night

Have you ever listened to the town at night?
It will speak to you, I promise.
It will tell you to get all your thoughts out,
or take you on a peaceful walk to the beach.
It will say, "Give me your burdens,"
Or it will sing you to sleep with a lullaby.
It will be willing to talk, but only at night.

Cassie Geisendorfer, Grade 5
North Shelby Elementary School, MO

I Am

I am a Christian, a helper, and a prayer.
I love Jesus.
I love God.
I do my best to worship Him.
I care about Him.
I am a Christian, a helper, and a prayer.
I like to help others.
I help other people worship.
I help my brother believe in God.
I help him to read the Bible.
I help him to understand the Word.
I am a Christian, a helper, and a prayer.
I pray with Jesus in my heart.
I pray and worship God at church.
I pray with my brother every morning.
I pray with my friends on the playground.
I pray every day and night.
I am a Christian, a helper, and a prayer.

Dani Urista, Grade 6
Desoto Central School, MS

My Little Brother

My little brother is five months old.
He's cute, cuddly, and crazy.
He smiles, snuggles, and is silly.
He's little, lumpy, and lazy.
His days are filled, it seems to me,
With eating, sleeping, and pooping,
My poor old mom spends her time
Into his little mouth, food scooping.
To me, it seems I spend my time
At this little lump looking.
My brother is the cutest in the world,
But I wonder what schemes he is cooking.

Courtney Marie Booher, Grade 5
Contentnea Elementary School, NC

Thanksgiving

On one day Pilgrims started to sail
Some of which began to look quite pale.
They sailed on a ship called the Mayflower;
Some survived, but only with God's power.

They had a feast with Indians who brought corn
After the harvest was born.
They looked around and realized
This is the place where they were bound.

Katie Lothrop, Grade 5
Evangelical Christian School, TN

Beyond A Book

Beyond a book there are hidden letters,
Letters that pop like popcorn into your eyes,
Every page that is turned,
Is like a pancake being flipped over and over,
Each picture has diverse colors,
Red as a cherry,
Yellow like lemonade,
And white as soft as bread,
Beyond a book is fear like no other,
Beyond a book is wonder far away,
Beyond your mind is an imagination,
But far behind is the key to a book!

Julie Miller, Grade 5
Wilt Elementary School, KY

Christmas

Christmas is filled with love
Christmas is when you give someone a turtle dove

Christmas Christmas
Christmas Christmas

Christmas is when you celebrate the birth of Jesus
Christmas is all about Jesus

Christmas Christmas
Christmas Christmas

Christmas is full of joy
My cousin plays with his toy

Cleon Davis, Grade 6
St Mark Elementary School, SC

Swim Meets

Sounds like cheering and yelling
Smells like sweat and heat
Looks like lots of nervous swimmers
Feels like chattering teeth
Tastes like sweet victory

Maryellen Dacy Newton, Grade 5
Briarwood Christian Elementary School, AL

Rocks

Rocks
Rocks
Rocks
Big Rocks,
Small Rocks,
Wet slimy smooth rocks,
Dry hard rough rocks,
These are just a few
Gooey rocks,
Heavy rocks,
Black, gray, white rocks,
Sandy colorful light rocks,
Shiny rocks, too
Dull rocks,
Round rocks,
Don't forget cave rocks,
Last of all, best of all
I like crystal rocks.

Dragan Petrovic, Grade 6
Lost River Elementary School, KY

Fences

Fences fences, they work so hard,
they try to keep things in the yard.
Short or tall. Big or small.
Oh how we love our fences.
Short or tall, on the ball.
Skinny or fat keeps in the cat.
Shaped like a log keeps in the dog.
Oh how we love our fences.

Jillian Ring, Grade 5
Elkhorn Elementary School, MO

Birds

Chirping, singing fun
Tweeting, eating all day long
Loves to sing nightly

Dallas Hoffman, Grade 6
Leland Middle School, NC

Storms

Storms rumble in the sky
turning it gray, shouting
BOOM! BOOM!
You run to your house to be safe,
rain pouring on your roof,
like water in the shower
when the pipe is broken
You tremble with fear
like a rabbit
being chased by a hunter
Lightning lights the sky.
You run to your mom
to snuggle in her arms, safe.

Kyle Eldridge, Grade 4
Crestwood Elementary School, KY

Grades

I am happy when I make good grades
It makes me strong and proud
Mom and Dad say study hard to which I sometimes frown
Reading is my favorite
Math is okay
Science test oh no! That really messes up my day
Social Studies makes me think about how life used to be
Especially during the times of Martin Luther King
Grades are very important
So are those special tests
But Mom and Dad are most proud as long as I have done my best.

Iyana Faison, Grade 6
Brogden Middle School, NC

Hot Pink

Hot pink feels like the sticky bubble gum dripping through the seams of my pocket.
Hot pink smells like the soft and cuddly fabric softener my mom uses.
Hot pink tastes like the sugar filled icing on my birthday cake.
Hot pink sounds like firecrackers on the Fourth of July.

Hot pink is a happy day at school.
Hot pink is Ashley's face after a good, hard laugh.
Hot pink is my winter coat covered with snow.
Hot pink is my gripper soft on my fingers while I write.
Hot pink is the color that makes me happy.

Hannah Martin, Grade 5
Cool Spring Elementary School, NC

The Soccer Ball

A sphere being kicked around on the green needly grass,
Blue like the ocean surrounded by the other seas,
Being stitched together feeling like bumpy holes keeping the ball alive before death,
Soft as rubber for my unhumanlike power,
Soaring through the air to meet its final destiny.

The ball is like a fighter jet,
Taking off to start the war,
Getting hit many times but it keeps going,
Getting hit once again, it plunges into the water,
The first half's over!

Spinning like a torpedo,
Ready to hit the head of a player
Then go back up for the next target,
Going through defenders,
Sending the ball back up like a cannon has just been shot.

The ball is like my child,
I take it almost everywhere,
The ball is cherished,
I eat, sleep and breathe soccer,
Knowing the ball is like gold I use it well.

Mason Smith, Grade 4
Goshen Elementary School at Hillcrest, KY

Independence Day

Sounds like explosions in the distance
Looks like the sky is cluttered with colorful dots
Smells like we are going to have a picnic
Tastes like Mom's famous chicken sandwiches
Feels like cool grass on a warm night.

Mark Herrington, Grade 5
Briarwood Christian Elementary School, AL

Wonder

I wonder how many planets there are.
I wonder how big the Earth is.
I wonder how many books have been written.
I wonder why Coke makes fizz.

I wonder how TV works,
I wonder how people make cars.
I wonder how old the sun is.
I wonder what it's like on Mars.

There are so many things I want to see.
There are so many things to behold.
It will take some time to find these things.
By then, I will be very old.

Juan Carlos Anzola, Grade 6
Haynes Academy for Advanced Studies, LA

Stars Falling from Heaven

I looked upon the sky,
And saw them, twinkling bright

They looked down on me from high,
And showed off dazzling light

Lighting up night's black curtain,
They set fire to the sky

The fire 'tis of Heaven, of this I was certain,
Getting closer, closer, closer by and by

Falling from Heaven,
Falling from the glory of our God

Quincy Leech, Grade 6
St Thomas More School, NC

Christmas Yum

Christmas is a time of fun
We might have a sloppy joe on a bun
I just might meet an old chum
I said, "Yum" to a sloppy joe
On Christmas Day I gave my dog a good nice mate
One of the presents, since I love to cook
Is a wonderful cookbook.

Rogelio Salguero, Grade 5
Hatfield Elementary School, AR

Me

I love to skate I love to roll also
I love to hip-hop which is my life and soul
I stay on the open road like all the
Time but one thang for show I keep
Jesus on my mind

My name is Ke I stay on beat and also
I can make the crowd scream
But now I keep it real so peace

Ki'Ana Hunter, Grade 6
Calloway Smith Middle School, AL

Katrina

It all began days before she struck.
If you were going to stay in the city,
You were testing your luck.
You had to get out.
You had to evacuate.
Then all of a sudden came that special date,
August 29, 2005.
Those who stayed,
Some were dead.
Some were alive.
The city looked like a war zone.
Searching for people where they were unknown.
Here we are over a year since she hit.
We're rebuilding the city.
You'd think for no reason,
Cause we're just going to get hit again,
During Hurricane season.

Jade Franke, Grade 6
Haynes Academy for Advanced Studies, LA

Thank You for Fighting for Our Freedom

I am glad to be an American.
It is the best for me.
It is fun to go outside
and see a baby blue sky.
The animals can walk
gracefully in the grass.
Families can picnic with others.
Waterfalls are very peaceful.
The angels are watching us;
the sunrise is shining for you.
We are sad for everyone that has died.
We thank you
for fighting for our freedom.

Laura Stelly, Grade 6
Leonville Elementary School, LA

On the Rocks

Rocks are everywhere.
They stand taller than the sand.
They're extravagant.

Olivia Lauderdale, Grade 4
Briarwood Christian Elementary School, AL

Dog

Dog
Strong, friendly
Runs very fast
Joyful, funny, happy, wonderful
My pet

Ashton Dement, Grade 4
Robert E Lee Elementary School, TN

Colors

Yellow is the color of the moonlight,
Pink is the color of hearts,
Orange is the color of the sun,
Red is the color of love,
Green is the color of grass,
Blue is the color of the sky,
Purple is the color of the sunset,
Black is the color of death.

Kaydee Elliott, Grade 6
Hayes Elementary School, OK

Veteran

V ictorious in war.
E xpose the truth.
T rained professional.
E veryone counts.
R ouse the troops.
A lways wins war.
N ow and forever we salute you.

Tara Kendrick, Grade 4
Cherokee Elementary School, AR

The Creeps

Big creepy mud lake
Surrounded by forest
Surrounded by fog

Charles Watt, Grade 4
Hillcrest Elementary School, TN

The Babysitter

When she came she sent me to bed
and then she said a bid
instead of going to my bed
I ran to the woods and hid

When my babysitter came
my friends and I hatched a plan
when she came to be mean to us
instead she left and ran

So whenever she came
and sent me to bed
she never was able to
because I sent her instead

Sean Rossi, Grade 5
Stokesdale Elementary School, NC

George Washington

G reat
E xpert
O riginal
R ight
G raphic
E xperienced

W illing
A wesome
old- **S** chool
H istorical
n **I** ce
N obility
G ood man
T errific
O ld
N oble

Ethan Thorla, Grade 4
East Jones Elementary School, MS

On Christmas

One sunny morn
I got up, then
whispered to myself
"it's Christmas." Then I
streaked under the
tree, counted the
gifts from old St. Nick,
on Christmas.
Then I found myself
filled with joy from
head to toes. I had
a certain amount
of gifts, can you
guess what it is?
The answer is 17
gifts from old St. Nick
on Christmas.
Woke my family from their slumber,
I even saw my tiny
dog Sassy was having
a great time on Christmas.

Spencer Newmister, Grade 4
Alvaton Elementary School, KY

Sports

I like sports, I don't know about you
There are many sports that you can do
Basketball, baseball, football, soccer
Golf's all right but you can't mock 'er
Then finally, there is hockey
When you get checked, it's really rocky

Steve Rosenzweig, Grade 5
Prince of Peace Catholic School, SC

A Day at the Beach

Walking on the beach
Standing in the nice sunshine
Playing with my friends

Kelsey Sheppard, Grade 6
Tomlinson Jr High School, OK

Deer Hunting

In the tree lines there stands…
A brown, soft deer,
With a ten point rack,
Glaring in the sun.

The smell of earth,
The crisp leaves beneath your feet,
The cold hitting you in the face,
That's the pleasure of a trophy buck.

Brett Kelley, Grade 5
Lewis County Intermediate School, TN

Beaches

I clench my toes
In the rough hot sand

Gleaming shells wash up
From the salty sea

The fish splash up
In the waves

I see the seagulls
Flee from the water

Crabs digging holes
Dolphins dive across the sea

The sunset goes down
The horizon line

Pink, blue, purple
Fill the sky

Olivia Brueckner, Grade 4
Easley Elementary School, NC

The Toad

I was walkin' down the road,
when I saw a toad;
I took him home,
where he growed, growed, growed.
I love that toad,
I really do,
but how he escaped,
no one knew.

Zach Garrison, Grade 5
Midway Covenant Christian School, GA

I Am

I am the light of tomorrow
I wonder what the future will hold for me
I hear voices crying out to me
I see people around me changing every day
I want a world with no drugs
I am the light of tomorrow

I pretend that I'm okay when I'm afraid
I feel sad when my loved ones die
I touch the sky when I'm happy
I worry if my brother's in trouble
I cry when my loved ones are sad
I am the light of tomorrow

I understand that no one can be perfect
I say that harsh words don't hurt
I dream of the future
I try to achieve every goal
I hope that I can
I am the light of tomorrow

Brittany Wilbourn, Grade 4
Walnut Grove Elementary School, AL

The First Shots

For when the troops came stomping
I knew I'd never see light again,
for at the end of the war
I might never open my eyes again

For when the first shots were fired
and the cannons hot,
the ground shook like an earthquake

For when the battlefields are lonely
and our men recuperating,
we pray for a victory over the enemy

For when the battlefields are raging
and all our men almost dead,
I thought to myself and said

I'm fighting for the land of the free
and the home of the brave,
I will not let my guard down for another man's rage.

Tyler Berkey, Grade 6
Myrtle Beach Middle School, SC

Thanksgiving

Red, brown, and orange leaves on the ground.
Thanksgiving day has come around.
After eating turkey I'll probably gain a pound.
I'm going to be sad when the sun goes down.
But I'll just have to think
when the next Thanksgiving day will come around.

Kelci Baumann, Grade 6
Guntown Middle School, MS

A Storm

It rumbles it crumbles.
Can you guess?
A storm.
We stay inside with no pride
that the storm is here to stay.
The lightning, the boom,
the feeling of doom that it will never leave.
The sky so dark.
Can you hear the thunder bark?
It rumbles it crumbles.
Can you guess?
A storm.

Maeve Mense, Grade 6
Our Lady of Lourdes Elementary School, NC

My Birthday

Smells like wonderful cakes
Sounds like laughter and singing
Tastes like cake and ice cream
Looks like presents and smiles
Feels like excitement and joy

Becky Thielman, Grade 5
Briarwood Christian Elementary School, AL

The Fall

The fall has many colors, colors, colors.
Fall may be brisk at times,
There are very beautiful leaves on the trees.
I think fall is better than spring.

During the fall I love to jump amongst the leaves.
Sure the spring is the time of love, but that is not for me.
It would kill me if there was no fall.
I think fall is better than spring.

Sometimes it can be warm or cold or in between,
It is almost exactly perfect that is why I like fall.
The spring is not as exciting.
I still think fall is better than spring.

What do other people think about fall?
I don't care because fall is for me.
And so you see, I think spring is not as pretty.
I think fall is better than spring.

Moriah K. Bechtel, Grade 5
Providence Academy, TN

The Green Grass and the Green Leaves

Green grass like the trees on the side of the nature road
Reminds me of the green leaves on the trees.
The leaves talk to me like a story of the wilderness.
You can see the blue open sky.

John Michael Folden, Grade 5
Temple Hill Elementary School, KY

Stars

The room was not bright,
I tried with all my might,
But couldn't see a sight,
I could only dream of such a night,
As the stars shone with all their might,
I stood frozen at the sight,
All the stars flooded the room with light,
It was no longer dark and night,
You could only dream of such a sight,
Wow, what a night.

Louie Pettit, Grade 5
Spring Branch Elementary School, MO

The Star Very Far

On a star away,
on a star very far

There lives dragons three,

Arien of the rising,
Gurrel of the setting,

and Lishia of the full moon

they dance around,
their tails swinging

their wings fluttering about,

With claws clicking
and paws treading gold,

and each their eyes aflame

and only a star away
only a star very far away.

Laura Carden, Grade 6
College View Middle School, KY

Fall

Leaves fall
d
o
w
n
DASHING in
to the pile
crunch! crunch!
all of the colorful leaves
on the ground
rust, lemon, cherry,
cinnamon wind
blowing every way
fall!

Kennedy Helveston, Grade 4
Alvaton Elementary School, KY

Love One Another

When it is time to pray, we need a place to stay.
All of God's people find a church, with a steeple and go inside each day.
We learn how to share, we learn how to care.
We try to help each other because we are all brothers.
And we love one another.

Dakota Flauss, Grade 5
Holy Rosary Academy, LA

On the River

When you're on the river kayaking, everything is peaceful.
All you hear is nature,
The birds go chirp, chirp, chirp,
The river goes splash, splash, splash,
The air is calm,
The water is cold when it hits your skin.
When you talk, your echo goes on for miles.
When you are having a bad day, it makes you feel at peace with the world,
Every time I close my eyes, I hear chirp, chirp, splash, splash,
And then all I want to do is kayak.

Hailey Dick, Grade 6
Woodland Presbyterian School, TN

Army Brat

I am the son of a soldier who's in Iraq.
I wonder if my dad will come home safely.
I hear soldiers saying bye to their family members.
I see buses leave with my dad.
I want my dad to be safe in Iraq.
I am the son of a soldier who's in Iraq.

I pretend that my dad is with me when I need him.
I feel that my dad shouldn't be in Iraq.
I touch my dad's bible and pray for him.
I worry that my mom will get frustrated.
I cry when I realize that my dad isn't home when I get home.
I am the son of a soldier who's in Iraq.

I understand that the army takes him to war because it is his job.
I say my dad is a hero and is brave.
I dream that my dad will never come back.
I try to help my family every day.
I am the son of a soldier who's in Iraq.

Joshua Hernandez, Grade 5
Walker Intermediate School, KY

Religion

R eligious people worship Gods.
E gyptian people believed in more than two Gods.
L atin American's religion was the center of life for rich and the poor.
I ndia believed in many Gods.
G od
I believe in one God.
O rthodox
N onbelievers have no faith.

Ariana Jelson, Grade 6
Clarksburg School, TN

Getting Along

A cat and a dog and a mouse sang a song,
About being friends and getting along.

They weren't taught by their mothers
That they should not like the others.
so none of them knew it was wrong.
This is really funny because,
Their moms don't know their own kids enough.

The simplest hint this poem sends,
Is that cats, dogs, and mice,
Are not supposed to be friends.

D.J. Dye, Grade 5
Cottonwood Public School, OK

Soccer Game

The first time I had a soccer game
Butterflies in my belly
On go my shin guards, plop
On go my socks, swoop
And on go my cleats, slip
The field, shaking nervously
Shorts to my knees
The sweet smell of green grass
The whistle blows, the ball at my feet
Dribbling down the field, wind in my face
Sweat rolling down my cheek
Whack! I shoot the ball and fall
Cheering is in the air, I scored!
The game went on
Tripping, kicking everywhere
1 to 1 and a few minutes left
I was quickly dribbling down the field again
I'm Open! Yelled one of my teammates
I passed to her with my ponytail waving
She kicks the ball, it's in!
The whistle blows, we won

Meghan Lovine, Grade 6
Beck Academy, SC

Homework

Homework is simple and easy to do.
I like Spelling, Math, and English, too.

When I do them, it gives me a chill
up and down my spine, what a thrill!

When I'm at school I do my work
when I do it I go berserk!

But, when I do my homework I have so much fun
just waiting for it to be done.

Madeleine Arnzen, Grade 4
St Mary Cathedral Elementary School, MO

The Baby Blanket

Hand made from needle and thread
It warmed me when I went to bed.
Blue, white, pink, and green are the colors
So soft it was under those covers.

My mom made it especially for me.
I can't wait to give it to my child.
For I will have so much glee
I am certain they will love it.

Courtney Harris, Grade 6
North Iredell Middle School, NC

Mom and Dad

Who wakes you up in the morning?
Who makes you breakfast?
Who takes you to school?
Mom and Dad do! Boo boo be doo!

Who gets you an after-school snack?
Who takes you to piano lessons?
Who cooks a yummy supper?
Mom and Dad do! Boo boo be doo!

Who takes you to Mass?
Who lets you have your own TV?
Who lets you have a cool race car bed?
Mom and Dad do! Boo boo be doo!

Who takes you on vacation?
Who takes you out to eat?
Who plays with you?
Mom and Dad do! Boo boo be doo!

Who keeps you safe from harm?
Who helps you grow big and strong?
Who lets you have lots of fun?
Mom and Dad do! Boo boo be doo!

Josh Green, Grade 4
St Mary Cathedral Elementary School, MO

Hope Is a Garden

Hope is a garden,
    Growing a dream…
As a lily soothes the soul,
    The lily is as fragile as a heart,
Once the heart is broken.

The flower is dead until the heart finds love again.
The rain drops on the flowers so clear,
    Like stained glass windows.
A door within the soul — once the door is opened,
    Hope is spread around.

Hope is a garden.

Taylor Bartlett, Grade 5
Breitling Elementary School, AL

The Sun

The sun
in the backyard
peeking through the clouds
east of my house
like
a smiling face
joy after a long rain
open eyes
floating,
in the bright blue sky.

Bayli Boling, Grade 6
College View Middle School, KY

Moon, Moon

Moon, moon being bright,
through the forest in the night.
The moon making it nice and clear,
so we don't have any fear.
The moon giving the slaves a way to go,
so they can escape their angry foes.
Giving sailors a way to follow,
so they don't feel any sorrow.
In a cloudy sky, the moon might
give you an awesome sight.
Moon, moon being bright,
through the forest in the night.

Robert Alberse, Grade 4
West Cary Middle School, NC

Colors

Colors you see all the time.
Colors ringing and sometimes dinging.
Colors on everything you see.
But black and white are really a fright.
They're not really colors.
But all the colors in the world
are really a bright sight.

Mallory Spivey, Grade 5
Drayton Hall Elementary School, SC

Swimming

Standing on the block,
Waiting for the buzzer,
Beeeep

Everyone dives into the water,
Like worms sliding in the ground,

The water jumps as I get out
Swimming
Swimming
Swimming

Tyler Habberfield, Grade 6
Eminence Middle School, KY

Flamingo

F unny to look at.
L ong, bumpy legs.
A mazing bright pink feathers!
M ini feather tails.
I t lives in zoos.
N ot a very good pet to have.
G ray feathers when a baby.
O h! That terrible sound.

Jody Vickers, Grade 4
Stephens Elementary School, AL

Horses

Horses running freely
neighing very happily
playing in all sorts of ways
going about their day

Kirstin Dawn Green, Grade 5
Etowah Elementary School, NC

Eagles

Up! Up! Eagles soar through the sky.
White, brown, and black.
Through the town.
I like to see them fly over my house.
Bald and Proud they fly.
They love to surf the sky.

Sean Botz, Grade 5
American Heritage Academy, GA

Eli

I have a dog named Eli,
That follows me around all day.
Whimpering and whining for me to play.
He bites and nibbles my feet.
Until I screech OWWWWW!!!

Teila Marlin, Grade 4
Cave City Elementary School, AR

Excalibur

Excalibur
the name itself has a ring
discovered by a boy at age thirteen

no ordinary sword
power within itself
a true treasure of Fincarya

some would say it's murderous
some would say it's fake
but I know the truth of it
the findings of a mentor
and the markings of a king

Wesley Hartgrove, Grade 6
College View Middle School, KY

Hope for the Coast

Hope was scarce
Nothing was there
A disaster had struck
The cities were bare

Many were homeless
With nowhere to go
Most could infer
Help would come slow

Help poured out from around the U.S.
In time of grief
When we needed help
That's what we got, Katrina relief

They gave us a new hope
The care that we sought
Giving us such a helping hand
So thankful they had not forgot

Our suffering was over
Recovery was done
After one year of pain
The coast saw the sun.

Allison Judge, Grade 6
Kitty Stone Elementary School, AL

Sad

Sadness is blue and dark green
It tastes like moldy bread
It sounds like quiet
And smells like overripe fruit
It looks like a thunderstorm
It makes me feel upset

Ellie Scheaffer, Grade 4
Cleveland Elementary School, OK

The Great Depression

Try as you might,
The fight begins,
Over money and food,
It started from within.

You want to help,
You think you're wrong,
Try as always,
You write your song.

You sing out loud,
To ease the pain,
The money gone,
And the loss remains.

Caitlin Kennedy, Grade 6
Bernard Middle School, MO

If I Were in Charge of the U.S.*

If I were in charge of the U.S.
I'd cancel school, work, golf shows,
And animal rights people.
If I were in charge of the U.S.
There'd be more football games, and basketball games,
And no tennis.
If I were in charge of the U.S.
You wouldn't have taxes,
You wouldn't have the Beach Boys
You wouldn't have soccer or homework
You wouldn't even have bills
If I were in charge of the U.S.
I would be able to hunt all year
Guns would be free.
And a person who got in trouble
And hit people every once in awhile
Would still be allowed to be in charge of the U.S.

Silas Nielson, Grade 6
South Nodaway Elementary School, MO
*Patterned after "If I Were in Charge or the World"
by Judith Viorst

Dirt Bikes

Dirt bikes are fast.
They are colored yellow, green, and blue.
They are big and they are small.
Dirt bikes are fun.

Dirt bikes are fast.
Their wheels are huge.
The tires have knobs.
The tires have flaps.
Dirt bikes are fun.

Dirt bikes are fast.
They make me happy.
I work with my dad.
He teaches me about my bike.
Dirt bikes are fun.

Boston Fausett, Grade 4
Hayes Elementary School, OK

The Price

Lollipops and presents are really nice,
But I wasn't the one to pay the price.
If it wasn't for Jesus
I would be dark.
I would be stuck in a world that wants to destroy me,
A world that wants to kill me.
If it wasn't for Jesus
I could not have seen the light that saved me.
I'm very thankful for what Jesus did
And all I have to give is my life,
And I did.

Sarah Shepard, Grade 6
Mount Zion Christian School, SC

Our Flag

Our flag is so great,
So mighty and powerful,
Our flag is red, white, and blue.

Red stands for hardiness and bravery,
White signifies purity and innocence,
Blue stands for the color of the Chief.
Our flag has fifty stars
    Which stand for fifty states.

Our flag flies high
Up in the sky.
Our flag flies free
For liberty
I love our United States flag.

Frankie Wachter, Grade 4
Heartland High School and Academy, MO

Sephra's Bio

Sephra
Nice, loving, fun, friendly
Lover of books, water, dolphins
Happy when reading, playing, having adventures
Who needs are Mom, water, food
Who fears ducks
Who wants the world to recycle
Oklahoma City
Kolker

Sephra Kolker, Grade 4
Cleveland Elementary School, OK

Kevin

I met him in kindergarten
round-faced and fat!
It was an odd way we met.
He challenged me to a drawing contest.

From them on,
no matter where I went, Kevin was there.
No matter where Kevin went, I was always there.
If I got in trouble, Kevin got in trouble.
We were in the same grade for four years.
Then I got held back.

But we always said we would be friends forever.
Then we met Brent and there were three of us.
Same thing though, one got in trouble, two got in trouble.

Every weekend we were together.

But all the same,
Kevin and I would always be inseparable!

Brandon Burris, Grade 5
Etowah Elementary School, NC

Snow

Very white diamonds
Falling from a gray blanket
White diamonds falling
Elissa Sutherland, Grade 4
St Thomas More School, NC

Basketball

Hitting the ground,
Hitting a hand,
Get shot through the hoop,
The net tickling my sides,
Driven in by the green team
I'm on the white team's side,
The last minute of the game,
The clock is ticking rapidly!
Sweat all over me,
I think I'm gonna die!
They count down 3, 2, 1!
I'm shot by the white.
The buzzer sounds,
I swish through the net,
We win!
We win!
Kyle McDonald, Grade 6
St Vincent Elementary School, MO

Book

Big, long
Reading, thinking, dreaming
Adventurous trip
Wind magazine
Sidney Burgess, Grade 5
Shirley Elementary School, AR

At the Beach in the Summer

In the summer sun,
I'm at the beach and having fun,
With the water at my feet,
The ocean waves keep a steady beat.
Juliana Lane, Grade 4
South Topsail Elementary School, NC

Butterfly

It's a butterfly
She is all around a tree
She goes east to west
Monisha Amin, Grade 5
Sycamore Elementary School, GA

Fall!!!

Fall is neat.
Fall doesn't make me sleep.
Fall has pretty leaves.
Fall brings us a cool breeze.
Danielle Rae Turley, Grade 5
All Saints' Episcopal School, TN

Texeen

Who can outrun the fastest hawk yet turn on a blade of grass?
Who can live through a lightning shock and walk upon shards of glass?
What beast can vanquish the fiercest foe and take the breath from a thief?
Who is a vermin horde's woe and destroyer of their chief?
She will come back if there is trouble, she'll make them march on the double!
Born in the fierceness of a lightning storm and stayed all night with the lightning warm
To show how wise and strong and swift to leave every good place with a gift
That gift, a child, a leader none the less, she shows the animals they are blessed
Yet, everyone fears her, this ghost of the night, eyes shining black, fur shining white
This fox of terror, and love, and compassion, there is none fairer
The animals shout her name in unison though they shout for no man.
For you've come to a conclusion, it is none other than…Texeen Rath Juskazon!
Abigail Oneal, Grade 5
Trenton Middle School, MO

About Basketball

Basketball is a fun sport
that a lot of people love but not everybody.
Basketball is a sport when you shoot a ball into baskets
and every time you get the basketball into the basket
you will get two points.
If you miss the basket you won't get any points at all
and you compete with another team from a different school or team
and sometimes you go to different schools
so you can try to compete and try to win
at the end of the basketball season they hand out trophies.
Jennifer Hughes, Grade 6
Dyer Elementary & Jr High School, TN

Bats

Bats are different forms of mammals.
They fly and eat bugs.
There are many different types.
There are devil bats, fruit eating bats, and 2000 more.
Bats are big. They are tall.
Some are even small.
There are other kinds of them that live around the world.
There are many more to learn about for me, and all the boys and girls.
Da-Vontay Blake, Grade 5
Drayton Hall Elementary School, SC

Understanding Love

I've always wanted to be hugged and kissed,
and I don't ever want that time to be missed.
I've always heard people say "I love you,"
but they don't mean it, they don't even know what love is.
I've wanted to hold someone so tight,
but sometimes it just didn't seem right.
I don't really understand love.
It is complicated,
but I guess I will one day when I really have it.
Now, here I go back into the world, still wondering what love really is.
Bessie Rowell, Grade 6
Desoto Central School, MS

Dreams

I dream of being taken away
to a land of fairies and magic
carpets and powers beyond belief.
I can do things like fly and save the world,
I'm everyone's hero,
never wanting to wake up
and in the distance
I hear a voice,
my mom,
and then I wake up
and I'm just me again.

Luke Sikinyi, Grade 5
St Teresa's School, GA

Ode to Erasers

Perched on top of my pencil,
you wait for the moment
when I flip you around to my paper.
Your talent, not taken for granted,
is exercised each day.
Your ability to eliminate mistakes,
as if time was turned back.
Your rainbow-colored siblings
patiently wait in my bag until your pencil dulls.
Then it is their turn to be the wonder of my day.

Emily Ferguson, Grade 6
College View Middle School, KY

Shopping!

Mom called me and we are going to the mall.
I came running down the hall
And jumped in the car.
We headed for the Lonestar State.
The high heal converse shocks too.
We're all in the mixed up shoe store zoo.
I picked up the high heals and converses.
Then we left the zoo type store.
On the way home, I let out a snore,
Mom I said, that was a bore.

Kayla Lane, Grade 5
Cottonwood Public School, OK

Baseball

Going to the field.
Just smelling the feel of baseball.
Going to the plate.
Trying to hit a homerun.
Going to take the field.
Pitch, strike.
Just loving the feel of baseball.
Hitting, catching, outfield, second, first, short, third.
Just loving the feel of baseball.

Ben Latiolais, Grade 5
Arnaudville Elementary School, LA

My Imagination

Your imagination is only you.
Maybe you don't think the sky should be blue.
Maybe you don't think the grass should be green.
Or anything like that in between.
You are you and I am me.
Accept yourself and happy you'll be.

Lauren Lewis, Grade 4
West Elementary School, MO

My Puppies

Playing with my dogs
running, barking, jumping on me
hearing things that my family does not hear
My dog is blond
My other dog is reddish brownish
playing hide and seek
My dogs are trained
Having them since they were little bitty babies
The weekends
getting the tennis ball
throwing the ball
Them catching it
Katie always getting it first
Ally being stubborn not trying
giving them both a treat
dogs love company
Grandma coming
Them trying to jump on her
having to let out a big streak
NO!
But I will always love my puppies

Rachel Miller, Grade 4
Alvaton Elementary School, KY

My Cat

My parents said I could have a cat.
They said I could name him,
(but make it creative).

I decided to name him Christmas,
and when I called him by his name
he would come.

Once I was taking a walk,
and Christmas followed me
all the way to the mailbox.

When I sat down on the edge of the driveway,
he curled up next to me,
and we watched the sun.

As we sat on my driveway,
he let me pet his warm fur
until the sun went down.

Wrenn Kleinschmidt, Grade 5
American Heritage Academy, GA

Halloween Fun!
Trick-or-treat to get candy.
Harry Potter look-a-like.
Others are werewolves, ghosts,
phantoms, or Frankenstein.
They can be scary,
creepy, spooky, eerie, and gooey.
Halloween is a thrill!

Tara Beltrami, Grade 6
St Joseph Institute for the Deaf, MO

Wonder
Wonder is a lone wolf
With interest in his mind
Seeking what is not there
Or what is not heard

Ashlee Knowlton, Grade 5
Herbert J Dexter Elementary School, GA

My Bedroom
My favorite room
my bedroom.
looking out the window
seeing the kids playing.
Can I play, too?
Sitting in my rocking chair
reading *Ramona's World*.
Sitting at my vanity
putting on funky make up!
Friends coming over
laughing, screaming
and even whispering!
Saying things we don't really mean!
Laughing over it.
I LOVE MY ROOM!

Jordyn Christiansen, Grade 4
Alvaton Elementary School, KY

We Pray for Our Soldiers
America is the best place for me.
As the sun shines,
the soldiers creep.
No one knows what will happen.
Missing their family so much
Hoping the soldiers return safely.
If they don't the angels take them
as the others are watching.
They're in Iraq everything seems so bad
like the hot and sunny days
to the hot and humid nights.
As the days go by,
we pray that the soldiers
will return home safely.

Victoria Smith, Grade 6
Leonville Elementary School, LA

How Love Feels
Love is something so big so bold,
And guess what, it never gets old,
It's so powerful and so strong,
It's something you haven't outgrown.

Tyrahn M. Brown, Grade 5
Macedonia Elementary School, SC

Quilts
Passing them down one by one
Each could have symbols or markings
It means different things to others
You should always cherish them
The best part is to snuggle up in it
Quilts come in different sizes and colors
One day a quilt could be passed to you

Carlie Pierce, Grade 6
North Iredell Middle School, NC

Colonial Church
A nglican,
B ruton **C** hurch,
D emanded, **E** ngland,
F oreign,
G od,
H oly,
I mmigrant,
St. **J** ohns, **K** ids, **L** ord,
M ary, **N** oah,
O fficial, **P** uritan,
Q ueen, **R** omans, **S** aints, **T** rust,
U nited, **V** irginia,
W illiam, **X** ylophone, **Y** ell,
Z eal

Jeremy Webb, Grade 5
Alvaton Elementary School, KY

Baseball
Baseball, it is fun, we run bases
and hit the ball.
We win, we cheer,
if not we will frown,
baseball it is fun,
we catch we throw we get them out.

Baseball, it has a field,
it is sometimes a prison,
it is sometimes dangerous,
it sometimes hurts, crowd goes wild.

Baseball it is fun,
my mom and dad come to games,
and sometimes don't.

A.J. Metzger, Grade 6
Dyer Elementary & Jr High School, TN

My Maple Tree
In the fall he holds me tight
In his branchy arms
He throws me high into the sky
I land in the leaves
His big brown bear claws
Take me in like a mother
And her pups

I see him smile
So many colors on his face
The sweet memories we have
Are so joyful

Then one day
A cold breeze takes me away
I watch from the window
He frowns
Leaves fall as tears

I'll wait for you
Until next fall
When I see you smile once again
I'll miss you
My Maple Tree

Emma Fields, Grade 6
South Oldham Middle School, KY

Christmastime
It's the end of this year,
And the holidays are here,
It is time to start giving,
The best time to be living.

Lea Sanchez, Grade 4
South Topsail Elementary School, NC

Christmas
C elebrating
H oliday
R eunions
I s
S pectacular
T o
M e
A long with
S now

Jack Forte, Grade 4
St Bernard Academy, TN

Seashells
Sun beats over them
Water splashes on seashells
So brightly shining.

Kayle Randolph, Grade 4
Russell Babb Elementary School, OK

Look at the Snow

Look at the snow fall to the ground.
So light and fluffy it won't make a sound.
The children go play out in the snow.
For they all know
When they wake up the next morning with glee
They'll find great things under their tree.
The next day at school they'll all be gabbing.
Except one little girl who's name is Ali.
Ali is different from you and me.
She has no money to buy a tree.
She has no sled to play in the snow.
All the kids know.
There's something different about her.
She has no sled, she has no tree,
But why is she always full of glee?
One day Betty Ann took her by the hand and said to her,
"Why are you so cheerful and full of glee,
When you are so ugly?"
Ali replied,
"My friend, I have Jesus in me. Can't you see?"

Ginger Werner, Grade 6
Mount Zion Christian School, SC

Sports

I am a sports fan.
I like to play it or watch it whenever I can.

Baseball and basketball are the ones I like best.
Although, I am interested in all of the rest.

When I play baseball, I like to pitch.
Who knows? Someday, I may be rich!

But I don't play for money. I play for fun!
Especially with my friends when we've just won!

It's nice to have a uniform that is cool and hip.
But most important of all is good sportsmanship.

Kendall Young, Grade 4
St Mary Cathedral Elementary School, MO

The Noun World

You see nouns everywhere.
A noun is a person, place or thing.
They are also thoughts, ideas, and feelings.
Did you know you are a noun?
There are many different types of nouns.
They are proper as April, common as mom.
There are plural and singular nouns.
Singular is one; plural is more than one.
Abstract and concrete.
Singular possessive and plural possessive.
They are all nouns.
Nouns are all over the place.

Kelsey Hall, Grade 5
Saffell Street Elementary School, KY

Whiskas

Died July 24, 2004

Old yellow cat,
With amber eyes
Though you have gone away

I think about you all the time
And how we used to play

Old yellow cat,
My furry friend
It's hard to understand

That you're no longer here with me
But in a better land

Alyssa Katherine Harris, Grade 6
Haynes Academy for Advanced Studies, LA

Big and Strong

I am big and fast
I can knock you out of this world
I am deadly horrible
My vortex can swing you to New York City
I am furious and fast
I turn like a twirling roller coaster
I am powerful like a wild dog
I am unstoppable
I am a twirling tornado

Kelsea Elizabeth Barton, Grade 5
Pembroke Elementary School, NC

I Remember

I remember when the TVs turned on
I remember when the Twin Towers were gone
I remember the panic and frustration
I remember the Pentagon
I remember hearing "It's gone"
I remember seeing them go down
I remember no sleep that night
I remember that terrible fright
I remember that nothing was right
I remember the hurrying in the halls
I remember so many calls
I remember seeing it happen
I remember that sad, sad day
I remember the lives that were lost, that I must say
I remember the brave souls, that were saved
I remember that all was quiet
I remember the sight of it
I remember when it hit
I remember it
I remember 9/11

Hallie Sartain, Grade 6
Bellwood Discovery School, TN

Fall

bright, colorful, leaves
got to rake all the leaves up
we jump in the piles
Thomas Sykes, Grade 4
East Jones Elementary School, MS

Dragonfly

Dragonfly,
A fairy.
Daintily jumping
From earth to ground.
Whizzing past your head,
Throwing fairy dust.
Dragonfly,
A fairy.

Emma Clinch, Grade 5
Austin Elementary School, GA

Snow

I am a snowman
I wonder if I will ever meet someone
I hear kids laughing
I see snow falling
I want to have a buddy
I am a snowman

I pretend the snow is everywhere
I feel excellent
I touch the white fluffy snow
I worry the snow will stop
I cry if I will melt
I am a snowman

I understand someday I will melt
I say that snow is everything
I dream of having fun in the snow
I hope I will be famous
I try to have fun
I am a snowman
Melisa Dedic, Grade 4
Wohlwend Elementary School, MO

Mockingbird

The mockingbird is a mimic.
He can copy other sounds.

Sounds like cars and trucks.
They sometimes act like clowns.

He can mimic the goldfinch,
The purple finch, and the robin.

Listening to mockingbirds
Just gets my heart throbbing.
Wade Creech, Grade 4
Northeast Baptist School, LA

My Goat

My goat's name is Jimmy Lee, he lives on a farm and eats grass every day.
Kids come and see him every day after school.
They come and see him and feed him.
They enjoy seeing him.
The goat is happy to see them every day and see their smiling faces.
Erica Webb, Grade 4
Brilliant Elementary School, AL

Turquoise

Turquoise looks like the winter sky as the snow falls
Turquoise feels like fun on a cool day looking at animals in the clouds
Turquoise tastes like the new ice-cream flavor down the street
Turquoise smells like fresh air on a cool November breeze
Turquoise sounds like the wind howling at your ears
Turquoise is the heart and soul of fun and freedom
Morgan Fryman, Grade 5
Geggie Elementary School, MO

Softball

I love Softball, it is by far my favorite sport;
Hitting home runs, catching fly balls, playing new positions all fall in my court.

Putting on a uniform and getting in my zone;
are all part of this sport along with listening to my coaches tone.

Sometimes he speaks calmly, but sometimes he screams,
although most of the time he tells me to do the right things.

I love Softball, it is by far my favorite sport;
whether or not I have a good game fall in my own court.
Madison DeBord, Grade 5
Paint Lick Elementary School, KY

Thanksgiving Day

Thanksgiving
Fresh turkey from the oven
Delicious apple pie aroma circulating in the air
Come and get it! The ham is done
Stuffing with gravy poured all over it
Hugging my family and saying I love you and have a good evening
Thanksgiving

Ashley Crawford, Grade 5
Sullivan Elementary School, TN

Levi

It stands for responsible, nice, smart and a hard worker.
It's the number 100! It means a perfect paper.
It's the sky, the water, and all the favorite stuff.
It's going to White Water with my church.
It's my granny who taught me to breathe better when I swim.
She explained it to me while we drove in her car.
Levi
I believe church is important because it helps you learn about God,
Jesus, and Moses.

Levi Carter, Grade 4
Vanoss Elementary School, OK

Friends

Friends are very good to have around when you have no one else to depend on, they are there when no one else is. Whenever you need anything friends will always be by your side. When you have friends put your trust in them, real friends will always have your back. A real friend can tell you lots and lots of secrets. If you can be a real friend make it happen.

Zaquoria Jefferson, Grade 5
East Marion Elementary School, MS

Xena

Sweet as sugar.
As soft as a teddy bear.
She is the sweetest horse I have ever met, I swear.
As the great-granddaughter of Dreamfinder,
She most definitely takes after her dad and her great-grandfather.
She is the most beautiful animal I ever laid my eyes on.
With good looks, a stunning appearance and lovable attitude nobody can resist.
She definitely caught my eye, when she was only a yearling.
Like her father, she is a muscular and has a big white blanket settled over her back,
As snow settles over the ground.
As she breathes out a sweet-scented breath,
I inhale deeply and once again recognize the beauty of her.
The feeling of her soft muzzle against my shoulder makes me warm inside and makes me love her even more.
As she calls to me from across the pasture, I can't help but smile and run over to her.
Like rain beating on a windshield, her hooves thunder over the ground;
As she races around with the other two-year olds.
Xena fills my heart with so much love that every time I see her,
I can't help but love her even more.

Isabel Moran, Grade 6
River Trail Middle School, GA

Fall

The best about fall is the smell of turkey, collards, venison, and duck. They raise my heart beat pump by pump! The best noises of fall are hearing the dirt bikes and four wheelers starting their engines. Hearing the hunter hunt and the sweet smell of the roaring, crackling fire smoke and the smell of marshmallows.

A couple of the best fall things are the tastes of pecans, and the sweet taste of maple syrup. And the taste of pumpkin pie. Apple and pecan pies. A thing I like is helping my Uncle Bill around the farm. And fishing in a canoe catching fish. That's my fall.

Josh Whitmore, Grade 5
Palmetto Christian Academy, SC

The Ballad of Hurricane Katrina

Evacuating a fearful town, before the rain came pouring down.
Adults and children and their pets, left the town to not get wet.
The left-behind families filled with fear, as the killer storm still drew near.

Lightning crashed and thunder boomed as flooding waters filled the rooms.
Wind blew houses, cars, and trees; it was a horrible sight for all to see.
Shrapnel and debris flew everywhere while fright and uncertainty filled the air.

It demolished houses and windowpanes, the destructive, massive hurricane.
Soon the terror came to an end, families emerged from their broken house and
Realized that they needed help and fast, who knew how long their few supplies would last?

People came and cleared the debris, and they set the surviving beings free.
New Orleans was cleared and rebuilt, after removing all of the rubble and silt.
New Orleans rose again as people saw their fabulous celebration of Mardi Gras.

Rachel Cannata, Grade 6
River Trail Middle School, GA

5th Graders

5 graders are the best
We study for the test
We study every night
To get the answers right.
If we pass all the test for the day
We get to go outside and play!

Travis Leek, Grade 5
Walton Verona Elementary School, KY

Veteran

V aliant efforts appreciated
E xult your bravery for us
T errorism will not be allowed
E ngulf the enemy
R epay for your service
A ble to protect us
N ation united

Wade Paul, Grade 4
Cherokee Elementary School, AR

Religion

God created all of the animals
And I am very blessed
Because I have six pets
And they are the very best.

Keegan Marchese, Grade 4
Holy Rosary Academy, LA

School Backwards

At my school they do everything
sdrawkcab
Recess at 03:7
hcnuL at 00:8
Art's ta 8:30
Then's myg at 00:10
htaM at 45:01
2nd recess at 11:30
(Finally I get the gnilleps right)
kcanS ta 03:2
It's so confusing my head spins
Os sometimes I write
sdrawkcab

Aidan Sokol, Grade 5
Prince of Peace Catholic School, SC

Ole Miss

Ole Miss is the best,
They're better than all the rest,
They hit, they run,
They tackle sometimes just for fun,
Ole Miss is better than all the rest.
Touchdown!

Emma Henley, Grade 6
Desoto Central School, MS

Black Cat

A tiny black cat
Was sitting in a tree
Along came a fat cat
And bit him on the knee
It hurt just a little
And he said "Owwee"
What bites a black cat?
In the month of Halloween!

Hunter Myers, Grade 4
Robert E Lee Elementary School, TN

Pumpkins

P umpkins
U nder
M y
P orch
K idnapping
I nnocent
N eighbors

Cody Wilson, Grade 6
Martin Elementary School, WV

The Beat of Our Hearts

The beat of your heart
Is the beat of my heart
And I got a huge feeling
That they shouldn't be apart
My beat your beat
Our beat is one
Together we can have a lot of fun
My beat is the lock
Your beat is the key
You open my heart
To another beat

Taylor Vinson, Grade 6
Blessed Teresa of Calcutta School, MO

School

School is so confusing and wild,
You have your populars, your geeks,
And the ones in between.
People are always being mean.
Go get the latest scoop.
What's the new kid's name?
Who got the new shoes?
People always know the news.
Who's the loser?
Who's the geek?
Something changes every week,
But that's what school is all about.
Hanging with your friends
And chilling out.

Alexandria Sneed, Grade 6
Desoto Central School, MS

Christmas

Christmas
Holly, jolly
Decorating, wrapping
Feeling very, very merry
Holiday

Kyle Collier, Grade 6
St Joseph Institute for the Deaf, MO

Homework

When I get home I have work to do
But I don't like to do it do you
Even though I don't like to do it
I finally get to it
And when I get finished
I'm glad I did it
And I want to celebrate
But I don't want the neighbors awake
Because it's so late!

Derek Watkins, Grade 5
Walton Verona Elementary School, KY

An Ode to Florida

Ode to Florida, with your hot, blue skies.
The weather,
the sun,
the laughter,
the fun.
My relatives, and friends,
the hot, summer sand,
Ode to my Florida,
my big and warm friend!!!

Cole McCubbin, Grade 5
Walton Verona Elementary School, KY

Veteran

V ery brave
E xcellent American Hero
T ogether they fight for freedom
E conomy devastated
R eady to be attacked
A ble to stand their ground
N ever back down

Steven Tyler Dobbs, Grade 4
Cherokee Elementary School, AR

Valentine Senses

I see people handing out cards
I smell freshly baked cookies
I hear Valentine songs being played
I taste sprinkled sugar on brownies
I touch a Valentine card from my friend
Valentine Senses

Kassie Compton, Grade 5
Sullivan Elementary School, TN

My Teacher

My teacher is the best,
Not at all like the rest.
She's sweet and kind to me
And anyone she may see.

My friends complain a lot
I just don't see why.
They whine and whine and whine
So much it could make her cry.

With the learning games we play,
She makes it really fun for us.
She makes us smile,
Each and every day.

Her eyes are oh so gentle,
While her spirit is very calm.
With her warm, loving smile
She shields me from the storm.

Brandon Noble, Grade 6
Haynes Academy for Advanced Studies, LA

Mom

My mom is allergic to everything,
She says she gets it from Aunt Ping.
I can't have a pet,
Because she's allergic to them when they get wet.
I am not allowed to go to the zoo,
Even if I cry boo hoo.
I really think she is being unfair,
It is not my fault she's allergic to hair.
My mom is allergic to everything,
She says she gets it from Aunt Ping.

Daniel Pannell, Grade 6
Desoto Central School, MS

Caterpillar, Butterfly

Caterpillar, crawling along
Caterpillar, small, slimy worm
Caterpillar, so cute, so green
Now it's time to make a small cocoon
Butterfly, now you are
Butterfly, spread your wings and soar
Butterfly, time to travel the world
From one stage to the next, you are so cute, so beautiful
What is your species, from one to the next you go,
We shall call you caterfy, a beautiful caterpillar, butterfly
Caterfy, what places do you wander
Caterfy, from land to sky, however shall I find you
Caterpillar, how do you figure out which one, to crawl or fly
    Caterpillar, butterfly,
      Caterfy

Sandra Steiber, Grade 5
Walton Verona Elementary School, KY

Tennessee

Tennessee is the place to be
There's no better place for me.

Memphis gave us Elvis
He could really shake his pelvis!

Nashville gave us country songs
They make you want to sing along.

Don't forget the Chattanooga Choo Choo
A train ride is fun for me and you.

Knoxville's Rocky Top and Orange Nation
Are the best in my estimation.

Tennessee will always be home
No matter how far away I roam.

Elizabeth Thompson, Grade 4
Sequoyah Elementary School, TN

Abraham Lincoln

Abraham Lincoln with his big towering hat,
Slim and tall with not an ounce of fat.
His shining black hair hid under his brim,
Except on his face with his beard and grin.
He kept our country as one and combined,
Although the South wanted to secede,
Had they lost their mind?
He was the one who freed all the slaves,
And established freedom in the United States.
His leadership qualities stood out from the crowd,
When he shared his motivating speeches, very clear and loud.
He was the sixteenth president and one of the best,
And to all other presidents, to beat him is the test.

Jeffrey Mullavey, Grade 6
River Trail Middle School, GA

My Good Friend

My dog is my good friend
Her favorite toy is a ball
That we bought at the mall
She likes to sleep a lot
She doesn't bark or bite
She's a Wire Fox Terrier
She may not protect our house like a barrier
But she is my friend to the end
And I love her so.

Taylor Grandinetti, Grade 5
St Teresa's School, GA

Autumn's Life

The lovely colors,
Wonderful thing about life,
Isn't it pleasant?

Madison Kimel, Grade 4
Briarwood Christian Elementary School, AL

I'm a Military Child

When my dad must go, I feel sad but I know that he will come home.
When my dad is about to go I ask him what if something bad might happen.
He tells me that I could never lose him because he is in my heart and he will always
Be part of who I will become so I should worry not.

When my dad goes some days seem very hard, but I am a military child.
So when I have scary thoughts, I just remember that my dad is the reason I can say I'm free.
He fights the enemy to keep our country free.

When my dad must go, my mom sometimes cries and I remind her that I am a military child
And she is a military wife so she doesn't have to worry because my dad is gone to win the fight.

Marissa Guevera, Grade 4
Walker Intermediate School, KY

Pointe Shoe Pink

Pointe shoe Pink looks like my Pointe shoes hanging up at home.
Pointe shoe Pink sounds like someone knocking on the front door when my shoes hit the floor.
Pointe shoe Pink smells like sweat off the dancers when they walk out of the room.
Pointe shoe Pink taste like a strawberry jolly rancher when I put it in my mouth for a snack.
Pointe shoe Pink feels like a pain of blisters popping on my feet.
Pointe shoe Pink is the color of my Pointe shoes
Pointe shoe Pink is the knocking noise that my Pointe shoes make when they hit the ground
Pointe shoe Pink is the sweat smell that comes off my feet when I take my shoes off.
Pointe shoe Pink is the taste of a perfect, delicious strawberry jolly rancher that I put in my mouth after practice.
Pointe shoe Pink is the pain of blisters that pop on my feet.

Rachel Ford, Grade 5
Cool Spring Elementary School, NC

I Am From

I am from helping out on Grandma's farm
And discovering kittens in the barn.
I am from working toward my writing dreams
And sewing pillow seams.

I am from having a variety of friends…
To all of us sticking together until the end.
I am from being the youngest out of three
With two annoying brothers always picking on me.

I am from cheerful summer days with my dogs
And singing all alone…sad songs.
I am from trying to move on when friends move away
By going on with life's activities day-to-day.

I am from hiding under a pine tree when I'm angry or sad
To expressing my feelings to Mom and Dad.
I am from "crying a river" to my cousin, Spencer, "building a bridge," and "getting over it."
I am also from getting in trouble, being grounded, and having to sit.

But, most of all…
I am from lots of love, having hopeful dreams,
And also from possessing great memories of many things.

Alyssa Martin, Grade 5
Burgin Independent School, KY

Halloween

Halloween is one of my favorite holidays,
When all the kids come out to play.
Witches, witches everywhere,
While all the ghosts come out to scare.
While the vampires and ghouls are passing out candy.
All I want is candy,
Fruity, Chewy, Sweet, and Sour,
Candy.
Doesn't it sound good.
Halloween is so great.
I just can't wait to go and say,
"Trick or Treat"
And get me a bag full of,
Fruity, Chewy, Sweet, and Sour,
Candy.

Tori Fizer, Grade 4
New Highland Elementary School, KY

Football Game

Sounds like the cheerleaders cheering
Smells like hamburgers and hotdogs cooking
Looks like football players doing their best
Tastes like nachos and cake
Feels like the cool football weather.

Ashlyn B. Boyd, Grade 5
Briarwood Christian Elementary School, AL

Little Stars

Trinkle trinkle little stars how wonderful are you.
I look upon you like mice with cheese.
Don't ever leave me please.
So while I let my eyes fall down I'll say,
"Until next time my special little stars."

Martha Acosta, Grade 5
Franklin Elementary School, OK

Christmas

Christmas time has come just right,
when snow came down it was a beautiful sight!

My grandmother made a potato pie,
and my uncle had on a Christmas tie.

Everyone there was filled with joy.
My little cousin Kyron played with his toy.

My mother said it was time to go.
We grabbed our stuff and went out the door.

The kids were running around making a snowman,
watching the snow melt in their hand.

We were going to grandma's house; we were on our way
to go wish everybody a Merry Christmas Day.

Nicole Faison, Grade 6
St Mark Elementary School, SC

My First Tooth Was Pulled

I pulled my tooth just yesterday,
And ouch was all I could say!
The tooth fairy came last night,
And left some money in the twilight.

When I woke up this morning,
I didn't see the tooth fairy.
But she left five dollars while rain was pouring,
And back to her castle my tooth did she carry.

A prized possession of mine,
That I will share with her.
Although I will never see it again,
I will forever cherish the day I lost my first tooth.

Olivia Grace Howell, Grade 4
Evangelical Christian School, TN

People

Some people fight
Some people bite
And some get along just right.
Lots of people are a mess
Few like to confess.
Some brush their hair
But some just don't care.
And some people are weird
Some people are funny
Or look like a bunny.
But each of us are different
And everyone is special in their own unique, magnificent way.

Abigale Roth, Grade 6
Poplar Bluff 5th & 6th Center, MO

Ode to Butter

He sits in the chair,
waiting for me,
brown-orange, with cream-yellow mixed in.
He looks up at me,
and is soft to the touch.
He yowls at closed doors,
and sleeps too much.

He doesn't like Cookie,
he loves chicken and fish treats.
He's worn out at the end of the day
from jumpin' around.
He's great,
though he sometimes bites.
But at the end of the day,
when I go to bed,
I know he's right there,
next to my head.

Amanda Hagan, Grade 6
College View Middle School, KY

Veteran

V eteran's Day we love you
E veryone's so sad
T o care for the ones who stand
E ven the ones who love you
R ights can sometimes hurt you
A merica we stand
N ever we will stop Veterans Day

Amie Reilly, Grade 4
Cherokee Elementary School, AR

My Picture Perfect Mom

I know my mother is an angel
Sent from heaven up above
For when her eyes gaze into mine
They show unending love.

Another way I know this
Is that she works constantly
To clothe and feed, and care for
Our whole family.

Though she's very busy
She has time for me
A game of catch, ping pong, or Clue
Just so you know, Mom, I love you.

Hayley Henley, Grade 5
Montessori School North Little Rock, AR

Cowboy

Cowboy
Short, soft
Playful, cuddly, barks
Loving, happy, sad, upset
My dog

Andrea Glass, Grade 6
Edmonton Elementary School, KY

Morgan

Morgan Mansell
brownish-blonde, green-eyed
play, dance, swim
I like playing soccer.
Morgan Mansell

Morgan Mansell, Grade 4
East Jones Elementary School, MS

Soccer Coach

Randy Whittaker
For the blue and white
Yelling and coaching
Louder than thunder
I will never forget him.

Addie Chaloupka, Grade 5
Salem Elementary School, AR

Flag

F lying high in the sky
L et us remember
A lways our freedom
G ive it respect, you and I

Madison Currie, Grade 4
Coleman Elementary School, OK

Merry Christmas

M erry Christmas
E very second's fun
R eindeer
R udolph
Y eah it's Christmas

C ookies
H iding in the snow
R iding in the snow
I love to come over
S now
T is the season
M aking cakes
A Christmas tree
S anta Claus

Ciera Eastmead, Grade 4
Tamassee-Salem Elementary School, SC

Rylee

My sister, Rylee,
Comes dashing through the door,
Shrieking out my name.
"You stop!"
"No!"
Darting for me like I'm a target.

Reece Triller, Grade 5
St Vincent Elementary School, MO

A Pencil's Life

When I am born,
I am the tallest I can get.
As I get older,
I get,
Dull, sharp,
Dull, sharp,
Over and over again.
I live for a week or two,
In Mrs. Lanier's class.
Or a month or two in another.
When I die,
I am short and dull,
And my head is all used up.
Then my life ends,
As I am thrown away.

Thornton Drury, Grade 5
Rainbow Elementary School, AL

Where I'm From

I'm from Barbie dolls, from softball.
I'm from building forts in the woods.
I'm from Kiss and Pat Benatar
From Parker Stevenson.
I'm from Tootsie Rolls
From Hardy Boys.
I'm from jokes of all sorts.
I am from being a teacher
And from big families and lots of love.
I am from "Suck it Up"
And "Come on slow poke."
I'm from "Trip man."
From all of this, there is me!

Jessie Norris, Grade 6
College View Middle School, KY

Thanksgiving

T he things I am thankful for are:
H ot food on the table each night
A lso friends and family
N ecklaces and jewelry
K ittens and doggies
S weets, candy, and other sugary things
G od, Jesus, and the church
I mportant things like weddings and love
V iolins and other forms of music
I am thankful for every day
N ever thankful for bad things
G ive thanks for all these things today!

Madison Pierce, Grade 4
Tamassee-Salem Elementary School, SC

The Teacher

The teacher.
the teacher shall touch my soul,
for He is in control.
The teacher.

The teacher.
Whom will provide for me?
He is in control can't you see.
The teacher.

The teacher.
He is in my heart and mind,
Can't you see He's very kind,
The teacher.

Sin lieth at the door,
come and teach me Lord;
for I will listen to your word,
The teacher.

Caroline Rhea, Grade 5
Providence Academy, TN

The Alien Attacks

In the night I get ready for bed,
Then I lay down my sweet little head.
I close my eyes and fall asleep,
But not before long, I awoke with a shriek!
I heard thunder clashing as I looked around,
Before long, I noticed the house had fallen down.
I ran outside, and I went into town,
And what I saw was lightning striking the ground.
I felt a vibration, a tremor, a shake,
And what happened next was a great earthquake!
The ground started cracking, the buildings did fall,
Then what happened next was the strangest of all!
What started was a hole in the ground,
Back went everyone in town.
A pod came up higher, oh my
Something came out that looked squishy as pie.
It was an alien, oh but it looked weak,
It looked terrible, horrible, tired, and meek.
But it pulled out a ray gun and shot everyone in town,
It aimed at me and pulled the trigger down,
I guess you won't be seeing me around.

Jeffery Littleton, Grade 5
Holsenbeck Elementary School, GA

My Friends

I have Jean Ann and Casie who love me so much
Allyson and Tori who love to cheer me up
Molly and Nia who love to go places
Kelsey and Katie who make silly faces
And of course me and Christina, who like to have fun
Those are my friends I love so much

Danielle Kelly, Grade 6
Brogden Middle School, NC

Hair

I have red hair,
But I'm not from Ireland

I have blonde hair,
But I'm not that dumb

I have brown hair,
But I'm not that pretty

I have black hair,
But I'm not a Goth

I have gray hair,
But I'm not old

I have green hair,
But I don't pick my nose.

Genevieve Servoss, Grade 5
St Thomas More School, NC

The Invincible Tornado

I cause devastation, I am furious, I am invincible
I am deadly, I am huge, I am powerful than you!
I cause many kinds of injuries
I am fearful. I am twirling with furious winds
I am devastating to humans
My vortex is bigger than the city of New York
My winds roar in the day and night
You may never know when I come
I sound like a rushing train
No one can stop me so don't try
I can throw you more than five miles
and make you touch the sky
I am a tornado…
I am your worst nightmare!!!

Brett Godwin, Grade 5
Pembroke Elementary School, NC

Hope Is Growing

Hope is a garden.
Hope is a tulip blooming in spring.
Hope is beauty.

Hope is a package with what you wanted inside.
Hope is a duck learning to swim, hoping to get it right.
Hope is when a baby is born.
Hope is the whistle of the wind.
Hope is a garden sleeping 'til spring.

Joel Brakel, Grade 5
Breitling Elementary School, AL

Raymond

Raymond is my cat's name
Sometimes he's not so tame

Orange and white he shall be
He likes to play with me

Bouncing, pouncing and hiding behind chairs
Raymond the cat has long furry hair

It hurts when he bites
He's asking for a fight

I put a sock on
To protect my palm

He bites my hand hard
And puts me on guard

When we get tired
We sleep by the fire

Raymond the cat is my best friend
other than Shaina, Sarah, Momma, and Ben.

Baylee Warnke, Grade 5
Canute Elementary School, OK

Bird

Bird, oh, pretty bird
Flying so gracefully
Landing in a tree
Helina Parker, Grade 5
Sycamore Elementary School, GA

Sunset

This is a place of wonder
melted in with dreams.
The sky blended with fire
where so much is to be seen.

Calm or alive?
No one really seems to care.
But, when it goes down,
you wish it was still up there.

Red, yellow,
pink, green,
you don't seem to notice
when you become a preteen.

Things as little as that
don't really seem to matter.
All we want to do
is chit and chatter.

So, next time it's up there,
just look up, and you'll see,
just how lit up
the sky seems to be.
Sadie Alexis Hill, Grade 6
College View Middle School, KY

A Grain of Sand

I'm a grain of sand
On a hot summer day.
I'm not like the others
In any particular way.

It doesn't matter
If I'm special inside.
When I could get washed away
With one simple tide.

I get stepped on every day,
By hot burning feet.
No one pays me any attention,
I hide myself underneath.

So often I feel
That nobody will ever understand.
They don't know what it's like to be me,
For I'm just a grain of sand.
Shuchi Goyal, Grade 6
River Trail Middle School, GA

Fire Fear

People fear fire; as much as they fear a mean bully in a middle school.
Fire, like a hot day in the middle of July.
Like a big ball of chaos that can damage somebody in a second.
Clearing everything in its path.
Fire is like a nuclear bomb, setting off at any time, and anywhere.
Fire stings as much as a belly flop into the pool.
It is hated as much as a person poking you too many times.
Destroying everything around and in front of it, like a bulldozer.
Leaving nothing behind as if it were a brave warrior.
Like the scariest mask on Halloween.
What a frightening thing fire is.
Sydney Williams, Grade 6
River Trail Middle School, GA

I Remember Squeaky

I remember Squeaky…
Brown fur, little eyes, squeaky voice, little nose

I remember Squeaky…
Sleeping on my pillow, playing in his cage, eating, crawling on my back

I remember Squeaky…
Exploring, watching TV, squeaking all the time, passing away

I remember Squeaky…

Byron Mitchell, Grade 5
Sycamore Elementary School, GA

Halloween

This is the night.
    The night of fright.
When all the ghosts and goblins
    Come out to play with our dreams.
        Filling them with the grim or fright.

This is the night.
    A night of scared children.
Wandering around the corner for candy.
    Seeing witches and werewolves when their parents can't.
        This is the night, that people come to scare us.

This is the night.
    The night of witches and more witches.
One named Winifred, who comes stealing the lives of children one by one.
    The black flame candle marks her time here.
Winifred's time is near.

    For all who think this is just a night of *Hocus Pocus*,
And when you feel the wind running through her hair,
    And you see the shadows of the moon at night,
And you sense the feeling of fright,
    You know that tonight is Halloween!
Abagail Meche, Grade 5
Arnaudville Elementary School, LA

My Cat Jasmine

I have a cat, its name is Jasmine.
She likes to take a nap and she's kind of fat.
She likes to play with a ball that I got at the mall.
All day, all night, she tries to fly in the sky.

Sometimes I try to do what she does…
And that's what makes her happy as a puppy.
We play all day, all night, in the sky by each other.

Alacyn Bridges, Grade 4
Tazewell/New Tazewell Elementary School, TN

Good Cake

I like cake with frosting, with frosting.
It has sugar with some flour, some flour.
You mix it with water and then you have cake, have cake.
You put frosting on the cake.
It doesn't matter what flavor, what flavor.
And then you have cake, have cake.

Jacob Shipley, Grade 4
Tazewell/New Tazewell Elementary School, TN

I Am Thankful

I am thankful for God
Or I would not be living,
For trees
Or I would not have air,
Books so I can read
And games to play.

I am grateful for my
Mom and dad
And schools to learn.

I would like to learn about
Being a police officer.
I like them because
They are nice and
Keep us safe.

Jevon Rogers, Grade 4
Lee A Tolbert Community Academy, MO

The Flag

The flag of our country,
    So proud and free,
'Cause the war you see
    Was not a pretty sight.

Every day and every night,
    The patriots will fight.
For our freedom and liberty.
    For our flag, you see,
Has fifty stars and thirteen stripes.

Our flag is a grand old flag!

Josh Toler, Grade 4
Heartland High School and Academy, MO

Family

F ellowship with
A ppreciation of
M y family, The Morgans/Graves/Wheeler's
I nspires me to
L ead by doing good deeds
Y ear round

Tairra Alise Wheeler, Grade 6
Nathaniel Hawthorne Elementary School, MO

Stardom

Stardom can be very tough
and when achieved, you get enough.
JoJo, Ashley, Zack, Ally, and AJ,
it's very tough, yes, they all say.
Paparazzi, reporters, and the fans,
people you don't know, man, oh, man!
They'll play a joke; they'll play a trick.
Sometimes I want to hit them with a stick!
Yes, stardom can be very cool
with big screen TVs and a swimming pool,
And, of course, there's lots of cash,
for stardom means having quite a stash.
Okay, okay, stardom's not so bad,
but trust me, it can make you go mad.

Kellie Freise, Grade 5
Immanuel Lutheran School, MO

All About Me

School is here, school is there.
School is everything you see.
It might be a little more fair if I told you more about me.

I transferred from Alaska.
"I'm cold," is all you'd hear.
Now I'm in Alabama,
And I'm having a party this year.

I am ten and a half years old.
Blonde, short, and sweet.
I sleep on a bed that is cold,
And it doesn't cover my feet.

When I first got to this state, I was a little afraid.
But then I learned to skate and now it's like a parade.
This year my tree is pink.
And yes I'm talking about my Christmas tree.
But now I've go to think, "Do I stick the ornaments on me?"

Now you know more about me,
And I want to know about you.
When I do, I will shout with glee,
Just like you should have done too.

Baylee McClellan, Grade 4
Stephens Elementary School, AL

Getting My New Puppy

The Christmas before last
Twenty five days felt like eternity
Upstairs shivering in my bed
Brrr!
Run downstairs
Try to wake up mom and dad
Slip on their shoes. Woosh!
Brother and sister
Come in the hall
We join them
Tired as fog, dad
We all went into the den
Ruff!
We see a puppy,
Pick her up
She barked and played around
She's as sweet as a piece of candy.
We looked at our other present
But, we mostly played with her.
Before we knew it the day was over.

Clark Hickerson, Grade 6
Beck Academy, SC

Obrie

Obrie Scarbrough
brown, white
talk, jump, draw
I like to rabbit hunt.
Obrie Scarbrough

Obrie Scarbrough, Grade 4
East Jones Elementary School, MS

Rainbow

Colors radiant
Beautiful hues in blue sky
Arching end to end

Clay Fowler, Grade 4
Broadway Elementary School, NC

The Colorful Rainbow

As the raindrop sprinkled down
and splashed on my skin drip, drop,
it slowly hit the ground in sheets.
The clear raindrop slowly slides
down my face onto the ground.
It became foggy.
Through the dew and mist
there was a beautiful rainbow,
but from behind the clouds
the bright shiny sun came out.
There was just a mist in sky
so that you can see the rainbow.

Lauren Searcy, Grade 5
Saffell Street Elementary School, KY

Horses

Some horses are really fast
Some horses are really slow
Some horses eat grass
Some horses really glow

Ashton Baggs, Grade 4
Horace Mann Elementary School, OK

Throwing the Cast Net

Carefully fold it
Bring it back and cast it out
The fish are pulled in.

Houston Butler, Grade 5
Our Lady of Fatima School, MS

Fall

In the fall, we learned education.
Sometimes we had a little frustration.
My teachers are quite pleasant,
They might even get a little fall present.
We may have some tears,
And maybe some fears.
But when we do,
We will all come through.
The trees stopped growing,
But just for now,
And in the spring,
They'll come to town!
That was my poem, about the fall,
I hoped you liked it, one and all!

Carmen Granger, Grade 6
Brogden Middle School, NC

My Dog Sandy

My dog Sandy.
Is as sweet as candy.
She loves to play and run.
We have lots of fun.

She loves to play with her toys.
She also loves to play with boys.
She loves to sleep on pillows.
She loves to eat marshmallows.

She loves to watch TV.
She also loves to ride on an ATV.
She loves to bark and bark.
At anything in the dark.

She sleeps with me in my bed.
She snuggles close to my head.
She is the greatest dog ever.
I hope she stays with me forever.

Dakota Wesley, Grade 5
Joann Walters Elementary School, AR

Silent

Silent cold water
Splashing on the sandy beach
As silent as can be.

Connor Eckstein, Grade 5
Bonaire Elementary School, GA

My Life

My life is neat,
My life is sweet,
In my life I like to eat.
I like to swing,
I like to sing,
I wish I have a ring
I wish I was cool,
I like to play pool,
I like to go to school.
My life is fun,
I like the sun,
Now my poem is done.

Trisha Hassebrock, Grade 4
Christian Life Academy, TN

Wondering

Wondering about the secrets kept,
Wondering if mine are told,
Wondering if my heart is broke,
Or if yours just turned cold,
Wondering why my eyes,
Seem to always fill with tears,
Wondering what could have happened,
Over the wasted years,
Wondering if dreams,
Could possibly come true,
Wondering if the future,
Holds room for two,
Wondering if everything,
Was always meant to be,
Wondering why I just cry
When you are close to me.

Darby McCarthy, Grade 6
Bellwood Discovery School, TN

Halloween

H aunted house
A black cat
L oud and spooky noises
L ots of pumpkins
O nly once a year
W itches
E veryone dresses up
E ating candy till you're sick
N ever dress up too spooky

Emily Hayes, Grade 4
West Elementary School, MO

Heaven

Looks like a city gleaming with gold
Sounds like harps playing real low
Tastes like the bread that God shared
Smells like nature floating everywhere
Feels like you're floating up in the air

Blake Coggins, Grade 5
Briarwood Christian Elementary School, AL

My Friend

My friend has brown hair.
We love to share. She loves to swing.
We both have a red bed.
We both have a cat named Pat.

My friend is nice.
Her name is Sadie. Mine is Katie.
Her last name is Mill. Mine is Hill.
We both love to read in bed.

We both love limes because they're a dime.
We spent a dollar on a collar for our pet cat.
We go to the same school.

I talk English, she talks Spanish.
We both hate math.
Our mom's names are Marisa and Melissa.
But no matter what we're best friends.

Katie Hill, Grade 4
Tazewell/New Tazewell Elementary School, TN

Football

I scream and cheer each Friday
When I see the Wildcats play
The team kicks off and how they run
Like a bullet that is shot from a gun
They run ten yards and get a tackle
The running back slips away and runs like a jackal
The game is a hard fought battle
The quarterback they cannot rattle
He runs the distance and makes the touchdown
And that is the best game in the whole town!

Riley Darden, Grade 4
Robert E Lee Elementary School, TN

December

December
At night I hear bells ringing.
I see presents at Christmas morning.
I smell cookies on Christmas.
I taste chocolate chip cookies on Christmas Eve.
I touch presents on Christmas day.
December

Austin Smith, Grade 4
Tamassee-Salem Elementary School, SC

Snow, White, Winter

Snow falls down
On Christmas eve night, like a baby's blanket all snug and tight
As we wake in the morning
To the glory of the light
Coming from the angel
Up top of the tree
And mistletoe hung as we can see
We open presents
From under the tree
That Santa has brought
For you and me
The snowman outside
Is looking quite dreary
He's beginning to melt
Like a popsicle in May
Or a block of ice
In a stack of hay
The wonderful joys
On Christmas day
Will only come once a year
But the memories will always stay

Darby Beane, Grade 6
Alvaton Elementary School, KY

If I Were a Girl Long Ago

If I were a girl long ago,
I'd work all day and night
Make food, make clothes that I'd have to sew
No mall to which I could go.

There wouldn't be computers,
There would not be TV,
No movies I could see.
It would be kind of boring, don't you agree?

The clothes would not be comfortable,
They would be hot as a summer's day,
They would be as stiff as wood,
And very hard in which to play.

My closest neighbors would be the trees,
No doctor for miles and miles.
I'm glad I live in modern times, it's terribly nice you see,
With all my modern technology.

Carly Stoltzfus, Grade 5
Providence Academy, TN

Christmas

Christmas is green, red and white,
It sounds like jingling bells,
It tastes like warm brownies,
It smells like a warm cup of cider,
It looks like a blanket of snow and a lot of presents,
It makes you feel happy, and loved.

Kaitlin Mingione, Grade 6
St Vincent Elementary School, MO

You Will See
Come with me
and you will see
the wonderful things
of Thanksgiving
the falling leaves
falling off of marvelous
trees
falling to the bottom

Come with me
and you will see
the things you need to see,
The feast of Thanksgiving
with the turkey a'coming
and the pumpkin pie on the WAY!

Brette Tennison, Grade 5
Palmetto Christian Academy, SC

Winter
Snow flying all around
Then gently hitting the ground
Christmas is coming
People cutting down trees

I love all the lights
And all the crisp, cold nights
People sleigh riding
And building snowmen.

Jared Runnion, Grade 6
Pleasants County Middle School, WV

Earthquakes
Scary
Killing many
One rumbling disaster
Surprising twist of a nightmare
Beneath

Alexandra Durazo, Grade 5
Broadway Elementary School, NC

Let's Go Eagles
Eagles, our team's mascot
Eagles, our pride and spirit.

Eagles win every game,
because it's hard to beat us,
we're undefeatable.

Your score might be twenty,
but ours might be forty,
because we're better!

Let's go Eagles!
Win, win, win!!!

Mackenzie Hobson, Grade 6
Dyer Elementary & Jr High School, TN

Thanksgiving, What It Means
Thanksgiving, it means fall,
It means families coming together with no fussing at all.
It means getting out of school, so we can sleep late
Oh yeah, it's great!
It means turkey and dressing with mashed potatoes,
it means homemade sandwiches with bacon, lettuce, and tomatoes.
It means fun for all.
But mostly it means giving thanks for all that we have,
and getting together with family, and friends.

Ben Johnson, Grade 6
Guntown Middle School, MS

My Joyous Night
Out into the night I rode on my stallion,
To the field we went as moonlit shadows
Quivered around us like a big black battle battalion,
Trees shook as wind passed through their limbs,
Raccoons scampered to get food from our old wineskins,
The grass was crisp and the field moonlit,
I then turned my horse as it spit,
I fled through the field and straight to the pond,
As I dodged a giant stick that looked like a wand,
My horse stopped, and so did I,
And when I jumped off my horse, the mud felt like a giant cream pie,
I jumped into the pond, and water cluttered around me,
As I came back up, I felt a heartwarming sense of glee,
For tonight was the night that I wouldn't go home,
For tonight was the night that I'd be alone.

Morgan Bishoff, Grade 5
Holsenbeck Elementary School, GA

Hurricane Katrina
Hurricane Katrina was big and strong.
500 miles wide, a mile was like a small prong
Going through MS, LA, and AL tearing up ground everywhere she went
Katrina left quite a huge dent.
Homeless because of the storm
People had to live in college dorms.
Louisiana Super Dome was filled
The roof was almost pilled.
It will never be the same
AL, MS, and LA are going through a big change.

Savannah Bond, Grade 6
Graham Elementary School, AL

Leaves
A leaf is a peaceful object that dances around in the air.
A leaf is a mindless object that flutters without a care.
A leaf is the color of dead grass in wintertime.
A leaf is like a poem without rhyme.
It gallops in the wind like a creature that was featured
On the daily news show.
And it doesn't know,
But it is being watched by thousands of people all over the world!

Rachel Barnett, Grade 5
Summit Hill Elementary School, GA

Pigs

My most favorite animals in the world
Is not one whose fur is soft and curled
but instead my favorite animal is
the one you least expect — Pigs!!
Pigs are very big, chubby, and fat
Even bigger than the world's largest cat.
Pigs sit around usually bored
But they don't spend as much time doing that
As they do at the grocery store.
Pigs play in the mud all day
Always shouting hip hip hooray!!!
I wonder what pigs would do at the beach
They'd probably get there and start to sleep.
And if pigs went to trick or treat
When they'd get home they'd eat eat eat.
If I were playing a game
Pigs would be on my team
At least that would happen, in my own dreams.
So now if you ask me what my favorite animal is
You'll know what I'll say — Pigs!!

Chad Yeager, Grade 6
Cathedral School, NC

Star Light

I see something shining,
Up at the dark night sky.
It's sometimes hard to be finding
But you see a lot of them up high.

It looks like a diamond,
It's the brightest thing.
It's sweeter than just lemonade,
You can see it in just a blink.

We sometimes find constellations,
It's like playing connect the dots,
When you look at the sky
There's a population.
There's a constellation that looks like a pot.

You think it looks like a star,
But it is just a dot,
It's gas that makes it shine,
It's hot like water boiling in a pot.

Gerardo Dominguez, Grade 4
Nesbit Elementary School, GA

Thanksgiving

Oh, thanks oh, thanks for this wonderful holiday.
We call it Thanksgiving.
We feast on turkeys and yams.
We feast until our stomachs explode.
Thanksgiving is when children burrow themselves
Thanksgiving is the greatest holiday of all.

Matthew Brooks, Grade 5
Debusk Elementary School, TN

My Sister

Angela is my sister, she is pretty as can be.
We have a lot of fun on the beach and at the sea.

Angela is my sister, she can climb a tree.
Sometimes we play chase, but she can barely catch me.

Angela is my sister, we have lots of fun.
We aren't together often, we're always on the run.

Angela is my sister, I miss her very much.
We live in different homes, but we always keep in touch.

Dustin Morrison, Grade 4
Brilliant Elementary School, AL

Grandma's Pork Chops

The wonderful smell drives me to the kitchen
to see what tasty meal you could be cookin'.
So I sneak around the corner and tip-toe down the hall.
When I enter the kitchen, you don't notice me at all.

Your salt and peppery hair is damp with sweat.
You're working so hard that you're somewhat wet.
You drop some pork chops in a carefully mixed batter,
because the taste of this dinner truly, truly matters.

You flip those tasty chops into the frying pan
and head to the sink to wash your powdery hands.
You carefully prepare macaroni and cheese,
and your mouth says a loving "Bless you" when I sneeze.

Your favorite perfume engulfs me in a hug,
and you give my braids a quick and gentle tug.
You ask me how I handled the tasks of my day.
You're the perfect grandma in each and every way.

Courtland Sutton, Grade 6
Charleston County School of the Arts, SC

Look at the Waterfall Below

The waterfall below is as strong as hulk
But as beautiful as a wildflower in different color varieties.
The waterfall is a fall of pure water in a beauteous form,
And is one of the purest waters in the land.
The fish may not swim in the powerful wind of the water
Still some may try and swim with all of its might
But very few make it to the waterfall and back.
The water may be cold but is life for some animals
Who drink this water to quench their thirsts
The waterfall may have minerals such as silver or gold
That the prospectors want
But some cannot reach the bunch of minerals of sort
The waterfall is a beautiful sight but a very strong type.
So look at the waterfall below.

Carey Jang, Grade 6
River Trail Middle School, GA

Snow

I like the weather when it snows.
It makes the outside look like it glows.
Snow is so white,
And snow is so bright.
I like to play in this weather.
The snow is as light as a feather.
When you smash it into a ball,
You can keep it until next fall.
In the freezer, it must stay
Until next time you want to play.

Dani Moore, Grade 6
Pleasants County Middle School, WV

Yellow Flower

Bright yellow flower
Floating upon the high tree
When spring is over

Ayana Ashworth, Grade 4
Hillcrest Elementary School, TN

Shopping

S hoes and clothes everywhere!
H aving to carry heavy bags.
O verflowing stores.
P eople rushing into sales.
P retty things all around.
I can't wait to try everything on.
N ever enough clothes or shoes.
G irls love to shop!

Kirstin Collins, Grade 5
Sullivan Elementary School, TN

Seasons

The air is cool and crisp,
Watch out for the wet mist.
The leaves are changing colors,
Red, yellow, orange, and others.

Winter is cold and bitter,
The weather makes me shiver.
Snow falling all around,
Like a white blanket on the ground.

The summer sun shines,
And leaves are quite fine.
Big and green,
Until falls Halloween.

Now the last one spring,
Where there's birds with their wings.
Where flowers are grown,
And a lot of seeds are sown.

Emily Kate Swan, Grade 4
Evangelical Christian School, TN

Last Year's Toys

Every year I get new toys.
I get filled with new joys.
But every year it's the same,
Last year's toys get lame.

Mikaela Knotts, Grade 4
South Topsail Elementary School, NC

Halloween

Halloween
Colorful pumpkins
Sweet pumpkin pie
Lots of noisy bats
Tangy sugar free candy
Lots of sticky wrappers
Halloween

Tyler Murphy, Grade 4
Tamassee-Salem Elementary School, SC

Nature

Nature, nature,
So beautiful and colorful.
Flowers in bloom,
Dancing in the wind to a beautiful tune.
The clouds in the air so white and puffy.
The sky so blue and beautiful.
The trees so tall with leaves of all color.
Nature, nature, is all around us and is so
Beautiful and colorful.

Jessica Blandford, Grade 6
Harrisburg Middle School, AR

Team Roping

T ime matters for this run
E normous horns on that steer
A wesome prizes for the winner
M ust catch that steer or else

R eady, set, go, here we go!
O pportunity now, release the rope
P atience matters for this run
I mpossible steer to catch for me
N ow's the ticket! You've got him!
G o! Go win the NFR!

Patrick Houchins, Grade 5
Frankford Elementary School, MO

Kasey

Kasey Shepherd
lazy, smart
play, draw, eat
I like playing sports
Kasey Shepherd

Kasey Shepherd, Grade 4
East Jones Elementary School, MS

Constitution

C lassic
O bligate
N ationalism
S croll
T homas Jefferson
I ndependent
T ake-up
U nited states
T actful
I dentity
O bey
N ation

Cole Mozingo, Grade 4
East Jones Elementary School, MS

George Washington

G ood
E ntrust
O bscuring
R ectify
G athering
E ncounter

W ork
A greement
S afety
H istoric
I dea
N ationwide
G avel
T all
O bligate
N ice

Jessie Kelley, Grade 4
East Jones Elementary School, MS

The Land

Grass is green
The sky is blue
Today is a beautiful
Day for you.

Brittany Wheeler, Grade 5
Franklin Elementary School, OK

Grandma

I love her
She is the best
She does everything for me
She is great
She might leave me someday
I don't want her to leave me
I love my Grandma!

Susan Ray, Grade 6
Brogden Middle School, NC

My World

The cars zooming on the highway.
The moon and sun in the skyway.

A cat by a tree looking at the crows.
Thinking of a treat knowing it must be sweet.

As he waits for his chance.
While the wind softly blows.

As the cars go by the birds start to fly.
Will the leaves start falling one by one or two by two?
Maybe on the ground for a day or two.

A dog on the porch lazily watching the cat.
Wishing he had energy like that.

The way I see my world.
Is a way that is beautiful.
Like a flower.
Getting bigger every year full of fear.

Joshua Logan Brown, Grade 6
Temple Hill Elementary School, KY

Rainbows

R ainbows stretch so far and wide
A hh I say when I see it in the sky
I see it when it stops raining
N ow I know my day will not be blue
B ecause the rain will stop
O h no I say
W hen it goes away
S ad because there is no more rainbow in the sky

Danielle Champagne, Grade 6
St Cecilia School, LA

History Facts

H unters gathered food for their family.
I ndependence has always been important for America.
S tories from ancient times help us the people understand
    why people in ancient time did such things.
T ime continually changes.
O bstacles were easily overcome by hunters and gatherers.
R ailroads paved way for larger and faster trade.
Y our future looks bright.

Kali Singleton, Grade 6
Clarksburg School, TN

Autumn

I feel the touch of the autumn chill.
I watch the colors brightly spill.
Across the land the chills, and the spills
Make autumn joyful, loving, and fun-filled.

Taylor Clark, Grade 5
Western Hills Elementary School, AR

Come to the Football Camp

See the giant football players
Hear the helmets hitting against each other, clang, clang
Touch the cold, delicious water bottles
Smell the sweat of the football players
Taste the dirt on the ground

Blake Davis, Grade 5
Bonaire Elementary School, GA

Yesterday

The first day of a new beginning
The last day of an old end
When time flies and multiplies
You never know where to begin
Lost in time, and lost in space
You can't tell which way to face
A place where you have no future
Or past, and yet
You want this place to last
A place where nothing new comes your way
Or maybe it does,
You just can't say
And something happened that you didn't know would
You couldn't expect it, or maybe you could
If you don't know this place
I don't know what to say
But to me this place is
Yesterday

Lyka Person, Grade 6
Brogden Middle School, NC

Ocean Blue

Waves are against the
Shore — roar — a surrounding sound,
A rocky view too.

Dorsey Shamblin, Grade 4
Briarwood Christian Elementary School, AL

Where the River Flows

The river falls and splashes
It's where I peacefully go
While the wind gives me a breeze and a melody

Nobody yelling
Nobody screaming
Just the sound of nature whispering in my ear

Amber Jordan, Grade 4
Cool Spring Elementary School, NC

Come to the Playground

See the children running like deer
Hear the children laughing like hyenas
Touch the soft warm grass
Smell the beautiful fragrant flowers
Taste the cold popsicle as it slips into your mouth

Elizabeth Priest, Grade 5
Bonaire Elementary School, GA

My Cat

Shadow.
Soft and sweet.
Pounces.
Loves him so.
Lovely cat.

Tyler Webster, Grade 5
American Heritage Academy, GA

A Trampoline

Fun in the sun.
Flying high,
     like you're going to die.
But you're alive for tomorrow,
     to do it again.

Katie Reed, Grade 5
St Vincent Elementary School, MO

Soccer

Score a point —
They get to kick!
They score a point —
You get to trick!

Fake left; fake right —
     sometimes…
They'll lose the fight.

Then go home
And lie down;
Just think…
You won a soccer game tonight!

Hendrix Harmon, Grade 6
Scotts Creek Elementary School, NC

Halloween!

Trick or treat,
Give me something good to eat.
While I am out late at night,
I hope I don't get a fright.
Just get a costume and dress up,
You can even be a rapper saying waz'up.
I am sure you'd rather be with the dead,
Than be sleeping in your bed.

Taylor Leigh Kerr, Grade 5
Midway Covenant Christian School, GA

Veteran

V iolent is what the war is.
E veryone will pray they will be ok.
T ortured is what the soldiers will be
E xperience is what they will use to win.
R ifles is what some used for guns.
A mbulance will come get hurt soldiers.
N ot everyone will be ok.

Haley Young, Grade 4
Cherokee Elementary School, AR

Orange

Orange looks like freshly squeezed orange juice on a hot summer day.
Orange feels like a big round pumpkin at the pumpkin patch in the fall.
Orange tastes like a nice juicy orange on a warm day in the spring.
Orange smells like a pumpkin pie fresh out of the oven.
Orange sounds like orange crispy leaves falling from the trees in the fall.
Orange is the beautiful color of fall.

Sydney Payne, Grade 5
Geggie Elementary School, MO

Autumn

October, the starting of this wonderful season
leaves falling, floating covering the forest green grass
footballs zooming into my hands like a bullet
hunting, shooting the creatures of the wild
orange, red, green leaves creating a masterpiece
fall break, running, enjoying no school and teachers
Thanksgiving, feasting, eating delicious foods like turkey and ham
cold winds etching my mom's windshield with frost
birds flying, gliding as the sun sets
crawling into bed anxious to see fall again tomorrow

Michael Dillon Chambliss, Grade 6
Alvaton Elementary School, KY

Autumn Is

Autumn is when you see the shades of red, orange, and yellow.
Autumn is when you have to rake up leaves.
Autumn is when you see children running and jumping in piles of leaves.
Autumn is when tree branches quiver in the wind.
Autumn is beautiful.

Davionne Blue, Grade 5
Parker Road Elementary School, MO

Midnight Garden

Water lilies spin in circles, as fairies dance under a starry sky
To wish there was such a thing as fairies in a midnight garden
I do believe in such a thing, in such a beautiful thing
The fairies' clothes are pretty pastels, which shine in the moonlight
I wish I could wear the pretty pastels, and dance in the moonlight with them
Over the water they shine like stars, fairies in their beautiful costumes
Their miniature flutes and harps sing with them to make a little night parade
Fairy wands wave in the air like majorettes in a band
It's such a beautiful sight to see them all like this
I wish it would go on forever

Leigh Cooper, Grade 6
Nature's Way Montessori School, TN

A Blessing for Christmas

May Santa Claus bring you lots of presents.
May you have great celebrations with yummy family meals.
May your Christmas tree and decorations be as bright as the stars.
May your milk and cookies disappear overnight.
And may you have Happy Holidays.

Julia Grace Gillen, Grade 6
St Francis Xavier School, AL

Sun

I like the sun because,
you can run and have fun,
in the sun, but when the moon
is about you have to go back to your hideout.

Austin Hostetler, Grade 5
Drayton Hall Elementary School, SC

Riding the Orphan Train

I am an orphan.
I wonder when my mom is going to come back for me.
I cry every night about her.
I hear my mom's voice in my head.
I touch the little bear she gave me before she left.
I see us playing at a park on the swings.
I am miserable without my mom.
I feel momless!

I want Mom to be at the very first stop.
I worry that someone else might take me first.
I pretend my best friend is my brother.
I want them to take us both.
I am very sad.

I don't understand why she is taking so long to return.
I say a prayer every night.
I dream about her every night.
I try hard every day to put my trust in my mom!
I hope she will come soon!
I am a lonely, sad orphan!!!

Everett Hatcher, Grade 4
Vanoss Elementary School, OK

A Painful Piercing

When I felt the hook in my ear,
My whole body was filled with fear.
While I was screaming,
the hook was just gleaming.

A man tried to pull it,
but it didn't move a bit.
My dad cut it in my path,
and at the end of the week it was a big laugh.

Chandler Stello, Grade 5
Drayton Hall Elementary School, SC

The Christmas Gift

He came from Heaven down to Earth
And in a stable His mom gave birth
The shepherds heard loud voices ringing
They looked in the sky and saw angels singing
Some wise men came from afar
Following a bright shiny star
He showed us how to love and pray
And this created our Christmas Day.

Madeline East, Grade 4
Evangelical Christian School, TN

My Bike Ride

The breeze was pressing against my face.
The colorful leaves were playing a silly game.
My bike skidded up the rocky road.
The streams trickled,
The chimes twinkled.
My bike came to a
silent stop.
There was nothing between me
and the sparkling lake.
My thoughts and worries
floated away
on the cool breeze.
Nothing
was holding me back.
Beauty
Had set me free!!!

Kaleigh Galvin, Grade 5
Big Creek Elementary School, GA

If I Were in Charge of the World

If I were in charge of the world
There would be no Homework,
We would have snacks in every class,
Class would be talking and
Playing games all day long.
If I were in charge of the world
I would change your wardrobe,
Your brothers would be nice,
I'll Change what time you have to go to school.
If I were in charge of the world
You wouldn't have brothers,
You wouldn't have mean parents,
You wouldn't have to go to bed early,
Or "Get off your cell phone"
We wouldn't have wars!
If I were in charge of the world
Gas prices would be 10 cents a gallon,
Kidnapping wouldn't exist,
Bullying at school would never happen,
Houses would only cost 1 dollar.
I would love to be In charge of the World.

Hannah Rose Fisher, Grade 6
Eminence Middle School, KY

Veteran

V ery brave
E ager to win the war
T ask force support truth and justice
E nlist in the armed forces
R epresent our nation
A bundance of respect
N o one will forget those that have served in the war

Sara Kate Garner, Grade 4
Cherokee Elementary School, AR

The Woods

Smell the fresh roses.
Watch the children splash and play.
Listen to birds sing.
Tylor Burchett, Grade 6
Martin Elementary School, WV

Life

I see, I saw
I hear, I heard
I talk, I speak
I try, I succeed
I do, I don't
I will, I won't
I can, I can't
I win, I lose
No, yes
Always, never
Lost, found
Friends, enemies
Mad, glad
Happy, sad
Colors, sizes, shapes
People, animals, things
The smile on your face
The choices that you take
The decisions you make
It's life
Mary Elizabeth Manchester, Grade 5
Prince of Peace Catholic School, SC

Racing Dirt Bikes

Everyone is leaning
against the handlebars.
The gates slam to the ground.
The race begins,
dirt flying everywhere.
I fly over the jumps and turns
getting about ten feet of air.
On each jump.
Dirt is flying everywhere.
Everyone is wrecking.
Suddenly I'm twenty feet in the air.
Accidentally I let go of my dirt bike,
I feel myself falling to the ground.
My bike lands on my legs.
Another racer runs over my feet.
Luckily, I had on steel toed boots.
I barely had the energy
to return to my racing trailer.
They fixed my dirt bike.
The wreck and race was over,
until next week.
Tucker Holton, Grade 5
Etowah Elementary School, NC

Friendship Forever

Friends are joyful.
Friends are nice they keep a promise
and never fight.
Friends are loving.
Friends are caring and
will always be sharing.
If you like your friend and
your friend likes you,
you will always have a dream come true.
Austen Clarke, Grade 4
Landmark Christian School, GA

Snakes

Snakes
Long, funnel-shaped
Slip through your hands
Slither through the grass
Is anything better than snakes?
Gaines Coker, Grade 5
Landmark Christian School, GA

Where Is the Love?

Where is the love?
The love we all have
But choose not to share

Where is the love?
The love we have at church
But what happens when
Church is over
We only show the love to people
We know

Where is the love?
The love we give our family
We should give the love
To everybody

After all, we are all brothers
And sisters

Where is the love
Inside of us
Stephanie Anderson, Grade 6
Bernard Middle School, MO

Fishing

I love fishing; it loves me!
I go fishing — just me and a breeze;
With a tree at my left,
And a tree at my right,
I sure hope I get a bite!
Josh Mathis, Grade 6
Scotts Creek Elementary School, NC

Clock

The clock moves its arms,
Restlessly clicking its tongue,
Impatiently waiting for
Each hour to pass.
Alexis Doza, Grade 5
St Vincent Elementary School, MO

Mr. Dinosaur

On the verge of extinction,
Your steps like earthquakes sound.
You travel where you please,
In swamp, river, or ground.
Long ago you lived,
Life always the same.
Some say a meteor hit,
Some say the ice age came.
Some creatures of your kind,
Still roam about the land.
Lurking in the water,
Or hiding in the sand.
Oh, Mr. Dinosaur,
Why did you have to die?
When a meteor hit,
And a cloud covered the sky.
Oh, Mr. Dinosaur,
I will ask again.
Why did you have to die?
For when you died, I was alone.
You were my only friend.
Jacob Schultz, Grade 6
Bellwood Discovery School, TN

The Spring Begins

A bright sun rose up
The time was beginning spring
It was very moist
Jazamaine Conner, Grade 4
Hillcrest Elementary School, TN

Heart

Heart
Small, smooth
Pumping, beating, pounding
Transporting blood to your body
Heart
Jacob Spillman, Grade 5
Trenton Middle School, MO

Winter Bliss

Winter days grow short
White flakes float quietly down
Warm flames soothe the heart.
Nathan Heppermann, Grade 6
Immanuel Lutheran School, MO

The Big Buck

In the wilderness I walk.
To see a big deer.
I try and try to hear a big deer.
But I can't hear leaf sounds in my ear.
Finally I see a big dear and I can hear the big deer.

So if you hear a big deer, you might not see a big deer.
And if you see a big deer, you might not hear a big deer.

The big deer walks the path
To the corn pile to eat some corn while he still has a while.
One gun fired, it woke them up out of their bed.
They all knew the big deer was dead.

But they never did see me again.
Because what they thought was that I had a big grin.

Tanner Stout, Grade 5
Temple Hill Elementary School, KY

Camouflage

Camouflage is the smell of my camouflage 243
Super mag going off after killing a deer.

Camouflage looks like my boots
walking through 2 feet of crisp, white snow.

Camouflage tastes like a deer steak
coming off the hot grill.

Camouflage sounds like the fall leaves
rustling under my feet in the woods.

Camouflage feels like the bark
on a rough oak tree.

Luke Fox, Grade 5
Cool Spring Elementary School, NC

Dancing in the Sky

Dancing leaves in the sky;
Flitter, flop, and float.
Crimson, red, dandelion, mahogany, and green;
Pirouette down to the ground.
Delicate, fragile, and speckled leaves;
Get crushed and squashed by a little child's feet.
Vivid and radiantly colored leaves;
Tell me stories of far off places.
Secrets spin around my head of leaves;
Whirling and swirling through my head.
Leaves dazzle and glisten in twilight;
By the light of the moon.
Leaves come and go, but they never stay;
Just like the four seasons, they return again!

Janina Pelzer, Grade 5
Summit Hill Elementary School, GA

Daddy

Daddy, Daddy, why don't you come home?
Without you I am alone.
Momma is worried about you
Alexus and I are worried too.
I cry as I sit and wonder why.
I want to see you every day
Or at the very least call you each day,
I love you very much
I just want to feel your touch
Daddy, Daddy, why don't you come home?
Because without you I am alone

Cheyenne Drayton, Grade 6
Brogden Middle School, NC

Skateboarding Is Fun!

Skateboarding is fun!
You can go skating with your friend anytime, anywhere.
It is exciting when you land a trick
you have been working on for a long time.
Ollie to kick flip, manual to pop-shove-it.
All the tricks I know and love.
Skateboarding is fun!

Jonah LeBlanc, Grade 6
Arnaudville Elementary School, LA

Snow

Snow is very pretty when it sparkles in the light.
When the sun shines on it, it is very bright.
I like to roll up snow to make a snowman.
Eyes of coal, an orange nose, and a hat of tan.

Launa Moore, Grade 4
Cave City Elementary School, AR

At the Fort

The letter was sent to evacuate,
on this legendary date.

When the Union troops answered No! No!,
Beuregard's top was about to blow!

On April 12 in "Sixty-one"
the fire rang from the musket gun

For three months, they'd rocked and swayed,
seeing if it'd been delayed.

When the fort was finally a pile of trash,
they sat there weeping in flame and ash.

When the flag finally appeared
the Confederate army jumped and cheered.

Gen. Beuregard had really won!
Anderson's troops were as good as done.

Evan Winn, Grade 5
Buckland Elementary School, NC

People

People
People
People
Smelly people
Dirty people
Big fat hungry people
Short thin small people
Those are just a few
Wide people
Long people
Good bad smart people
Crazy people too
Lazy people
Hyper people
Don't forget funny people
Last of all best of all
I like athletic people

Robert Frantz, Grade 6
Hayes Elementary School, OK

The Poor Turkey

The poor turkey must not be late,
For he might end up on someone's plate.
The poor turkey, feathery and fat,
Must watch out for the farmer's hat.
If he sees it come near,
He must run in fear.
The poor turkey must not be late,
For he may end up on someone's plate!

Caleb Amason, Grade 6
First Assembly Christian School, AL

Light Is Shining Over the Mountains

Light
is shining
over the mountains
The sun is falling below
The world is
Now so
dark

Jake Harding, Grade 5
Easley Elementary School, NC

The Hulk

Please don't sulk
while we're on the hulk,
When we're twisting and turning
and whirling all about.

Please don't shout
we will get on again and again
until the end,
We will get back in line
and everything will be fine.

Emily Wallace, Grade 6
Harrisburg Middle School, AR

Haunted

I was haunted by the big bad boogey man that lived under my bed
scratching and watching every move I make.
A move or a groove but he always watching me!

What haunts me now are crazy clowns.
They make people laugh but not me,
no they can scare, they can wear frizzy hair,
and they are CRAZY!

What will scare me the most in the future are rabid robots.
They act nice at first, but then they get worst,
and then they turn on everyone.
They shoot lasers from their eyes and some could even fly and drive.
This is what Scares me the most!!

Matthew Lee, Grade 5
Eminence Middle School, KY

Abraham Lincoln

Abraham Lincoln had an amazing life.
He had many brothers and sisters, and also a wife.
Abe was the United State's sixteenth president,

He was born as a Kentucky resident.
A log cabin is where he was born,
He and his family were farmers and they grew many things like corn.

As a young child he loved reading,
He always borrowed books from neighbors, coming and leaving.
When he was little he had no real education,

And yet he made the U.S. into a new creation.
Abe was against slavery and the Mexican War,
He was the president during the Civil War.

Then surrender came upon Robert E. Lee,
Abraham Lincoln was full of glee.
People know him as a man with a big tall hat,

We honor him today, with the Lincoln memorial where in a chair he sat.
Abe was the man, who kept our nation together,
He'll always be an important man in U.S. history forever.

Willa Tseng, Grade 6
River Trail Middle School, GA

Oh No!

Hot and humid really dry as we packed up for our vacation drive.
I ask mama what to bring, but she said, "Look out the window and please predict."

So I brought my short, tank tops, and no sweaters.
I think I got carried away, I thought it was summer today!
Father said, "It's time to go!"
So I put my stuff in a plastic bag and went off.
I saw only mountains very far from home.
I gasped and yelled, "Oh no! We're in winter."

Jackie Antiveros, Grade 5
Etowah Elementary School, NC

Hope Is Growing

Hope is growing
  Everywhere you see.
It's relaxing in greens,
  An angel in heaven resting in peace.

Wars everywhere…fighting for freedom…
  A prayer to God
From children in need…

Hope is in everyone —
  It's in you.
  It's in me.
  It's growing in everyone.

Cassidy Barclay, Grade 5
Breitling Elementary School, AL

The Old Marsh Ditch

Oh, old marsh ditch, people digging by you.
So peaceful, so beautiful.
A home to all birds.
Your water, sparkling.
And glimmering in the sunlight.
Just like a peaceful dancer.
The birds, feeding and singing their peaceful songs.
Now, you're gone, so much fun, taken away.
I don't see many birds now.
And I don't hear many songs now.
We have destroyed you.
So sad, so sad.
Your water used to be clear.
But now it is dirty and muddy.
I miss you so dearly.

Parker Jaquillard, Grade 5
Christ Episcopal School - Middle School, LA

Childhood

Childhood is being afraid of the dark.
Childhood is screaming while watching a scary movie.
Childhood is jumping on the bed until your parents get mad.
Childhood is dreaming about what you will be in the future.
Childhood is having a favorite toy.
Childhood is having a baby-sitter when your parents go out.
Childhood is wondering why you don't have a brother.

Manny Minjarez, Grade 6
Lost River Elementary School, KY

God's Promise

God's promise is a rainbow so colorful and bright
to never flood the world again through any day or night.
It comes after rain storms it's such a beautiful sight.
Whenever the sun is shining it shines reflected light.
The colors in a rainbow are very very bright.
Now you know about a rainbow so hold it very tight.
God's Promise!

Ashlyn Irvine, Grade 4
Lewis Vincent Elementary School, LA

Love

Love is in the air
So I hope you are being fair
because in the shadows it hides
Waiting for you to come by
So be ready to fly
because in any moment your dream will come true
Your love will be waiting for you

Karol Serafin-Molina, Grade 6
Brogden Middle School, NC

At Night

Icky sticky crawly things,
I know they're there though they can't be seen,
  they sit and wait till I close my eyes
then BOO they jump out I'm not surprised!
Please mom please that's why I can't sleep,
So, can I stay up to 5:00 A.M. watching TV?

Ketera Chatman, Grade 6
Graham Elementary School, AL

The Outdoors

I saw birds flying up high,
  When the bus went by.
I saw rocks in a pile,
  When my friend smiled.
I saw a cat climb a tree,
  Then it looked at me.
I heard machines running,
  While fall leaves were turning.
I felt the cool breeze,
  While looking at aging trees.

Michael Lee Van Buren, Grade 6
Temple Hill Elementary School, KY

My Life

My life is pretty, my life is sweet,
My life is boring, but most of all my life has beat.

And, if that beat is broken
My life will all fall
Fall like the waters in a cascading falls
So when it reaches the bottom it will just drift away
And I will be a mere speck of sand in the nighttime bay.

My life is pretty, my life is sweet,
My life is boring, and my life has a beat.

But that beat will never be broken,
For I can withstand, I can, I can, I can withstand

My life is pretty, my life is sweet,
My life is boring, but most of all my life has a beat

Jackson M. Buck, Grade 6
Brogden Middle School, NC

Football

Football is the best sport
Football people can get hurt
Football you can run the ball
Football you can throw the ball
Football you can kick the ball
Football is a good sport for boys.

Latoddric Fortenberry, Grade 5
East Marion Elementary School, MS

Fall

Fall, oh, fall
How beautiful
From the leaves that fall onto me
To the food baked just for me
Now it is time for bed
There is a story to be read
Thinking of times
Of a new fall to come.

Josiah Corson, Grade 4
First Assembly Christian School, AL

Oops!

Oh no! It's a Bomb!
I just set a Bomb!
The timer says thirteen minutes!

I don't think I should run,
That would be wrong,
What should I do?

Let's see, I need scissors!
I need to find scissors!
I have to cut the wires myself!

In the movies it's a breeze,
So why can't I do it?

All I have to do is
Cut this wire right
Here…

Emmon Roth, Grade 6
Brogden Middle School, NC

Red

Red is scarlet,
Red is a rose,
Red is a fire truck,
Or a funny clown's nose.
Red is a pair of painted lips,
Giving you a great big kiss.
As you can see,
Red is not an easy color to miss.

Caroline McLeod, Grade 5
Endy Elementary School, NC

Halloween on Oct 31

Halloween is a great time of year
to
get all the candy you want.
Halloween is a fun time of year
to
show off new costumes like
a
witch or a funny clown.
Halloween you're so much
fun…
If only every day were Halloween
it would be
so much fun!!!

Kristi Prince, Grade 5
Walton Verona Elementary School, KY

Thanksgiving Day

Thanksgiving
Warm family fire
A spicy apple pie
The happy screams of children
The sweet juicy turkey
Kids playing two hand touch football
Thanksgiving

Hunter Blakley, Grade 5
Sullivan Elementary School, TN

Summer

Roses are red
Violets are blue
Summer memories rock
And stick like glue.
The pools of water
And the buttery smell
Of tanning oil on the beaches,
And late night movies
Filled with snakes and leeches.
Oh how I hate how fast
Summer days go by.
When summer has left I sit
There and cry.

Brandon Dillard, Grade 6
St Mark Elementary School, SC

Veteran

V ery sad when they die
E xtremly violent
T alk to the family
E veryone's there for the family
R etrieving the dead
A re always saving lives
N ever ready to die

Brittany Moffitt, Grade 4
Cherokee Elementary School, AR

Thunder

Thunder is so loud
Thunder makes me very scared
Thunder is scary

Clark Brucken, Grade 5
Etowah Elementary School, NC

Mountains

Mountains
Trees, blurry, wet
Foggy, cold, pretty
Big
Hills

Deana Sowell, Grade 5
Shirley Elementary School, AR

To That Special Someone

I'm waiting here for that someone
Every day and night.
Needing someone to hold me tight.
To cheer me up when I'm sad.
And make me smile when I'm mad.
I need someone that will always care.
Someone that will always be there.
Even when I'm right or wrong.
And always there to keep me strong.
Someone to show me there is no fear.
Someone always there and always near.
Always helping me to get through.
Someone there to say I love you.
Someone to be there when I'm cold
And always there for me to hold.
Someone there for me to think of.
Someone there to show me love.

Breget Picazo, Grade 6
Brogden Middle School, NC

Flowers

Flowers are beautiful.
They are so clean.
They make you happy.
The sun makes them shine.
  Oh, so, beautiful to me.

Bees love them too.
They take their nectar to make honey.
  Oh, so, good.

They are yellow, blue, and even red.
They are the best.
The butterflies love them, just like me.
This is over. So long,
  Good-bye!

Stephanie Alderson, Grade 5
Oark Elementary School, AR

Hockey

Rough, tough, you can't get enough.
There's fighting and slashing, tripping and stuff.
Two minutes, four minutes, five minutes, or
Get the puck in the net and then you score!
The helmets and padding
You'll think that they are nice
After you slip and fall
On the hard, slippery ice.
One period to go,
Your team is doing bad.
Get you head in the game.
Make the opponent mad.
You score three more goals,
Ahead by just one.
The clock runs out.
Your job is done!
Your team has won.
Everyone is glad.
You are picked as star one.
What a great game you had!

Montana Cole, Grade 5
Landmark Christian School, GA

The Stuff I Like and Don't Like

I like to swing.
I like to sing.
I like to ring bells.
I like to sail on a boat.
I like to mail.
But don't like to fail.

I like to sell stuff,
Like dogs, art, and snails.
I like to play in the sand
With a cool kind of pail.

Macey Leigh Barnes, Grade 4
Tazewell-New Tazewell Elementary School, TN

The Baseball Family

My family is like baseball positions:
My dad is the pitcher,
and nothing starts till he throws,
my mom is the shortstop
and usually backs up my dad.
Our cats Tom and Smokey are at first and second
for they love to pull off double plays on each other.
Our dog, George is the right fielder;
he can get any ball that he has to get.
I am the left fielder;
I do crazy things.
My sister is the center fielder,
and she can call me off.

Daniel Yeiser, Grade 6
College View Middle School, KY

What If...

What if God did not love us.
What if we never knew God
What if God never took the time to bless us
Because we have not blessed Him
What if we let sin take us over
What if there was no God
Well do you know,
I do
There would be no world.

Nia Scott, Grade 6
Brogden Middle School, NC

Seth, the Big Green Dog

Seth runs and then jogs and begins to faint.
Then all of a sudden, he steps in some paint.

My best friend was over and was on the swing.
She screamed, and I heard her, "Oh my, your dog's green!"

I came outside and held my breath.
Then he looked at me like I'd sentenced him to death

I got out the bucket and then the brush.
I grabbed hold of his collar and told him to hush.

I threw in the soap and then the shampoo.
He jumped out of the "tub" and then took my shoe.

Now he wiggles and waggles all sparkly and clean.
And because of this bath, he does not look green.

Stephanie Driskill, Grade 6
College View Middle School, KY

Day or Night

Day or night, which do you like?
Are you scared of the dark,
Because someone might shoot your heart?
Or do you love the night?
Because the moon is so bright.
I love the days,
Because I can see the sun's rays.

Hunter Harrell, Grade 4
Stephens Elementary School, AL

Hope

Before the cries of laughter and before the shouts of war,
there is a special word we all are looking for.
It hides beneath the shadows and over the sky above,
it is our life, our care, our love.
and even in the darkest of nights we will search,
until it is found, until we find our torch.
Our torch to light our way,
because we know we will find it someday.
Hope.

MacKenzie Prickett, Grade 6
Myrtle Beach Middle School, SC

4x4 Trucks

4x4 trucks
Loud ringing pipes,
Big mud grip tires,
Lifted up on lift kits,
Gas hogs.

4x4 trucks are awesome,
Trucks to play in the mud.
Sharp trucks to
Take duck hunting
Take deer hunting
4x4 trucks.

Dillon Reinhard, Grade 6
Harrisburg Middle School, AR

Frog

A gentle caring animal
Happily leaping from
Lily pad to lily pad.
Yet a little afraid about
What he is going to do.
When is he going to eat,
Or how will he find some flies?
Flies are nowhere!
He still has a care in his heart.
Soon a fly comes.
"Ribbet," the fly is gone
And the frog is jolly.
The frog's lunch had been served.
And all is well.

Hassan Haddad, Grade 5
Nesbit Elementary School, GA

My Room

My room
is very big
and it's very cozy

My room
has mirrors
everywhere.

I have a piece
of candy waiting for me
on my desk.

My floor is filled
with clothes
like a one-way nightmare

But, my room is the best
place I could be!
It's my space! My joy!
My room!

Bethany Roberson, Grade 6
Dyer Elementary & Jr High School, TN

Moment by the Sea

Waves charge like an army in war towards the diamondy shore.
Foam comes up, sizzling and chewing away like acid through the sand.
CRASH!!!

A ginormous wave surfs in,
Drenching the most daring people,
That stood like victims in front of the waves.

Little rocks stand in the open,
Rocking weakly against the waves.
Some getting cleared away completely.

Hearing cries of joy coming from excited, happy families.
Prancing around in the warm water,
Splattering the sparkly water in their faces.

Treading like a torpedo through the waves, counteracting them.
Noticing the water is like liquidy crystals, dancing on a blue blanket.
Sand sparkles, showing off its bright coat of crème-colored clothing.

Jumping into the silver waves,
SPLASH!
Hoping the moment will last forever.

Alisa Trudel, Grade 4
Goshen Elementary School at Hillcrest, KY

World War 2

A soldier never knew, a war like World War 2;
So much blood and gore, he's thankful it isn't anymore.

It started when Hitler took Poland by surprise
They didn't believe it when they saw with their own eyes,
England declared war not out of the blue
When Hitler fought France, he fought England too.

Then Hitler fought Russia; Big mistake,
Russia could wipe them away like a rake.
Japan bombed Pearl Harbor; now, that was messing with America.
America declared war; there was mass hysteria.

The war seemed like it took a century
Many lives were claimed, but eventually,
The Allies pushed Hitler back into Germany
Then the Allies had France to free.

When they won in Europe, parties broke out,
But Japan was still fighting, there was no need to shout.
Then we dropped the atomic bomb…
It sent them into an eerie, long, qualm.

Then the war was won, but everyone remember,
How sad it was when your loved one was a member — of World War 2.

Raghav Kaul, Grade 6
River Trail Middle School, GA

Nature

I feel the wind hit against my face.
I see the moon out in the early morning.
I see grass and leaves that are on the ground.
I also see birds up in a tree.
And cars going by.

I hear a dog barking.
I hear a farm tractor in the distance.
I can hear the neighbors raking leaves.
And the crunching sound under their feet.

Nature is a vision for all to see.

Nicholas Robert Grinnell, Grade 6
Temple Hill Elementary School, KY

Thanksgiving

Gathering friends around our tables
Telling ancient tales and family fables
Yelling oh my and what a hoot
Thinking about the time the dog ate your boot
Laughing and sharing
Listening and caring
Holding hands and praying together
Remembering times that will last forever.

Shannon Griffiths, Grade 6
Queen of Angels Catholic School, GA

What's Baseball?

Tapping homebase and *rehearsing* your swing
The pitcher *flings* the ball at homeplate
You *pound* the ball with a metal bat — *Ping!*
And *dash* the bases in a diamond shape
Sliding into home base like a bullet
If the catcher *tags* you
you're out in the dust — MAN!
Next player *tramping* up to bat
Grumping to the dugout
That's baseball!

Eric Lee Bagshaw, Grade 4
Price Elementary School, KY

Unleashed

Another day has passed
And I'm still waiting to be
Unleashed
To be surrounded in the
Excitement I bare
To be hovered in the
Domains of life
To be closed in by the sweet and sugary things
To be heart warmed by the
Family who stands close to me
While I sit here on my window sill
Waiting to be unleashed

Bailey Bowlin, Grade 5
Walton Verona Elementary School, KY

Dancing

Dancing is a way of expressing,
Even more than a way of dressing.

Dancing is a form of art,
For talented, funny, and even smart.

Dancing is my favorite thing,
Just like my friend who loves to sing.

We dance together in talent shows,
All the latest moves we'll be sure to know.

Dancing is my life, my world, and my passion,
Dancing is my heart, I'm always in action.

Brianna Stinson, Grade 6
Orange Grove Elementary School, MS

Mom/Daughter

I love her so much	She loves me too much
I always let her know	She tells me too much
But she needs to clean her room	My room is mine
She is so rude to her brother	He bugs me all the time
I give her ground rules	I have too many rules
Sometimes she disobeys me	So I sneak around them
So I have to punish her	She yells and screams at me even if I do simple things like tell my brother to shut up
Oh well,	Oh well, I guess I'll live
You gotta love her	You gotta love her

Rebecca Swanson, Grade 6
Beck Academy, SC

A Barrel Racer's Run

Walking into the arena, then
BAM goes the horse running toward the barrel.
Turning tight, tight, tight;
CRACK goes the rider's whip
running through the gap.
Turning again around the barrel
BOOM goes the rider's feet.
Running toward the last barrel,
the rider turns tight and kicks;
then BLAST goes the horse.
ZOOM! Running for home;
running past the timer.
"WHOA!" goes the rider,
now hoping for a good time.
"Great run!" BLASTS the announcer's voice.
It's a 15.47!
"YEAH," goes the crowd!
It puts her in first place.
That's the run of a barrel racer.

Cassie Adkins, Grade 6
Immanuel Lutheran School, MO

Bengals

B utt-kicking
E ven better than last year
N ever quits
G reat head coach
A wesomely talented
L eader of the offense is Carson Palmer
S econd Super Bowl loss in 1988

Daniel Tilley, Grade 5
Walton Verona Elementary School, KY

My Guitar…

At the pluck of a string,
It makes a wonderful sound,
Sometimes I play it soft,
And other times I play it loud.
My guitar's name is Marilyn,
I play her all the time.
I love writing new songs
Even if they don't rhyme.
When I first started playing
It was so very hard,
But I wouldn't trade the world
for my guitar!

Haley Wilkinson, Grade 4
Brilliant Elementary School, AL

Joy

The roses' gentle sway in the wind
The roll of distant thunder
A sun shining brightly
A moon gleaming softly
Is this what brings you joy?

The fall of delicate snowflakes
The blanket of white it makes
Is this what brings you joy?

A Christmas tree aglow at night
A glass of milk for Santa
The steady
Comforting
Beat of the rain
As it hits the window pane
The warmth of a fire spewing out flames
Is this what brings you joy?

A child's laugh
A baby's cry
A cradle that's filled with toys
Is this what brings you joy?

Joy
Kaitlyn Adkisson, Grade 6
South Oldham Middle School, KY

Crazy Legs

Crazy legs I see something jumping.
Crazy legs come out of the bushes.
Oh my, who is that?
It is green with yellow spots.
With webbed feet, "Yuck."

Come out now, you are scaring me.
I promise not to scare you; he or she.
Oh there you are.
I see you through the fog.
You are a big fat green frog.

Samantha Allen, Grade 5
Etowah Elementary School, NC

Peyton

Peyton Ramsey
nature, couch potato
play, watch, sleep
I like a nature trail.
Peyton Ramsey

Peyton Ramsey, Grade 4
East Jones Elementary School, MS

The Orange Tin Man

There once was an orange tin man,
who lived in a very bright can.
He had a dog named log,
who is a smelly hog.
That is why the man bought a fan.

Dylan Lamendola, Grade 4
Judsonia Elementary School, AR

Christmas

Christmas is a time to share.
It is also a time to care.
You can go outside and play.
On this very snowy day.

Triston Dunham, Grade 4
Horace Mann Elementary School, OK

The Knight

I thought I was lost,
But to my aid came a knight,
With a lion on his shield,
A bow with arrows strewn on his back,
The storm blade in his hand,
A falcon on his shoulder,
As a sign of pride.
For he was victory itself,
And he alone,
With no other aid,
Would undoubtedly win the war.

Marco Neblett, Grade 4
Herbert J Dexter Elementary School, GA

The Flag

The flag is red, white, and blue,
It sounds deafening in the wind,
It tastes like a nation coming together,
It smells like a fresh beginning,
It looks like a country coming forth,
It makes you feel proud.

Eric Buchheit, Grade 6
St Vincent Elementary School, MO

Friendship

Met you as a stranger,
Took you as a friend,
Hope we meet in Heaven,
Where friendship never ends.

Sydney Bourque, Grade 6
St Cecilia School, LA

One Day of Life*

I was born this day.

Now is the time
To come out and play.
Even though I am a day old,
I can still play.

I died, but I'm in the sky.
You will see me one day.
When the angels come out and play.

Jonathan Zavaleta, Grade 5
Debusk Elementary School, TN
*In memory of Troy Lane

Blue Crane

It soars high,
Over the clouds and in the sky.
At night it flaps its wings to a steady beat.
Moving slowly on its feet.
It's peaceful and quiet,
As the wind passes by it.
The sun makes its wings shine,
As its life slowly passes in time.
Dipping its head in the blue,
Catching fish it will do.
Frogs will sing to the beat,
The crane will stand to its feet.
Another time will pass by,
As it floats to the sky.
The sun will sink in the horizon
As it leaves the beautiful pond.
The sun will shine once again,
For the life of the Blue Crane,
Will never end.

Mattison Bond, Grade 6
Southwestern Middle School, NC

Rockets

Rockets are fast, rockets are fun
there should be a rocket for everyone
we'd have space suits and other cool good keeps
no one could hear because of the beeps
that's what I want that's what I see
when it all comes down and lands in the sea
let's email NASA and see what they say
when we ask "may we ride a rocket today."

Matthew Graves, Grade 6
Graham Elementary School, AL

Destruction

I'm a huge twirling structure
You don't want to mess with me
I'm nothing but pure evil
I will grab and sling you before you would know it
You don't want to look into my eye
I bring many injuries
I destroy towns even states
I'm as mean as a snake and as vicious as a tiger
I come at any time and any place
You can't stop me
I can outrun anybody
Who am I? I am Wolverine the tornado

Jeremiah Delano Chavis, Grade 5
Pembroke Elementary School, NC

Friday

Today is Friday!
Oh joyous, wonderful Friday!
    Friday brings warmth and happiness,
    Friday gives food and wealth to the poor,
    Friday is the pinnacle of the week,
    Friday is — what? Are you sure?
Today is Thursday; oh Thursday you make me sick!

Kassidy Joyner, Grade 6
Benton County School of the Arts, AR

Lions

They are as proud as a king,
Yet as humble as a servant.
Some are like a mountain,
While some are as cowardly as a mouse.
Like a bear, ferocious and strong,
But all of them can be as gentle as kittens.
Their teeth are as sharp as a razor,
And also as white as a dove's feathers.
Their grace and beauty are equivalent to those of a swan.
The lions' roar is like the sound of a meteor hitting the Earth.
They are as smart as any human,
And their speed is so great,
A lion is almost as fast as a light particle.

Ernest Lai, Grade 6
River Trail Middle School, GA

My Fat Cat

I have a cat, he's very fat.
He's crazy, but very lazy.

He thinks he's the king of my bed,
And he thinks we're scared of his large head.

He's very sleepy sometimes, but leapy.
Like I said, he's crazy, but very lazy.

A.J. Witherspoon, Grade 4
Tazewell/New Tazewell Elementary School, TN

Christmas

Christmas is great and jolly.
I always feel happy when I see Aunt Holly.
Christmas is a great big feast,
But my cousin thinks Santa is a beast.

Christmas is beautiful and bright,
But the Christmas tree is such a sight.
Christmas is filled with lots of love.
Especially with the joy from above.

Christmas spirit fills the air
That makes it fun everywhere.
I love to play in the snow,
On my way to the Christmas show.

The Christmas lights are so beautiful and bright,
I love to see them shine during the night.
Christmas is a great time of year,
Because the season is so dear.

Ashlea Berry, Grade 4
Stephens Elementary School, AL

Leaves

Leaves are falling all around
Children are jumping up and down
Leaves are swirling and dancing about
Children are laughing and wanting to shout
"Hooray, Hooray fall is finally here."
This time of year fills us with cheer.

Sarah Matson, Grade 5
All Saints' Episcopal School, TN

The Safety Man

My dad is a safety man.
To keep people safe, he'll do what he can.
He teaches people how to be safe when they drive,
instead of being in an accident on television live.
He's acquainted with his customers, this to you I will tell.
They will sometimes call him on his cell.
My dad is a safety man, and I can't tell you how,
but if you don't know much about safety,
just ask him now!

Shelby Youtsas, Grade 6
Family Life Christian Academy, LA

Rudolph

I am Rudolph.
I wonder if I'll be the head leader.
I hear my sleigh bells ring.
I see Santa packing up.
I want to have a regular nose.
I am Rudolph.

I pretend it's Christmas forever.
I feel me passing school.
I touch Santa.
I worry reindeer might bully me.
I cry when they be mean to me.
I am Rudolph.

I understand I have a red nose.
I say I am normal.
I dream I have a normal nose.
I hope I go down in history.
I try to be normal.
I am Rudolph.

Sydney Hallett, Grade 4
Wohlwend Elementary School, MO

Carrie

C aring and loving
A n artist
R abbit drawing one by one
R ainbow pictures everywhere
I 'm always in a good mood
E ven when it is raining

Carrie Miller, Grade 4
Tamassee-Salem Elementary School, SC

About Me

Hello!
My name is Michaela
If I were a color,
I'd be blue
Like a Sapphire
If I were an animal,
I'd be fast, clever, and beautiful
Like a horse
My favorite place is home
When we wake up on Christmas morning
And open our presents
My favorite snack is pizza sticks
the pepperoni kind
from the little store
I really get upset
When I'm playing
and I have to do my homework
I love listening to Christmas music
When we decorate the tree
before Christmas

Michaela Smith, Grade 4
Pine Tree Hill Elementary School, SC

Blue

Blue looks like the night sky against the white stars on our American flag.
Blue feels like soft material rubbing against my skin.
Blue tastes like a blueberry muffin in the oven.
Blue sounds like the ocean waves pounding against a boat.
Blue is the color of me.

Macy Brooks, Grade 5
Geggie Elementary School, MO

I Am a Military Child

I am a Military Child.
I pretend that I will go off to war and gift for our country.
I feel good when Dakota makes me laugh a lot.
I touch pictures when I am very happy and sad.
I worry that my dad will die in the war.
I cry in the inside when I am very sad.
I understand that my dad had to go to war in Iraq.
I say that every war in the world should end.
I dream to fight for our country for peace.
I am fun to play with and a kid who likes to watch action movies.
I wonder if my dad likes Korea.
I hear army men shooting and throwing their bombs.
I see the planes lifting off during my soccer games when I am playing.
I want my dad not to die in Iraq so I can see him.
I respect the flag because it is the sign of our country.
I hope our country will be safe.
I am a Military Child.

Andrew Figueroa, Grade 4
Walker Intermediate School, KY

Night Lights

The darkness falls across the land,
It's nighttime in my world.
Like time drifting across the sand,
My thoughts of the day swirled.

I close my eyes, but cannot sleep,
For my head is full of fluff.
I try to think of happy thoughts,
To end a day that has been rough.

The light shines through the window,
And falls onto my bed,
I rise to peer out into the dark,
And see a magnificent sight instead.

The moon is beautiful, bright, and clear.
The twinkling stars glisten in the night.
They are so big it seems they're near,
And close enough to hold on tight.

I stare into the night sky for what seems to be an hour.
I'm mesmerized by what I see and start to feel so sleepy.
I guess I didn't realize the night lights held such power.
They rid me of my rushing thoughts and no longer leave me weepy.

Victoria A. Hodgson, Grade 6
J D Meisler Middle School, LA

Goodbye

Goodbye, Goodbye
I said with a sigh.
My heart feels like it is jarred.
Saying goodbye is hard.

No one to talk to, no one that heard.
Just a geek, just a nerd.
I can say this personally.
In loving memory.

Love is the one thing.
It can never be broken.
Not even death can make me sing.
My love is broken.

Tears, Tears, no fears.
Sadness: a disease.
It is no breeze.

Goodbye, Goodbye.
I say with a sigh.
Goodbye.

Seth Blake, Grade 6
Buckhannon-Upshur Middle School, WV

Hope Is Growing

Hope is a garden
  full of thoughts,

Thoughts that make me wonder…
  Why is there war?
  Why is there sickness?
  When will we have peace?
  Will hope remain?

Hope is love and faith in everyone's heart,
  Together we love, together we care.

Hopes are dreams that have not been accomplished.
If there is no hope, what would we have left?

Laurel Elliott, Grade 5
Breitling Elementary School, AL

Cafeteria Lunch

I can't tell you about cafeteria lunch.
Your belly will feel like jelly
The mice walked on the rice
The corn looks moldy and the bread is old and hard
The eggs are rotten and the soup was forgotten
The buns are soggy and the fish is loggy
The chicken was licked and the beans were picked.
I think I'm going to riot
From eating that diet.
But that's just the cafeteria lunch!

Sarah Hassan, Grade 6
Brogden Middle School, NC

Hate

Hate is such a strong word, yet it means so much
You hear it every day as you walk past,
It haunts you every night,
You hear it so much

For it is lonely,
No one is there for it,
It is the loneliest of all emotions,
What is wrong with the world, for it has turned to hate.

Rachel Vizy, Grade 6
Orange Grove Elementary School, MS

The Beach

Tastes like cold lemonade from the cooler
Sounds like seagulls soaring through the air.
Feels like sunshine on your face
Smells like breezes and salty air.
Looks like blue skies everywhere.

Kaitlyn Brooke Scott, Grade 5
Briarwood Christian Elementary School, AL

Veteran

V ery, very sad and hurtful
E very soldier tries very hard
T ogether they make a difference
E very night and day soldiers die
R eload tanks and they make a difference
A ttack is in a war which lasts very long
N ever stop trying for our blessed country

Haleigh Watts, Grade 4
Cherokee Elementary School, AR

Granddaddy's Lake

I love to go to Granddaddy's lake,
Where the water is deep and smooth like glass,
Where tall trees reach for the periwinkle sky,
And the flowers grow in the thick, green grass.

I love to go to Granddaddy's lake,
Where I see my cousins, uncles, and aunts,
Where our family gathers in the Alabama summer,
To watch the rippled waters dance.

I love to go to Granddaddy's lake,
Where we ski and tube and ride the boats,
Where after-dinner cruises are so common,
And we never have to wear our coats.

I loved to go to Granddaddy's lake,
Where times were sweet and family was near,
Where the sun always shone on that little lake house,
I'll never forget the memories so dear!

Elizabeth Cummings, Grade 6
Providence Classical School, AL

Future 5th Graders

5th grade is not a time to play,
We get 50 pounds of books each day.

Pens, pencils, and books galore,
More studying than ever before.

The new Spanish teacher is really nice,
Now let me give you some advice.

Homework that takes you all night,
If your brain gets bigger, don't fright.

Not much time for lunch,
No time to munch and crunch.

Homework piles so tall,
If you wear your backpack you may fall.

Talkers run laps in the hot sun,
It isn't so fun.

So, 4th graders prepare,
And be aware.

Brenna Elmore, Grade 5
St Thomas More School, NC

Homework

Homework makes my brain go dead,
Homework makes my eyes turn red.
Homework makes me want to cry,
Homework makes me want to die.
Homework makes my hands throb,
Homework makes me want to sob.
I had rather go outside and play,
That is how I want to spend the day.
Then I will go to bed,
And rest my aching head.

Mason Jones, Grade 4
Brilliant Elementary School, AL

Country Boy

C ountrified
O utdoors
U nlimited work
N ice people
T alking southern
R ural areas
Y ellow corn

B arns
O utside
Y ellow-bellied snake

Brett Hampton, Grade 6
Clarksburg School, TN

Lithographic Pencil

Lithographic pencil
Sticky fun,
Bright colors
Drawing crazy,
Different colors,
Too many,
Making dizzy,
Fall over.

Shelby Graves, Grade 4
Russell Babb Elementary School, OK

Wind

Wind is the one who calls my name.
It's the one that blows through my hair,
It whispers, "I'll be back someday."
Wind, you give me hope and joy.
Can I call you hope and joy?
Wind please come back…
Someday.

Katie Hicks, Grade 6
Alpena Elementary School, AR

Ocean Fish

water, fish, swim, wave
cold-blooded, long, big, bite
coral reef, no legs

Colby Stringfellow, Grade 4
East Jones Elementary School, MS

My Favorite Season Is Fall

The leaves want to fall.
It's autumn's call.
Yellow, orange, and red.
They make a soft bed.
The plentiful hues
Glisten in morning's dew.
The fog and mist
Make my list
Of reasons to hide
Safe and warm inside.

Brooke Roebuck, Grade 5
Cottonwood Public School, OK

People

White people
Black people
Tall people
Small people
Skinny people
Wide people
People, people
Different kinds of people everywhere.

Alivia Nolting, Grade 5
Immanuel Lutheran School, MO

All About Me

Hello!
My name is Parker.
If I were a color,
I'd be blue,
Like the Colt's color
If I were an animal,
I'd be strong and powerful
Like a lion
My favorite place is on my trampoline
When I'm on vacation
And when I'm done with chores
My favorite snack is popcorn
The full bag with all the butter
on it from Wal-Mart
I really get upset,
When the coach didn't play me
And I had to sit on the bench
I love listening to salsa
When I go to sleep at night.

Parker Robinson, Grade 4
Pine Tree Hill Elementary School, SC

Fishing

wax worms, fishing pole
catching, hooking, reeling, breams
bait, worms, crickets, fun

Rachel Wilson, Grade 4
East Jones Elementary School, MS

Christmastime

Santa is very fat.
He also wears a big red hat.
Santa has presents to enjoy,
For every girl and boy.
Santa has reindeer on his sleigh,
He wishes for you to have a good day.

Desni Briggeman, Grade 4
Horace Mann Elementary School, OK

Air

Air is full of life yet
you cannot see it.
It can be cold or hot.
It can blow hard or soft.
Sometimes it even whistles.

Chris Hughes, Grade 6
Armorel Elementary School, AR

Autumn Leaves

Autumn leaves are like fireworks.
They light up the sky as they fall
Leaving bits everywhere.

Devon McLeod, Grade 4
First Wesleyan Christian School, NC

My Hero

I have a twenty-year-old brother named Drew,
He loves to be in a band crew,
Drew has a disease called Cystic Fibrosis,
When he is sick he gets an I.V.
He coughs a lot and it gets annoying,
He thinks God has a great goal to accomplish
In the future.
He loves his family and friends
And will fight till the end,
My family and friends will keep him in prayer,
A good thing will happen we just don't know where.
Drew is my only brother
And will never want another.
Each and every day I'll be a good friend.

Zachary Stavropoulos, Grade 6
Woodland Presbyterian School, TN

America's Flag

America's flag, red, white, and blue —
  With stripes of red and white.
And stars on top of a background of blue
  Make our flag just right.

For American patriots
  Our flag stands.
And for all who were before us,
  Our flag stood tall.

To be pure —
  And to be true,
They gave their lives
  To the red, white, and blue.

Laurel Moriarty, Grade 4
Heartland High School and Academy, MO

Moon

There is the moon shining so bright.
It gives us light in the night.
It makes the tides low and high.
The stars look as it goes by.
On the moon people found ice.
It is not made out of cheese, too bad for the mice.
There are lots of craters on the moon.
There might even be more soon.
Some nights the moon is new.
Mr. Armstrong left a footprint on it with his shoe.
One day it will be half.
It looks like my nail I can't help but laugh.
Near or far it is always there.
You can even find it at a fair.
Try to look for it tonight.
It will look like a round light.

Kimberla Prevost, Grade 6
St Cecilia School, LA

Fall to Winter

Leaves blow in the winter breeze
Leaves change to red, yellow, orange and brown before a freeze
Children hope it snows on a December night
To see the snowflakes in the light
We tried to stay up with a light
On Christmas night
To see a reindeer taking flight

Kelly Woodard, Grade 4
Evangelical Christian School, TN

Skittles

S alt and pepper fur he has
K ittens he and his brother still are
I love him dearly, yes I do
T iny is he yet a little bit chubby
T errified of open windows
L et's play, he says
E verything's a toy
S o so very cute

Brooke Dedmon, Grade 4
Briarwood Christian Elementary School, AL

Overwhelmed

Surge of numbers, torrent of shapes,
leaving division in their wake.
A parade of little 3s and 9s
marching forward in a line.
Plusses and checks running through my head,
then finally settling as if in bed.
Multiplication twitting and flying,
while I sit, frustrated and trying.
With all this math making tracks in my brain,
getting it done can be a strain.

Griffin Reed, Grade 5
Meramec Elementary School, MO

Football

Looks like a hot sunny day
Sounds like a loud cheering crowd
Smells like kraut on hot-dogs
Tastes like salty peanuts crunching in my mouth.
Feels like a million dollars when your team wins.

John Mason, Grade 5
Briarwood Christian Elementary School, AL

Describing Tests

A test:
A mind-boggling sheet of writing
Don't be fooled by the look of innocence.
Having a test to take is like
Being in a narrow room with nothing but a fence,
Being a marble-sized bug stuck in sap.
Oh, no! I have a test to take.
I'll just go take a swim in the lake.

Kacey Berkbuegler, Grade 5
St Vincent Elementary School, MO

Fall

Fall is a good season.
A good nice fall family time.
A laughing good season
A lucky good season.

Selena Leon, Grade 5
Debusk Elementary School, TN

Monday

I hate Monday, it's the first day of school
When I walk in I feel so cool
My sister says I'm not
But my teacher says I am
So let's forget it and start all over again.

My classes are boring
I'm almost snoring
They wack me with a ruler
And say I'm a drooler
This is Monday
As you see
I've always thought Tuesday
Was better for me.

Corrine McDowell, Grade 6
Brogden Middle School, NC

All About Me

Hello!
My name is Brooke.
If I were a color,
I'd be lime green
Like the color of Hannah's book bag.
If I were an animal,
I'd be real pretty
Like a puppy and a horse.
My favorite place is home.
When I am in my room
And there is no one there.
My favorite snack is ice cream,
the Oreo cookie and cream kind
from Baskin Robbins.
I really get upset
when my sister comes in my room
and I have to get her out.
I love listening to the radio
when nobody is in my room
and they are aggravating me.

Brooke Dixon, Grade 4
Pine Tree Hill Elementary School, SC

Corned Horn

Once I saw a dragon,
Sitting in a wagon
He was eating corn
But it got stuck on his horn.

Alex Rains, Grade 4
South Topsail Elementary School, NC

I Am an Army Son

I am an army son that loves his dad and wants to keep him safe.
I wonder if my dad will have to go back to Iraq.
I hear aircraft overhead and gunfire in the background of soldiers preparing.
I see soldiers returning from Iraq at the hospital with wounds from the war.
I want the war to end so all the soldiers can return home.
I am an army son that loves his dad and wants to keep him safe.

I pretend not to worry that he will return.
I feel the stress of other kids as their dads are gone.
I touch his picture, clothes, and car while he is gone to make me feel closer to him.
I worry each day he is gone because I don't know what is happening to him.
I cry when I think about the friend that I lost to the war.
I am an army son that loves his dad and wants to keep him safe.

I understand my dad wants to protect the United States and the people.
I say he is a hero.
I dream about the day he retires and I won't worry about when he'll leave again.
I try not to let him see that I worry.
I hope people understand what it is like to have your parents at war.
I am an army son that loves his dad and wants to keep him safe.

Samual Delle Donne, Grade 5
Walker Intermediate School, KY

The Other Side

My great-grandpa lived to be 100 years old.
He worked in the hot and he worked in the cold.
His wavy gray hair and his dark blue eyes
Told me the stories of the other side.
His old wrinkled skin told of his long days in the sun
As he drove his bulldozer till he was done.

My great-grandpa, Bert, was the first to create a road cutting down trees
In the misty, cool breeze.
You might have driven up one of his roads.
If you have then you'll remember the story that I have told.
My great-grandpa Bert cut the road on the mountainside.

So now when you go to hike on the Appalachian Trail
You'll find it leads you to Max's Patch.
Then you can see far and wide
And you too can see the other side.

Jaclynn Estes, Grade 4
Sequoyah Elementary School, TN

In the Fame

Juked my brother because I showed him my strength
My body formed a spin move; it was as fast as lightning
In my head I heard roars from the crowd proclaiming my success
A sudden zone change
Got the game winning ball from the effort I gave
Bashful I became as the word got out
Perseverance was the key to winning success

Gatlin Claybern, Grade 5
Cline Elementary School, KY

New Year Already

What New Year's here already
This CANNOT be true,
I must have slept in late on Christmas
And nobody knew
I missed the hot chocolate,
The marshmallows…
Gingerbread house…
I must have been sleepin' like a mouse,
And WHAT my presents aren't there,
I'm getting angry and my nostrils began to flare,
Mama! Mama! I began to shout, but as I look around
She is nowhere in sight, and OH MY LANTERNS,
I see Santa Claus out in the night, and wait, wait,
Is it a bird or a plane, NO it's my mother,
WHAT it was all a dream,
And what I have presents, once again,
And now my poem can have a beautiful end.

Miya Goodwin, Grade 5
Romine Inter District Elementary School, AR

Silver Sun

The moon is like a silver sun
In the black curtain of the night
The stars are its fellow friends
That fade at dawn
The moon is like a guardian angel
That watches us through the dark night
When the sun comes up in the morning
Its duties are done
Until the black night comes again
And the moon takes place as our silver sun

Rachel Scott, Grade 6
Bernard Middle School, MO

Move Along

The waves blow on and the boats move along,
so soon he reached the shore.
"Let us move along," shouted the boy.
"NO! We will not move along
we will not stay aside we'll just hide
in our blankets and say bye-bye."
"NO! 1. You will move along.
Also 2. You won't say bye-bye."
"So as soon as we leave we will get some ice cream.
So let's move along as we sing a little song."

Jada Reddin, Grade 4
St Mary Cathedral Elementary School, MO

Never Give Up

Never give up on a test or anything.
Believe in yourself, that you will make an A on a test,
Your parents are counting on you.
Accomplish your dreams.
Never give up.

Lynnsey Murry, Grade 5
Western Hills Elementary School, AR

Friends

Friends, they care for you, love you.
Best friends are people who keep secrets,
And do not talk about you behind your back.
Friends help you
if you do not know how to ride a bicycle.
If you hurt yourself, your friend
should be right beside you to help you,
And most of all friends are to love.

Chreyshayla Lognion, Grade 5
Romine Inter District Elementary School, AR

I Remember Libby

I remember Libby…
Her soft pink tongue, her soft brown ears,
her black shiny nose, her pretty brown fur.

I remember Libby…
Going for a walk, walking with mom,
prancing down the big long streets, watching her eat.

I remember Libby…
Her smell, her face, her soft bark, her wiggly tail.

I remember Libby.

Kirsten Swanda, Grade 5
Sycamore Elementary School, GA

Music

You've come a long way since Miss Mary Mac.
Clapping hands and talking smack.
You've come from America to strut
From far away to I got nerve.
From this land is our land to it ends tonight.
I'll know you'll be here in the morning.
You've had soul, heart, rhythm, and sometimes passion
You talk about the blues and the hard times
Music, how would we live without you

Quianna Lewis, Grade 6
Brogden Middle School, NC

Mr. Tough Guy

I am the fastest thing in the world no one can catch me
I can twirl so fast I look invisible
I'm deadlier than a rattlesnake
I cause devastation wherever I go
I will get so furious you don't want to mess with me
I am the most powerful thing in the world
I am bigger and worst than the Tasmanian Devil
I'm meaner than a Mountain Lion
I'm unstoppable, I'm the biggest and the most
powerful thing in the world, you can't catch me
You better watch out 'cause I'm a tornado

Shateah Lynn Mitchell, Grade 5
Pembroke Elementary School, NC

Leaves

Rustling under your feet,
As you walk through the garden,
Over to the old oak.
Raining leaves around the yard,
In all colors of the rainbow.

Kellan Fluette, Grade 6
Chapin Middle School, SC

Snakes

Smooth
Slimy, thick
Thin, slick
Sly, slippery
Reptiles

Leassa Kellerman, Grade 5
Marion Elementary School, MO

The Mud Flood Day

Today was a mud and flood day
And the clouds were very gray.
It rained especially hard
So my friends and I played cards.
The rain made it cold,
And I woke up freezing in my household.
The rest of my family felt the same,
The rain was the only one to blame.
Then I read a book
And in the kitchen I went to cook.
Today was a mud and flood day
And the clouds were very gray.

Aunesty Chrystal, Grade 4
Cleveland Elementary School, OK

Opposites

I discovered a robot
and took it home with me,
But when I said stand up
He sat down with glee.
I cannot shake him,
I may have to bake him!
If I say cook,
He cleans!
The opposite of me!
He's a nice guy, yes,
But no commands
Does he hear.
I am saving my money for a hammer
And then I am going to go bammer!
Or slammer!
Whichever comes first,
But it's going to happen!
Sooner or later!

Garett Brock, Grade 6
Alpena Elementary School, AR

Who Am I?

I'm nice, smart, and athletic.
I dance and ice skate and play.
I'm a student and athlete and jokester.

I sound like music,
I feel like dancing.
I move like an ice skater,
And look like a silly boy.

I'm as hot as the sun,
And smart as a dolphin.

I wait for an airplane to go home.
I long for school at St. Joseph's.
I hope to see my mom and dad.
I dream of getting my driver's license.

My name is Kalin.

Kalin Khera, Grade 5
St Joseph Institute for the Deaf, MO

School Is Cool

Roses are red,
Violets are blue,
Mrs. Daniel is cool,
And Mrs. Barrett is too.

I like reading.
I like writing.
I like everything,
Except fighting.

Stay in school
So you can be cool!

Dylan Little, Grade 5
Cottonwood Public School, OK

Leaves

The leaves were
F
a
l
l
i
n
g
from the trees because
of the beautiful fall breeze.

The trees had bright colored
LEAVES
It felt 40 degrees.

Alisha Bostic, Grade 4
Easley Elementary School, NC

Christmas Tree!

I am a Christmas tree
I wonder if I will stay green
I hear my branches being bent out
I see myself being tall
I want to be decorated
I am a Christmas tree

I pretend I'm huge
I feel the warm lights
I touch the ornaments
I cry when my branch gets broke
I am a Christmas tree

I understand if they don't want me
I say it's ok if I don't get picked
I dream of being the most decorated tree
I hope I'll go away
I try not to fall
I am a Christmas tree

Stephen Hemann, Grade 4
Wohlwend Elementary School, MO

I Can't Write a Poem*

I am sick
I broke my fingers
I don't want to
Make me
My head hurts
My pencil broke
I hate writing

Times up? Uh oh!!!
All I have is this
list of excuses!!!
You like it? Really!!!
No kidding!
Thanks a
lot!!!
Would you like to see
another one?

Sam Warren, Grade 6
Armorel Elementary School, AR
*Patterned after "I Can't Write a
Poem" by Bruce Lansky*

Pumpkin Pie

Pumpkin pie is a treat
For my family and I to eat.
The aroma makes me want to jump!
Makes my belly round and plump.
Thick layers of pumpkin pie
Makes me just want to die.

Hanna Pigg, Grade 4
Coleman Elementary School, OK

Christmas Time

Snow, Snow, Snow.
I can tell Christmas is on its way!
Snowy cars, shoveling snow, and no school.
Oh! I can't wait!
Snowmen with carrot noses, snow angels, and snowballs.
Can I go outside and play?
Christmas trees, presents, and ornaments.
Hey! Where did the star go?
Hot cocoa, warm red fires, and big fluffy blankets.
Brr! It's cold!
Santa, Rudolph, and Frosty.
Ho! Ho! Ho!
Christmas Day is here!!

Maria MacLean, Grade 6
Old High Middle School, AR

A Friend

A friend is someone who's always there
Always cares
Always shares
They're there for you when you are down
They make you smile instead of frown
A friend is nice, kind, and polite
And hardly ever starts a fight
A friend is someone whom you can depend
She'll be there for you until the very end.

Lenae Allison Cordell, Grade 6
Maplewood Middle School, LA

Snowflakes

Cold as the ice age
Too tiny to see
All are different as you and me
Like twinkling stars of the endless outer space sea
Like little silver pieces of jewelry
They melt in golden rays of light
They dissolve in the grass of height
They turn into water that people like
That ends the life of a little snowflake tyke

Uma Kaladi, Grade 4
Nesbit Elementary School, GA

I Am From

I am from playing with trucks in the smooth dirt.
I am from riding bikes in the cold air
and watching birds fly over my head.
I am from a loving family that cares about me.
I am from drinking milk and eating cookies
after a hard day of school.
I am from eating crawfish and crabs
when my dad gets back from work.
I am from a great place to live.

Clay Hebert, Grade 6
Arnaudville Elementary School, LA

Shy Person

I'm the shy person,
That says nothing at all.
Talk to me anytime,
I'll shrug my shoulders.

I don't like to talk,
Especially in class,
Not even a group,
Nor two.

I might ignore you,
But please,
I don't mean it,
I just don't know what I'll do.

Shrugging my shoulders is what I'm good at,
And I just love doing this.
One thing I'm going to ask you is,
Do you know what this means?
It means I don't want to reply.

Jenny Huy, Grade 5
Nesbit Elementary School, GA

Fireworks

They light up the midnight sky,
Making peoples hearts soar.
Their graceful shapes seem to fly.
Leaving people wanting more.

Impatient watchers wait for them to begin,
As they stare into open space.
Once they go off they make a big crackle,
Making watchers run all over the place.

Camilla Warrington, Grade 6
Brogden Middle School, NC

Christmas

Christmas is a time for laughter and joy.
I bet you want that special toy!
But, that's not what Christmas is about,
It's about giving and singing out!

While you're sleeping in your bed,
Santa and his reindeer are above your head!
Now he's creeping in your house!
He's as quiet as a mouse.

Once you awake,
You run through the house like an earthquake!
When you see what's under the tree,
Nobody's there, but the presents and me!

You should really keep in mind,
At Christmastime always be cheerful and kind!

Cierra Bolding, Grade 4
Lula Elementary School, GA

I Am Haunted

I was haunted by the thought of one day waking up to a weird and worryful slimy thing
laying on my bed, a snake, a slimy slithery scary snake.
What if it wraps tightly around me and strangles me to death?

I was haunted by thinking that there are monsters in my closet
waiting 'til the very short second I shut my eyes to drag me into their mind tricking mystery world.
You know like Dracula and the Boogieman, only I think the Boogieman lives under the bed.

I was haunted by huge hairy hungry spiders.
They were so creepy and crawly. I always got to thinking that they would stare at me
then attack me for my really red blood.
But now I don't think that made much sense.

I am now haunted by the thought of going to a cemetery on a dark scary night
when there was a full moon and there was scary little spiders crawling in the
little cracks of the stones, just waiting for the very moment I can't see and trip over one of the stones.
Then BOOM, all of the dark dreadful dead people come out of their graves and attack me.
I don't even want to know what will happen next.

I will soon be haunted by the thought of a new day going outside and a bunch of vultures attack me
because they think I am a giant gross possum.

I am haunted
I am very haunted!

Rachael Moore, Grade 5
Eminence Middle School, KY

The Destroying Beast

I am a gigantic, unstoppable, beast that will huff and puff and blow you away. I am an incredible, supersonic, angry, spinning
tornado that will rip you into bits. I am bigger and stronger than the devil. I am so mean you will wish you were never born. I
am ugly and I can destroy the whole world. I am a deadly, petrifying, terrible wind storm and I am a horrible beast. You better
watch out for me!!

Destiny Locklear, Grade 5
Pembroke Elementary School, NC

I Am From...

I am from the white blurry room of the doctors the dirty blonde hair of my first puppy dog
I am from the dirty, yet delicious flowers of my own forest
I am from the bruises of bad things I have done
I am from the clear, blue water of the neighborhood lake and
I am from fluffy clouds of the high flying swings
I am from the warm bath water
I am from the little boat and yellow squeaky ducks
From the dirt of the tile to my mother's warm arms and the coldness of the old wedding ring
I am from the shiny, sparkling stars of the black open sky
I am from the warm delightfulness of fresh baked cookies on a cold winter day
I am from the long lost goldfish that swam in the fishbowl now sitting in the
old garage full of toys from my toddler years and the best Christmas presents
I am from the screen of endless fun known as television
I am from the fluffy blue bed and ocean scene room of my own
From all four to two legs of sprinting energy
I am from the build ups of support from family and friends
I am from the cold stiff water of winter
I am the only me and no one can be the same as me.

Austin Baeckeroot, Grade 4
Big Creek Elementary School, GA

Christmas

C hristmas is here!
H appy Holidays to you.
R inging bells here and there.
I ce cold snow everywhere.
S inging Christmas songs.
T rees that are decorated.
M istletoe to kiss under.
A ll kids dreaming of presents.
S ee the lights on homes.

I cicles hanging from roofs.
S anta is coming!

C andy canes peeping out of the stockings.
O rnaments sparkling.
M erry people shopping.
I ce cold snowmen that have been built by kids.
N ew gifts for the kids to play with.
G reen and red colors everywhere!

Jodi Blanton, Grade 6
Alvaton Elementary School, KY

Horses/People

Horses
fast, furry
galloping, eating, trotting
mustangs, Clydesdales, workers, farmers
gossiping, reading, singing
talkative, spoiled
People

Chaffin Hart, Grade 5
Briarwood Christian Elementary School, AL

Love

Love is powerful.
It can change someone's life forever.
Mentally and physically.
Love is fabulous!
But it can be harsh…
And once you know it
It turns into
Hate.

Daniela Thielisch, Grade 6
R D and Euzelle P Smith Middle School, NC

Trees

Everywhere you look,
You're likely to see a tree.
A tree of any shape and size,
with colors of the rainbow.
Red, green, or yellow,
littered on the ground.
But unfortunately we lose these precious greens,
to metal monsters with razor teeth, wedge head, and chain claw.

Jack Adamson, Grade 6
Bellwood Discovery School, TN

Black

Black is the color of the night,
Filling your head to the brim with fright;
Black are the shadows, when the sun is out;
But, in the black, everybody give a shout;
So, why are you scared of an owl's "whoo,"
When in the dark every ghost shrieks a "boo?"

Marisa Boyd, Grade 6
St Anne Catholic School, SC

Our Flag

Our flag stands high in the sky,
   It is a colorful flag.
It stands so straight in the sky.
   It is a flag of justice
That was stitched with heart full of love.
   I love the flag that was stitched above.
It was stitched with kindness
   And handmade for our country.
It is a thoughtful flag.
   The soldiers look at it with love.
It shows liberty and freedom
   And justice for all.

Emmily Johnson, Grade 4
Heartland High School and Academy, MO

Swimming

I went swimming in a swampy habitat,
When I jumped in I went kersplat.
It is too bad I did that
I should have played with my cat.
There's something long and spiky and very grim,
I'd better swim now, or he'll give me a trim.
I shouldn't go swimming in a swampy habitat
Or else with an alligator I may combat.

Sophia Gabrielson, Grade 4
Cleveland Elementary School, OK

The World Series

9th inning, 2 outs, 3 balls, 2 strikes.
World Series
The batter steps in the box,
it's a bad thing if he gets hit,
because he's as fast as a fox
But first Smoltz steps off the mound,
But, he looks deep down, his power he has found,
Smoltz lobs, right down the middle,
The batter sobs, because it's fast as a fiddle
STRIKE! You're out.
Hear the announcer saying,
"They won the World Series, the crowd is going insane"
Fifteen years later,
Smoltz is in the Hall of Fame.

Matt Zibanejadrad, Grade 5
American Heritage Academy, GA

Countryside

Turkeys squawking,
chickens squealing
Maw and Paw are
inside a-eatin'.

Me and you are
having a ball,
while the turkeys
have no fun at all.

We laugh, we cry,
we eat, we sigh,
we eat everything
'till the turkey is dry.
We do it all in the
COUNTRYSIDE.

Lezlie Tollison, Grade 6
Guntown Middle School, MS

Flowers

F uming scents all around
L oving times will be found
O ut of the world into your brain
W hen will it happen all over again
E arly sun beams peeking through
R evolving around you
S unshine on the wet shiny dew

Lillian McEntire, Grade 5
Montessori School North Little Rock, AR

Veteran

V ictorious over our country
E quipment in the camps
T ake down the enemies
E xtreme danger on the battle field
R epair the tanks and
A mbush the enemies
N ever give up, soldiers.

Eric Day, Grade 4
Cherokee Elementary School, AR

What Am I?

What am I?
I can be hilly, I can be flat.
What am I?
I have lighthouses, five of them.
What am I?
My capital is Raleigh.
What am I?
I have three regions.
What am I?
I AM NORTH CAROLINA!

Ashley Foster, Grade 4
Moyock Elementary School, NC

Fall

Wind singing,
Bells are ringing.
Leaves flying here and there,
Oh, beautiful fall is here.

People are starting to wear coats,
Even the animals wear coats even goats.
You can see rabbits running round,
So move your feet on the ground.

Nathan Bennett, Grade 4
North Elementary School, NC

My Name

M agnificent
A thletic
R ight handed
T alkative
H ealthy
A nnoying

W onderful
I mpressive
L aughs a lot
L oveable
I nconsiderate
A ctive
M ean
S ensible

Martha Williams, Grade 6
Lloyd-Kennedy Charter School, SC

The One the Only Me

I am funny and nice
I wonder if I will be wealthy
I hear whistling
I see me
I want good friends
I am funny and nice

I pretend to fly
I feel emotion
I touch water
I worry when I will die
I cry when I think about someone dying
I am funny and nice

I understand that I will have to grow up
I say love
I dream about friends
I try to do better in school
I hope I will live a long life
I am funny and nice

McKinzie Devereaux, Grade 6
Hayes Elementary School, OK

Bearcats

B est team in the region.
E laborate on defense.
A very skilled team.
R acing for the sweet 16.
C reative minds on offense.
A very passionate team.
T eam everyone wants to be like.
S uper effort.

Zach McNeil, Grade 5
Walton Verona Elementary School, KY

I Am a Baseball

I am a baseball,
small and round.
I'm hit high and hard.
There is the fence.
Thump! I'm hitting the ground.
Now I bounce over the fence.
It is a ground rule double, and
the last play of the game.
The Cardinals win, and
the crowd goes wild!

Brandon Kapp, Grade 6
St Vincent Elementary School, MO

Fall

F un
A utumn
L eaves
L ater

Kristen Roberson, Grade 4
East Jones Elementary School, MS

Autumn Leaves

Autumn leaves
are like a soaring bird in the blue sky,
swaying in the breeze.

Ryan Hammond, Grade 4
First Wesleyan Christian School, NC

Family Closet

My family is like a closet:
My dad is the distressed jeans
Working so hard.
My mom is a belt
Keeping things held together.
My sister is like Nike Shocks
Energetic as can be.
My brother is earrings
Cute but sometimes gets in the way
And I am the Polo
Completing the whole outfit.

Meredith Coomes, Grade 6
College View Middle School, KY

The Beach

Soft waves lapping,
Everyone is laughing,
Warm sand on the land,
Quieter than the sound of mice.
You may hear a gull cry,
In the light blue sky.
Moonlight shines to light the night,
Just as the sun so bright.
Millions of animals in the sea,
Are intriguing to you and me.
As the land we live on,
The beach is a home to many.
What a beautiful creation,
For all to see.

Brittany Brooks, Grade 6
Haynes Academy for Advanced Studies, LA

The Sports I Play with My Friends

Basketball, baseball, soccer, and football
Are the sports I play with my friends.
When homework is done,
We meet in the sun.
Dribbling, catching, kicking, and passing,
We play sports together.

We try hard.
We have fun.
And that is why
We play sports together.

Noah Elliott Patton, Grade 4
Evangelical Christian School, TN

Season

Winter, spring, summer, fall.
Oh! Boy I love them all.
Swimming, leaves falling, flowers blooming and snow,
How much I like them,
you'll never know.

Summer and spring makes me sing.
Swimming and when kids voices ring.
Winter and fall leaves snow.
When each comes I have a ball.

Fall and winter are cool.
We like our time out of school.
We plan to have lots of fun.

Spring and summer and fun,
We have fun in the sun.
Our time is short.
We have fun of a different sort.

Max Vaughn, Grade 5
Joann Walters Elementary School, AR

A Wonderful World

It's glowing inside.
There's nothing to hide.
My family is on my side.

Just look at the moon, shiny and bright.
Look at the stars glowing at night.
Look at the sun giving off so much light.

Just look at the flowers, where the bees crawl.
Look at the trees standing so tall.
Look at the ground hiding beneath leaves of the fall.

Just look at the ocean, past piles of sand.
Look at the streams cutting through the land.
Look at the waterfall pounding like a band.

Just look at the animals, all perfectly matching.
Look at the monkeys squeaking and scratching.
Look at the birds peacefully hatching.

Just look at your fellow humans, as they progress.
Look at the children playing at recess.
Look at the adults seeking success.

Just look at the Earth, God made it for you and me.
You'll appreciate it if you can really see.
No one else is as powerful as He.

Safiyah Elkomy, Grade 5
Islamic School of Central Missouri, MO

Bad Things Happen (to Me)

One day I went to town
And just walked around.
All of a sudden a baseball came at me.
I ducked and it missed
Then it bounced back and hit me.
I had amnesia for a few days
And at school I thought I was in first grade.

One day I jumped a horse
Over a pole that was long and low.
The horse stumbled
And I fell off head first.
I woke up two weeks later
With a bump on my head
And it really hurt when I went to bed.

One day I was playing soccer
And I was about to score.
Then I got slide tackled from behind.
My leg started bleeding.
It made a big mess.
And guess what
I had to clean it up.

Clint Shannon, Grade 6
Jackson Christian School, TN

Zilla

Zilla is my pet lizard,
he is not very big.

But when people hear his name,
they think he is the size of a pig.

Zilla likes to eat bugs,
like the ones he finds under the rug.

Zilla is my best friend and
this poem has come to an end.

Shannun Swiney, Grade 5
Magnolia Springs Baptist Academy, AL

Governor's Palace

A ssembly,
B uilding,
C apitol,
D isliked,
E xamples,
F avor, **G** overnor,
H ighness, **I** mpress,
St. **J** ohn, **K** ing,
L awmakers, **M** embers,
N oble, **O** wners,
P alace, **Q** uills, **R** oyal,
S igned, **T** axes,
U nited,
V irginia, **W** illiamsburg,
X eno,
Y awn,
Z enith

Lane Gibson, Grade 5
Alvaton Elementary School, KY

The Wild

There are many animals in the wild.
They are impressive to a child.
Lions are the kings.
Birds like to sing.
Deer are amazing to me.
But you have to go to see.

James Robert Blake, Grade 4
Contentnea Elementary School, NC

Storm

Rain striking roofs
Thunder booming loudly
Lightning flashing, shooting down trees
Fighting, seeing who is stronger.
They'll fight the night away
Until finally they rest,
Letting the sun come out
Until the next fight comes again.

Erica Storey, Grade 4
Atkinson Elementary School, NC

The Best Day Ever!

The beach is so awesome!
I can't say that enough that the beach is so grand
My favorite part is soaking my feet through the sand
The beautiful beach means everything to me
As I watch and learn the waves rush up against my ankles
I knew this was going to be the best day ever!
As I watch from far away every day I was hearing something new
The beach is awesome
I can't wait till I go again!

Taylor Hogan, Grade 5
Stokesdale Elementary School, NC

Blue

Blue
Looks like a beautiful night sky.
Blue
Feels like a perfect summer day.
Blue
Tastes like sweet sugary blueberry.
Blue
Smells like fresh violets.
Blue
Sounds like an amazing rhythm.
Blue
Is everything but mostly surprising because of what it is and what it could be.

Dajsha Townsend, Grade 5
Geggie Elementary School, MO

Why You Should Always Train Your Dog

You should always train your dog because, you know those big holes
they will probably never stop until you get old old old.
Most of the time when you look down you will see
dirty slobber all over your knee!
You probably know by now
your untrained dogs howl.
When they rip up your flower
they think they have the power,
You will probably never see another bird fly
because your dog can jump so very high.
Instead of letting your dog rip up your month's pay
you should teach him how to stay,
If your dog used to be very bad,
once you train him you will be very glad.

Brittany Francisco, Grade 4
Lewis Vincent Elementary School, LA

My First Deer

In a stand a top a tree I wait for a glance for something to see.
I raise my gun and at the first noise I hear ready to shoot my first deer.
There he stands slender and tall with antlers that look 8 feet tall.
I pull the rifle to a firing position pull the trigger with great anticipation.
After the smoke clears from my gun I look, what I have done?
I would like to say on the ground there he laid.
But to my dismay all I could see was him on his way.

Kyle Price, Grade 4
Brilliant Elementary School, AL

Ocean Blue

Ocean blue is like a warm cup of tea in the morning
Ocean blue feels like you're in the ocean
Ocean blue looks like a blueberry patch
Ocean blue tastes like a blueberry punch
Ocean blue reminds me of the ocean blue

Alex Pfeil, Grade 5
Geggie Elementary School, MO

I Remember Grampa

I remember Grampa…
His funny laugh, his calm voice, his soft eyes, his silent naps

I remember Grampa…
Understanding, always listening, helpful, willing

I remember Grampa…
Making me smile, caring for me, loving me, rising up

I remember Grampa

Kaylee Floyd, Grade 5
Sycamore Elementary School, GA

I Went for a Walk

I'm walking in the night,
I look up and see the moon shining oh so bright.
I walk into an alley, suddenly, there is no light.
I turn slowly and what do I see?
A very big man staring at me.

I try to run,
But he catches me and says, "There will be no fun."
I yelp for help hoping someone might hear,
I listen so hard straining my ear.
I listen for a sound,
Finally, I hear something walking on the ground.

Then out of the blue,
I see a shadow, but I knew it couldn't be true.
Then I heard a police man pull out his gun and say "freeze,"
then everything was quiet even the breeze.
When I got home my parents and I sat down to talk,
I went to bed and thought, I never should have went for a walk.

Benjamin Bruce, Grade 5
Blackburn Elementary School, MO

Christmastime

Christmastime is almost here.
So let us give a big, loud cheer.
Wouldn't you like to ride in Santa's sleigh,
And then shout, "Hurray!"
Be good little girls and boys.
Play nicely with your toys.
If you don't, it might not be shocking,
When you find a lump of coal in your stocking.

Genevieve Palmich, Grade 6
Queen of Angels Catholic School, GA

In the Night

In the night, the silent night
In the thick coated, black striped silent night
With the cricket's chirp and the world's wind
Everything here God did send
Just standing outside in the wild, wild world
Everything here I want to keep forever.

Tess Hartis, Grade 4
Chester Park Elementary School of Fine Arts, SC

Good Night

It's night so lie down,
Lie down on a cloud.
Forget about all that has been done,
Forget about all of the things that have been done to you.
Lay your head on my leg,
Sleep as I will keep you safe for you are my sweet.
Close your eyes and listen to my song,
Though sung with the birds.
All is fine when you and I are together safe,
Together with only love and voices with us.
The song I sang is great,
With you in between my quilt made with love.
Throughout the night I will sing,
Sing for you to fall asleep.
If you awake,
I will be holding you in my arms,
In the morning we will sing together.
Together, forever you will remember me.
For you will sing my song for your loved ones.

Gabrielle Sellers, Grade 6
Orange Grove Elementary School, MS

The Lost Sheep

From the depths of the castle's dungeon lay
The silversmith suffering and sad.
The king didn't like him so he would say,
"Why do you make me so mad?"

Death would tease and taunt and sing;
Inside him a battle was waging.
Sin would dance and prance and sting;
The war in his soul was raging.

From the core of the twilight's crawling,
From the lip of the raven-black night,
Came the voice of temptation calling,
Luring and holding him tight.

Mercy and courage dismounted,
From the heavens where God lives in love;
The blood of his Savior was counted,
Offering him strength from above.

Ariel Huhn, Grade 5
Providence Academy, TN

Sick

Today I'm "sick," and out of school,
My mom believed me, she's such a fool!
I told her that my tongue was pink,
I feel so nauseous I can't think!
I told her that I have Chicken Pox,
But I just colored with red dots.
I told her that my feet were blue,
She didn't know it wasn't true!
I told her that I'm turning purple,
And that I've growing orange gurples
I told her that my hair is growing out,
And I'm becoming short and stout!
And when it came to Saturday,
I was "better" and went out to play.

Colleen Zelenski, Grade 6
Hayes Elementary School, OK

The Raven

A caw!
Black birds
Ruby eyes
Swift fliers
Dark as night
Come out at twelve.
Midnight is the time of lost treasures.

A caw!
The raven is here
A lost, dark soul.

Grace Long, Grade 4
Atkinson Elementary School, NC

Thanksgiving

T ime of thanks and cheer,
H appy people come to eat.
A ll day we meet with family,
N o sadness comes about.
K indness is here to share,
S o come on in and take a chair.
G od gave us this wonderful day,
I think we should stop and pray.
V oices sing with thanks to God,
I n rhythm we play with laud.
N ice people are all about,
"**G** od is good!" we shout.

Nick Kerns, Grade 6
Victory Christian School, OK

Summer

Flowers, sunshine, swimming,
Butterflies, play, barbecue
Family, soccer

Abby Baravik, Grade 4
East Jones Elementary School, MS

Daddy

My daddy loves me very much.
He takes care of me right to the touch.
He always tucks me in at night,
And helps when I'm in a fight.
Dad encourages me to be the best.
But it sometimes gets me stressed.
He's always by my side.
Sort of like a personal guide.
That's why I love my daddy so much
Right to the very touch.

Addie Lewis, Grade 6
Pleasants County Middle School, WV

People

Some people sleep and sleep
and some are very active
Some people are not pretty
and some are very attractive

Some people nag and nag
and some don't try to fight
Some people smile and smile
and some don't show any light

Will Swihart, Grade 6
Central Arkansas Christian School, AR

Grandparents

Grandparents are fun.
Grandparents are wrinkly.
Grandparents can't run.

Grandparents can run
When their grandson
Is stuck in a car
Rolling afar.

They let you watch TV.
And you can sit on their knee,
Then you watch them snore and sleep.

If you're still young
You have to take a nap.
Oh, but I grew out of that!
But it's good to get some sleep
Every once in a while.

Ella Klott, Grade 5
Frankford Elementary School, MO

Turkey Time

The hunters will hunt.
The turkeys will be hunted.
Go away turkeys!

Savannah Murr, Grade 5
St Joseph Institute for the Deaf, MO

The Summer of Summers

The lake feels so crisp
Honeysuckle smells so sweet
The tree's shade is nice

Ciara Wallace, Grade 6
Tomlinson Jr High School, OK

Falling Food

Some people fall far
yet they never leave the ground
Some people are very very lost
but finally are found.

Some fear to gain knowledge
yet many fear to lose it instead
Some people are very hungry
yet some remain overfed.

Jason A. Justice, Grade 6
Central Arkansas Christian School, AR

Books

Books!
Pages and pages.
They try to attack my brain,
Never wanting me to stop reading.

Courtney King, Grade 5
St Vincent Elementary School, MO

Veteran

V icious and victorious soldiers
E ager to battle
T rouble is around the corner
E quipped with weapons
R eady to go
A ttacking the enemy
N ever let down our country.

Charles Latham, Grade 4
Cherokee Elementary School, AR

The Laughing Kookaburra

Kookaburra
Australian bird
Living, laughing, flying
Eating small reptiles for dinner
Kingfisher

Connie Nichols, Grade 4
Indian Springs Elementary School, AL

Season Call

I hear the cool wind blowing
and the old crows crowing.
When I hear that special chime
I know that it's Thanksgiving time.

Deanna Hopper, Grade 6
Guntown Middle School, MS

Tea for Three

Some folks, at their house, for two make tea,
but at Grammy's house we serve tea for three.
The guests at this party, are no mystery you see,
'cause it's Grammy, Granddaddy, and little ole me.

Our table is spread upon the floor
with water-colored tea, cookies, and more.
Grammy pours and Granddad sips,
being very careful not to burn his lips.

With cloth, napkins, and tiny china cups,
we pretend to be living it up!
We laugh and talk and visit awhile,
making memories that, for years, will bring a smile.

If you look quite clearly, you will see
I love them and they love me.
And we three will always agree,
Tea Parties are best shared, not by two, but by three.

Hannah Eastin-Burkart, Grade 6
Center Place Restoration School, MO

Brown

Brown sounds like the crunching
of my dad's favorite cereal on a cold winter morning.
Brown looks like dead leaves
that are on the lawn over night.
Brown feels like a smooth little turtle
sitting in a mud puddle after a hard rainy evening.
Brown smells like a Native American
after a war with smelly gun powder.
Brown tastes like my favorite candy bar
that I accidentally left in my back pocket last night.
Brown sounds like my grandma's dog
Oreo barking at the food in my hands.
Brown looks like dirty socks and a uniform
after a hard baseball game.
Brown feels like a soft rocking chair
that a mother sits in to rock her baby to sleep.
Brown smells like a dog's cage before cleaning.
Brown tastes like a burnt piece of toast
in the morning with cold cereal.

Amanda Lankford, Grade 5
Cool Spring Elementary School, NC

Lies

Lies start out small and thin.
Then go on and on and may never end.
Lies are knots in you that twist and turn.
Liars are untrustworthy and not good friends.
Lies make you stressed and sometimes mad.
So why don't you stop telling those horrible lies.

Sara Wallace, Grade 5
Parker Road Elementary School, MO

So You Want to Be a Monster

So you want to be a monster
Here's what it's about
Here are some great tips to help you out.
You don't look like one
But you are already mean
We will get you a costume
So you can be a big, green, ugly machine.
I may not like you
You may not like me
We'll get you some ugly teeth
To help you with one thing.
You may be weird
You may not be nice
But if I help you there will be a price.
So you want to be a monster
Now you look like one
It matches your personality
100 to none.

Sami Dixon, Grade 6
Knollwood Christian School, AL

Inside a Girl's Mind

Inside a girl's mind is very complicated,
It might be who she likes or who she hated
Some people try to figure it out,
But never know what it's all about
It's full of rumors or facts,
It's who stabbed who in the back
Anything you want to know, it's there,
All up under her style of hair
So once again, it's difficult
Being nosy isn't an insult
Be careful what she hears,
Because it'll be there for years
Inside a girl's mind is her own world,
She knows everything about boys and girls.

Madeleine Monson, Grade 6
Our Lady of Fatima School, MS

Autumn

Leaves fall to the ground
cooler weather is now here
scarecrows and pumpkins

Anna Lea Strickland, Grade 4
Briarwood Christian Elementary School, AL

Veteran

V ictory is ours as we stand.
E quipped soldiers strong and sturdy fight for freedom
T rained troops tortured, but still fighting
E ager to win and are
R unning from vicious bullets
A rmed forces are fighting and about to give up
N ever give up and fight for our country.

Preston Wiles, Grade 4
Cherokee Elementary School, AR

Personalities

Some people play and run
and some stay in all day.
Some people eat and sleep
and others play all day.

Some people like their jobs
and others do all the work.
Some people are good and polite
and others just love to smirk.

Bo M. Smith, Grade 6
Central Arkansas Christian School, AR

Math Mom and Me*

I am a kid	
	I am a parent
I like to learn	
	I like to teach
I love my parents	
	I love my kids
I hate cleaning	I hate cleaning

My favorite subject is
Language Arts

	I like Math
I love the beach	I love the beach

I like to go to Florida	
	I like Pawleys Island
I like cold weather	
	I like warm weather
We are Family	We are Family

Bryce Conti, Grade 6
Beck Academy, SC
*A 2 voice poem

Big Big White Bear

A big big white bear.
Playing in the big white snow.
That big big white bear.

Kelsie Hunter, Grade 6
Livingston Middle School, TN

Winter

Winter is so cold
But yet so bold.

Santa brings toys
But only to good girls and boys.

You get lots of treasures
Including lots of pleasures.

When the snow starts to melt
The trees are now svelte.

Lara Bannister, Grade 5
Etowah Elementary School, NC

Orange

Orange looks like a beautiful cold day of autumn looking at me around the corner.
Orange feels like sleek, sparkling, shouting, fireworks on the 4th of July.
Orange tastes like a crisp, darkened, sweet, pumpkin pie.
Orange smells like beautiful, fragrant, luscious, flowers on a fresh spring day.
Orange sounds like an angry, ferocious, growling tiger cat.
Orange is a super special color.

Lauren von Seelen, Grade 5
Geggie Elementary School, MO

Fall

A ll the leaves are swirling through the air
each as **U** nique as every one of us
T urning wondrous colors
dancing **U** pon the wind
the feeling of **M** agic sneaking up on the breeze
we cannot neglect this awe of **N** ature

Chloe Carll, Grade 4
Geggie Elementary School, MO

A Rhyme of Where I Am From

The country's tall grassy fields are the place for me.
The country is home and comfy.
It is the place I want to be.

I have ridden my golf cart every day…until it broke down.
Now, I just run around outside and play.
I may then decide to sway on my tire swing.
After that, I will usually go in the living room and sing.

Sometimes I will step out onto my back porch
And observe the peaceful water rippling on Herrington Lake
Before I step back inside to eat some of my favorite foods…like steak.

When it's time for bed,
My mom clearly has it said.
I pile my blankets on my head
And nestle down in the bed.

I close my eyes and pray
To rise
When the sun peers over my homestead.

Liz Marcinek, Grade 5
Burgin Independent School, KY

September 11th

September 11th, what a sad, sad day that put everyone in dismay.
When the first tower crashed, it was a terrible sight,
to see the people running with all their might.
Then the second tower came rolling down to the ground.
People were hoping that their loved ones were safe and sound.
Yes, it was a sad, sad day for people who lost their family members
in such a terrible, terrible way.

Autumn Rhoda, Grade 6
Desoto Central School, MS

Winter

The snow is falling, and everybody is excited. The houses are covered with lights in the neighborhoods. We see the Christmas trees through the window. Kids are out for Christmas break, and parents are off from work.

It's Jesus' birthday, we all say hooray! Because Jesus' birthday is today! People are out at 5:00 AM to buy Christmas presents, and people are getting decorations ready. Lights, wreaths, Christmas trees; they're all so pretty.

The houses are covered in blankets of snow, with icicles hanging from them. Children throwing snow balls and making snow angels, and parents making hot cocoa for them. The flea markets are covered with customers.

Christmas is coming Thanksgiving is gone, Merry Christmas and a Happy New Year!

Hanna Niebuhr, Grade 5
Palmetto Christian Academy, SC

Neon Green

Neon green looks like a bright light in the distance.
Neon green feels like a smooth, creamy, soft rock.
Neon green tastes like a juicy green apple.
Neon green smells like a beautiful new flower at bloom.
Neon green sounds like a cool crisp winter breeze.
Neon green is like a sweet, beautiful bright sensation you get when you read this poem.

Ben Schroeder, Grade 5
Geggie Elementary School, MO

Blue

Blue is the color of my bathing suit, when I go to the ocean.
Blue is the sound of the rain falling into the ocean water.
Blue is the smell of blueberries, mixed in with cotton blossoms from the flower bed opening.
Blue tastes as good as the sweet honeysuckles near the ocean.
Blue feels smooth and softer than a baby.
Blue is the ocean.

Haley Campbell, Grade 5
Cool Spring Elementary School, NC

I Am From

I am from having fun in preschool, to a splash of fun at Marine Life and playing hide-n-go-seek 'till dark.
I am from skateboarding, Tower of Terror at Disney World, a splash of Shamu at Sea World, and a staple in my eye.
I am from cops and robbers, making funny faces and murder in the dark 'till ten.
I am from Granny, Momma, Pop-Pop, little brother and big sis.
I am from Mello-Jello, Ju-Ju, It's Friday It's Friday, and to be kind an generous.
I am from dirt bikes, Skate Spot, and Biloxi white sand between my toes.
I am from all the loving and caring people and all the people that let me be who I am.

Julius Medina, Grade 6
Arnaudville Elementary School, LA

A Starry Night

Look up in the sky late at night and look at the beautiful stars
They wink they shine with a great deal of pride as if they are staring at you
But they are so far away we can't possibly see what's balled up inside
Sometimes there are many other times there are few but looking up in the sky will remind you
To be nice to be happy and live up to your dreams even though a star is a star as we can all see
And not to be scared to show who we are but to be who we really think we are
They will help us believe all we want to believe

Morgan Saucier, Grade 6
Orange Grove Elementary School, MS

It's Autumn!

October is nearly over
November is almost here
December is fast approaching
It's almost the end of the year
Leaves are falling
Air is chilling
Mom is baking
Dad is raking

It's time to pick some pumpkins
And celebrate with a feast
Giving thanks to our Lord and Savior
Born near oxen, lamb and beast

So come close to the fire
Some stories soon you'll hear
For it is truly Autumn
My favorite time of the year!

Eric Putnam, Grade 5
Palmetto Christian Academy, SC

Fall

I am green, yellow, red and brown.
I fall all over the ground.
Bet you can't guess what I am.

Man, you guessed!
I'm fall leaves.

Hope you don't jump on me.

Justice Bowers, Grade 6
Madisonville Middle School, TN

Excuses for Math

I can't think today,
My brain ran away.
Does 3 + 4 = fish?
Or does it equal a doggy dish?

I can't think today
My sister stole my brain away.
Does 2 + 2 = a dirty shoe?

I can't think today because
I just don't want to.

Hayden Harkey, Grade 5
Cool Spring Elementary School, NC

Winter

There is snow and ice
that you can play in outside
on a wet dark night.

Sierra Totte, Grade 6
Tomlinson Jr High School, OK

Spring

Spring is a time for us to share,
The time when love is in the air,
Spring is a wonderful time of year,
The time when people show no fear,
When newborn animals live and grow,
In this world we've come to know,
Spring always makes me feel so glad,
It's impossible to be sad,
Since spring comes only once a year,
It makes me glad and filled with cheer,
There's bees and birds at every place,
Buzzing around at their own pace,
So people spread your wings and fly,
Get off the couch and play outside,
Spring is a time for frolic and fun,
It is great when you get in the sun,
Now it's time this poem is through,
So good-bye from me to you!

Megan Bardwell, Grade 6
Model Middle School, GA

Activities

So messy!
Sticky glue
messy paint colors
squishy clay
doesn't that sound fun?

Painting pottery
is my favorite.
A cat shaped bowl
was my masterpiece.

Using a skinny paintbrush,
I painted the:
ears and nose pink,
eyes blue,
fur brown,
and base purple.

I used a lot of purple.
It is my favorite color.

Today my masterpiece
sits on my dresser.

Samantha Cramer, Grade 5
Etowah Elementary School, NC

Lacrosse

Lacrosse is so fun.
I love to play games with friends.
I win every game.

Charlie Greer, Grade 6
Beck Academy, SC

My Horse Sundae

I love to ride on Sundae.
She is a pretty bay.
She loves to run and run,
Because she has so much fun!

Grace Breakstone, Grade 4
Evangelical Christian School, TN

What's Thanksgiving?

The smell of roast turkey
the laughter of family
jackets, boots, and hats
for the snowy, cold day outside

Hot and steamy inside
Snowy and cold outside
the feeling of Thanksgiving is here.

Keely Mitchell, Grade 6
Guntown Middle School, MS

My Dog

He waits for me at my pa's
And granny's every day after school.
He comes at the edge of the road.
I get off the bus at 2:28
We play football when I get
Done with my homework.
He's my dog he is protective of me.
I trust him he trusts me.
I have known him since he was a puppy.

Ethan Boone, Grade 6
Temple Hill Elementary School, KY

Night

I love night,
The moonlight
Is so bright.
Sometimes it
Can be a fright,
Some people have
Night flights.
Then they can
See the beautiful lights.
Night can be
A beautiful sight.

Madison Carr, Grade 6
Armorel Elementary School, AR

Cool Pet Monkey

I would love to have a pet monkey,
Although his cage would be junky.
I'd maybe even give him pajamas,
Although he might want bananas.

Andrew Paquette, Grade 4
South Topsail Elementary School, NC

Dreaming Hurts

I woke up Friday morning it was half past twelve.
Ouch, my throat is sore!
There was no way I'm going to make it out the door.

Since it was a school day, I just prayed
because I've had perfect attendance.
My throat still hurts really, really bad. What will I do?
I'm really, really sad.

I eat veggie soup with crackers.
I'm sitting on the couch watching TV.
When all of the sudden I start shaking.
Then my mom wakes me up out of my dream.
It was a dream?
Oh my, dreaming really hurts.

Hunter Denney, Grade 5
Etowah Elementary School, NC

Mountains

M ountains are beautiful
O ver valleys and
U nder the sky
N ear the flowing rivers.
T owering over you and me
A lways so high in the sky
I ce falls on them also
N ever will mountains fall
S o there is no need to worry.

Ellie Mulvaney, Grade 4
Briarwood Christian Elementary School, AL

Night Spirit

Gliding silently through the dark, summer night
Hiding in the shadows, no one ever sees him
Swiftly, silently looking for a victim
Locating his prey, flying fast, giving chase
Snap! Gulp! The owl got a mouse.

Elizabeth Ellis, Grade 5
Shannon Forest Christian School, SC

Trees

Can you hear the whisper of the wind?
The talking of the trees? The laughing of the sun?
The giggling of the clouds? The roaring of the chain saw?
The chain saw cut down the trees.
Without the talking of the trees, the clouds will not giggle.
If the clouds will not giggle, the wind will not whisper.
If the wind will not whisper, the sun will not laugh.
If the sun will not laugh, the Earth will be lonely.
If the Earth is lonely he is in anger.
If the Earth is angry the people will drown in his tears.
They will fall in his frustration.
They will spin in his headaches.
So if you cut down the trees, you erase mankind little by little.

Elizabeth Keller, Grade 6
Statesville Middle School, NC

Kitty the Kitten

Kitty tried to catch a mouse
　　He ran around the house
　　　　CRASH!!!
　　　　　　BOOM BANG!!!
　　　　　Grrr!!!
He wrecked the house
　　Even though he didn't catch the mouse
　　　　THEN
　　　　　　WHACK!!!
　　　　　　WHACK!!!
　　　　　　　The mother was back
　　　　　　　　And the kitty got whopped

Christopher Morgan, Grade 6
Edmonton Elementary School, KY

Love

I've found it before,
and I've somehow found it now,
Love…
we share it with one another,
like we've shared with no other.
I'm glad we're together,
and I'm happy we share our feelings this way.
You've shared so much love for me,
and you know I do the same.
You're my guardian angel sent to me from Heaven,
and I hope you're here to stay.
You came to me when I needed you most.
You cared for and protected me,
always close and dear.
Love…
I've found it before,
and I've somehow found it now.

Kelly Donathan, Grade 6
Leland Middle School, NC

The Flag

The flag that flies high in the sky,
Stands for life and liberty;
The flag is our country's emblem.

When I see our flag in the sky,
I think of the patriots;
Who died for our country.

This is a sign to the world,
Of a free country;
One united nation.

An inseparable union,
For the people;
And by the people.

Hannah Gibson, Grade 4
Heartland High School and Academy, MO

The Soccer Game

Six seconds left
with the ball at my right.
I dribbled down the field
with all of my might.
I fiddled and faddled
through all of the battle.
I made a hard shot and
what do you know we
won the game with zero seconds to go!

Logan Altman-Duelge, Grade 5
St Teresa's School, GA

Sand

Sand is
Like a spider's web
It can stay
On your fingers
Even get in your hair
Sand is
Like the stardust in the air
It can go anywhere

Karl Ivey, Grade 4
Herbert J Dexter Elementary School, GA

My Behavior

My behavior is sad,
I am really bad.
My mom is mad,
I like to flab.
I am like a crab,
Snapping at mom and dad.

Michael Long, Grade 6
Pulaski County Middle School, GA

My Best Friend

My best friend was a dog
Not like any human you see.
I loved her with my whole heart.
She was an angel to me.

So I named her Angel,
It's easy to see why,
Such a feisty spirit
Locked up inside.

Her barking came later
So noisy and loud.
Our neighbors could not stand it
The way she would howl.

They wanted her gone.
They gave us no choice.
They didn't think my angel
Had a terribly nice voice.

Sue Ellen Harrod, Grade 5
Providence Academy, TN

What Thanksgiving Means to Me

Thanksgiving to me is like the sweet aroma of spring,
like seeing all the little joyful faces you see opening their presents at Christmas.
But the good thing is it's all mixed in to one holiday called Thanksgiving.
This is what Thanksgiving means to me.

Adam Grubbs, Grade 6
Guntown Middle School, MS

America

Freedom isn't free, it's got a really hefty fee.
They don't do it for fame or glory or to tell an exciting story.
They fight for the land that they love, they are watched over from someone above.
Their families hope they'll be okay, they pray for them every day.
So they risk their lives to pay that fee so
it will stay America, Land of the Free.

Ricky Andrade, Grade 5
Joann Walters Elementary School, AR

You Are Special to Me

Life has been hard but you still push on
Troubles come sometimes often and fast but stay strong
Even with tears you last
You are special to me
I may not be all you want at times
But I appreciate you not only in my heart but also in my mind
So today I honor you because it's your day
I wish somehow for you to have love, laughter, prosperity, joy and
your favorite gifts all on a tray
I know that will give you things that you dream
Then I can say within my heart I love you so much
You are special to me

Jerrica Collins, Grade 6
Douglass Elementary School, TN

July's Party

All the months are invited They came by ones
They danced all year long and had so much fun
When January came the snow fell, fell, and fell
Next came February and hearts were passed out
Then March came, it rained, and rained,
April brought flowers but it still rained
Then May came, and brought Tons of flowers
June brought the sun, and she shined all she could shine,
July fired off fireworks, they even made the month's flag out of fireworks
August brought the clouds, so the sun played
Hide-in-seek with the months
Then came September, which brought workers since it was Labor day
Next was October, she brought cooler weather and candy for Halloween
November brought a wonderful Thanksgiving Dinner
She also brought coats to wear to keep warm
The final month came it was December,
she brought presents for everyone
They laughed and played 'til dark came
And everyone said "goodbye"
and went back home.

Keri Marlin, Grade 6
Eminence Middle School, KY

Nighttime

At night you hear the frogs
that croak and hear the grasshoppers sing.
But the best part of all is
when you see the stars gleam.
They shine
just like you and me.
The moon is never bare
it glows in the night sky.
You're usually asleep
but when you're up,
you'll see most miraculous things.
At night there is magic in the air.
But when the sun rises,
You think that tonight's
going to be a great night.

Elizabeth Tomon, Grade 5
St Teresa's School, GA

The Giant Web

Stretching from branches,
figures moving inside it,
like a busy house.

David Sides, Grade 4
Briarwood Christian Elementary School, AL

Day Dreams

Day after day I go through my head,
Thinking thoughts that need not be said.

But, today I will share them with you,
Because I think that is what friends ought to do.

Rich gold mines, so hard to find,
Not being wakened from bed until nine!

Surely these two things cannot be compared,
But still there is more that needs to be shared!

Great big worlds, so wondrous and sweet,
Like what candy looks like before you eat!

Beautiful animals that talk to you,
You like them, and they like you too!

Trees that dance and sway in the breeze,
Things unexplainable, beyond all of these!

So much more! I wish I could go on,
But that would take too much paper to write upon!

So good-bye, good-bye, farewell, my friends,
Unlike this poem our imaginations have no end.

Samuel Crain, Grade 5
Palmetto Christian Academy, SC

Leaders

Leaders have determination.
They have motivation.
Leaders have intimidation.

You can tell who leaders are.
They stand out in a crowd.
It's because they stand lofty and proud.

Leaders have a good attitude.
Whether they win or lose.
They make friends with all.
They always help you back up if you fall.

Leaders can be tough.
They know how to handle things when times get rough.

But leaders always have,
Determination, motivation, and intimidation.

Kirsten Webb, Grade 6
Woodland Presbyterian School, TN

The Planet We Lost

The planet we lost was my favorite.
When I go to bed.
I dream of that wonderful planet that goes around the sun.
That beautiful icy planet.
That beautiful great name Pluto.
My favorite planet we lost.
Good-bye icy lost planet!
The planet we lost!

Chassity Whittington, Grade 4
Lewis Vincent Elementary School, LA

Changing Seasons

Summer
free, relaxed
hot, sunny, bright
Swimming, sweating, thinking, wishing
Cold, snowy, peaceful
Wonderland, playground
Winter

Mary Katherine Connell, Grade 5
Briarwood Christian Elementary School, AL

Ship in the Sea

Dark, blue sea foam waves crashing among ships
You can almost hear the ships colliding with the waves
The scary, gray clouds hypnotizing the eyes of sea goers
How the waves are so big and the boat yet so small
The boat's filling with water, as the captain shouts.
Suddenly a wave,
Then you faintly hear the words…
"Pull back!"
And then…

Ann Mossy, Grade 6
Christ Episcopal School - Middle School, LA

Santa

Hey Santa it's that time of year
to celebrate with good cheers
so come on with your reindeer
and give me good gifts and gear
now it's time to bring good gifts
so come out of the snow and drift
and celebrate for a new year
and make me happy with good cheer

Kaneishia Jackson, Grade 6
Graham Elementary School, AL

Truly Elegant

The sunlight in your hair
makes my heart leap in the air
The beauty in your face
makes my heart start to race
The gaze in your eyes
makes my heart start to fly
The gentleness in your words
makes me want to be heard
The sweetness of your ways
makes me go through a phase
The grace in your steps
touches my heart to the depths
The love in your heart
makes me never want to part
It's definite that when you and I met
you were truly elegant

Lillian Claire Dickinson, Grade 5
American Heritage Academy, GA

Music

Dancing, rhythms, clapping,
Soft, slow tunes
Wild, crazy beats
Is anything more fun than music?

Mallory Terrell, Grade 5
Landmark Christian School, GA

To Watch Rain Fall

To watch rain fall
is to watch wonders grow.
To watch rain leave
is to watch fantasy go.
A single drop of rain
is worth a million to come,
no one more than any other.
They are a sign of passion,
personality, and friendship.
To watch rain fall
is a sight to see.
It drains all worries and fears from me.

Cody Conway, Grade 5
Alpena Elementary School, AR

The Bad Luck Leprechaun

I went out to the grass of green,
I met a leprechaun that was very mean.
The leprechaun gave me a painful pluck,
And all day long I had bad luck.

Blaine Greenwood, Grade 4
South Topsail Elementary School, NC

Jungle

The jungle seemed loud
When I stopped it seemed louder.
I heard monkeys chattering
Tigers growling
Cheetahs running.
Then all was quiet.
There was just the rain.

Sarah DeMaria, Grade 5
Faith Christian School, SC

A New Painting

When one face meets another
When one world unites again
When a babe sees the light,
And when someone comes to God.

It's the beginning of a new,
A picture is painted.
The edges sharp
And the colors fine.

The painter is God
He brings love to one another
Peace to the Earth
Life and good health.
And a new beginning.

Meghan Littles, Grade 6
Home School, MO

During Fall

During Fall
there're lots of leaves.
During Fall
I hear a sneeze.

During Fall
I rake a lot.
During Fall
the leaves all rot.

During Fall
the leaves all fall.
During Fall
we have a ball!

Leah Bush, Grade 5
Midway Covenant Christian School, GA

Weather

The weather the weather
is unpredictable and we know
not whether it will
rain or snow the weather
is out of our control.

Steven Munoz, Grade 5
Cool Spring Elementary School, NC

My Room

My room has
a big ugly TV in it.
My room is white.

My room has
lots of games.
My room is my favorite.

My room is where
I lay my head
to go to sleep.
My room is
my room.

Isaiah Fields, Grade 6
Dyer Elementary & Jr High School, TN

Serena

S weet
E xcellent
R eally good student
E specially
N ice
A wesome

Serena Davis, Grade 6
Martin Elementary School, WV

Christmas

C hrist
H oliday
R eindeer
I nside
S anta
T ree
M om
A wesome
S urprise

Bradley M. Swartz, Grade 5
Shirley Elementary School, AR

Fall

Fall is coming quick.
Trees are losing their bright clothes,
Leaving them naked.

Whitley Bailey, Grade 4
Stephens Elementary School, AL

Winter

Though winter is rather cold
It's fun for young and old
The snowmen stand around
As snow covers the ground
You also see kids walking merrily
To see friend and family
So, put on your gloves and we'll have some fun
    Just before the day is done

Faith Barnes, Grade 6
Community Christian School, NC

Friends

It's good to have a lot of friends
And you know they're always there
If you have a group of friends
they'll try and make things fair
But if they all leave you and you
want another one
Come and find me…
We'll have tons and tons of fun!!

Catherine Hancock, Grade 5
Briarwood Christian Elementary School, AL

Jumping Around

The tiny frog hops
on a lily pad then jumps
into the water

Molly Lattner, Grade 4
Briarwood Christian Elementary School, AL

I Have a Sister

I have a sister that is an angel.
whenever I play with my sister I feel as
if I was in heaven when I am sad my
sister cheers me up by making me laugh!!

Whenever my cousin is mean to my sister I
defend my sister because its my job to take
car, listen, feed, watch, and love her.
and I'll always lover her and be there for her.

Yasmine Hernandez, Grade 4
Alvaton Elementary School, KY

Try

Cheat for anything, and fail anytime,
    Give effort for something, and succeed within
Everywhere you wish and everything you care,
    Never be disappointed with your effort in the air
Effort will guide you to true achievement,
    Scholarships, admissions, and everything you believe in
Cheating, however, is a crime like none other,
    It builds up inside you and destroys your true dreams
No matter where you go or how you see it,
    Cheaters never win, and winners never cheat

Sahil Patel, Grade 6
Haynes Academy for Advanced Studies, LA

My Pet Octopus

My pet octopus can really be a pain
When he pulls me out of bet at night again and again
And again

I take him by the tentacles and we play WWF throw down time
He always wins and never do I
Because he chokes me and pops me in the eye

Ohhhhh that octopus, I can't stand
Maybe if I think hard enough
I'll find a way to destroy him with a very evil plan

David Asmar, Grade 4
Cool Spring Elementary School, NC

Math

I don't like math,
math doesn't like me.
When math comes around at 12:15,
I hide in the bathroom 'till someone finds me.
There's no point to math,
it's completely crazy.

What's that you say?
It's 12:15?
Oh my,
I think I'm going to die!

Jack Bernard, Grade 5
Meramec Elementary School, MO

Yippee!

One snowy night it snowed like stars
raining from the sky
a little girl prayed for school to be out
and hoped it wouldn't dry

the next morning when she got out of bed
she looked out her window to see
a white wonderland of snow piled high
then she yelled, "schools out! Yippee!!!"

Haley Doyle, Grade 5
Qulin Middle School, MO

Maddy

I wake up — something cold in my ear
I open my eyes and see my little dog near
She buries under blankets
She tries to push me out
When I don't come, she begins to pout
With her unhappy face she persuades me out and wants to race
When I head for school
I see her watching me go
That tells me she'll always be my friend — I know

Elayna Seago, Grade 6
Scotts Creek Elementary School, NC

Fall

Fall is here
I'm starting to see many deer
Leaves are turning many colors
I went to show my little brothers
Now it is getting cool
I dress warmly to go to school
Fall is here
That's why it's my favorite time of year.
Price Burgess, Grade 5
Friendship Christian Academy, MS

¡Rain!

Rain, rain, rain
Falling on the ground
Rain, rain, rain
Makes me feel down
Rain, rain, rain
Keeps me in all day
Rain, rain, rain
Please, go away!!!
Karlie S. Cauthen, Grade 5
Walton Verona Elementary School, KY

A Leaf Life

I'm a leaf I fell,
from a tree today
now I'm free
it was fun falling from the tree
my brothers, sisters, and me
go WEE down from a tree.
Navalla Ennis, Grade 6
Edmonton Elementary School, KY

Country Life

Country life is peaceful
Birds chirping in the morning.
Coyotes howling at night
But it is no fright.
When you live the country life.

Cows roaming the pastures
Farmers feed them hay.
It is great to wake up to a
Country life day.

Country life is beautiful in the autumn.
Farmers combine their corn
And put on their overalls and get
Ready for winter

Country life is peaceful
Country life is great
Country life is beautiful.
I'm glad I live the country life.
Colby Lawrence Garrett, Grade 6
Temple Hill Elementary School, KY

Sun Rays

The sun ray catches your eyes like a new quarter,
Giving you warmth and love.
Making you sleepy like a tired kitten,
Or making you sizzle like a frying pan.
The sun rays remind you of good days and memories,
Making you think back and wanting that exact moment right now.
You feel as welcome as the sun shining through a rainy day,
Or a rainbow appearing after a tornado.
You feel feelings you have never felt,
When the sun rays shine on you.
You breathe in the fresh air like you never had before,
Smelling the wonderful flowers.
All this happens because the sun rays bring love to all things.
Hailin Liu, Grade 6
River Trail Middle School, GA

Snow

Crunch, Crunch,
Snow crackling under my boots,
Climbing higher and higher into the bright white snow on the hill,
Pulling my brown and candy apple red snow sled up to the top,
Getting on, pushing off, zoom,
Gliding down as fast as possible,
Then pulling it back to the top,
To start the process over again,
Rolling with my dog his fur turned white with snow,
Running by the bare oak trees,
Rolling back and forth making angels,
Rolling the bottom to be the biggest,
Then the middle just a little smaller,
Then the top the smallest,
Running into the house to get buttons eyes and a hat,
Found them,
Racing back,
You put on the eyes, and buttons, and I'll put on the scarf and hat,
Wait don't forget his smile,
Mom come look it's a perfect snowman.
Dylan Ross, Grade 6
Alvaton Elementary School, KY

The Wild Tornado

I'm a tornado.
I'm horrifying.
I'm unstoppable.
I'm devastating.
I'm as powerful as Mr. Incredible.
I'm like thousands of bricks pounding on your head.
I'm as fast as Dash.
If anyone steps in my way, they will be smashed into pieces of meat.
I'm scarier than Freddie Krueger.
I will kill you.
I'm a tornado.
Tristin Clark, Grade 5
Pembroke Elementary School, NC

Melik Dukes

Strong, handsome, smart
Brother of Tony Drequan, Ronald, Ammia, and Monique
Who loves God, Mom, and Dad
Who feels good about having a loving family
Who needs education, family, and a home
Who gives love, friendship, and compassion
Who fears nightmares, snakes, and wolves
Who'd like to see Reggie Bush
Who dreams of being a football star
A student at Colerain Elementary
Boo Boo

Melik Dukes, Grade 5
Colerain Elementary School, NC

My School

I want to tell you about a school I love very much,
    It's really cool with just the right amount of God's touch.
My friends there are very important to me,
    There is no other place I'd rather be.
They have a basketball team so good and great,
    Although we have never made it to state.
If you are ever looking for another school,
    Try Ava Victory Academy — it's cool.

McKenzie Matlock, Grade 6
Ava Victory Academy, MO

Snowflakes

Snow falls to the ground,
small white flakes of cold perfection.
Fragile shapes of white,
whistle through the night,
and quietly land on cool clean ground.
Without a sound,
swiftly flows through the air,
until the evening wind carries it away.

Kelsey Culp, Grade 4
Saul Mirowitz Day School - Reform Jewish Academy, MO

My Pawpaw

My pawpaw is my hero.
I love him a lot.
But as we all know, he died.
Two years has past.
I miss you pawpaw.
I just want you to know, I love you.
December will be three years now.
How is the Lord sweet, nice, does he take care of you?
Every Christmas I listen to Christmas in Heaven.
I still cry.
Dad say's it's okay to cry when you need to.
I guess I'll see you in the next ninety years or so.
When I die and go to heaven.

Taylor Teal, Grade 4
Lewis Vincent Elementary School, LA

Black Smith

T hanks for sharing your talent
H ow neat your art work is
A nyone would enjoy a gifted artist like you
N ice of you to come
K ids and adults loved the experience

Y ou taught us about black smithing
O ur fifth grade classes enjoyed your talent
U nder the autumn trees

Cody Shipley, Grade 5
Sullivan Elementary School, TN

My Best Friend

My best friend.
    She is my hero.
        Has a brittle body, but the best face.
            She is my grandmother who will one day fade away.
                But we will meet again someday.

Brittany Hanks, Grade 6
St Cecilia School, LA

Grape Pie for Ann

Ann loves grape pie.
She never wastes a bite.
She was going to make some more.
But there weren't any ripe.

She doesn't know what to do.
Should she ask her neighbor?
What should she do?
This is too much labor.

She should just ask the baker.
That's what she should do!

Hannah Wilson, Grade 4
St Mary Cathedral Elementary School, MO

Winter Is Here!

Outside everything is covered with snow
But inside, time for hot cocoa.
Winter break from school;
Kids think that is really cool.
Animals hibernate in trees, caves, or underground.
And we kids are living the life above ground!
The weather is cold, and people wear coats.
If they stay out too long, they'll get sore throats.
During Christmastime, we give gifts.
When we're done, we go play in the snow drifts.
Snowball fights are so, so great,
But when they're done, you've probably lost a teammate!
Ice skating is fun too.
Except when you can't, your rear goes "Boo hoo hoo!"
To wrap things up, winter is very cool.
Oh, did I mention…no school?

Zachary Harris, Grade 4
Sequoyah Elementary School, TN

Home

My home is a place
That is secure.
This I know for sure.
My mom and dad and
Sister and I make my home
The place to be.
With laughter, family trips, and fun
Activities, my home is one you
Should come and see!
My home is filled with things
From the past,
And some new things that will last.
Making memories is what my family
Does best.
Which makes my home
Stand out from the
Rest.

Sophie Tatum, Grade 6
Woodland Presbyterian School, TN

The Terrible Mean Tornado

I am a terrible mean black tornado
I will destroy your life forever
I am a mean, angry, gray, black tornado
I will kill anything that gets in my way
I will destroy your homes and barns
You would wish you were never born
I am a beast and I look mad
I smell like dirty trash
I can even break down a road
I am coming to kill you forever
I am an incredible tornado
I will throw you over the world
Like in a crocodile's mouth

I am gigantic and I am tough

I am coming to get you.
You better run because you can't hide.

David Locklear, Grade 5
Pembroke Elementary School, NC

He's My Hero!

T he one that guards me!
H ome is where you belong!
A hero in my heart!
N othing is more important than family!
K ids cheer and family and friends cry!

Y ou are my hero every day!
O ur country is praying for you!
U nited Families are joyful!

Abby Childress, Grade 5
Sullivan Elementary School, TN

Pop

My paw paw has a little car.
He zooms and zooms and never parks.
When he is bored he drives so far.
By the time he's home it's after dark.
He's 85 and they call him pop and
When he's 90 he still won't stop!

Kaley Quimby, Grade 4
Brilliant Elementary School, AL

My Cat Pouncer

Mouse eating machine
Yo-yo bouncing fool.

Catches
A lot of
Toys.

Pounces
Over dogs
Unusually
Noisy
Cat
Eats
Really bad eggs.

Lorysa Ann Jameson, Grade 6
Temple Hill Elementary School, KY

Swimming

I swim in the pool
Every day after school
My coach is so much fun
He likes to sit in the sun.

I like to swim laps
And when I'm done
I feel like I could collapse.

My sister swims really good
But only if I could
My life would be so much better
Only if I could catch up and get her.

Haley Davis, Grade 4
Lewis Vincent Elementary School, LA

Harp and Drums

Harp
Gentle, soft
Tuning, playing, plucking
Strings, keys, rhythm, drumsticks
Beating, tapping, hitting
Loud, noisy
Drums.

Corina Lopez, Grade 5
Harahan Elementary School, LA

Death

As you are, I once was,
As I am, you shall be.
Take my hand and go
Down the valley of the shadows with me.
I'll take you to heaven,
Let's have some fun.
Death is your friend,
Don't be afraid.
Your toll is paid,
So take a ride.

Adam Howell, Grade 5
Etowah Elementary School, NC

Puppies

Puppies
Puppies
Puppies
Long puppies
Short puppies
Cutie, pretty, beautiful puppies
Different, weird, dumb puppies
These are just a few
Ugly puppies
Sad puppies
Happy, cheerful, bright puppies
Black, white, brown puppies
Named puppies
Shy puppies
Don't forget funny puppies
Last of all best of all
I like Basset Hound puppies

Jessica Butler, Grade 5
Tates Creek Elementary School, KY

Jesus

J ehovah Jirah
E xcellent God
S ufficient for me
U p in the Heavens
S ees everyone

Anna-Elizabeth Lewis, Grade 5
Midway Covenant Christian School, GA

Creepy Costumes

C reepy
O ooh
S cary
T wisted
U nique
M akeup
E asy and fun
S uits

Paige Dunn, Grade 6
Martin Elementary School, WV

Wind Coyote

The mighty wind coyote howls like a baby
Crying for its milk. But do not feed this dreadful sound,
Or it will turn into a swift adult chasing a rabbit
Around

Swirling until it blows with rage and frustration.
Then it takes it all out on the world around it.

Mariyka Auber, Grade 4
Big Creek Elementary School, GA

It's So Cold

It's so cold, I thought as I strolled.
The morning sun had looked like gold
Until I found out it was 280 below,
Then it started to snow.
All I could think was it's so cold,
The snow covered everything like a giant blindfold
How was I ever going to get home?
Was this going to be my tomb?
What did you say? It's time to go in?
But I barely had time to begin.

Emma Astrike-Davis, Grade 5
Montessori Community School, NC

Lonely Robin

Lonely robin perched on a branch,
Continuously calling out for a mate,
Or at least an acquaintance or friend,
Wallowing with only the leaves from the big oak.

Weeping with a great craving for friends,
The wind banishes his little cry,
No one knows the depth of the loneliness,
Only the inside of his red feathery chest.

Perched alone with nothing of his own,
No others in sight,
No sign of life,
No allies around.

Heard a squeaky sigh just in the distance,
Flew away with great anticipation,
Succeeded the task at hand,
To find the mate that made his day.

Lauren Ledet, Grade 5
Larose Cut Off Middle School, LA

I Wish

I wish that there were no such thing as school.
And our horrible teacher was just a ghoul.
I wish my parents would be nice to me,
And my brother and sister would let me be.
I wish that I could play games more,
And I could turn this place into a gore.
I wish, I wish, I wish…
But I'm stuck here no matter what I wish for.

Nicholas Schallon, Grade 5
St Dominic School, TN

I Wish I Could Fly

I wish I could fly
Up in that big blue sky.
There I sat on my bed to wish I had wings to fly.
In the instant I grow my wings
And I jumped
Up to find
I could fly.

Madison Vincent, Grade 4
Ode Maddox Elementary School, AR

Friends

A friend is always by your side,
Even if you cheated or lied.
They will never abandon you,
Doesn't mater what you do.
They will never leave you out,
That is right without a doubt.
You might play sports and have fun with them,
Or be in school with your pencil and pen.
Friendship is a valuable treasure,
It will bring you much pleasure.
It means a lot to me,
I think you can see.

Rishi Chandrasekhar, Grade 6
St Michael Parish School, WV

Flight 93

These people gave a lot to save our country's source,
That plane crashed before it hit the White House's court.
The people on that flight had friends, family, and relatives,
They saved us from the wrath of the mean old nasty terrorists.
I still remember this day on 9/11 too,
This day of bravery and courage; you should remember it too!
The people that were on that plane really had some guts,
To save George W. Bush and not let our country get cut.
But do you know what I think?
I think those people were brave,
To save George W. Bush, they picked the right way.
We will always remember that day and Flight 93,
Because of those people we are all still free.

Christian Hodge, Grade 5
Holsenbeck Elementary School, GA

snow

snow is very white
i like to build a snowman
we got out of school
Jessica Copeland, Grade 6
Livingston Middle School, TN

Presidents

Presidents,
Presidents,
Presidents,
Tall presidents,
Short presidents,
Big fat Taft presidents,
Skinny tall honest presidents,
Those are just a few.
Old presidents,
Dead presidents,
White long beard presidents,
Nice presidents, too.
Mean presidents,
Cool presidents,
Don't forget smart presidents,
Last of all best of all,
I like Bush presidents.
Erin Norrie, Grade 6
Hayes Elementary School, OK

Rain

The rain falls outside
I hear it as it bellows,
making the world smile.
Kristen Belford, Grade 6
Armorel Elementary School, AR

Smart, Funny, Cool Boys

Tall boys
Short boys
Smart, funny, cool boys
Awesome, poor, lonely boys
Those are just a few!

Weird boys
Cool boys
Friendly, kind, helpful boys
Fair, puny, enjoyable boys
Fantastic boys too!

Entertaining boys
Incredible boys
And don't forget cheerful boys!

Last of all
Best of all
I like comical boys!
Korey Thompson, Grade 5
Salem Elementary School, AR

Candy Canes

Candy canes, candy canes, all around
Candy canes, candy canes, on the ground
Candy canes all red and white
The white as clean as snow
The red as bright as a fire place glow
Candy canes, candy canes, in the halls
Candy canes, candy canes, on the walls
Candy canes, candy canes, all hard when wrapped
Candy canes, candy canes, all sticky when lips can be heard smacked
Candy canes, candy canes, filled with joy
Candy canes, candy canes, are almost like toys
In the candle light, they look so bright
They try to glisten with all their might
Candy canes, candy canes, please be here next Christmas
Candy canes, candy canes, please oh please, you must!
Courtney Weber, Grade 6
Beck Academy, SC

Ohio

I love Ohio.
I love the cold, winter wind nipping at my skin,
Colorful presents wrapped especially for me at Christmas,
and the taste of delicious turkey on Thanksgiving.
I love Ohio.

I love the sweet smell of my grandparents' house because it makes me feel at home.
I love hearing the sound of my cousins' laughter before I walk in the door,
I love the feeling of seeing old friends for the first time in years.
I love Ohio

I love the sound of screaming people on roller coasters at Cedar Point,
I feel the shaking of Grampa's boat moving swiftly across the water,
And the sound of Grampa's birds squawking, screeching, and screaming.
I love Ohio.

I love the sound of the roaring crowds for Ohio sports teams,
I love the smell of happiness when I run into my relatives' houses,
I love the flash and click of the camera making memories forever.
I love Ohio.
Christian O'Malley, Grade 4
Big Creek Elementary School, GA

I Am Haunted

I was haunted about an awful alligator living under my bed at night.
I felt like if I stuck one little toe under my bed he would
grab me under and eat me.

I am haunted about grizzly, gassy ghost making scary,
freaky, frightening noises in my room.
And the ghost making things move all over my room
and taking me and eating every bit of me.

I will be haunted later about something destroying,
burning down my house. Breaking in and taking me.
Courtney Barrett, Grade 5
Eminence Middle School, KY

Thanksgiving

Thanksgiving is a time for family.
It's about family and friends being together.
It's a time for fun.
No school, no homework.
No time to sit around,
or just playing video games all day.
It's a time to play, run, jump, or be free.

Thanksgiving, it's not just about food!
It's about being with the people you love.
Whether it's watching the football game,
or riding bikes down the roads.
It doesn't matter what.
As long as you're having fun,
or giving thanks to the Lord!

Emily Finch, Grade 6
Guntown Middle School, MS

Household Rug

A simple rug is like a dog,
So furry, so soft.
A simple rug is like a rainbow,
So colorful, so beautiful.
A rug is like a magic carpet,
A flea's house,
The shoes' paradise.
A rug is anything, but we think of it as a…rug.
Yet right under our feet —
Paradise is happening.

Morgan Mahurin, Grade 4
Herbert J Dexter Elementary School, GA

Nouns

Nouns are quite useful.
Why…Even I use them all the time.
People, places, and things are all nouns.
Wow! Even thoughts, ideas, and feelings are nouns.
Without nouns we wouldn't make sense.
I'd be down with a frown,
if there were no nouns.
Plural nouns bring us further in nouns.
Common nouns are easily found.
Wow! Are nouns important or what?

Shawn Loveless, Grade 5
Saffell Street Elementary School, KY

Billy, My Cat

Billy is a boy he is black and white
he likes to claw people and things every night.
When he is thirsty he gets a drink out of my sink
he is cute and soft as can be
forever he will be.

Christine Long, Grade 5
Walton Verona Elementary School, KY

Fall Leaves

I look out my window;
Into my backyard;
To see something pretty;
You don't have to look very far;
All colors of the rainbow;
Shades of orange, red, and yellow;
As the wind blew by;
I saw some leaves fly;
What was left of the leaves;
Still in the trees;
Made a rustling sound;
To reveal all the bright green leaves that are still around;
Thinking about what I have just seen;
Can make me feel oddly serene.

Caitlin Murray, Grade 6
Queen of Angels Catholic School, GA

My Paw Paw

My paw paw is nice and great.
He is a guy that you would not hate.
He's not too big. He's not too small.
He's strong enough to catch me when I fall.

My paw paw's not too mean, not too nice.
He's a guy that loves me as sugar and spice.
He's not too fast, not too slow;
He's a guy who will bring me places if I can go.
I love my Paw Paw.
How does he sound to you?

Hannah Moore, Grade 5
Enon Elementary School, LA

Summer

Smells like fresh air
Feels like hot sunshine
Tastes like juice
Looks like flowers blooming
Sounds like birds chirping

Carson Seay, Grade 5
Briarwood Christian Elementary School, AL

Thanksgiving Breeze

Thanksgiving, Thanksgiving
you bring the autumn breeze
Thanksgiving, Thanksgiving
you light up all the trees
Red, yellow, and purple all come in twos
it makes me feel like running with no shoes
Thanksgiving, Thanksgiving
you leave us once again
Thanksgiving, Thanksgiving
you won't be back till next year
Thanksgiving, Thanksgiving
I'll be waiting till then

Drew Pannell, Grade 6
Guntown Middle School, MS

My Pencil

This is my pencil;
It is yellow and strong.
It is made of wood,
And it can write a song.

This is my pencil;
It has an eraser.
On every test
It will give the answer.

Cooper Lawrence, Grade 5
Heber Springs Elementary School, AR

Together

They were in school together,
Elementary through high school.
They were in college together.
They worked together,
They got married together.
They had kids together,
They grew old together.
They died together,
They got buried together.
These two people,
Who were husband and wife,
Did everything together.

Brianna Cochenour, Grade 5
North Shelby Elementary School, MO

Egypt

Sitting gently on the Nile.
Under E, it will be filed.
The houses flat and not that tall.
The greatest wonder of them all.

Nicholas Matteson, Grade 6
Bellwood Discovery School, TN

Clouds

My blue imagination
    with cats,
        dogs,
    turtles,
        clowns,
everything I want.
My mind is crazy —
    swirls,
    stars,
doodles.
Getting dizzy,
        and dizzier,
            and dizzier.
Then
    back to reality.

Rachel Mudd, Grade 5
St Vincent Elementary School, MO

I Think of Soldiers

I am happy to be in America.
Today I saw a comet pass
through the sky.
While I looked at the lines in
the green leaf,
I thought of the soldiers
in the desert wasteland called Iraq.
Then I stood still
and prayed for the soldiers
and their families
I thank God
that He is protecting them.

John Miles Jr., Grade 6
Leonville Elementary School, LA

Christmas

Christmas "O" Christmas,
full of wonderful colors,
one is red and one is green,
You put the bright lights
on the Christmas tree,
then you run around it full of glee,
You jump up and down
and scream with joy,
then it's off to play with the toys.

Garret Johnson, Grade 5
Drayton Hall Elementary School, SC

I Can't Write a Poem*

My tummy hurts.
It's boring.
I can't rhyme.
My pencil broke.
My eyes hurt.
I don't like writing.
I am tired.
My dog ate my pencil.
I am hungry.
I want to go home.
I have a seeing problem.
I forgot how to spell.
I have a blister.
I have a bad back.
I forgot my name.
I can't think.
Time's up? Uh oh!
All I have is this dumb list of excuses.
You like it? Really? No kidding.
Thanks a lot.
Would you like to see another one?

Angel Huffman, Grade 6
Armorel Elementary School, AR
*Patterned after "I Can't Write a
Poem" by Bruce Lansky

My Name

C heyenne is my first name.
H ey my life is fun.
E ating chocolate is my thing.
Y es it's great.
E arly in the morning I go to school
N othing at school is exciting.
N o it's just learning.
E verything I do is still fun.

S mith is my last name.
M y middle name is Kimberly.
I know my name I
T hink you do too and this is
H ow I explain my name.

Cheyenne Smith, Grade 4
Stephens Elementary School, AL

My Duty

I have a duty,
It's blazing in my heart,
To fight for my country,
Against the world apart.

I'll fight for happiness,
I'll fight with glee,
I'll fight in uniform,
Bronze and burgundy.

With my skills and all,
I'll beat the enemy,
I'll make them fall.

With sheer determination,
And pure loyalty,
I'll become a hero,
Between the lines of destiny.

The tale I lead is not foretold,
So I must be very bold.

Laboni Hoque, Grade 4
Brookwood Elementary School, GA

Halloween

H aunted houses
A xes with scary costumes
L aughter in the distance
L icking sweetness off our lips
O n the street, trick-or-treaters
W itches on brooms
E ar piercing screams
E veryone having fun
N ice treaters giving candy

Laila Wyatt, Grade 5
Arnaudville Elementary School, LA

Mean vs Nice

Some people visit and some talk,
others are quiet all day long.
Some people are nice and some are funny,
others are mean and do wrong.

Some people are rich and some are loaded,
others are poor and have nothing to eat.
Some people are kind and some share,
others are greedy and never share treats.

Seth Koettel, Grade 6
Central Arkansas Christian School, AR

Fire

Laughing and crackling,
as the flames lick the ground.
Creeping toward us, as we hide.
Its heat feels like anger,
growing stronger by the second.
The smoke seems like hands,
trying to grab us and pull us into its great, orange mouth.
It reaches the wall and tries desperately to get into the room,
but it doesn't have a chance.
The water gushes down in a fury,
the flames screaming and hissing as they die.

Scott Berson, Grade 6
River Trail Middle School, GA

God's Love

I love the God of heaven and Earth.
He is the one who created us.
I would rather have God than money untold.
The God of my life will never grow old.

God sent His Son from heaven to us.
He was born on Christmas in a stable barn.
When He was born He was laid in a trough.
Sometimes it kills me to think how much He loved us.

The Lord formed miracles from water to wine.
He healed the sick and healed the blind.
The Pharisees hated Him more than a prisoner.
He came because He loved the sinner.

Then God let His Son be beaten and bruised.
The Lord let Himself be beaten and bruised.
Then He was nailed to the cross to die.
For if He had not would we live with him in the sky?

Aaron Lewis, Grade 5
Providence Academy, TN

Sun-Sun-Sunflowers

Make me think of grace
makes me sad when they hang down
oh they light up bright

Abby Johnson, Grade 4
Briarwood Christian Elementary School, AL

Pumpkin, Pumpkin

Pumpkin, pumpkin, on the wall, who's the best of them all?
Is it you or is it me?
Do you see?
Pumpkin, pumpkin in the well
who's the best of them all?
Do you know who?
Pumpkin, pumpkin, next to me,
is it me, you see?

Shelby Sexton, Grade 5
Drayton Hall Elementary School, SC

You're Gone

Now that you're gone
I feel so alone
I liked the way you looked at me
And the sweet things you said
I'll miss you and I'll keep you in my heart
But why did you leave
My whole world is falling apart
They say it's okay to cry
But right now, I want to die
Well, now you're gone
And I'm all alone
I hope you have a good life
You'll always be in mine

Amber Daley, Grade 6
Rock Mills Jr High School, AL

Dance

In my dance class I do all so many things.
In acro I do flips and flings,
For jazz I spin and turn,
Hip-hop is where I do the worm,
During ballet I tiptoe across the floor,
I shuffle to tap class like never before,
As you can see, dance is my favorite to do,
So while doing this hobby I will never be blue!

Lauren Ray, Grade 6
Sanford Elementary School, WV

Resurrection by Recycling

The tennis ball waits in its can,
Pushing to be set free,
And laughs with joy as it flies through the air.
The ball yells in pain as it is hit too hard,
And it breaks somebody's string.
It looks sorrowfully at the TV,
Which shows tournaments that remind of its youth.
It cries when it is thrown into the recycling can,
But soon finds itself in a new container,
Filled with pleasure,
And the will and strength to be flung around again.

Jay Reynolds, Grade 6
River Trail Middle School, GA

Fight Night

Night is day,
Day is night,
Every night I love to fight,
When I come home,
I'm all beat up.
When I start to hurt,
My girlfriend cheers me up.
Casey Jones, Grade 6
Harrisburg Middle School, AR

December

December is cold and white
When animals go to sleep for the night

Hot chocolate is brewing
What is she doing
We'll make a snowman tonight

The trees are out the lights are up
Is that a present in sight

Oh yes it is
I really can't wait

For Christmas is coming tonight
Lauren Keeling, Grade 5
St Thomas More School, NC

Giggles Wiggles

I love Giggles
She is so cute
Even though she wiggles
I love my Giggles
Taylor Nay, Grade 6
Martin Elementary School, WV

My Ode to Dogs

This is about my ode to dogs,
Not cats or pigs or monkeys or hogs.
For they guard and guard
From their house in the yard.
They can even sniff, not see, in the fog.
Ann-Elise Siden, Grade 6
Beck Academy, SC

Daughter

D are all your dreams.
A lways believe in yourself.
U ncover hidden talents.
G o on adventures.
H ave fun and be happy.
T reasure tiny miracles.
E mbrace life.
R each for the stars.
Porsha Jackson, Grade 6
Scotts Creek Elementary School, NC

What Is Christmas?

Beautiful lights, wrapped presents,
Fresh-baked cakes and getting all dressed up.
But no worship.
Many people think this is what Christmas is about,
And when they don't get what they want, they pout.
They are wrong because the most important part of Christmas is missing.
Where is Christ, our Lord and Savior?
Christ is in our hearts and everywhere we go.
No matter what, He is always there from our head to our toe.
The most important gift we have received is the gift of forgiveness.
With this gift, there is no darkness.
Jesus gave it to us when He died on the cross for our sins.
All of us — you, me and even twins.
Helping others, sharing a smile,
Feeding the homeless, and thinking of others because they are worthwhile.
Not one day, not one week or one month, or midyear
But all year.
This is what Christmas is about!

Victoria Vicidomina, Grade 6
St Mary Magdalen School, LA

Adamant Green

Adamant green feels like a hand shield clashing with a mithril sword.
Adamant green looks like my fave shirt that is warm when it is cold.
Adamant green sounds like armor clashing together (chain mesh).
Adamant green tastes like yucky spinach which Popeye the sailor man eats.
Adamant green is the color of grass too wet to dry out.
Adamant green is the seaweed growing on a sunken vessel.

Andy Beall, Grade 5
Cool Spring Elementary School, NC

The Powerful Tornado!!!

I am powerful and no one can stop me.
I will go through your house, no doubt about me.
I am dangerous, and I am fast.
I can out beat you leaving a great blast.
I am windy taking out trees and cars.
Stay out of my way, you never know, I might bring down the stars.
I am a huge storm, great and strong.
I am a tornado, nature is where I belong.
Toni Amelia Floyd, Grade 5
Pembroke Elementary School, NC

Halloween

Halloween is a special day
when ghouls and goblins come out to play.
Halloween is such a special day
that I might play and get some trick-or-treating on the way.
Halloween is a fun holiday to dress up and have fun by eating candy.
Even though it's one day to play,
I still think every day is Halloween to scare and have fun
with all the ghouls and goblins every day.

Harrison Sanders, Grade 5
Parker Road Elementary School, MO

The Girl

It started on a winter day;
I was having lunch at school.
Looking at a crowded table,
I wondered where to sit.
A girl waved me to her seat;
She looked dazzling!
My friend bumped and nodded to the girl.
When I sat beside her, she smiled at me;
I smiled at her; my feelings emerging.
Boy, I love that girl!

James Albert McCall, Grade 6
Scotts Creek Elementary School, NC

Chocolate Cake

Chocolate cake is so yummy and sweet,
Sometimes messy, always a treat.
Mostly soft, but sometimes crunchy.
I like having chocolate cake on my birthday.
Some people like having it as dessert.
Many chocolate cakes are big and fancy
Others are small and plain.
It doesn't matter if it's big or small.
It's still chocolate cake
And I like them all.

Jack Ulibarri, Grade 4
Sequoyah Elementary School, TN

Thanksgiving Senses

I see turkey on the table
I smell pumpkin pie spices filling the rooms
I hear people talking and laughing
I taste savory ham
I feel hot buttery rolls in my hands, yum!
        Thanksgiving

Austin Boggs, Grade 5
Sullivan Elementary School, TN

Daddy

I lay still in my bed.
As thoughts roam freely through my head.
Then I hear a knock on my door.
My mom falls to the floor.
She said it was all her fault
I answered quickly and said no it's not.
Tears were streaming down her face
I handed her the some tissues just in case.
She stopped crying when she heard
The ring of phone outside my door.
When she answered she heard a familiar voice
Then she started to rejoice.
When she got off the phone she said to me
Daddy is going to be "ok" my sweetie.

Natalie Berry, Grade 5
Shirley Elementary School, AR

The Ocean Blue

Smashing like cymbals
A beautiful aqua blue
And a horizon

Emma Baker, Grade 4
Briarwood Christian Elementary School, AL

Our Flag

I love our flag,
    The red, white, and blue.
Some flags are older,
    And some flags are new.
It's nice to hear the flag's flapping sound.
It takes courage to enter war
    Because of the dying and
    Because of the gore.
A good citizen would take a stand
    For the people of America
    And for liberty's land.

Andrew Mullin, Grade 5
Heartland High School and Academy, MO

Night

I hear the nice, soft birds
Chirping in the silent blue sky
I feel the cold wind
Taking me away
To a silent night wall surrounding me
And I fall asleep, my eyes shut,
Dreaming and dreaming
When I wake up
I am warm in my home
With the fire.

Nick Delfino, Grade 4
Chester Park Elementary School of Fine Arts, SC

Bird's Eye-View

I'm a bird, high in the sky,
All the people watch me soar and fly.

I see children, playing in the streets,
I see generals leading their army fleets.

I see players, shooting their goals,
I see children skating on rolls.

I see girl-scouts, selling their cookies,
I see baseball players, beginning as rookies.

I see lumberman cutting down trees,
I see beekeepers, tending to bees.

Now you know all I see,
Maybe one day you'll be like me,
You'll be in Heaven, and see all I see.

Taylor Phillips, Grade 6
Model Middle School, GA

My Sister

My sister loves
Me so
Much, she adores
Me and can't get
Enough of me,
I love her
With all my
Heart, she brings
Me joy, laughter
And faith, if
I ever
Lost her I
Think I would
Faint, she is
Only three and
Filled with
Glee, in her
Eyes she sometimes
Wants to cry, but
After all she is the
Best sister of all.

Madison Warren, Grade 6
Armorel Elementary School, AR

Soccer

Once you kick the ball
It leaps into the air
The net swishing
As the goalie dives
And misses
Diving into empty space

Dillon Garrett, Grade 5
Bonaire Elementary School, GA

Monkey

Athletic.
Climbing tree to tree.
Having fun with its friends.
Hanging,
   and swinging
   is a monkey's life.

Libby Clifton, Grade 5
St Vincent Elementary School, MO

Holiday

Fourth of July
See red white and blue flags
Smell corn cooking in the house
Hear booming fireworks in the air
Juicy meat
Flags
Fourth of July

Ashley Poore, Grade 4
Tamassee-Salem Elementary School, SC

Clouds

Clouds are God's warriors
Watching over us,
While an angel sits upon one,
Keeping us safe
Like a lion protecting its cub.
Clouds are like cotton
So soft and snug.
But each one slips away
As fast as they came,
Sailing up to heaven.
Saying a swift good-bye
To the sky
It once lived in.
Saying good-bye
To the ground
It once looked upon,
Taking an angel with it,
Leaving behind peace and sorrow.

Jade Johnson, Grade 4
Crestwood Elementary School, KY

Baseball

In the summer, I'm played with.
In the winter, I'm at rest.
When I leave the pitcher's hand
I know the adventure begins.
Then I hear the umpire say
"out"
or "safe"
And it starts all over again.

Nathan Carroll, Grade 5
St Vincent Elementary School, MO

Boys

Boys,
Boys,
Boys,
Messy boys,
Fun boys,
Funny, smart, dumb boys,
Silly, loving, bright boys,
Those are just a few.
Ugly boys,
Gross boys,
Young, middle-aged, old boys,
Responsible, respectful, wild boys,
Plain boys, too.
Playful boys,
Mute boys,
Don't forget loud boys.
Last of all, best of all,
I like cute boys.

Jacki Wiederholt, Grade 6
South Nodaway Elementary School, MO

Stars

Stars,
Glittering in the beauty of the night sky,
Striking the darkness with light,
Filling the air with hope,
Scaring away
All bad things that hide
In the shadows of your heart.
Saving you from darkness.
Stars

Justin Kennady, Grade 4
Crestwood Elementary School, KY

Family

My name is Kevin
I have a big family
That is eleven

Kevin Jorgensen, Grade 4
John Will Elementary School, AL

Kittens

Kittens, kittens, oh so furry,
So small and cute.
Eyes colorful and different,
Tails thin and smooth.

Always into trouble,
Maybe, make that double.
Never knowing anything
About the outside world.

Kittens, Kittens on the couch,
Kittens, Kittens all about.
Kittens, Kittens everywhere,
Kittens, Kittens licking my hair.

Madison McMurray, Grade 4
Moyock Elementary School, NC

Dedicated to "Baby"

Baby was a dog
that would parade through a field.
She was special.
A loving white German shepherd,
both pleasant and sinister.
Her beauty was indescribable.
She was my first dog,
and she was the best ever.
Gentle, good with kids was she,
but then arrived that horrid day.
Baby was crushed by a car,
and I cried for days.
So this is for you, Baby,
the best dog ever.

Ally Nolting, Grade 6
Immanuel Lutheran School, MO

Tornado!

Rushing, rushing
A tornado is coming right before my eyes!
I saw homes being destroyed
And I could not help but cry
Help us! Help us!
We can't find a place!
We walked and we walked,
But we could not find a home!

Amber Nicole Parris, Grade 6
Scotts Creek Elementary School, NC

Baby Boys

All snuggle in the crib. Tucked in tight.
As they sleep the whole night.
Ducks and sheep make a little noise.
Just to comfort a sweet baby boy.

Awake in the morning because of the bird's song.
Beautiful music trails along.
Curious in every little way.
Even when they wake in the mid day.

Seeing new friends stuffed with fluff.
With cute button noses which are quite tough.
Watching them grow till they start to talk
You can't keep up. They start to walk.

You are amazed how the years have past.
When his first toy becomes his last.
Yet you will still remember that special day
When you were introduced to your sweet baby.

Miranda Snow, Grade 6
West Cary Middle School, NC

I Am a Tree

I am an oak tree, towering over the town;
my bark is knobby, elderly and brown.
I hear the creek moving in the wind;
my arms are extended, and always bend.

I am an oak tree, broad and tall;
my leaves turn brown in the fall.
I see kids playing in the field;
from the sun, my leaves are a shield.

I am an oak tree, old, yet strong;
birds nest in me while they sing a song.
Oh me, I have acorns galore,
and squirrels are eating my whole store.

I am the oak tree, ancient and giving;
I just thank God that I am still living.
I give shade, food, and much more;
and I've never felt better, right down to my core.

Elizabeth Woodard, Grade 6
Christ Episcopal School - Middle School, LA

Math

One times one is two,
or three times three is four?
Math is so confusing!
My hand is getting sore.
Seven minus eight is nine.
Four plus four is none.
Math is definitely not the least bit fun.
Why can't I figure it out?
This world will never know.
They tell me what the answer is…all I say is, "So?"
Eight times eight is blah blah.
Four plus four is who cares?
Five rabbits came and four left,
what was left of the hares?
My teacher says to stop, and try to figure it out,
but the only progress I am making is learning how to pout.
I needed to ask someone, but I didn't know who.
I'll ask my teacher! She'll know what to do!
Turned out I was right, she helped me, and I understand.
She told me everything,
now *I* have the upper hand.

Kara Oliver, Grade 6
Viola Elementary School, AR

October

Feeling the soft breeze blowing my hair
Touching the red, yellow, and green leaves on the ground
Hearing the cars driving by
Smelling the pumpkin pie being made
Seeing the leaves change colors on the trees

Hope Donohue, Grade 5
Briarwood Christian Elementary School, AL

Canopy

Thick, high, home for frogs
birds, snakes, all of them live there.
It makes you feel free.

Katherine Smith, Grade 4
Briarwood Christian Elementary School, AL

My Dog Suzy Q

She likes to hunt deer
She likes to swim in the pond
She always runs when I say c'mere.

I let her in when it's cold
She keeps me warm at night
I wish she could be with me when I'm old.

Together there's nothing we can't do
That's why I love
My dog Suzy Q.

Tré Tolar, Grade 5
East Marion Elementary School, MS

Pencil

Pencil
Pointy, hard
Sitting, writing, erasing
Has a sharp point
Toothpick

Erin Plunkett, Grade 5
Bonaire Elementary School, GA

Snowy Mountains

That snow white top
That crisp winter air
The view of mountains everywhere
From the bottom to the top
The roads wind around
All the way up and back to the ground
It's my favorite place to go
Especially when there's snow.

Taylor Cowan, Grade 5
Midway Covenant Christian School, GA

Homework

I wish homework was loads of fun
Then every day I'd have it done
But instead it's not that way
I get an *F* instead of an *A*

Caroline Lawe, Grade 4
St. Thomas More School, NC

Snowmen

A snowy, sunny morning is the best
For building snowmen and all the rest

It's a day where there's no school
I made a snowman that's really cool

My snowman has a carrot nose
But all snowmen come and go

But there is no need to sigh
When a snowman passes by

Because there is always next time.

Jonathan Titus, Grade 6
Brogden Middle School, NC

Lawmaker

L abor
A ctive
W orking
M aker
A mbition
K nowledgeable
E ncore
a **R** gumentative

Jake Noble, Grade 4
East Jones Elementary School, MS

Thanksgiving

I think Thanksgiving is about eating and having fun with other people.
Gathered around to be eating turkey and dressing.
All from the same family.
Thanksgiving is about being free
and able to go outside wherever we want to where the sun is shining.
That's what Thanksgiving is about.

Kyle Martin, Grade 6
Guntown Middle School, MS

Circle of Destruction

There was no person to be seen. There was no one in sight,
except for one man in a bomb shelter avoiding that turbulent night.
He crept out and stumbled onto a broken road.
It creaked as if carrying such a burdening load.
The town lay in rubble as it gave off an eerie glow.
What happened last night the man had to know.
He looked at the dying sun and immediately knew.
For this was the end and the start of something new.
He looked away and stared in disbelief.
As a woman approached him with a sigh of great relief.
The forests were burned down and the oceans all dried,
Yet all hope had still not died.
This circle of destruction and they are Adam and Eve,
As a new circle will start, this one will leave.

Shoham Das, Grade 6
Haynes Academy for Advanced Studies, LA

Dogs

Dogs are playful creatures. They come with many features.
Some are slim and tall. Others are chubby and small.
Some dogs bark real loud. Other dogs barely make a sound.
Some dogs live in a backyard. Some dogs live in a house and act like a guard.
Some dogs are very hairy. Some dogs are almost barely.
Some dogs are playful and nice. Others are mean and will bite.
Dogs are my favorite pets. When my mom asked me if I wanted one I said yes.
He comes inside when it gets cold. He is, in human years, 10 years old.
He is big and black and hair, he doesn't lack.
Raven is his name. Running is his game.
A dog is a smart animal. It will come to you when you call.
Dogs will return a ball. And you can teach them how to crawl.

Chelsea Bogac, Grade 6
Holy Rosary Academy, LA

Light Blue

Light Blue looks like the ice that the Charlotte Checkers glide across while they play.
Light Blue sounds like the puck sliding across the ice while the players try to get it.
Light Blue smells like the hot dogs at the concession stand.
Light Blue tastes like victory when the Checkers score
Light Blue feels like the cool air from the freezing ice.
Light Blue is one of the main colors for the Charlotte Checkers team.
Light Blue is the sound of the stereo blaring at the game.
Light Blue is the smell of the sour sweat dripping off the players
Light Blue is the taste of victory when the Checkers win the game.
Light Blue is the feel of the crowd as they cheer on their team.

Landon Ellis, Grade 5
Cool Spring Elementary School, NC

Summer Vacation

Summer vacation the best time of the year.
Kids run out of school letting out a cheer.
The parents run, scream, and hide.
The kids are out you cannot deny.
The parents are mad and ground you all day.
Like a prisoner in your room with nothing to play.
You sit on your bed and stare at the wall.
If you jump out the window you will definitely fall.
You sneak by your parents and get away safely.
You are free to run, hop, and skip playfully.
You and your friends run to the field.
The parents are mad; they will get you next year.

Reed Scott, Grade 6
Queen of Angels Catholic School, GA

A Horrifying Day

While playing outside one horrifying day
I see a burning plane flying over to crash this day
The terrorists started taking over the day
That's why 911 is such a bad day!

Markell Harkless, Grade 5
Eastside Elementary School, GA

Garden

Oh, garden! Oh, garden!
How wonderful you are.
You twinkle and shine
Like a Christmas star.
You are, you are
The wonder of the world.
You can warm a heart in an instant.
A part of you will always be a part of me.

Mason Garrett Wagner, Grade 4
Ode Maddox Elementary School, AR

Prayers

My prayers are listening and my bells are ringing.
The angels above are singing,
cause my prayers reach to the heavens for God to answer.
My prayers are clinging to the air to reach the heavens,
my prayers are answered, one by one.

Rebecca Harrington, Grade 4
Brilliant Elementary School, AL

Veteran

V ery dangerous troops
E very one of them armed and dangerous
T anks at the ready
E very soldier at the ready
R ed blood everywhere
A lready too many soldiers killed or wounded
N early won the war

Jordan Smith, Grade 4
Cherokee Elementary School, AR

Droplets Dropping

After the rain fell
Rain droplets were dropping down
From the green, dark leaves

Loveday Glandon, Grade 4
Briarwood Christian Elementary School, AL

I Am Having So Much Fun

Oh I am having so much fun
playing in the sun
The birds are in the sky
and we have been watching them fly and fly
we hope to see the moon
Now we are ready for bed
and now we have dreams in our heads

Heather Wideman, Grade 5
Graham Elementary School, AL

Lulu Rap

Don't get mad when you see me with my pen and pad
Writing my work down and becoming so glad.
I know my a's and b's and my one, two, threes
Making non-believers fall to their knees.
360 degrees is the radius of a circle
I'm telling the truth and don't mean to hurt you.
Put me to work, I'll pass the test.
No clowning around, you know I'm the best.
Blue is the color of my J's, with a smile like the sun rays.
When I step in the school, they be like
Zoom, zoom be quiet in the room, room.
Because you know I'm the girl who rocks her work!

Olivia Witherspoon, Grade 6
Calloway Smith Middle School, AL

Fall Festival

Rushing, Dashing, Leaping
Finally finding
my friends.
Hopping, Running going to get our hair spray painted.
Orange, red, purple, blue
all different colors.
Looking beautiful
kind of like twins.
Jumping so high in the bouncy balloon.
So loud it sounds like drums.
What a fall festival.

Rachel Waild, Grade 4
Alvaton Elementary School, KY

Baseball Game

Smells like peanuts fresh from the oven
Looks like diamond green and brown
Sounds like fans screaming for a home run
Tastes like a cold Coke in my mouth
Feels like a ball being handed to you by the player

Mary Elizabeth Whorton, Grade 5
Briarwood Christian Elementary School, AL

Left Behind

I drag behind
not knowing what to do.
All I can think of is
how I miss you.

You spring ahead
without a word.
My head spins in circles
and I see imaginary birds.

I am lost
my heart beats hard.
Monday was my birthday
and you didn't give me a card.

I know this sounds random
this poem I write,
but I am just tired
of being left behind.
Emily Alton, Grade 6
Brogden Middle School, NC

The Walk to the Park

When I went to the park
I saw my best friend Mark
Played a game of basketball
And he asked me to the mall
We were sitting in the heat
Bobbing to the strange beat
He took me straight home
Then later we talked on the phone
Adriana Swain, Grade 5
Graham Elementary School, AL

Britt!

I have a horse her name is Britt.
She really knows how to get up and get.

When I ride upon her saddle.
When I get off I can only waddle.
Conner Seither, Grade 5
Walton Verona Elementary School, KY

The World

The World is a place,
The best place to be,
It's a great playground,
For a he or a she,
It has tons of wildlife,
So full of green,
It's the perfect home,
For you and for me.
Daniel Kim, Grade 6
Bellwood Discovery School, TN

Tiger

Tiger
Ferocious, mean
Killing, roaring, biting
Very good predators
Animal
Tanner Andersen, Grade 5
Bayyari Elementary School, AR

Pink

My favorite color
Nobody can deny
Oh how fine it is
Prettiest color in the world
Quick to make you love it
Red's best friends
So whenever you're down
The color pink will lift you
Up
Skyla Renner, Grade 5
Sullivan Elementary School, TN

Butterflies

Butterflies so cute
They fly so high in the sky
You can run after them
Trying to catch them but can't
So beautiful you can't imagine it
Different colors so cute
Butterflies everywhere I look.
Kaitlyn Hunter, Grade 6
Poland Jr High School, LA

My Favorite Sport

My favorite sport is basketball.
It is a lot of fun to play.
You get to
shoot,
pass,
and slam dunk
the ball.
The most fun is when I get the ball.
I see my grandparents saying,
"Go Jesse, go!"
Basketball is a lot of fun.
One time, I got down the court,
And I was covered with guys.
They were all over me!
I passed to my friend.
He passed back to me.
14-17!
I shot the winning goal.
My favorite sport is basketball.
Jesse Turner, Grade 5
Shannon Forest Christian School, SC

The Mad Man

There once was an old man asleep,
he likes to ride in his blue jeep.
But one Wednesday,
he ran away.
You never heard a single peep.
Gracie Chapman, Grade 4
Judsonia Elementary School, AR

Big Old Fish

There once was a big old fish.
He got served on a plastic dish.
I'm sorry to say,
That he couldn't stay
Now he's an angel fish.
Seth A. Smith, Grade 5
Salem Elementary School, AR

Sunset

Sunset comes, I glide
Off the cool ice rink and watch
An artist paint the blue sky
Pink.

The faint
Colors of the sun
Disappear along
With the fun.

But tomorrow is
Another day to
Frolic free laugh
And play!
Kaitlin Gillespie, Grade 5
Elon Elementary School, NC

Dirt Bikes/Street Bikes

Dirt bikes
fast, loud
racing, speeding, jumping
blue, white, yellow, orange
wheeling, racing, spinning
fast, gigantic
Street bikes
Shawn Adams, Grade 6
Lost River Elementary School, KY

Shark

Fast
Eats meat
Swims underwater
Unkind, vicious, scary beast
Hunter's
Hunter Yarbrough, Grade 4
Robert E Lee Elementary School, TN

Duck Calls

Worn duck calls dangling from lanyards decorated
With waterfowl bands are considered family
Heirlooms in Arkansas.

Some Arkansas middle schools discourage students
From toting duck calls on campus because of the
Crescendo of practice calling during fall recesses.

It is not uncommon on Arkansas highways to
Hear muffled quacks coming from 4x4 pickups
As callers practice their "highballs."

Drew Parker, Grade 6
Harrisburg Middle School, AR

Crisp! Crunch! Cool!

Leaves are falling all around
Geese honking make a pleasant sound.

Flying in a V-shaped form
Geese are escaping the winter storms.

Trees are painted orange and red
Children do not want to go to bed.

The fair is coming to town
People come from all around.

Children in costumes go about
They are hoping for candy no doubt.

The weather is getting crisp and cool
It is time to forget about the pool.

Fall is pleasant, crisp, and clean
And the leaves make a lovely scene.

Taylor Hetrick, Grade 5
Forest Avenue Academic Magnet School, AL

Merry Christmas

M erry in the morning
E xcellent when you open presents
R eady for toys
R eady to love
Y es! It's Christmas

C heerful when you know Christmas is coming
H appy when it's Christmas break
R unning and playing with your presents
I n warm pieces
S neaking candy
T rees shining bright
M ary in the manger scene
A t the Christmas tree getting presents
S pecial when you're with your family

Jordan Grant, Grade 4
Tamassee-Salem Elementary School, SC

Family

Matt
athletic, funny
playing, studying, working
College student, gamer, boy, car driver
talking, feeding, dressing
Pretty, sweet
Mom

Timothy Robertson, Grade 5
Briarwood Christian Elementary School, AL

Outdoor Sounds

I heard my cats meowing, my dogs barking,
Coyotes howling in the woods at dark
I was in my room looking outside
At the colorful leaves that were falling
With the moon light shining on them
I heard the hooting sounds of the owl
Coming from the tree
In my back yard
Outdoor sounds make me happy.

Hazel Kline, Grade 6
Temple Hill Elementary School, KY

Karate

Mental tasks with distinguished discipline is in store
It all awaits on the work of my application
Attention focused for so long
Bravery is a requirement to become a part
Bones will crack and shatter
Training must be endured
Skills must be challenged to be a master
Difficulty will be the first element to master

Jonathon Kinser, Grade 5
Cline Elementary School, KY

Canoe Ride Bliss

Have you ever enjoyed a canoe ride?
The gentle breeze as you abide.
The rolling waves, the pleasing sun.
In the water let your fingers run.
Just take it all in and make a wish.
Before your eyes is a flying fish.
Don't miss a minute, don't hurry, and don't race.
Just gaze up into the void of space.
The birds of the air, the fish of the sea.
Oh aren't canoe rides filled with glee.
The inky black waves that engulf the land below.
The fish move along with the water's flow.
The birds always cooing, the wind rushing by.
I just saw a bullfrog eating a fly.
And now that our time is all done and through,
I think I'll go rent me another canoe.

Alex Gachassin, Grade 6
St Cecilia School, LA

The Moon

It's trapped by Earth's power, a slave it's become. It once was a free asteroid. Now it's under Earth's thumb. It's forced to travel around the Earth again and again only twice in the year seeing the Sun. It's cold all night but has no day. (That would be weird any way.) It's one silver beauty alone in the sky. It's one little child lost in a crowd of stars called the Universe. Once in a while it will go away. (I wonder where it goes?) I guess only the moon knows.

Hayden Kesterson, Grade 4
Sequoyah Elementary School, TN

The Most Wonderful Time of the Year

Lights, decorations, ornaments on the tree, 'tis the time of year again to sing with glee.
Presents will be wrapped, cookies will be baked, anxious little children waiting to hear Santa's sleigh.
Warm cider with delicious turkey and yummy food galore.
Loving families celebrating the lord. Oh my it's so much, I can't wait 'til Christmas Day
to celebrate with all my words.

Meagan Molter, Grade 6
Queen of Angels Catholic School, GA

The Mournful Echoes

The echoes they say
This was a wonderful place just the other day.
The place was busy and the people were kind,
You'd really think that they would mind
To have to leave such as this kind.
It had tents and jails and was well thought out,
There was even one big winding route.
This place was used to live during the gold rush,
Even people eating mush were happy here.
But then the deposits of gold were all done
So the people without looking back, glanced to the sun
And made their way to their next sites where they would pass many nights.
And never would they think of the town left behind where people had been so kind.
Never to think of what happened there only to care of coming things
The hope of gold and diamonds and rings.
If only they could see what happened to the land. It became all soil and sand.
Today those towns are empty without a soul in sight no light, not dull or bright.
Ghost towns they became and many more the same.
And today you can hear the mournful echoes sounding a bit like some geckos.
They tell us the story of the days long ago when the people they cared not for such things
Only gold and silver and diamond rings.

Keerthana Srinivas, Grade 6
River Trail Middle School, GA

I'm Haunted

I was haunted by the dreadful dark who would play those tricky tricks on me.
Like when I would see something that wasn't really real.
Also I would see a big green monster that would come get me and I wouldn't sleep that night.

I am haunted by the movies *Nightmare on Elm Street*. I live on Elm Street.
I am haunted of that frightful Freddy Krueger would kill me in my dreams.

I am haunted of going to war.
I might not come back.
I would leave my family hurt and heartbroken.

I'm haunted!

Mason Wells, Grade 5
Eminence Middle School, KY

Rudolph

I am Rudolph.
I wonder if I will guide Santa's sleigh.
I hear all the reindeers' bells.
I see all the elves working hard.
I want to guide Santa's sleigh every year.
I am Rudolph.

I pretend to claim my fame.
I feel like I always save Christmas.
I touch the roof of every house.
I worry the children will wake up.
I cry if people laugh at me.
I am Rudolph.

I understand I may not be the lead reindeer every year.
I dream of Christmas every day.
I say that I love the North Pole.
I hope Santa appreciates me.
I try my best every Christmas Eve.
I am Rudolph.

Leah Meissner, Grade 4
Wohlwend Elementary School, MO

WWII

Patriot fighters, the bravest of all,
facing the odds of certain death.

They'll do as they're told,
no questions to ask,
doing the most dangerous, hardest of tasks.

They're ready, they're willing,
they're waiting to fall,
showing absolutely no mercy at all.

They'll die for their country
as they're trained to do,
they'll fight, they'll win, and
they'll come home to you.

Ben Harrison, Grade 6
Brogden Middle School, NC

Fred the Dog

My dog likes to play.
My dog is really cool.
My dog's eyes are blue.
My dog has feelings for people.
My dog likes to hunt.
My dog likes to ride my 4-wheeler with me.
My dog puts his paws in my lap.
My dog loves to run.
My dog is my best pet.

Blake Ferguson, Grade 6
Temple Hill Elementary School, KY

Christmas Gift Wishes

If I could grant a wish for you,
I would wish for a toy or two.

I would wish for a plastic army man,
And I would wish for a small toy van.

Next, I'd wish for plenty of Legos,
And a great, big model stegosaurus.

May you get a telescope to look at the stars,
And a remote control for your new cool cars.

I would wish you even get a great big doll.
May you have the best Christmas of all.

Nate Hills, Grade 5
Heber Springs Elementary School, AR

My Grandma's and Grandpa's House

My grandma's and grandpa's house is the best.
My grandma is the best. My grandma has candy and pop.
My grandma is the best.

My grandma's and grandpa's house is the best.
They play games with me and they watch TV together.
I love my grandma and grandpa very much.

They give me hope.
They give me love.
They give me money.

Chelbi Decker, Grade 4
Hayes Elementary School, OK

My First Hunting Trip

Every Christmas the men in our family go on a quail hunt
I was finally part of our family's Christmas tradition
It didn't take long to get there and it was cold

In target practice I shot my first shotgun
Then we hit the field
Two hardworking dogs accompanied us
It didn't take long before the dogs went on point
I focused, my heart was racing, the dogs moved in
I took my position by my Papa,
Birds like rockets, up from the ground
I saw one. I pointed and pulled the trigger

BOOM!

A quail came falling out of the sky
Dog retrieved. I took it from the dog's mouth
I got my first quail
The cycle went on and on
Fifty was our goal and fifty was what we got
Our quail dinner was delicious

Buck Brown, Grade 6
Beck Academy, SC

Red Bellied Black Snake
Snake
Very shy
Eats and swims
Can lay up to 40 eggs
Venomous
Eric Hill, Grade 5
John Will Elementary School, AL

Colors
Green is for the grass below
White is for the pretty snow
Yellow is for the colorful leaves
Brown is for the droopy trees
Orange is for the bright sun
Purple means to have some fun
Black means the day is done

What do you think of colors?
Megan Cambron, Grade 5
Ascension Elementary School, KY

Kittens
Kittens
Cuddly, furry
Purring, playing, eating
Always there when you're down
Pets
Blair Brewer, Grade 5
Bayyari Elementary School, AR

I Remember My Great-Grandma
I remember my great-grandma…
Loving, caring, cooking, fun

I remember my great-grandma…
Kissing, cleaning, reading, laughing

I remember my great-grandma…
Sleeping, hugging, sweet, and now dead

I remember my great-grandma
Maria Mora, Grade 5
Sycamore Elementary School, GA

Fall
I love the fall with trees so tall,
All the leaves orange, red, and brown,
They decorate the ground.
The weather gets colder
As the year gets older.
Oh, how I love fall,
The greatest season of all.
Tristan Scott, Grade 4
First Assembly Christian School, AL

I See
I see the trees as I pass on the highway.
I see signs and other cars.
I see the same thing over and over.
I see my reflection in the window.
I see me!
Amber Kent, Grade 5
St Dominic School, TN

Winter
Winter is coming.
Black bears are hibernating.
People are skiing.
Brooke Baird, Grade 4
Stephens Elementary School, AL

Too Late Now
Even though everyone laughed at him
He kept going.
Even though no one believed in him
He kept going.
Even though everyone made fun of him
He kept going.

He never gave up.
He persevered.
He got up time after time.
His love shone true.
Why did I never see it?
And now it's too late.

It's too late now.
I let him down.
I let him go.
So now he's gone.
Lost forever.
And now it's too late to do anything…
Lynn Tran, Grade 6
Brogden Middle School, NC

Nature
I see the sea that is so blue.
It has beasts that eat their feasts.
I see the trees with beautiful leaves.
The wind is cool at night,
Invisible at sight.
The earth that gives birth,
With its cool dirt.
The fire gives us warmth
During winter storms.
This is nature
That I love so much,
I feel your touch.
David B. Corder, Grade 5
Macedonia Elementary School, SC

It's All My Fault
What a call,
For me to make you fall,
It makes me want to bawl.
You skinned your knee,
Beneath the tree,
Because of me.
And now I see,
That you are mad at me.
I am sorry.
Maria-Jose Malaver, Grade 6
Queen of Angels Catholic School, GA

The Mime
Way back when
In my great-grandmother's time
There was a man named Jerry
And he was a mime
He took his job so seriously
He never said a word
And his walk was so funny
He looked like a bird
Emily Wetherington, Grade 5
Quail Run Elementary School, GA

A Road to Nowhere
I'm on a road,
Don't know where it ends
I'm not sure of the path ahead
Where do I turn?
Where do I end?
Haven't any money,
I'm nowhere to be found,
Starving for food
The rain is pouring down.
Wishing for a hood
Miss my family and my friends
It's only me all alone

But I fell back to Earth
It was only a dream.
Alice Tiller, Grade 4
Lynn Fanning Elementary School, AL

Dogs
The sun is setting
The time is short
I don't have much time with my dogs
My beagle is gentle, soft and sweet
My lab is hyper, sweet and rambunctious
I love them and they love me
I can hardly stand it when it's time to go.
Brooke Conley, Grade 4
Moyock Elementary School, NC

The Devastating Tornado!!!

I am as dangerous as a rattle snake
I am the path of Destruction
I am so powerful the whole world can't stop me
My winds are so fast they sound like a rushing train
I cause so many injuries that I can't keep count
I will sweep you up into my vortex where you can't get out
My powers are unmatchable
Stand clear of my path, for I have no mercy
Though in my calm I bring you stillness and peace
I may come in day or night you better watch out stay alert
I AM A TORNADO

Trevor Jordan Bullard, Grade 5
Pembroke Elementary School, NC

The Little Girl's Prayer

In a little country church just outside of town
a little girl walked to the altar and gently knelt down
she folded her hands and bowed her little head
then she began to pray and this is what she said…
Father, I love You and I know You know what's best

but this is my mother laying here at rest
I know You need her but Daddy does too
and I don't understand why You brought her to me if she
was gonna leave so soon
I'm gonna miss her really bad you see
'cause I want her to play outside when the wildflowers grow
to pick beautiful red roses from her garden
and to sleep with me at night
Daddy needs Momma to do
all the sweet things Daddy never could
like kiss my forehead when I'm in bed asleep
and Momma needs Daddy to chop wood for the winter.
So Father, I guess You need her bad right now
to take her away from me so soon. I just don't know how
but I trust in You to help us through each day
and to hear my daddy and me each time we pray.

Precious Marion, Grade 6
Edmonton Elementary School, KY

Mrs. Harsh

Mrs. Harsh, always joyful and fun,
Smiling, sharing, caring for everyone,
You're as cool as reading to me,
You're always calm and collected as can be,
So, forever, you'll be remembered by thee.

Becky Thomson, Grade 4
Moyock Elementary School, NC

God Loves Me

I can see God loves me. He gave my soul to me for free.
God loves everyone on Earth. He knows we all have worth.
Jesus came to help us all. He picks us up when we fall.
Then He died for all our sins to keep us safe from Satan's pins.

Cody LeBoeuf, Grade 5
Holy Rosary Academy, LA

Snowflakes

All different shapes.
Twirling around to the ground.
They are fun to watch.

Abby Parks, Grade 4
Briarwood Christian Elementary School, AL

Miss Bad Stuff!!!

I am powerful like thunder.
No one can stop me.
I'm bad and wild.
I can knock you down if you get in my way.

I have a twirl that is deadly.
I am furious.

I am horrible.
I am painful.

I can hurt you like you've never been hurt before.

I am scary.
I can scare you like it was Halloween night.

I am a bad tornado.

Shayla Ann McRae, Grade 5
Pembroke Elementary School, NC

Our Flag

The flag that I love waves high and bright.
We stand for the great flag
    Because we have liberty and justice.
Can we see how great our forefathers fought?
Or do we not know what they fought for our flag and freedom?
Our flag is here for every living thing that is in this world.
Do we stick together like we should?
Or do we go our separate ways
    Not doing what our country needs.
Our flag is great,
    And I will stand here for it every day.

Aubrianna Allen, Grade 5
Heartland High School and Academy, MO

Fall

I took a walk in the fall.
The trees were so very tall.
That it made me feel real small.
I heard the birds make their beautiful call.
But I did not see them at all.
Then the leaves began to fall.
The colors were so pretty and all.
I tried to put the colors on the wall.
But you can't copy fall.

Ron Locklear, Grade 5
Pembroke Elementary School, NC

Animal

Birds singing in trees
Dogs barking from house to house
Shy deer in the woods
Dustin Ferguson, Grade 4
Tamassee-Salem Elementary School, SC

The Lord I Know

Mysterious like the wind,
Gentle as the snow,
That's the Lord I know.

Fierce like an army,
Calm as the sea,
The Lord will provide for me.

Wise as all creatures on Earth combined,
Powerful like a tsunami,
He is many things, you see.

The Lord is many things,
As most of you can see.
But this I really know,
He cares for you and me.
Clayton Laird, Grade 5
Midway Covenant Christian School, GA

Love

Love is always cool
And it may always rule.
Like father and mother
And grandparents and brother!

Love is very, very kind.
It will always be like that every time.
Love is always peaceful,
Love is always sweet.
Love is never queasy
But love is always neat.

It is cool and it is pure
But love will always be very sure.
Love is warm and it will always be real.
It is always something great to feel!
Kristen Harris, Grade 6
Brogden Middle School, NC

Veteran

V ictorious
E xuberant
T angy
E nergetic
R emarkable
A dvise
N ow and forever, we are in the USA.
Jadin Haley, Grade 4
Cherokee Elementary School, AR

The Night

One night, where the stars shine bright,
The owls go out to fly beyond the mysterious sky,
Where the wolves prowl and the coyotes howl, at the moon in the sky,
Where the crickets chirp and frogs make big, loud burps,
The foxes hide in their den, and the music begins
With mysterious beat of sound.
Now you hear a big bear bound.
As the big owls scream,
And the tiger drinks from the stream.
Where it's sometimes violent,
It's seldom silent.
Though it can be a fright,
It's just about all the time night.

Amber Westenkirchner, Grade 5
Quail Run Elementary School, GA

Do You Know Who I Am?

I am a sky scraping horrible beast
I'm as furious as a bull
I'm as strong as the Golden Gate Bridge
If you fall in my vortex you better watch out
I might throw you a mile
I'm more petrifying than a giant spider
I'm more angry than a hurricane
I am devastating
I am horrible
I'm more determined to knock over a building than a wrecking ball
I travel at the speed of light
I am deadly
I am incredible
I am disastrous
My winds are louder than a freight train and its whistle
Watch out there's no telling where I'll turn up next
I'm as tall and gigantic as a dinosaur
I'm as tough as T-Rex
Do you know who I am
I'm a strong but furious Tornado

Sean Marshall, Grade 5
Pembroke Elementary School, NC

The Best Dog Ever

Like a best friend, you greeted me when I returned from school.
Like a brother, you made me happy when I was sad.
When you licked my chin it was like hitting a game-winning home run.
When you wagged your tail, it was like eating ice-cream.
Your golden, yellow fur was as thick as a forest.
Your deep, black eyes were as dark as the midnight sky.
Your rough, damp nose was as great as playing sports on a summer day.
When we swam in the pool, it was like being on a roller coaster.
Playing tug-of-war with you was more fun than I could ever imagine.
As I woke up every morning, and saw your face, you made me smile.
Tara, I will miss you very much.

Jason Delay, Grade 6
River Trail Middle School, GA

Running Deer

I hear the tree limbs snap
because of the wind
I hear hoofs pound the ground
because of the running deer
Colorful leaves lie dry on the soil
the fall smell outside never goes dull.
The leaves crunch
and a shadow appears among the trees
The pounding of hoofs come near
I know for sure that it's the running deer
There's a warm feeling in the red and brown leaves
knowing that Christmas will come soon
That deer runs away

Corrina Hall, Grade 6
Guntown Middle School, MS

Come with Me to the Center of the Sun

Come with me to the center of the sun
Where I hope you bring the SPF Infinity
For it is so hot here,
Bring tons of water
Oh, come with me
To the center of the sun!

Devin Leitch, Grade 4
Herbert J Dexter Elementary School, GA

Lake and Desert

lake
enjoyable, noisy
swimming, fishing, playing
ducks, water, cacti, sand
wandering, starving, tiring
burning, arid
desert

Connor Brewton, Grade 5
Briarwood Christian Elementary School, AL

Me

Tiffany, 11
Happy, friendly, awesome
Daughter of Tim and Shelly
Sister of Molly
Best friend of Angela
Owner of a cat
Who enjoys a good game and shopping
Who feels happy, sometimes mad, evil to little siblings
Who fears bulls and mountain lions
Who would like to see Salt Lake City
Who feels strongly about pets and family
Who will spend the summer at home
Born in Chillicothe, now a resident of Trenton
Norman

Tiffany Norman, Grade 5
Trenton Middle School, MO

My Country

We live in a country that allows freedom of speech,
Liberty, justice, and strength.
We live in a country with God as our guide;
He helps us and leads the way.
We live in a country that is united together,
Containing the fifty states.
We live in a country where we can respect our flag;
Respect the red, white, and blue.
We live in a country where we can be proud,
Proud of our country so pure.
We live in a country so brave and so bright,
Surely our country is great.

Seth Acup, Grade 5
Heartland Academy, MO

Daydream

When I stare into space, my mind starts to spin,
And my amazing journey starts to begin.
I'm riding on a dragon, up in the air.
It looks so far away, the earth down there.
I see from above castles of gems, and mountains of snow.
All of a sudden, the dragon starts to slow.
Now I'm flying with silver wings,
And enjoying the flight with these wonderful things.
And then I see a cloud out there.

Would I do it? I dared.
I flew through the cloud, against the icy air.
Then I came out with the wind in my hair.
Now I'm in Japan, with Ninja all around.
Then they attack, I dive under the ground.
At the center of the earth, I feel I could melt,
This horrible heat, it's too much I have felt.
Now I snap back, and no one can deny
The glint in my eye
As I think about
The magical, the imaginary, and the impossible.

Paige Cary, Grade 5
Elon Elementary School, NC

Playing Piano

P racticing piano every day
L essons taken once a week
A lways moving fingers across the keys
Y oung is when piano playing begins
I mprovising comes in handy
N otes are on a staff
G ood teachers make good players

P laying forte (loud) and piano (soft)
I love playing piano
A piano has 88 keys, 52 white and 36 black
N ever give up
O nce you begin, you'll love it 'till the end

Austin Yoders, Grade 5
Bellwood Discovery School, TN

Electrical Storm

The wind is howling,
A thunderstorm is brewing,
Lightning is crackling.
Caleb Madden, Grade 5
Lloyd-Kennedy Charter School, SC

Thanks to All the Soldiers

America is a great place to me.
God and the angels are watching
over all the soldiers fighting for us.
the water falling
in their face,
the grass and mud
in their face,
having their guns and cannons
I bet they feel bad
for having
to kill people
I know I would.
Fighting through
the morning and night
All the soldiers,
I thank you.
Molly Jeane, Grade 6
Leonville Elementary School, LA

Mother's Love

To this world came two girls
Lovely as can be
Mother's love for these girls
would always be
one girl two girl beautiful
as you can see
The love you share will always be
De'Oushia Jefferson, Grade 5
East Marion Elementary School, MS

Basketball

Basketball is dribbling
up and down the court.
I bounce it up and down
and I turn around
and shoot to score.
It falls in the basket
and it hits the floor.
Sara Gilbert, Grade 4
Brilliant Elementary School, AL

Sunlight

Brightly shining orb
Big ball of fire in blue sky
Shimmering on earth
William Cox, Grade 4
Broadway Elementary School, NC

Rain

Oh God,
On our earth
The beautiful earth
The god of rain
For a long time
He has not been kind
And the people around
Are suffering along
So we pray to you
To give us back
A lot of rain
To make this earth
Green and happy again
Sahej Chhabra, Grade 5
Briarlake Elementary School, GA

Thanksgiving

T hanksgiving is for
H elping
A nd
N ibbling on food,
K neeling to aid,
S eeing fall colors,
G iving happiness.
I
V ow to bring happiness and believe
I n the
N eed to
G ive.
Collin Holloway, Grade 4
Cleveland Elementary School, OK

A Christmas Day!

When you see the snow fall
When you see the rain
You start to get a picture
That looks kind of insane
But once you know that feeling
That just wants to say
Oh! Oh my, is it really,
Christmas Day?

When you look up the chimney
And start to dream and stare
Are you really wondering,
Is Santa still up there?
Then you get a feeling
That really starts to grow
And when you hear that cheering voice
Saying, Ho, Ho, Ho, Ho, Ho!
You start to wonder and say,
Is it really Christmas Day?
Beonika Hughes, Grade 6
Brogden Middle School, NC

Ode to Math

From division
To multiplication
From subtraction
To addition
From parenthesis
To exponents
They never come
With ease
For it takes time
To learn your 1, 2, 3's
Carly Beard, Grade 5
Meramec Elementary School, MO

Bubble Gum

Juicy Fruit is very juicy.
Extra lasts all day and
Double Bubble gets me in trouble.
So I don't get to go out and play.
Haley Foster, Grade 4
Brilliant Elementary School, AL

Fences

I'm a fence, I'm a fence,
I need a good rinse.
I'm a fence, I'm a fence
I need a rain trench.
I'm a fence, I'm a fence
I need to be fixed with a wrench.
I'm a fence, I'm a fence
don't turn me into a bench.
Patrick Calumpong, Grade 5
Elkhorn Elementary School, MO

Devin in Heaven

Devin was eleven,
And went to see a reverend.
Who sent him to Heaven,
Where he saw Kevin and Evan.
Devin Karr, Grade 5
Oark Elementary School, AR

Basketball

B ounce the ball.
A round the court.
S hoot the ball in the basket.
K ills to lose.
E ach time we win we say, good game.
T ake the ball and off I go.
B ounce the ball.
A round the court.
L eap up and touch the sky.
L eft and right I go.
Zoey McMichael, Grade 4
Hayes Elementary School, OK

Mrs. Gabriel

Mrs. Gabriel is a single rose on a thorn bush
She is an angel in disguise, always following behind me
A shadow underneath my feet.

Maci Lester, Grade 6
Pulaski County Middle School, GA

Happy Feet

Socks and shoes and leather laces
These feet like to dance in wide open spaces.
Singing and dancing make these feet move
To any rhythm that has the right groove.
Happy feet, happy feet move in proper stride
To the million sounds of music
That you just have to try.

Amber Throckmorton, Grade 6
Pleasants County Middle School, WV

Don't Leave Me

Don't leave me
Don't you dare leave me
Without you I have nothing to love
I have nothing to give
Nothing to do
If you leave I will fall apart
We've been together right from the start
You're the only reason I live
Please don't go
Don't you dare
I truly think we're the best of friends
If you leave you'll be breaking my heart
So its either you or me
Make the decision now
You can't decide so why are you still standing here
It's too late
I've decided for you
Now go

Tatum Gates, Grade 6
Brogden Middle School, NC

What Is Red?

Red is a rose growing every day,
Sunset that grows but never stays.
Red is the salsa spicy and hot,
It's so spicy you want to jump on the spot.
Red is like fireworks booming and bright.
It's such a lovely world what a beautiful sight.
Red is like fire growing stronger every minute.
It's way too hot so don't get in it.
Red is like tulips growing in the grass,
But don't get in the poison oak or you will get a big rash.
Red is the color of poisonous frogs,
Red is the color of Santa Claus.
Red is the color of summer in the sun,
It's also the color of having fun.

MiKayla Love, Grade 6
Lost River Elementary School, KY

A Rain Storm

A raindrop starts dripping from a leaf.
The rain falls slowly from the sky.
The clear water falls slower and slower.
Now the rain is falling harder.
The rain is falling faster and faster.
When you walk outside, it is pouring down rain.
The storm gets louder and louder.
Now there is a light mist all around.
When you walk outside, it is really slippery.
Now the storm stops,
and a rainbow comes out of the bright blue sky.

Keaton Walker, Grade 5
Saffell Street Elementary School, KY

Love Hurts

Love hurts.
It slams you down.
No one cares.
It sways you back and forth.
Between two worlds.
You go on in life thinking.
No one to save you now.
The person you love.
Not what they seem.
Stay away.
Save yourself before it's too late.
Your lover's out to get you.
You're filled with fury.
You try to run but you're pulled back in.
"It's life," they all say.
Ph, yeah right.
So just remember one thing before I leave.
Love purely, truly hurts.

Kayla Shiflette, Grade 6
Dyer Elementary & Jr High School, TN

The Search for Treasure

In the early morning,
In my warm sweater I search for treasure,
With pleasure I measure,
How heavy the beautiful pearl is
The Earth.

Amanda Poroch, Grade 5
Austin Elementary School, GA

Big Feet

There once was an old woman with big feet.
She sat down and heard a tweet.
It wasn't a bird.
That's not what she heard.
It was her feet.
That made the tweet.

Kendra Reece, Grade 6
Livingston Middle School, TN

Scared

Have you ever felt sad or scared
Not knowing what will happen
Tomorrow
Scared to show your feelings
Or share them
Frightened to know to
Expect bad things to happen
Always
Yet depression of the blues are
Always there
Like something is following you
And doesn't go away
When you have the slightest
Hope of happiness
And when you turn around it's
Gone?

Jordan Cushman, Grade 6
Bernard Middle School, MO

Halloween/Christmas

Halloween
Dark, cool
Walking, tricking, treating
Parties, candy, trees, goodies
Eating, wrapping, shopping
Merry, bright
Christmas

AJ Floyd, Grade 6
Lost River Elementary School, KY

Soccer in the Fall

Soccer is very fun —
Soccer is when you run.
You especially want the soccer ball —
But you play soccer in the fall.

You want the ball to stay alive —
Just make sure your ball does not dive.
Get the ball in the net for a goal —
Soccer is drifting deep down in my soul.

Emily Hester, Grade 4
North Elementary School, NC

My Dad

Thank you, Dad,
for fighting for our country.
You are the best of all of the rest,
and you're even smart too.
I really miss you when you are gone,
but I understand why.
That's why I wrote this
just for you.
Thank you, Dad,
for being you!

Jenifer Jacobs, Grade 5
St Teresa's School, GA

Who Am I

I am a military brat; I travel around the world.
I like to support my dad and love the person he is.
He's a helpful person; he's very helpful to me.
I like when he comes in with a smile on his face.
I worry about my dad, especially when he went to Iraq.
My dad is always trying to protect our family and me.
Who am I? I'm a military brat, and I would like to be like my dad.
The man that comforts me when I'm happy or sad.
My whole life, I have moved from place to place.
Meeting so many friends I can't remember their face.
I have been to Germany and now back to the states.
I don't know many civilians that could understand.
Yes, I will be a military brat until I am a man.
It makes me want to travel when I'm older as a matter of fact.
My family and I have been around the world and back.
My dad joined the Army and I became an Army Brat.
That's why it says "A Family of One" on our welcome mat.

Anthony Brantley, Grade 5
Walker Intermediate School, KY

Yellow

Yellow looks like Hines Ward for the Steelers running a 33 yard touchdown pass.
Yellow sounds like crazy Steeler fans going crazy
Yellow smells like the sweat running off the players.
Yellow tastes like nacho's and cheese on my tongue.
Yellow feels like the victory of the Steelers
Yellow is the color I spray painted
Yellow is the sound of all the fans screaming
Yellow is the smell of fresh candy in the air.
Yellow is the taste of soda in my mouth.
Yellow feels like Jerome Bettis handing me the game ball

Jared Lancaster, Grade 5
Cool Spring Elementary School, NC

I Am a Military Brat

I am a skater who is supportive of my father.
I wonder if I will be in the military.
I hear cannons at the range.
I see soldiers going off to war.
I want my dad to stay here.
I am a skater supportive of my father.

I pretend that I am a pro skater.
I feel the wind in my face when I am going down a steep hill.
I touch my heart when I am saying the pledge.
I worry if I will wake up and my dad will be gone.
I am a skater sportive of my father.

I understand that my dad has to serve in a war.
I say Psalms: 25:4 "Show me your ways O Lord, teach me your path."
I dream one day there will be world peace.
I try to stay happy when something bad happens.
I hope the war will be over soon.
I am a skater who is supportive of my father.

Brandon Paiva, Grade 6
Walker Intermediate School, KY

The Flame of My Mother's Love

T he light of my mother's love illuminates the stars,
H ow she loves me I've always known,
A nd I know that someday I will be the same,
N othing will change her view of me,
K ind and loving my mother is,
S o today I am thankful for my mother's love.
G old — the color of my mother's heart and
I ntegrity is what she shows the most, but
V itality is her main aspect.
I n the entire world I love her the most,
N eeded, I am, for her to love,
G leeful I am for her love — deep as the sea.

Raymond Wray, Grade 5
Robertsville Middle School, TN

wilderness

the trees blow frequently
they blow with the wind freely
they are tall giants

Richard Ford, Grade 6
Livingston Middle School, TN

Nightmares

So distant yet so real.
Makes you feel as cold as steel.
Wanting them to disappear.
Like vapor in the atmosphere.
Then something happens beyond belief.
All of a sudden you wake up with great relief.
Then it's back to bed
Where more nightmares go swarming in your head.

Chris Rice, Grade 6
Brogden Middle School, NC

The Unstoppable Tornado

I am powerful, and nothing can stop me

I am unstoppable, if you are in my vortex I will
throw you into an alligator's mouth before
you know it

I am dangerous to people, my huge and
twirling, zooming strong winds will carry
you into the sky

No one can stop me or outrun me
I am strong, powerful, fast and dangerous

You will know when I am coming, the wind gets
strong and it will sometimes rain

I am a horrible, deadly, tornado!

Hillary Woods, Grade 5
Pembroke Elementary School, NC

Thanksgiving

Thanksgiving
Family and friends chatting,
turkey sizzling,
stories being told
Different food from your different families,
new foods you never knew
People hugging me and others,
feeling hot food in your mouth
Cousins playing,
grandparents watching TV,
parents helping with cooking food
Food smells drifting in the air make you wonder
if it tastes good or not,
when you smell dessert,
you think the same thing
Thanksgiving.

Vincent Alig, Grade 4
Tamassee-Salem Elementary School, SC

My Little Brother Bobby*

B is for the best on the field at tee-ball
O is for O my when he makes good grades
B is for best in the whole world
B is for buying him presents when he's sick or hurt
Y is for yaking around the house

Kristen Chedville, Grade 4
Lewis Vincent Elementary School, LA
*Dedicated to my little brother Bobby

Why Won't You Use Your Wings

Why won't you use your wings?
Is something wrong?
Just spread your arms and flap those things!
Think of a very sweet song.
Are you scared of what you might see?
Don't be!
Whatever it is, it might set you free!

Raylyn Bunch, Grade 5
Windsor Elementary School, NC

Birthday

Smells like burning candles
Feels like heaps of presents
Sounds like singing "Happy Birthday"
Tastes like cake and ice cream
Looks like all my family and friends.

Katelyn Simmons, Grade 5
Briarwood Christian Elementary School, AL

I Am So Tired

I am so tired I can sleep for months.
I am so tired I can sleep for years.
I am so tired I can sleep for a century.
I am so tired I slept an hour on Thanksgiving.

Harold Thomas, Grade 6
Armorel Elementary School, AR

I Cannot Clean My Room Today

I cannot clean my room today,
I cannot see,
My eyes are swollen,
My hands are broken,
My legs are sprained,
I simply cannot clean my room today.
What? What's that you say?
You're taking my to the skate park today.
Let's go!

Evan Plott, Grade 5
Cool Spring Elementary School, NC

What Do Girls Know?

What do
Girls
Know?

Boys
Girls
Everything
Make-up
Slug bugs
Softball
Boys
Phones
Boys
and especially
BOYS!

Jonathan Porter, Grade 6
Armorel Elementary School, AR

Our Glorious God

Jesus is the Son of God,
We walk in His ways,
He calls us — young and old,
To follow Him all our days.
We must always give to God,
All our worship and praise.
Mighty and glorious is our God,
That's what the Bible says.

Benjamin Frank, Grade 5
Holy Rosary Academy, LA

My Fence

Fences Fences
tall and brown,
Fences Fences
tall and round,
Fences Fences
oh, how we need you,
Fences Fences
oh, how we weed you.

Sam Marrow, Grade 5
Elkhorn Elementary School, MO

Nature

Nature is pretty
I like it,
It's like a breath of cool air
It is so cool
It is rainy some days
like cats and dogs
Nature is beautiful
so pretty and quiet, it is
never ending!!

Joshua L. Ransom, Grade 5
Pembroke Elementary School, NC

Fish

Cute little fishes
Swimming around in clear tanks
For people to see.

Nissa Johnson, Grade 5
American Heritage Academy, GA

Soccer

Soccer is so fun to play
You can do it both night and day.

Dribbling, heading, juggling too
Those are some things that we do.

Being a goalie is so cool
You get to watch the other team drool.

Fielder and forward are some more
Of the positions you have, to score.

A coach, some friends are all it takes
A team and fun are what it makes.

Win or lose it's all the same
I just love to play this game.

Peyton Beall Clark, Grade 4
Evangelical Christian School, TN

My Favorite Time of the Year

My favorite time of the year will
be and always be Christmas.

We miss a lot of days. But we always
have work at school waiting on us.

We also have presents at school
and at home.

My whole family is there to enjoy
the day.

Raqueal Caesar, Grade 6
St Mark Elementary School, SC

Do Yo Pants Hang Low?

Do yo pants hang low?
Do they drag on the flow?
are they baggier than you?
are they tan are they blue?
can you throw them on
your shoulders when they're hot
or when they're not?
Do yo pants hang low?

Stephanie Bradfield, Grade 6
Armorel Elementary School, AR

James Madison

J ester
A chievement
M agnificent
E conomical
S afekeeping

M aintenance
A cknowledge
D arling
I dol
S weet
O bey
N ice

Richanna Sockey, Grade 4
East Jones Elementary School, MS

Dog

Outrageous, daring
running with speed and power
sweet but fierce
a dog

fun, playful, a character
of no other
a dog
in lazy moods, drooling
hairy, furry
but also very loving
a dog

a four-legged animal
smart and very wise
they know when to eat
and when to go outside

They can be a handful
but also a very close friend,
a dog they are, and a dog they will be
until time comes to an end
a dog.

Ayana Roddey, Grade 6
Brogden Middle School, NC

Winter Summer

Winter
Chilly, windy
Freezing, shoveling, cuddling
Ice, snow, sun, grass
Living, sweating, drinking
Hot, green
Summer

Daniel Watson, Grade 5
Nathaniel Hawthorne Elementary School, MO

Candy

A sweet sweet treat
my favorite thing to eat
That precious goody goes down my throat
and every bite I have to note
Every piece a different taste
but still I must keep up my pace
Candy colors, colors, colors galore
every color a new taste to explore
There is chewy, crunchy, chunky, to munch
every one so good for my lunch
A sweet sweet treat
my favorite thing to eat

Katelyn Restrepo, Grade 6
Riverwood Middle School, NC

Christmas

When most people think of Christmas they think of gifts,
Well when I think of Christmas I think of Jesus.
Jesus, born of Mary, was and still is our God.
So don't think that Christmas is all about the gifts,
This holiday is truly about our Lord, Jesus Christ
Who died on the cross for our sins,
And who is so good to us,
And we are so unappreciative of that.
We need to thank Jesus for everything.
So this Christmas worship him as our Lord and Savior,
So on Christmas say this to Jesus,
Happy Birthday, Jesus!

Michaela Yount, Grade 6
Statesville Middle School, NC

I Am Uglier Than Jason

I am a big killer machine.
I will eat you with one crunch.
Children hate me because I am a beast.
You will not like me because I am a beast.
I am ugly.
You can't hide.
'Cause I will find you!!!
I am speedy.
I will get you.
I will destroy you at any time.
I am your worst nightmare!!!

Cameron T. Harris, Grade 5
Pembroke Elementary School, NC

Wintertime

Wintertime is finally here
So hip hip hurray and shout and cheer
Snow sprinkling while you are asleep
You wake up to your alarm clock beep.

You look out your window
You see snow every where in the meadow
Go tell your mom and dad
But remember don't be sad, be glad!

You go to look at the snow
But the wind starts to blow
You might want to go in, or you might will catch a cold
The weather might be very cold.

Go ahead and get ready for church
While snow sprinkles on the birch
Remember wintertime is finally here
So hip hip hurry and shout a cheer.

Katey Shafer, Grade 5
Sullivan Elementary School, TN

Dame School

I am a girl and I go to school
There are no boys, so I think it's cool.

Here at Dame School we can learn knitting
I'm glad because we are always sitting.

My school is at a lovely home,
My teacher's name is Mrs. Comb.

We have a strict lesson, it is manners
We are having a party and I'm one of the planners.

We are freezing in these petticoats
Waiting for the heavy boats.

Ashley Kirton, Grade 5
Alvaton Elementary School, KY

The Sea Shore

Gigantic waves crashing,
Beautiful sea shells come ashore,
Sticky seaweed tangling our feet,
Bright sun shining all around,
Oh! The sea shore!

Happy children laughing and playing,
Young teens sunbathing with their friends,
Cheerful mothers relaxing on a blanket,
Sleepy babies napping under an umbrella,
Oh! The sea shore!

Emily Brown, Grade 5
Midway Covenant Christian School, GA

Things People Do

People say things
that sting.
People do things that
make you mad.
People say things
that hurt.
People do things that
make you sad.
Even though sometimes
it's hard, when
times are rough,
just remember
you're not alone
in this cruel world,
Look up and remember
God, went through
the exact same thing.

Reba Bass, Grade 6
Riverwood Middle School, NC

Thanksgiving

Thanksgiving is a special holiday.
You give thanks for:
Health,
Family,
God,
and
freedom
that we have today.
So we can gather with our family.

Nelson Brown, Grade 5
Paint Lick Elementary School, KY

Fairies

Fairies
Pretty, small
Dance, fly, sing
Small people with wings
Pixies

Rachael Wright, Grade 4
Russell Babb Elementary School, OK

Jack and Shelby

Eyes like ours
They don't like water
Feet like smooth velvet
They are little when it's a kitten
Ears stick up
They don't like being dropped
Fur like smooth velvet
They shed their fur
Happy when they cuddle up with you
Angry when they scratch you.
Cats are cute.

Elizabeth Grinnell, Grade 5
Temple Hill Elementary School, KY

Joy of Christmas

Christmas is upon us with all its many joys.
The decorated houses, and Christmas trees, and toys.
Excitement shines brightly in the eyes of boys and girls.
Christmas is such a magical time all around the world.
All the children wonder whether they've been good or bad.
Will Santa leave them presents? If not, they'll be so sad.
On Christmas Eve the children find it very hard to sleep.
They're tempted to sneak down the stairs to try to take a peek.
Was that reindeer hooves up on the roof or Santa Claus himself?
Does he deliver all the toys alone or does he get some help?
Christmas morn' arrives at last, kids jump out of their beds.
Thoughts of what awaits them keep running through their heads.
The excitement that they feel is almost too much to contain.
Will they get books or bikes, games or trikes, or maybe an electric train?
There, under the Christmas tree, wrapped up in ribbons and bows
Are dolls and bats and balls and hats and even some winter clothes.
The gifts have all been opened, the family's been fed.
It's Christmas night and time again to scurry off to bed.
All will soon be sleeping, dreaming of the day they had.
Goodnight to all the children, goodnight to Mom and Dad.

Casey Weisler, Grade 6
Haynes Academy for Advanced Studies, LA

Number One

You can take me apart, and put me together again.
I'll still be the same.

When you multiply me, subtract me, divide me and even add me,
it's more times the fun.

I know I can be odd at times,
but I can be even too.

But most of all if I lose or win
I can always go back again.

Sean Anderson, Grade 5
Meramec Elementary School, MO

I Am From

I am from the presents I open on my birthday.
I am from the drawings of nature that I make on my favorite holiday,
Earth Day!

I am from the beautiful birds that fly around my house
To the awesome animals in my room...
Such as a small mouse!

I am from the stick I've been carving for a week.
I am from the spaghetti and pizza that I love to eat!

I am from all of the 28 states that I have been to and seen,
But most importantly, I am me!

Jake Robertson, Grade 5
Burgin Independent School, KY

Watch Them Grow

Flowers grow, children grow.
They sprout into something beautiful.
They are delicate, soft, and loving.
Sometimes it is hard to escape their beauty.
But soon enough you watch them go,
And surely do you know, they will be back again.

Elissa Leise, Grade 5
Saul Mirowitz Day School - Reform Jewish Academy, MO

I Am Haunted

I was haunted by the goblin ghost
That lives in my closet, he jumps out
And gives me quite a fright.
I was haunted by the icky, sticky mice.
That creep and crawl on the carpet floor.

I am now haunted by the thought
Of my house catching on fire and
Falling to pieces and losing all of my
Special things. I am now haunted
By the creepy crawling spiders
On my carpet floor.

I will be haunted by the thought of
Never learning how to swim and I drown
In the pool and die and never see the light again.

I Am Haunted!

Sabrina Smith, Grade 5
Eminence Middle School, KY

Past

My identity unknown,
My friends gone,
My family left.
I'm all alone.
Living a forbidden life
Just trying to get by.
When I see you and I break down and cry
I know you're the only link to my past.
I don't want to know, don't want it to last.
I just want this moment to end,
Then it happens.
You notice me.
You walk over and say, "Is it really you?"
I get up and run
Knowing I can't run for long
Because you start singing that luring song.
I can't resist.
I slowly walk back
Look up and see your face.
You smile at our little chase.

Sherilyn Queen, Grade 6
Newbern Middle School, GA

Liberty

L aws
I ndependence
B irth of freedom
E xpress the way you feel
R ights to do and say what you want
T raditions expressed
Y outh using liberty to show independence and freedom

Sabrina Murillo, Grade 6
Clarksburg School, TN

All About Me

Hello!
My name is Joseph
If I were a color,
I'd be gold
like a gold rod.
If I were an animal
I'd be powerful and fast
like a tiger.
My favorite place is skateland
When I'm skating
and buying candy.
My favorite snack is ice cream,
The kind with vanilla, chocolate, and strawberry
When it's homemade.
I really get upset
When I have to stay with my grandma.
I love listening to rap music,
When my folk's are not around.

Joseph McClendon, Grade 4
Pine Tree Hill Elementary School, SC

Sissy

Sissy is the heart of our home.
Without her we would feel all alone.
She is the most beautiful dog we have ever seen.
If you could only see her, you'd know what we mean.
She has big brown eyes that glow in the dark,
And she would let us know if there was a fire, or even a spark
Sissy guards our house both day and night.
And even though she is way too old to play,
she sits around and waits for a treat.
She will not bite your hand even if it's meat.
When she lays down, she crosses her two front feet,
so she looks like a lady if you should happen to meet.

Marty McMahon, Grade 5
Etowah Elementary School, NC

Christmas

Looks like Christmas with pretty lights
Smells like Christmas with garland hanging
Tastes like Christmas because of all the food
Feels like Christmas because of the warm fire
Sounds like Christmas with Christmas carols.

Emily Sanders, Grade 5
Briarwood Christian Elementary School, AL

All About Me

Hello!
My name is Maddison
If I were a color
I'd be blue
Like the water at the beach.
If I were an animal
I'd be something that swims and jumps
Like a dolphin or a fish.
My favorite place is the beach
When I am on summer break
And feeling playful.
My favorite snack is gummies
The kind that smile back at you
From my cabinet in the kitchen.
I really get upset
When I am sick and it's sunny
And I have to stay inside.
I love listening to 89.7
When I am in the car
And it's my favorite song.
Maddison Flowers, Grade 4
Pine Tree Hill Elementary School, SC

Tornado

Awesome monstrous storms
Destroying what's in its path
Leaves nothing behind
Harley Douglas, Grade 4
Broadway Elementary School, NC

Jungle Ride

Hip hop the monkey jumped
Slink slide the snake went by
Hiss growl the leopard leaped
On my jungle ride

The jungle made me quiver
The jungle made me shiver

The sounds at night, a fearful fright
While the moon it shone so bright

The tigers growled
The monkeys howled
The lions prowled
On my jungle ride

Morning comes and all awake
The zebras grazed
The monkeys played
But the lion goes to sleep
On my jungle ride
Garrett Andradez, Grade 6
Brogden Middle School, NC

Basketball

Basketball is thrilling
Basketball is cool
Basketball is my favorite sport
I love the excitement
The chance to get a point
We run plays 1, 2, 3
I always hear swoosh, swoosh, swoosh
I hear the buzzer ring
I look to see
Home 23 and Guest 22
We won the game!
People in the crowd
Jump to their feet
I just smile knowing
I made the winning point
Cody Booth, Grade 5
Riverside East Elementary School, AR

Waterfall

Falling! Falling!
The cool water is calling.
It starts to drop;
Where will it stop?
Falling into a giant pool;
Gosh! The water is cool.
See the beauty far and near —
If you listen, you can hear.
A waterfall, so tall,
Is sounding the call.
Come and see! Come and see!
This waterfall is great!
I can hardly wait
To feel the cool mist
And check this waterfall off my list.
Cody Pannell, Grade 6
Scotts Creek Elementary School, NC

Fun Hot Summers!

The sun shining brightly
Warm wind blowing everywhere
Ice cold Pepsi in my hand
Seeing a dog walking on a track.

Kids splashing in the pool
Going to the beach on a hot day
Surfing with my cousin
Playing Volleyball!

Having a picnic at the park
Eating Culver's frozen custard
And having my birthday
I LOVE SUMMER!
Shelby Watson, Grade 4
Alvaton Elementary School, KY

Hatshepsut

H is for Hyksos
A menhotep
T hutmose
S yria
H ieroglyphic
E gyptians
P haraoh
S ungod
U pper Egypt
T ruth
Kristan Crabtree, Grade 6
Clarksburg School, TN

Friends for Life*

From babies to preschool,
friends for life,
from kindergarten to fourth grade,
friends for life,
from fifth to twelfth grade,
friends for life,
When we get married,
friends for life,
when we die and go to heaven,
friends for life,
No matter what's wrong friends for life.
Kelsey Howton, Grade 6
Harrisburg Middle School, AR
*Dedicated to Paige, Maria, Zoe,
and Alyson H.

Math

Math math
Is not a blast
Math math
Oh I wish it will go by fast
Math math
Oh I hate it
Oh look at the time
it's the time oh I hate it!
Brandon Helm, Grade 5
Zalma Elementary School, MO

The Best Day Ever

One day I was walking along
I saw a beautiful horse
in a field
I tried to catch it,
but it ran as fast as a Jaguar
I tripped over a log
that afternoon she let me tame her
so I did
after that I loved to ride her.
Kayla Groce, Grade 4
Alvaton Elementary School, KY

Friends

Friends
Companion buddy
Considering helping giving
Talking behind your back, leaving you out
Stalking hurting fighting
Back-stabbing heartbreaking
Enemies

Heather West, Grade 5
Zalma Elementary School, MO

Christmas

C andy canes being eaten
H appy people opening presents
R eaching to the top of the tree to put the star on
I think it's the greatest holiday
S anta up all night
T rying to fix the lights
M any kids playing in the snow
A pple pie baking in the oven
S o many gifts to be opened

Tyler Darnell, Grade 5
Sullivan Elementary School, TN

Halloween

Ghosts and goblins
What do you need?

Witches on their brooms
Don't be so keen.

Skeletons light up the sky, the stars, and the moon.
Don't be so scary and mean.

Scarecrows and pumpkins are all around,
I see it must be HALLOWEEN!

Emily LaPorte, Grade 5
Arnaudville Elementary School, LA

Halloween

Halloween is best of the year
Halloween is almost here
Halloween draws friends near
Halloween is scary it feels dary
Halloween is the most coolest and ghoulest holiday ever!!!

I LOVE HALLOWEEN!!!

Jenna Good, Grade 6
Richard H Gettys Middle School, SC

My Friend Wade

W e laugh all day
A nd talk all night
D inosaurs make us laugh and fight
E verybody knows we're best friends so never let the fun end

James Wilson, Grade 4
Tamassee-Salem Elementary School, SC

Poetic Nature

Nature is like a poem
Beautiful,
And everything has their special place,
Flowers like words so amazing.
Poems are like Nature

Michelle Bennett, Grade 4
Saul Mirowitz Day School - Reform Jewish Academy, MO

Christmas

Christmas is the time of
Year for boy and girls to
Start to cheer.
On Santa's sleigh there are lots of toys.

Everyone's heart is filled with joy.
Happiness is all around,
No one feels upside down.
In the middle of the night,

I get a big fright.
Thinking about a big, jolly man,
Coming in sight.
Down the chimney with all his might.

With all his presents in his sack.
I always look for him back.
From year to year people say Santa is near.
IT just seems forever for him to appear.

Drew Adams, Grade 5
Joann Walters Elementary School, AR

Flowers Grow

Flowers grow in a lot of places
Some grow in vases.
Some are pink, yellow, and red
And some are on the dresser by your bed.

Flowers are purple, blue, and white
You cannot see them at night.
I think they smell good
And if you don't, you should.

Jordan Downing, Grade 4
Stephens Elementary School, AL

The Earth

The rising of the sun, the waking of the Earth
The rushing of water, the rustling of leaves
The song of a blue jay, the hop of a frog
PART OF ME, ALL AROUND
The roar of a lion, the dive of a dolphin
The crashing of waves, the blowing of wind
The rising of the sun, the waking of the Earth

Carla Robinson, Grade 6
Greenville Montessori School, NC

Ode to My Pacifier

Oh pacifier, what would I do without you
you stayed in my mouth even
when I eat I
loved you so

But I'm too old for you now
I cried without you
so pacifier…

We had so much fun and I
wish we could still
but now
I'm going to have to say good-bye
to you, oh boo hoo!

Hannah DeLisle, Grade 5
Walton Verona Elementary School, KY

Christmas

Oh the best part of Christmas
is being filled with love
and being surrounded by
the ones you love!

CaeLynn Johnson, Grade 4
Moyock Elementary School, NC

The Saltwater Crocodile

The crocodile lays
Basking in the hot dry sun
Sleeping among trees

Jaylin Craig, Grade 4
John Will Elementary School, AL

The Hurricane

Growling like a vicious bear.
Pushing you over with his breath
(Just like my brother)
Striking you with a burning sword
Like a knight on a horse.
Thrashing like a murderer,
He'll drown you in the sea,
Always watching you with his eye.

Cole Sauer, Grade 5
St Vincent Elementary School, MO

Daisy

Dog gone cute!
She'll cheer me up
and take me down
at the same time.
My best friend in the world!
Scared of many things,
But not scared of me.
You and me, Daisy,
Best buds forever!

Holly Blandford, Grade 5
St Vincent Elementary School, MO

I Am…

I am courageous and loving.
I wonder if the world will ever depart us.
I hear the heartbeat of a long lost friend.
I see the strong love of my family every day.
I want to always be successful in life no matter what obstacles I face.
I am courageous and loving.

I pretend that I am as shy as a butterfly, but I have the heart of a lion.
I feel a fairy's touch as soft as a cloud.
I touch my heart and feel that it hasn't stopped.
I worry if I will ever get another friend that will replace the loss of the other.
I cry when a part of my family leaves me to go somewhere special forever.
I am courageous and loving.
I understand that I will never be alone.
I say that hope can change anything.
I dream the Earth will be as quiet as snow falling.
I try to get outstanding grades.
I hope that nothing good can change in the future.
I am courageous and loving.

Tobi Shitta-Bey, Grade 5
Big Creek Elementary School, GA

Friends

Worries are the locks our pride is the key
yours plus mine is the best of best because we were made to succeed.
We are always best friends till the very end
through the thick and also thin.
You know this and I do
to every word in this poem is very true.
We always know when each other are sad
because we don't act weird and usually never feel bad.
We have to know things like this and stick together
through good and even bad weather.
Each day and night we know that there may be a fight. But that is okay
I still have no worries tomorrow or today.
No person or object could tear us apart
because now we are truly connected from our hands to our hearts.

Sarah Huddleston, Grade 5
Dawson Springs Middle School, KY

The Shot

Ten seconds left down by two,
Oh my! What should I do?

I dribble down the court
With the clock ticking…
five, four, three, two
I throw up a prayer
and look in the air
And what do I know it went in!

WE WON!
The crowd raises me in the air
And I said "Thank you Lord for answering my desperate prayer!"

Mike Schlesinger, Grade 6
Brogden Middle School, NC

My Life Is a River

My life is a river
Sometimes flowing lightly and gently
Moving along with relaxation
My life is like a river
Sometimes rough and rapid
Waiting for the sun to shine
Looking for the rainbow in the sky
My life is like a river
There are gentle turns everywhere
I like the smooth waters
I do not like the rocks and currents
They are my struggles in my life
I enjoy the nice peaceful waters
My life is like a river
Having ups and downs
Twists and turns
Trying to conclude them out

Andrew Kim, Grade 6
River Trail Middle School, GA

Mom

Even though we fight sometimes,
we always make it through.
We both have our own opinions,
but we always seem to agree on one thing.
And that thing is,
our love that we have for each other.

Melissa Bowen, Grade 6
Desoto Central School, MS

A Wish

I
walked
to the bus stop
with my friend Gus.
And watched him get onto the bus. As I turned
around I saw a wish woman standing there
and she said, "Want a wish for one
penny?" I said "Yes!" Then
she asked, "What will
it be?"   I then
found   out
she   was a
big   fat
Phoney!
P ut fake item in mind
H onest to no one
O ne who lies
N ot true
E yes open to trick
Y et it fails true words.
P.S. I paid for that!

Katie Clair, Grade 4
Landmark Christian School, GA

Ocean

When the tide comes in,
great for surfing and pretty,
big waves, lots of fun.

Matthew Martin, Grade 4
Briarwood Christian Elementary School, AL

Bonnie and Clyde

It is a cold winter day.
I walk outside,
And feed the horses hay.
I yell, "Here Bonnie, here Clyde."
Nothing but pure silence!
I walk around and around again.
Finally, I jump the fence.
I shake the feed in the bucket of tin.
Then I found the horses in the corner.
I walk over there and feed them their hay.
I start to cuddle them, just to get warmer.
Then, I walk away from that wonderful day.

Stetson Erickson, Grade 5
Etowah Elementary School, NC

The Beach

Stepping out onto the beach.
The water is as blue as the sky.
The waves seem so very high.
As I kneel down to feel the sand,
A little crab crosses my hand.

I step back with fright.
But am comforted by the sunlight.
It feels so very warm on my face.
But soon the sun goes down without a trace.

It's getting late now it's time to go.
But I must have one more dip in the waters below.

Ashley Prager, Grade 5
Etowah Elementary School, NC

Friendship

Friendship is like a storm.
The feelings you get are not always warm.
Sometimes the skies are gray,
It's not always like a sunny spring day.

Friends are something you need.
Friendship starts off as a seed.
It blossoms into a flower,
But is so delicate it can die within an hour.

So as you can tell,
Friends are not for sale.
And as you can see,
Friends are special to me.

Rachel Cash, Grade 6
Statesville Middle School, NC

Personality

Some people like to eat
and some are picky
Some people eat meat
and some think it's icky.

Some people like to fish
and some like cards
Some people eat out of a dish
and some play darts.

Parker Schuetzle, Grade 6
Central Arkansas Christian School, AR

Baseball

fun, cool exercising,
baseball, left fielder, catcher, third base
base, catch, home plate

Tristin Houston, Grade 4
East Jones Elementary School, MS

What Is Pink?

Pink is the frosting
On my birthday cake.
Pink are the roses
That match the girls' noses;
Strawberries in the patch
Ready to be matched.

Pink is the gum
That is stuck on my shoe.
Pink is the opposite
Of the color blue.

Pink is the seashell
Hiding behind the bronze bell,
Cherries for the pie;
A stylish bow-tie.
Pink is the color of the paint
That made my mother faint!

Chandler Wilson, Grade 5
Trenton Middle School, MO

Happiness

Summer brings laughter
swimming with the ones you love
children at the beach

Jessica Kimball, Grade 6
Tomlinson Jr High School, OK

Witch Named Zoom

There once was a Witch named "Zoom,"
who flew on a really big broom!
She flew so high…
that she touched the sky.
Then landed right back in her room.

Briana Iorio, Grade 5
Springfield Elementary School, SC

At a Baseball Game

At a baseball game these are the sounds you hear,
Crack!
Thump!
Swish!
And the sound of a glove catching a baseball.

At a baseball game these are the things you feel,
Excitement,
Your rear hurting from the seat,
Joy
And relief that the team that you cheered for the baseball game won!

Mariah Hiatt, Grade 5
Walton Verona Elementary School, KY

Sisters

I am an older sister	I am a younger sister
15 years old	11 years old
Learning to drive	Wishing to drive
10th grade is so fun	6th grade is awesome
Old school, old friends	New school, new friends
Exams, reports	Tests, quizzes
So much to do	So much to do
On the computer	Playing outside
Love to read	Love to read
Little sisters get into everything	Older sisters get to do things first
Siblings can be annoying	Siblings can be annoying
But, I love my life	But I love my life

Haley Thornton, Grade 6
Beck Academy, SC

Blue

Blue looks like the beautiful ocean waves.
Blue feels like my cozy blanket straight from the dryer.
Blue tastes like fresh picked blueberries.
Blue smells like a fresh made blueberry pie coming out of the oven.
Blue sounds like the rain is falling off my bedroom window.
Blue is the best color ever!

Ali Calcaterra, Grade 5
Geggie Elementary School, MO

Autumn

Raining like a cold shower,
Squirrels gathering acorns,
Going on hay rides like riding on a four wheeler
Getting in from the cold and drinking warm apple cider,
Leaves falling like a dog shedding,
Kids raking and jumping in the leaves like a fox pouncing on its prey,
The start of deer hunting,
Getting out costumes,
Going trick-or-treating on Halloween,
Eating turkey on Thanksgiving,
Fall!!

Brittini Christiansen, Grade 6
Alvaton Elementary School, KY

I Am

I am a girl who dreams of being the best pediatrician I can be.
I wonder if I will ever succeed my life dream.
I hear the babies crying.
I see myself being my life dream a pediatrician.
I want to accomplish my college dream and become a pediatrician like in my dreams.
I am a girl who dreams of being the best pediatrician I can be.

I pretend to nurse my baby doll to health.
I feel that I am the pediatrician of my dreams.
I touch my stethoscope and feel the power it holds
I worry sometimes will I succeed in my greatest life dream.
I cry sometimes when I do not think I can succeed.
I am a girl who dreams of being the best pediatrician I can be.

I understand I have to work hard.
I say if I cannot succeed try, try, again.
I say my name is Doctor Amy.
I dream I am helping children nursing them to the best health.
I try to work hard so I can accomplish my greatest life dream.
I hope my dreams come true.
I am a girl who dreams of being the best pediatrician.

Amy Cobb, Grade 5
Pine Ridge Elementary School, GA

Friendship Can Last Forever...

Friendship is something to share with a wonderful person;
and once it's there, you've got to make it last.
Friendship isn't something to be taken for granted.
It's something to be nurtured and cared for and caressed.
Friendship can last forever…if you want it too.
Friendship isn't tough and rough; it's wonderful and gentle and tender.
Friendship is mysterious; but it asks that you share secrets.
Friendship is more like a flower than a tree;
the wrong things can hurt it easily,
but the right things can make it more beautiful than anything else your life has known.
Friendship is something to be treated as the best of all blessings;
and as your own little miracle that will keep coming as long as we're FRIENDS!!!

Taylor Thompson, Grade 5
Romine Interdistrict Elementary School, AR

Jamillah

Jamillah is a true friend. Always has my back. She never lets me down.
When I want to go down. When I am in trouble she says something to make me happy.
That is why I love my best friend Jamillah.

Bri´anna Caldwell, Grade 6
Brogden Middle School, NC

Steve Irwin

I was having a good day until my mom broke the news to me that Steve Irwin had died. While swimming in the deep blue sea,
a sting ray had a fright. He had a passion for animals so we could love them and not kill them. Only Steve Irwin had enough
love or courage to show the world that he loved animals like nobody else.

Hunter Allen, Grade 4
Lewis Vincent Elementary School, LA

Purple

Purple is the color
of the sky when
a long day is over.
Purple is the color
that I dream of at night.
Purple is the color of my little sister
when she's happy.
Purple is the color of rain.
Purple really is my color.

Tiffani Jordan, Grade 4
Stephens Elementary School, AL

Monsters

Monsters, monsters
Big and black
Monsters, monsters
Claws and fangs
Monsters, monsters
Their so cool
Monsters, monsters
I am one too.

Chase Croslin, Grade 4
Cave City Elementary School, AR

Stars

Stars, stars, everywhere
Stars, stars I dare to stare.
But when I look upon a star,
I feel Jesus in my heart.
And that's why I wish upon a star.

Trae Hill, Grade 5
Faith Christian School, SC

Teachers

Teachers,
Teachers,
Teachers,
Precise teachers,
Intelligent teachers,
Perverse, perky, etiquette teachers,
Insane, emotional, disastrous teachers
Those are just a few.
Bold teachers,
Repulsive teachers,
Blistered, peevish, squeamish teachers,
Hairless, identical, disabled teachers,
Skeptic teachers, too.
Mischievous teachers
Possessive teachers
Don't forget queasy teachers
Last of all, best of all,
I like imaginative teachers.

Makayla Hilsabeck, Grade 6
South Nodaway Elementary School, MO

Buddy

This is my dog,
His name is Buddy.
He's so cute,
Except when he's muddy.

This is my dog,
He's very furry.
When he's outside,
He'll run and he'll scurry!

This is my dog,
He doesn't make me sad.
In fact I think,
He makes everyone glad!

Kelli Rawls, Grade 5
Heber Springs Elementary School, AR

Personalities

Some people talk and talk
and some people listen
Some people feel in the dumps
and some people glisten

Some people follow their heart
and others do just what they're told
Some people are not courageous
and others are very bold

Sara Randolph, Grade 6
Central Arkansas Christian School, AR

Stars

Stars
you sparkle like glitter,
you shine like the ocean shimmering
in the sunlight.
You jump you dive
like dolphins leaping into the water.
You sizzle and twirl like a ballerina,
but quickly you will fade away,
leaving behind a memory

Shalynn Payne, Grade 4
Crestwood Elementary School, KY

Books

Books are special, I like to read
From this world I am freed.
Imagination takes me places world wide
Understanding the small world I like.
From the books I can seek
The beautiful minds I do see
Sharing good hearts from letters
We people hold hands together

Kevin Nguyen, Grade 4
Robert E Lee Elementary School, TN

Christmas

Christmas
Gifts, decorations
Loving, kissing, hugging
The best time of your life
Holiday

Fernanda Torres, Grade 5
Bayyari Elementary School, AR

Whisper

Walking down a path at night,
forever walking,
forever walking.
Stars are falling from the sky,
forever walking,
forever walking.
The sound of footsteps follows my flight,
forever walking,
forever walking.
Waiting, waiting for morning light,
forever walking,
forever walking.

Ruth Simberloff, Grade 5
Nature's Way Montessori School, TN

Disappear

You see me here, you see me now,
Now you don't see me now at all.
Am I here or am I there?
I could be here, I could be there,
I could be anywhere. Do you give up?
I'm right in front of you!

Phoebe Burns, Grade 5
Holy Family Parochial School, AL

My Grandma's Dead

My Grandma died
She is not alive
It feels like getting stung
by a bee in its hive.
It felt so bad
To let her go
Yet the gates of heaven
Had already shown.
Jesus took her away
Just like that,
Now, if I had one wish
It wouldn't be for her to be back.
She would be in pain
I would shout
and she'd die again,
so I would pout
But she's still with me, spiritually.

Taylor Locklear, Grade 5
Pembroke Elementary School, NC

She Is an Angel

She sits by herself at school.
No one pays attention to her.
She wears old unfashionable clothes.
Her hair is all knotted up.
She walks home alone
With her head bowed down.
She comes back to school the same.
Her voice is of an angel
Singing her heart out in choir.
She is so quiet in class
Seems like she has never sinned
People trip her all the time
Then she hurt herself
Blood trickling down her leg.
I took off my jacket
and wrapped it around her leg.
When I did that she smiled and said, "Thank you."
Later when I died and went to heaven I saw something.
A girl angel with my jacket
She came up and said, "Thank you," and hugged me.

Audra Clark, Grade 6
Pleasants County Middle School, WV

Thanksgiving, Thanksgiving

THANKSGIVING, THANKSGIVING
Oh how I like when that turkey and ham is calling my name.
The ham is like an orange so juicy in my mouth.

THANKSGIVING, THANKSGIVING
Oh how I like Thanksgiving.
When those mushy mash potatoes melt in my slobbering mouth

THANKSGIVING, THANKSGIVING
Oh how I like when my mom, Misty,
Makiiah, And Malayah are all around.

THANKSGIVING, THANKSGIVING
Oh how I like Thanksgiving

Brittany Watkins, Grade 6
Eminence Middle School, KY

A True Friend

A true friend is someone who is kind and caring.
It's not just about sharing.

But, it's the way they feel about you.
A true friend is there for you
when you need a shoulder to lean on!

A true friend will always be there for you
in good times and bad.

A true friend will love you unconditionally.
YOU ARE A TRUE FRIEND!

Hannah Martin, Grade 5
Arnaudville Elementary School, LA

Shoes

Shoes,
Shoes,
Shoes,
Red shoes,
Blue shoes,
Stupid, expensive, light up shoes,
Good looking, basketball, clearance shoes,
Those are just a few.
Black shoes,
Purple shoes,
Light weight, old shoes,
Warm, cozy, leather shoes,
Rough shoes, too.
Soft shoes,
Yellow shoes,
Don't forget new shoes.
Last of all, best of all,
I like my shoes.

Zeb Coleman, Grade 5
South Nodaway Elementary School, MO

God Bless Americow

God bless Americow,
The land of the dairy.
They who dwell upon this land,
Give magnificent milk.
From the farmlands,
To the barns,
To the pastures where we graze.
God bless Americow,
The land of the dairy!

Abby Lammers, Grade 4
Saul Mirowitz Day School - Reform Jewish Academy, MO

A Helping Hand

Autumn Leaves
A gentle tear
A helping hand
A blooming rose
A quiet giggle
A helping hand
A rippled pond
A special love
A helping hand
A natural spring
A giving soul
A helping hand
A comforting friend
A cool drink
A friend's hand
A helping hand…
My Hand

Jordyn Miller, Grade 4
Saul Mirowitz Day School - Reform Jewish Academy, MO

Fall Feelings

Fall is my favorite season,
I like it for so many reasons.
The leaves turn orange and red,
And the gentle wind blows on my head.
Baseball ends and that makes me sad,
But football is starting so it's not so bad.

Colton Mears, Grade 6
Desoto Central School, MS

Iwo Jima

The world was at war,
To stop a tyrant, that's what for.
Men fought and died,
While their loved ones cried.
They fought land and sea,
No victory was thought to be.
But they never gave up the cause,
Not once did they pause.
On an island in the sea,
A victory was to be,
After many deaths,
As slow as a dying breath,
A flag was raised.
Which was many times praised.
At Iwo Jima,
The greatest of victories.

Matt Ruhlin, Grade 6
River Trail Middle School, GA

My Butterfly

Butterflies flying
Through the air
Sometimes gliding
They are everywhere

I never noticed them
Until you were gone
They seem to come around
When I feel all alone

Wings full of color
So big and bright
Moving at all times
Through the day and night

Butterflies tend
to make me feel good
Just as you
always would

Butterflies will carry a message
To heaven above
I miss you Whitney and I send my love
Butterflies are everywhere.

Marissa Tennison, Grade 6
Poland Jr High School, LA

Neil Armstrong

As Neil Armstrong thinks back to his adventures in space,
He remembers "putting a man on the moon" was the big race.
His rocket took off with a thundering noise,
Watching the cheering and clapping of some young boys.
Going through the deep, forceful atmosphere,
The destination was very clear.
The big, glowing Earth could be seen from his window.
Now he was in space, where gravity was close to zero.
This rocket was on a course to the pale-white moon.
Neil Armstrong hoped they reached there very soon.

Now he could see the moon, it was very close by.
It was like the moon was looking at him, as if a great big eye.
Finally, they landed on the "round ball of cheese."
Armstrong declared, "Stay together please."
They hovered the ground, like a bird flying low,
Watching comets go by, as if observing a light show.
Neil Armstrong planted an American flag into the moon's rocky surface,
Showing America's pride and spirit and also our space travel purpose.
When Armstrong and his crew reached back home where the bright sun shined,
He declared nationwide "That's one small step for man, one giant leap for mankind."

Kunal Potnis, Grade 6
River Trail Middle School, GA

Black

Black sounds like a black cat hissing in the night…
Black tastes like a black Hershey Chocolate bar melting in the palm of my hand…
Black feels like a slimy, slithering black snake…
Black smells like burning hay in the night…
Black looks like fire burning everything in it's path…
Black.

DJ Groff, Grade 5
Cool Spring Elementary School, NC

A Kiss from a Dolphin

It was summer.
I was on a cruise that went to Mexico and lots of other places too.
We were in the area that the dolphins were kept.
I was six,
young,
and excited.
The lady took us to the dolphins
and set us beside one
with our life jackets on.
We touched the
smooth,
blue
dolphin.
The sun glinting off it's back,
It was beautiful.
The dolphin then kissed my sister and I on the cheek.
It was a memory made.
That beautiful, blue dolphin kissing me on the cheek.
Since then, dolphins have been my favorite animals in the world.

Ellison Dew, Grade 6
Beck Academy, SC

My Sanctuary

My Sanctuary,
is a place way deep into the forest,
where you can hear a bird's song.
Where a stream runs by,
at night my sanctuary is silent,
during day it is lively and green,
My sanctuary has a waterfall
that mixes into the warm steamy water.
My Sanctuary has giant climbing trees,
where you will always find me.
The banks near the crystal blue are colorful
and filled with all the flowers in the world.
My Sanctuary is guarded by a wall of briars.
The plants can walk and talk,
and nobody ever shouts.
My Sanctuary is a place of peace
and just where I Belong!

Sam Perry, Grade 5
Holsenbeck Elementary School, GA

Love Is More Than a Song

People say love and don't mean it.
Love can make you sad.
Love can make you happy.
Some people don't really know the meaning.
BUT love may come and go.
But true love will stay forever.

Breoshia Nicole Jackson, Grade 5
East Marion Elementary School, MS

The Color Green

Green is the color of the clovers I pick up
Green is the color of the lime in my water
Green is the color of the grass waving at me in the wind
Green is the color of the leaves on a tree
Green is the color of the salad I eat
Green is the color of my friend's eyes looking at me
Green is the color of the sour apples I consume
Green is the color of the ball I play with
Green is the color of the moss growing in my woods
Green is the color of the shirt I wear
Green is the color of the cards for my board game

Douglas Carson, Grade 5
Cline Elementary School, KY

Blue

Blue looks like the sky during a nice wonderful day.
Blue feels like a sad person about to cry.
Blue tastes like the best blueberry that I would love to eat.
Blue smells like a blue jolly rancher about to bring me joy.
Blue sounds like the waves splashing against the shore.
Blue is the color of the sky with the sun in it shining on us.

Nihal Shrimal, Grade 5
Geggie Elementary School, MO

What Is Pink...

Pink is the color of your lips when they get a kiss.
Pink is when a flamingo is taking a trip.
When you're wearing a pink dress on Valentine's Day.
Pink is when your feeling happiness in your heart.
When a rose is giving to you by love.
Pink is when a princess is getting married.
Pink is when you're having a slumber party with your friends.
Pink is the color of butterflies.
Pink is the color of the sunrise.
Pink is the color when you're happy to send,
Pink is the color when it's the end.

Carla Rodriguez, Grade 6
Lost River Elementary School, KY

The Bahamas

Pretty, graceful, calm,
lips kiss by the lovely waves
feet dance on the sand.

Austin Files, Grade 4
Briarwood Christian Elementary School, AL

Sharks!

Sharks, sharks swimming in the sea
If you see one let it be.
Big or small they all have teeth
So be careful when in the reef.
Brown and gray and dark green too
They are the prehistoric sharks we knew.
East or west on every coast
Sharks are remoras' favorite host.
Even if you see one that you adore
You had better head for safer shores!

Parker McKellips, Grade 4
Sequoyah Elementary School, TN

A Perfect Holiday

My perfect holiday
Would be on Christmas Day.
There would be you and me
Under the brightly lit Christmas tree.
There would be crystal white snow
Outside with a beautiful glow.
It would be an amazing sight
On that Christmas night.
Glistening holly leaves
On festive Christmas wreaths.
Christmas carolers singing
And jingle bells ringing.
The snow is falling softly
And everyone's filled with glee.
Opening my special gift
As my holiday spirits lift.
I couldn't have wished for
Anything better or more.

Alyssa Gebhardt, Grade 6
Haynes Academy for Advanced Studies, LA

The Deep Blue Sea
Down in the deep blue sea
There's just so much to see.
Down on the sandy floor
From eels to whales that soar.
Down in the deep blue sea
There's just so much to see.
You see the coral reefs
But on land the trees have leaves.
Down in the deep blue sea
There's just so much to see.
Instead of in the sky like on land
The stars are in the sand!
John Mark Heard, Grade 6
Alvaton Elementary School, KY

Snow
Snow is white.
It sounds like silence.
It tastes like water.
It smells like fresh air.
It looks like white polka dots.
It makes you feel like PLAYING!
Karsten Lowman, Grade 6
St Vincent Elementary School, MO

Glue with a Crew
The milk-white glue
Was given to a crew
To make sure they fixed
Everything they mixed.

They would never run
If something wasn't fun
But the crew
Always had their glue.

To start fixing
They wouldn't be mixing
Because they needed a little white dot
Right on the spot.

So, everything was right
Because of the might
Of the milk-white glue
That belonged to the crew.
Patrick Seelinger, Grade 6
Cathedral School, NC

Lions in a Zoo
The lions feel sad
They want their home back so bad
I wish they could go.
Darell Hawley, Grade 5
South Nodaway Elementary School, MO

Sweet
Violets are red, sugar is sweet,
but not sweeter than you,
I love you like candy,
you're as soft as a sheep,
that's why I wanna love you.
Elizabeth Adair, Grade 5
Franklin Elementary School, OK

The Outdoors
H unting is
U nderstanding
N ot
T aunting
I t's cool to be
N ot indoors, but in the
G reat outdoors
Brandon Lloyd, Grade 6
Martin Elementary School, WV

Fall
Fall is not too cold
not too hot the weather is
great and just perfect
Malcolm Batchelor, Grade 6
Tomlinson Jr High School, OK

Joy to Friendship
Summer brings friends out
playing on the sandy beach
water on my toes.
Giovanni Cruz, Grade 6
Tomlinson Jr High School, OK

Katora
Katora Culpepper
brown, dog lover
run, jump, dance
I love to eat apples.
Katora Culpepper
Katora Culpepper, Grade 4
East Jones Elementary School, MS

How to Play Softball
You have to hustle for muscle
You have to speed to succeed
You have to hit to play
You have to have a good day
Hit with all your muscle
To get to first you have to hustle
If you have speed
You will succeed
If you play you will have a good day
Arielle Rimoldi, Grade 6
Queen of Angels Catholic School, GA

Beautiful Butterfly
Hi, I saw a beautiful butterfly.
I thought it was going to die.
Because it couldn't fly.
Then I saw an open cocoon.
And I thought it would fly soon.
And that made me happy as a loon.
Stephanie Cusey, Grade 6
Cottonwood Public School, OK

Light
The shining of light
is so bright.

It lights up our way
when we have nothing to say.

It's always there
when we're not feeling fair.

This great thing
will make you think

Out of it, we get to have a ton
of fun.

It makes us want to go out and say,
"I'm feeling great today."
Logan Reeder, Grade 5
Stokesdale Elementary School, NC

My Cat Aubie
My cat is feisty,
My cat is sweet,
My cat attacked my neighbor's feet,
He's orange with stripes,
He sleeps at noon,
He doesn't like the color maroon,
He's wild he's crazy he sleeps by daisies,
He attacked his own sister,
It left a large blister.
Cate Joseph Rasco, Grade 5
Graham Elementary School, AL

Blankness
Everything around me,
Not dark and not light;
Only one thing I can see
Is the blankness of the white.
I feel like time will never end,
Because all of the colors blend.
So no dark or light is seen in here,
To tell the time of day or year.
Lindsey Helms, Grade 5
Elon Elementary School, NC

America's Flag

America's flag is for me and for you.
    Its colors are red, white, and blue.

Soldiers fought and fought for our flag.
    Please don't think I'm a drag.

The flag stands for our great country, in which I live.
    Our soldiers, their lives they give.

America's flag is for me and for you.
    Its colors are red, white, and blue.

Jordan Paul, Grade 4
Heartland High School and Academy, MO

O' Mighty Chocolate

Chocolate, o' chocolate, o' mighty chocolate
You're so chocolatey,
And so sweet.
You make me feel warm,
From head to feet.
Chocolate, o' chocolate, o' mighty chocolate,
Your sweetness,
And your creaminess.
You put me in
My state of dreaminess.
Chocolate, o' chocolate, o' mighty chocolate
White chocolate,
Milk chocolate,
Dark chocolate galore.
Oh how I wish
I had more, more, and more.
Chocolate, o' chocolate, o' mighty chocolate
How you come in all different types
And color,
Now you know that I am your
One true lover.

Chris Chang, Grade 6
River Trail Middle School, GA

Butterflies

Butterflies are pretty things.
They have pretty colored wings.
They fly really really high
They even soar through the sky.

I love it when they land.
They fly right over the sand.
They're very cute little fellows.
They're soft like little marshmallows.

There are a lot of butterflies where I stay.
I hope they never fly away.
I wish a butterfly was me.
I wonder what could I see.

LeJasmine Singletary, Grade 6
St Mark Elementary School, SC

It's Fall

The best time of year is fall
When the leaves turn colors
When the leaves shake hands with the ground
It's fall

This time is when the oxygen
Is as crisp as a winter's morning
This time is so fun it makes you run
It's fall

This time is when the leaves are falling madly
This time is when you can hear
The crunch of leaves under foot
It's fall

This time is when we must praise God
For what He has done for us
So be thankful for God has created all life
It's fall

Caleb Presley, Grade 5
Providence Academy, TN

Basketball Game

Looking at my teammate open for a pass.
Feeling the basketball leaving my hand.
Smelling the sweaty boy that is guarding me.
Hearing the crowd cheering as we score.
Tasting the cool Gatorade that I will drink.

Joshua Laatsch, Grade 5
Briarwood Christian Elementary School, AL

Camping

Camping is like finding a hidden treasure.
    Even though it's not buried, it still is a pleasure.

When the day in the woods is finally done,
    The night at the campsite is so much fun.

Sitting around the blazing fire ring,
    We all roast marshmallows and sing.

Some tell ghost stories big and small.
    Some look for stars in the sky to fall.

The creatures in the woods seem to never get sleepy.
    The sound of the coyotes is a little bit creepy.

You can hear them through the dark, misty night.
    Even though it is a fright, you know it's all right.

It's sad to leave when the camping is done.
    However, you know next time will be more fun.

William Ewell, Grade 4
Sequoyah Elementary School, TN

Thanksgiving

Thanksgiving is a special time of the year.
It is a time we give thanks for what the Lord has done,
is doing and will do in everyone's lives.

Thanksgiving isn't just about giving thanks for
what we can do that other people cannot do.

Some people call the USA spoiled
because we can do a lot of stuff that they won't do.
They can get hurt or killed and that is why the USA is spoiled.

T.J. Brinkley, Grade 4
Magnolia Springs Baptist Academy, AL

Sisters

I love my sister she is a lot of fun
We go outside and play ball in the sun
There are times we argue, fuss, and fight
My mom will settle it and make it all right
When my sister gets home from school we talk
So we go to the park to take a little walk
At the end of the day we love each other
But we always wish for a little brother!

Nakayla Twymon, Grade 5
Graham Elementary School, AL

Camping

Looks like beautiful painted mountains and trees
Smells like fresh pine and campfires
Tastes like fish and bacon
Sounds like the relaxing, calming sounds of night birds
Feels like the warm, cozy feeling of the outdoors

Carrie Orteza, Grade 5
Briarwood Christian Elementary School, AL

Fall

I see a plane fly over my head;
I wave.
The wind is blowing;
The trees sway back and forth,
back and forth.
The leaves fall on top of my head.
The sun is shy and is only peaking
through the tree branches.
I look at the branches above my head;
they are sprinkling leaves on top of my head
like a sprinkler does to the flowers.
I heard a bird sing;
it sounds like a sweet lullaby.
I watch the cars as they pass by.
As the sun says its good-byes;
I go inside
until the sun rises above my head again.

Caroline Christy, Grade 6
Scotts Creek Elementary School, NC

Thankful

I am thankful for having
Mom and Dad beside me.

I am thankful for having food
So I can eat every day.

One day in life
I want to have a change
and meet new people.
Then I can have people to talk to
When I am sad.
I am thankful I can
Change my life
So I will help other people
And be what I want to be.

Armoni Smith, Grade 4
Lee A Tolbert Community Academy, MO

Waves Crashing

Insane surfers ride
huge or tiny sharks swim in
crashing against sand

Connor Armstrong, Grade 4
Briarwood Christian Elementary School, AL

Say No to Girly Girls!!!

Baseball is for boys,
Gymnastics is for girls,
But I think softball is the best sport in the world!!!
Hitting the ball with all our muscle,
Out to the fence so the outfielders hustle!!!
Running on the corners of the diamond one by one,
Once you get home your work is done!!!
Running home and sliding in the dirt,
Making sure you don't get hit,
So you duck head first!!!
After you win,
Another day you come out to play again!!!

Mary Bryce Pring, Grade 6
Queen of Angels Catholic School, GA

A Blessing for Gymnasts

May your grips not slip during your bar routine.
May you have balance during your beam routine.
May your body follow your brain's instruction.
May your floor routine be flawless.
And may all your routines be 10s.

Emily Sears, Grade 6
St Francis Xavier School, AL

Autumn Leaves

Yellow, orange, gold
many colors falling down
like rain very crisp

Grant Hester, Grade 4
Briarwood Christian Elementary School, AL

Rainbows

Rainbows are a sign of God's love and peace.
They remind me of bumblebees.
At the end of some rainbows there is a pot of gold,
And sometimes your fortune is told.
Rainbows are fun to leprechauns,
Because they get to hide and run.

Rainbows appear while the skies are blue,
They have a magical touch of happiness too.
Rainbows make a smile,
That's always worth the while.
Rainbows appear after the rain has fallen,
They even sometimes appear while the rain is falling.

Rainbows are made of rain and sun,
In my opinion they are fun.
Grace White, Grade 4
St Ann School, TN

With Freedom Comes Responsibility

I think that there should be freedom to all that live,
But with freedom comes a GREAT responsibility,
Thou must not steal;
Thou shall not kill.
With freedom comes responsibility,
Wish for wisdom,
Because to have wisdom is to have freedom.
Amethyst Chiantaretto, Grade 5
Paint Lick Elementary School, KY

Steve Irwin

Steve Irwin was a valiant lad,
For a love of animals was what he had.

He grew up with all of the crocs,
He captured them amongst the rocks.

As he grew older a zoo he led,
He helped all creatures to be fed.

A wife he found, she was a prize,
About all animals she was wise.

They had two lovely kids named Bindi and Bob,
Following the foursome was a huge mob.

Once while Steve was diving in the sea,
A terrible fate was to be.

While he was making his kind of art,
A stingray stung him in the heart.

A fatal sting it was to be,
Steve Irwin you shall never see.
Rachel Walsh, Grade 6
River Trail Middle School, GA

Kaizer

I hear Kaizer meow.
She is as furry as a hairy pillow,
orange like a lion,
black like a panther,
white like a dove,
and brown like a monkey.

Her eye is golden as if King Midas touched it.
She is fast as lighting
and furious as a starving coyote hunting for dinner,
but I still love her.
She's my alarm, my family, my one and only kitty cat, Kaizer.
Tiffany Barragan, Grade 6
Magnolia Springs Baptist Academy, AL

Love

Love is kind and true.
 Love is for me and you.
  Love is wonderful and peaceful too.
   Love is when you're all alone.
    And you will remember your family's love.
Shanice Daniels, Grade 5
East Marion Elementary School, MS

Glistening Glass

The glass in the window is
shiny and bright!
Glistening in the sunlight,
then blowing down with a crash!
Now that wonderful, glistening thing
is now in little pieces in the trash!
No-one will ever see again
that pretty glass with a picture of a flower.
Gone.
No more to delight,
No more tonight.

Mara Craig, Grade 6
Alpena Elementary School, AR

The Tree

The tree has branches like arms, refusing to let go.
Its leaves are like clumps of snow.
The tree has colors as bright as a paint pallet.
It has a trunk like an unyielding door.
The tree has forks like a comb.
It has a life like an immortal spirit.
The tree has patience like a teacher.
It has knowledge like the ancient Earth.
The tree has breath like life.
It is as still as death.
The tree dances like swaying ocean waves.
It loves like peace.
Madison Rudnick, Grade 6
River Trail Middle School, GA

The World's Smallest Pocket Guide

The world's smallest pocket guide I carry in a part, that's useful fluffy red, it's called my little heart.
He comes with me everywhere to help me know what's right.
He's useful summer, winter, fall, day, dusk and night.
I talk to him when glad
I talk to him when blue
The next time when you need some help you should ask yours what to do.

Carrie Nowell, Grade 5
St Thomas More School, NC

I Love Where I Am From

I am from Mom working at Danville's American Greetings Factory
And Dad managing the Lexington Habitat for Humanity Office.

I am from living on a farm in the country off of Highway 68
In a GIGANTIC white house with barnyard animals that, to me, are first-rate!

I am from sharing our home with Nanny and Papaw…
Learning useful lessons of cooking meals, repairing chicken pens, to building birdhouses,
And realizing that my grandparents are two of my best friends!

I am from traveling to Palau with Nanny to the small Pacific Island
That was home to her long ago…
From staying with Aunt Regina
To shopping and buying Palauan *bling.*
What a wonderful thing!

I am from touring this tropical place
To having my uncle taking me to met Palau's president face-to-face!

I love my family, who are from places all over the world,
And I love the places where I have been…

This is why I love my family and where I am from!

Kae-lynn Bradshaw, Grade 5
Burgin Independent School, KY

Tornados

I am vicious, I will kill and torture everything in my path. I will tear you to pieces. You better go far away from me or you will be dead. You don't know when or where I'm coming from. If you step in my path you will be dead! I come in the daytime and nighttime. You cannot stop me. I am faster than any wind in the whole world! I am a grand slam tornado. I have a different name every time I come to destroy. I can be up to a mile wide and suck up everything in my path. I can swallow you up and digest you. I am a tornado.

Devon M. Oxendine, Grade 5
Pembroke Elementary School, NC

Autumn

Autumn is…
Pretty orange and yellow leaves are falling off the trees,
People are putting pumpkins out on their doorsteps
Stores are loading with fall decorations, the sweet smell of fresh pumpkin pie in the air.

Kids are excited getting their outfits ready.
It's chilly outside and farmers are starting to get their stalks ready for the winter.
That's what autumn is!

Caroline Rathman, Grade 5
Palmetto Christian Academy, SC

Blue

Blue looks like the ocean on a summer day.
Blue sounds like the ocean waves splashing in spring.
Blue tastes like the blue kool-aid I drink.
Blue feels like a beautiful marble.
Blue smells like the morning sky over the ocean.
Blue is the beautiful dolphins in the ocean.
Blue is the sound of the blue-shark chasing his food.
Blue is the smell of the elegant ocean waves
Blue is the salty ocean when it swishes up my mouth.
Blue is the feel of the ocean waves on a summer day.

Jesse Pacilli-Wilkerson, Grade 5
Cool Spring Elementary School, NC

Colorful Leaves

Comes where chlorophyll
goes, they're red, yellow, orange,
and brown and are cool.

John David Imbusch, Grade 4
Briarwood Christian Elementary School, AL

A Soldier

A soldier stands in the middle of the battle field,
Without even a shield.
All alone by himself,
Undisappointment towards oneself.

For we have just won all the wars,
With a body full of sores.
They have just fought for the red, white, and blue,
Then they come home and tell us too.

`Dakota Vance, Grade 5*
Joann Walters Elementary School, AR

Fall

Colorful ground all lushes and true.
Every single color except for brilliant blue.

Wind is twirling all around.
Twirling around I can hear the beautiful sound.

Patrick Holland, Grade 6
Queen of Angels Catholic School, GA

10 Different Ways to Hold Your Science Book

You could hold it with your toes,
You could hold it on your nose,
You could hold it with your feet,
You could hold it — asleep!
You could hold it on your head,
You could hold it on your bed.
You could hold it — with pencil lead!
You could hold it with paper fans,
you could hold it with metal cans,
But whatever you do,
I'd just stick with my hands.

Christie Sanders, Grade 4
Landmark Christian School, GA

Index